SETS, MODELS AND RECURSION THEORY

STUDIES IN LOGIC

AND

THE FOUNDATIONS OF MATHEMATICS

NORTH-HOLLAND PUBLISHING COMPANY
AMSTERDAM

SETS, MODELS AND RECURSION THEORY

PROCEEDINGS OF THE SUMMER SCHOOL
IN MATHEMATICAL LOGIC
AND TENTH LOGIC COLLOQUIUM
LEICESTER, AUGUST-SEPTEMBER 1965

Edited by
JOHN N. CROSSLEY
University Lecturer in Mathematical Logic;
Fellow of All Souls College, Oxford.

1967
NORTH-HOLLAND PUBLISHING COMPANY
AMSTERDAM

Library of Congress Catalog Card Number 67–21973

PRINTED IN THE NETHERLANDS

PREFACE

This is the second time that the proceedings of a Logic Colloquium have been published, but in this case the Leicester Colloquium was augmented by a Summer School in Mathematical Logic organized by Professor R. L. GOODSTEIN and Mr. R. F. WHEELER of the University of Leicester. There was a combined attendance of about 100 persons. Two levels of courses were provided and the advanced lectures are published here except that Dana Scott's lectures on Set Theory have been replaced by Carol Karp and R. B. Jensen's papers. Scott's lectures are now scheduled to appear in the Proceedings of the A.M.S. Set Theory conference in Los Angeles, 1967. The other papers in this volume were presented at the Logic Colloquium which was recognized as a meeting of the Association for Symbolic Logic.

We are very grateful to the University of Leicester for making this Summer School possible.

Oxford, February 1967 JOHN N. CROSSLEY

CONTENTS

A PROOF OF THE RELATIVE CONSISTENCY OF THE CONTINUUM HYPOTHESIS

CAROL KARP
University of Maryland, USA

The purpose of this paper [1]) is to make available to the mathematician with limited background in foundations, a comprehensible proof of Gödel's famous theorem on the consistency of the continuum hypothesis [1]. The theorem says that if set theory without the axiom of choice and generalized continuum hypothesis is consistent, then it remains consistent when these principles are added as axioms. The set theory used here is Zermelo-Fraenkel-Skolem set theory (**ZF**), but the proof adapts readily to set theories with classes. The present proof is complete modulo that material ordinarily found in introductory courses in mathematical logic and axiomatic set theory.

The present construction is Gödel's original one as found in [1], the model of constructible sets, but the proof that the constructible sets do indeed form a model of **ZF** for which one can prove the axiom of choice and the generalized continuum hypothesis within **ZF**, is simplified by the use of a calculus of set-theoretical formulas of a special form, the $\Sigma_1^{\mathbf{ZF}}$-formulas. Indeed, the only tedious part of the proof is showing that the model can be defined in **ZF** by a $\Sigma_1^{\mathbf{ZF}}$-formula.

A personal note on the style. Throughout the paper I have maintained a clear distinction between informal set-theoretical arguments and arguments that can be formalized within **ZF**. This is done in order to make the idea of the consistency proof more accessible to the general reader. For instance, it permits an informal proof of some of the basic properties of constructible sets with the details involved in carrying this out in **ZF** tucked away in an appendix. This is dangerous of course and in the classroom I would surely stay more closely with **ZF**. The satisfaction sign $\models$ has been omitted in order to conform more closely with ordinary mathe-

[1]) This paper was prepared with the aid of NSF grant GP-1586 and GP-5456.

matical usage. Thus if $\mathscr{A}(v_0, v_1)$ is a **ZF**-formula and x, y are sets, "$\mathscr{A}(x, y)$" will be written for "$\models \mathscr{A}(x, y)$". Logical symbols $\sim$, $\rightarrow$, $\forall$, and so on, are used both formally and informally, but which use is intended is always clear from context because variables $v_0, \ldots, v_n, \ldots$ are always **ZF**-variables, $x, y, z, \ldots$ are only used informally, $\dot{\in}$ is the primitive predicate symbol of **ZF**, $\in$ is only used informally, and so on.

Finally, a note on the background of this proof. The calculus of $\Sigma_1^{\mathbf{ZF}}$-formulas and their fundamental properties are due to A. Lévy and much of this material can be found in his memoir [2]. Lévy has been using this technique for proving the generalized continuum hypothesis from the assumption that every set is constructible for a number of years. The proof is close to Gödel's original proof, but placing it in the setting of $\Sigma_1^{\mathbf{ZF}}$-formulas clarifies it considerably. The present proof that the constructible sets form a model of **ZF** uses a technique borrowed from P. Cohen's work for proving the replacement schema.

My original proof used primitive recursive set functions in the way that the present proof uses Σ_1-definable set functions. I am indebted to R. B. Jensen for pointing out that the proof goes faster this way. The essential difference is that in order to conclude that the Σ_1-definable functions are $\mathscr{L}$-absolute, we must first show that $\mathscr{L}$ defines a transitive model of **ZF**. The primitive recursive set functions can be shown to be $\mathscr{L}$-absolute immediately. They are in fact absolute relative to many classes that are not models of **ZF**. Thanks are due also to Dana Scott for his stimulating set theory lectures delivered during the summer school at Leicester, England, during the summer of 1965.

1. Preliminaries

The axiomatic set theory used in this paper is Zermelo-Fraenkel set theory (**ZF**). The construction can however be modified to apply to a Von Neumann-Gödel-Bernays set theory with classes. The theory **ZF** is regarded as a formal first-order axiomatic theory with variables $v_0, \ldots, v_n, \ldots$, and *prime* formulas (or *atomic* formulas) just those of the form $(v_i \doteq v_j)$ or $(v_i \dot{\in} v_j)$. The formulas are built from atomic formulas by use of the propositional connectives $\rightarrow$ and $\sim$, and the quantifier $\forall$. All other logical symbols such as $\wedge$, $\vee$, $\leftrightarrow$, $\exists$, $\exists!$, are regarded as abbreviations. All individual constants, all function symbols, and all predicate symbols other than $\dot{=}$, $\dot{\in}$, that appear in the formulas, are defined symbols and must be formally introduced into the theory in accordance with the rules. Whenever a set constant, operation, or relation, is informally denoted by a special symbol, then that symbol with a dot over it is the corresponding formally defined symbol in **ZF**.[2])

The axioms of **ZF** are the universal closures of the formulas in the following list. In order to simplify the formulas, new symbols are introduced by definition as soon as possible.

Axiom of extensionality: $(\forall v_3)(v_3 \dot{\in} v_1 \leftrightarrow v_3 \dot{\in} v_2) \rightarrow v_1 \dot{=} v_2$.

Axiom of regularity:

$(\exists v_1)(v_1 \dot{\in} v_0) \rightarrow (\exists v_1)(v_1 \dot{\in} v_0 \wedge (\forall v_2)(v_2 \dot{\in} v_1 \rightarrow \sim v_2 \dot{\in} v_0))$.

Pairing axiom: $(\exists v_0)(\forall v_3)(v_3 \dot{\in} v_0 \leftrightarrow v_3 \dot{=} v_1 \vee v_3 \dot{=} v_2)$.

Definition: $v_0 \dot{=} \{v_1, v_2\} \leftrightarrow (\forall v_3)(v_3 \dot{\in} v_0 \leftrightarrow (v_3 \dot{=} v_1 \vee v_3 \dot{=} v_2))$.

Definition: $\{v_1\} \dot{=} \{v_1, v_1\}$

Union axiom: $(\exists v_0)(\forall v_2)(v_2 \dot{\in} v_0 \leftrightarrow (\exists v_3)(v_3 \dot{\in} v_1 \wedge v_2 \dot{\in} v_3))$.

Definition: $v_0 \dot{=} \dot{\bigcup} v_1 \leftrightarrow (\forall v_2)(v_2 \dot{\in} v_0 \leftrightarrow (\exists v_3)(v_3 \dot{\in} v_1 \wedge v_2 \dot{\in} v_3))$.

Definition: $v_1 \dot{\cup} v_2 \dot{=} \dot{\bigcup}\{v_1, v_2\}$.

Definition: $v_1 \dot{\subseteq} v_2 \leftrightarrow (\forall v_3)(v_3 \dot{\in} v_1 \rightarrow v_3 \dot{\in} v_2)$.

Power set axiom: $(\exists v_0)(\forall v_2)(v_2 \dot{\in} v_0 \leftrightarrow v_2 \dot{\subseteq} v_1)$.

Definition: $v_0 \dot{=} \dot{\mathscr{P}} v_1 \leftrightarrow (\forall v_2)(v_2 \dot{\in} v_0 \leftrightarrow v_2 \dot{\subseteq} v_1)$.

Axiom schema of replacement: $(\forall v_2)(v_2 \dot{\in} v_1 \rightarrow (\exists ! v_3)\mathscr{A}) \rightarrow$ $(\exists v_0)(\forall v_3)(v_3 \dot{\in} v_0 \leftrightarrow (\exists v_2)(v_2 \dot{\in} v_1 \wedge \mathscr{A}))$, where $\mathscr{A}$ is any formula having no free occurrence of v_0.

Definition: $\mathscr{Z}(v_1) \leftrightarrow (\forall v_2)(\sim v_2 \dot{\in} v_1)$.

Axiom of infinity: $(\exists v_0)((\exists v_1)(v_1 \dot{\in} v_0 \wedge \mathscr{Z}(v_1)) \wedge (\forall v_2)(v_2 \dot{\in} v_0 \rightarrow$ $v_2 \dot{\cup} \{v_2\} \dot{\in} v_0))$.

Definition: $v_1 \dot{=} \dot{0} \leftrightarrow \mathscr{Z}(v_1)$.

The pairing axiom is provable from the others, but it is simpler to take it as an axiom than to prove it. We are assuming background in set theory roughly equivalent to Suppes [3]. This formulation of **ZF** is equivalent to his, provided that cardinals are identified with alephs. Since we will always have the axiom of choice when dealing with cardinals, this identification

---

[2]) It is assumed that set-functions are always defined as total functions. Thus an n-place function symbol F must be introduced into **ZF** by a formula $\mathscr{D}_{\mathrm{F}}(v_0, \ldots, v_n)$ such that $\vdash_{\mathbf{ZF}} (\forall v_1 \ldots v_n)(\exists ! v_0)\mathscr{D}_{\mathrm{F}}$. In cases where the usual notation for a set-function is unsuitable, the dot is omitted. For example, the notation {, } for pair appears in **ZF** just as it appears informally.

presents no problems. Notation used here is not always the same as Suppes'. Brackets $\langle,\rangle$ are reserved for functions. Thus if $\mathrm{T}(x)$ is a set-theoretical term, then $\langle \mathrm{T}(x) | x \in y\rangle$ is that function on y whose value at x is $\mathrm{T}(x)$. A sequence is a function whose domain is an ordinal. Thus $\langle a_\xi | \xi < \delta\rangle$ is the sequence of domain δ (or *length* δ) whose ξ-th term is a_ξ, and $\langle a_0, \ldots, a_{n-1}\rangle$ is the sequence of length n whose i-th term is a_i. Lower-case Greek letters used informally stand for ordinals, used in **ZF** are variables restricted to the formula $\dot{\mathrm{O}}\mathrm{rd}(v_0)$, "$v_0$ is an ordinal". Unless indicated otherwise, exponential notation refers to cardinal exponentiation on sets. Thus $x^y = \{f | \mathrm{Fcn}(f) \wedge \mathrm{Dm}(f) = y \wedge \mathrm{Rg}(f) \subseteq x\}$ and if n is a natural number, x^n is the set of all sequences of length n with terms in x. If κ is a cardinal, that is, if $\kappa = \aleph_\alpha$ for some ordinal α, then $\kappa^+ = \aleph_{\alpha+1}$, the first cardinal larger than κ. The relation of cardinal equivalence between sets is written "$\approx$". For other notation and terminology, see the appendices.

It is convenient to prove the axiom of choice for the model of constructible sets in the form, "every set can be well-ordered". Thus the formulas expressing the axiom of choice and the generalized continuum hypothesis are

$$\mathscr{AC}: (\forall v_0)(\exists v_1)(\dot{\mathrm{S}}\mathrm{eq}(v_1) \wedge \dot{\mathrm{R}}\mathrm{g}(v_1) \doteq v_0)$$

$$\mathscr{GCH}: (\forall \kappa)(\dot{\mathrm{C}}\mathrm{ard}(\kappa) \rightarrow \dot{\mathscr{P}}(\kappa) \dot{\approx} \kappa^+).$$

In fact, the powerful class form of the well-ordering principle is proved for the model; the form that says that there is a function on ordinals definable in **ZF** whose range is the entire universe.

There is an important induction and recursion principle for sets that is not always discussed in textbooks on set theory, though Mendelson [4] has a discussion of it in his chapter 4. With the aid of the axiom of regularity, it can be shown within **ZF** that every set is in some $\mathrm{V}(\alpha)$ where V is the function on ordinals defined by transfinite induction thus:

$$\mathrm{V}(0) = 0$$
$$\mathrm{V}(\alpha + 1) = \mathscr{P}(\mathrm{V}(\alpha))$$
$$\mathrm{V}(\lambda) = \bigcup_{\xi < \lambda} \mathrm{V}(\xi) \quad \text{if} \quad \mathrm{Lim}(\lambda).$$

When we say that V can be defined within **ZF**, we mean that there is a **ZF**-formula $\mathscr{D}_\mathrm{V}(v_0, v_1)$ such that $\vdash_{\mathbf{ZF}} (\forall \underset{\cdot}{v}_1)(\dot{\mathrm{O}}\mathrm{rd}(v_1) \rightarrow (\exists! v_0)\, \mathscr{D}_\mathrm{V}(v_0, v_1))$, $\vdash_{\mathbf{ZF}} \mathscr{D}_\mathrm{V}(\dot{0}, \dot{0}) \wedge (\forall \alpha, v_2)(\mathscr{D}_\mathrm{V}(v_2, \alpha) \rightarrow \mathscr{D}_\mathrm{V}(\mathscr{P}(v_2), \dot{s}(\alpha))) \wedge (\forall \lambda, v_3)(\mathrm{L}\dot{\mathrm{i}}\mathrm{m}(\lambda) \wedge$

$\dot{\text{Seq}}(v_3) \wedge (\forall \xi < \lambda)(\mathscr{D}_V(v_3,\xi,\xi) \rightarrow \mathscr{D}_V(\dot{\bigcup}(\dot{\text{Rg}}\, v_3), \lambda)))$. The condition $\dot{\text{Lim}}(\lambda)$ may be defined by $\dot{0} \dot{\in} \lambda \wedge \dot{\bigcup}\lambda \doteq \lambda$. One of the basic theorems about **ZF** is that a function defined by ordinal recursion from **ZF**-definable functions is itself **ZF**-definable.

The axiom of regularity is often called the axiom of restriction because it has the effect of restricting the universe to the union of the $V(\alpha)$'s. This assumption is not really necessary to the development of axiomatic set theory. See Mendelson [4] chapter 4, for a discussion of this point. However, many authors, the present one included, prefer to work with the axiom of regularity because it is convenient to be able to think of sets as being built up from the empty set by a succession of set-formations.

Define the rank $\rho(x)$ of a set x as the least ordinal α such that $x \subseteq V(\alpha)$. Then the induction and recursion principles for ordinals induce induction and recursion principles for sets as follows:

Induction principle for sets: Let $\mathscr{A}(v_0)$ be any **ZF**-formula. Then in **ZF**, $(\forall v_0)(((\forall v_1 \dot{\in} v_0)\, \mathscr{A}(v_1)) \rightarrow \mathscr{A}(v_0)) \rightarrow (\forall v_0)\, \mathscr{A}(v_0)$.

Principle of definition by recursion: Suppose that G is a **ZF**-definable set function on the universe. Then there is a unique **ZF**-definable set function F such that if $n+1$ is the number of places of G, then for all $x_1, \ldots, x_n$, $F(x_1, \ldots, x_n) = G(\langle F(y, x_2, \ldots, x_n) | y \in x_1 \rangle, x_1, \ldots, x_n)$.

The induction principle can be proved by ordinary transfinite induction on the rank of sets. The recursion principle can be proved by using the principle of definition by ordinal recursion to define $H(\alpha, x_2, \ldots, x_n) = \langle F(x_1, x_2, \ldots, x_n) | x_1 \in V(\alpha) \rangle$. Such a definition is $H(\alpha, x_2, \ldots, x_n) = \langle G(\langle H(\rho(y)+1, x_2, \ldots, x_n)`y | y \in x_1 \rangle, x_1, \ldots, x_n) | x_1 \in V(\alpha) \rangle$. Then $F(x_1, \ldots, x_n) = H(\rho(x_1)+1, x_2, \ldots, x_n)`x_1$.

We are assuming background in mathematical logic equivalent to the first two chapters on Mendelson [4]. The version of the Löwenheim-Skolem Theorem that we need is, however, a little different than the one found there.

THEOREM (TARSKI-VAUGHT). Suppose that A is a model of a first-order theory **T** having $\aleph_\alpha$ symbols and that the universe of A can be well-ordered. Then A has a subsystem of cardinality at most $\aleph_\alpha$ which is also a model of **T**.

Outline of PROOF (assuming no primitive functional symbols): Proceed at first with the usual Henkin-Hasenjaeger argument as found in proposition 2.34 of Mendelson. Adjoin $\aleph_\alpha$ new individual constants

b_λ, $\lambda<\omega_\alpha$. Call the resulting theory $\mathbf{T}^*$. Let $\mathscr{A}_1(v_{i_1}),\ldots,\mathscr{A}_\lambda(v_{i_\lambda}),\ldots,\lambda<\omega_\alpha$, be a sequence consisting of all formulas of $\mathbf{T}^*$ in one free variable. Make a corresponding sequence $b_{j_1},\ldots,b_{j_\lambda},\ldots$ (the witnessing constants) from the new individual constants choosing b_{j_λ} to be the new constant of least index different from b_{j_β}, $\beta<\lambda$, and not appearing in $\mathscr{A}_\beta(v_{i_\beta})$, $\beta\leq\lambda$. For $\lambda<\omega_\alpha$ let B_λ consist of b_{j_λ} together with the b's which appear in $\mathscr{A}_\lambda(v_{i_\lambda})$ and are not in $\bigcup_{\beta<\lambda}\mathrm{B}_\beta$. Then the B_λ's are pairwise disjoint and $\bigcup_{\beta\leq\lambda}\mathrm{B}_\beta$ consists of just those b's which either appear in some $\mathscr{A}_\beta$, $\beta\leq\lambda$, or are witnesses for some $\mathscr{A}_\beta$, $\beta\leq\lambda$.

We now define a mapping σ on the new constants into A, the universe of the given model A. Suppose R well-orders A and that a_0 is the R-least element of A. For $b_\xi\in\mathrm{B}_\lambda$, let $\sigma(b_\xi)=a_0$ if $\xi\neq j_\lambda$. Interpret $(\forall v_{i_\lambda})\,\mathscr{A}_\lambda(v_{i_\lambda})$ in A using the part of σ already defined to interpret any b's that may appear. If it is true, let $\sigma(b_{j_\lambda})=a_0$, and if false, let $\sigma(b_{j_\lambda})$ be the R-least element of A making $\mathscr{A}_\lambda(v_{i_\lambda})$ false.

Now we are ready to define the submodel. Let A^* be the expansion of A obtained by assigning $\sigma(b_\xi)$ to the new individual constants. Then A^* is a model of $\mathbf{T}^*$. Let $\mathrm{A}_0=\{\sigma(b_\lambda)\mid\lambda<\omega_\alpha\}\cup\mathrm{C}$, where C is the set of denotations in A of the original individual constants of $\mathbf{T}$, if any. Let A_0^* be the restriction of A^* to A_0. An easy induction on the number of occurrences of logical connectives shows that for sentences $\mathscr{A}$ of $\mathbf{T}^*$, $\mathscr{A}$ is true in A^* iff $\mathscr{A}$ is true in A_0^*. The only non-trivial case is quantification and by the definition of σ, it is clear that $(\forall v_{i_\lambda})\,\mathscr{A}_\lambda(v_{i_\lambda})$ is true in A^* iff $\mathscr{A}_\lambda(b_{j_\lambda})$ is true in A^*. Thus the proof is complete.

2. The method of inner models

Our task is to show that if **ZF** is consistent, then so is **ZF** plus the axiom of choice and the generalized continuum hypothesis. The traditional method for proving that an assumption is consistent with a theory is to produce a model for the theory in which the assumption holds. This is the method in set theory too, but because we are dealing with the foundations of mathematics, the model must be produced in a special way in order to make the proof convincing. Gödel used an inner model, the only kind used for consistency proofs in set theory until P. Cohen's generic models arrived on the scene in 1963.

Gödel's model is an example of a simple type of inner model that might be called a *definable transitive inner model*[3]), where the universe is replaced by a transitive subuniverse defined within **ZF**, the membership relation is just the original one restricted to the subuniverse, and where the axioms of **ZF** relativized to the subuniverse, are provable within **ZF**.

2.1. DEFINITION. Let $\mathscr{M}(v_0)$ be a **ZF**-formula. The relativization $\mathscr{A}^{(\mathscr{M})}$ of a **ZF**-formula $\mathscr{A}$ is the result of replacing all quantifications $(\forall v_i)(\ldots)$ in $\mathscr{A}$ by $(\forall v_i)(\mathscr{M}(v_i)\rightarrow\ldots)$.

2.2. DEFINITION. A **ZF**-formula is (provably) transitive iff $\vdash_{\mathbf{ZF}}(\mathscr{M}(v_0)\wedge v_1\dot{\in}v_0)\rightarrow\mathscr{M}(v_1)$. A **ZF**-formula $\mathscr{M}(v_0)$ defines a transitive inner model of **ZF** iff $\mathscr{M}$ is a transitive formula and $\vdash_{\mathbf{ZF}}\mathscr{A}^{(\mathscr{M})}$ for all axioms $\mathscr{A}$ of **ZF**.

Since $(\exists v_i)(\ldots)$ is regarded as an abbreviation for $\sim(\forall v_i)\sim(\ldots)$, the relativization of an existential quantification to $\mathscr{M}(v_0)$ is equivalent to the replacement of $(\exists v_i)(\ldots)$ by $(\exists v_i)(\mathscr{M}(v_i)\wedge\ldots)$. Thus $\mathscr{A}^{(\mathscr{M})}$ says that $\mathscr{A}$ holds in the subuniverse defined by $\mathscr{M}(v_0)$. Therefore if $\mathscr{M}(v_0)$ defines a transitive inner model of **ZF**, then given any model of **ZF**, the submodel obtained by restricting the universe to $\{x|\mathscr{M}(x)\}$ is again a model of **ZF**.

Suppose that $\mathscr{B}$ is a **ZF**-statement for which we are able to describe a formula $\mathscr{M}(v_0)$ defining a transitive inner model such that $\vdash_{\mathbf{ZF}}\mathscr{B}^{(\mathscr{M})}$. Then we have a convincing consistency proof for $\mathscr{B}$ relative to **ZF**. For suppose $\vdash_{\mathbf{ZF}}\sim\mathscr{B}$. Since the logical axioms and rules are still good relative to $\mathscr{M}$ and since the relativized axioms of **ZF** are provable in **ZF**, $\vdash_{\mathbf{ZF}}\sim\mathscr{B}^{(\mathscr{M})}$. But then $\vdash_{\mathbf{ZF}}\mathscr{B}^{(\mathscr{M})}\wedge\sim\mathscr{B}^{(\mathscr{M})}$ and **ZF** is inconsistent. Hence

2.3. THEOREM. If **ZF** is consistent and $\vdash_{\mathbf{ZF}}\mathscr{B}^{(\mathscr{M})}$ where $\mathscr{M}$ defines a transitive inner model of **ZF**, then **ZF** and $\mathscr{B}$ are consistent.

Gödel's model is called the *model of constructible sets*. We must describe a **ZF**-formula $\mathscr{L}(v_0)$, read "v_0 is constructible", such that

I. $\mathscr{L}(v_0)$ defines a transitive inner model of **ZF**.

II. $\vdash_{\mathbf{ZF}}\mathscr{AC}^{(\mathscr{L})}$.

III. $\vdash_{\mathbf{ZF}}\mathscr{GCH}^{(\mathscr{L})}$.

[3]) This notion, though similar, is not the same as Shepherdson's notion of complete inner model in [5]. Shepherdson works in a Von Neumann-Bernays-Gödel set theory (**NBG**) with classes so that his models interpret not only the notion of set but also the notion of class. What is more important, the notion of complete inner model is, "X is a transitive class and the axioms of **NBG** are satisfied when the universe is restricted to X", a condition expressible in **NBG** because the theory has only finitely many axioms. Our notion is, "$\mathscr{M}$ is provably transitive and the axioms of **ZF** are provable when the universe is restricted to $\{x|\mathscr{M}(x)\}$".

It turns out to be convenient to replace II and III by

II′. $\vdash_{\mathbf{ZF}}(\forall v_0)\,\mathscr{L}(v_0)\rightarrow\mathscr{AC}$.

III′. $\vdash_{\mathbf{ZF}}((\forall v_0)\,\mathscr{L}(v_0)\wedge\mathscr{AC})\rightarrow\mathscr{GCH}$.

IV. $\vdash_{\mathbf{ZF}}\mathscr{L}(v_0)\rightarrow\mathscr{L}(v_0)^{(\mathscr{L})}$.

Conditions II and III follow from I, II′, III′, IV, for relativizing proofs of II′ and III′ to $\mathscr{L}$, we obtain proofs of $(\forall v_0)\,(\mathscr{L}(v_0)\rightarrow\mathscr{L}(v_0)^{(\mathscr{L})})\rightarrow\mathscr{AC}^{(\mathscr{L})}$ and $((\forall v_0)\,(\mathscr{L}(v_0)\rightarrow\mathscr{L}(v_0)^{(\mathscr{L})})\wedge\mathscr{AC}^{(\mathscr{L})})\rightarrow\mathscr{GCH}^{(\mathscr{L})}$. Thus II and III follow from IV.

3. The model of constructible sets

A restricted quantifier in a formula is one of the form $(\forall v_i)\,(v_i\dot{\in}v_j\rightarrow\ldots)$. A restricted formula is a **ZF**-formula with all of its quantifiers restricted. We follow Lévy [2] in calling such formulas Σ_0-formulas. A $\Sigma_0^{\mathbf{ZF}}$-formula is one that is equivalent in **ZF** to a Σ_0-formula. Recall that a **ZF**-formula has only predicates $\dot{\in}$ and $\doteq$, so to determine whether or not a formula with defined symbols is a $\Sigma_0^{\mathbf{ZF}}$-formula, it is necessary first to eliminate all function symbols and all predicate symbols other than $\dot{\in}$ and $\doteq$. The Σ_0-formulas are important for models of set theory because such formulas have for given arguments $a_1,\ldots,a_n$, the same meaning in any transitive class containing $a_1,\ldots,a_n$ as in the whole universe. This is the content of lemma 3.1.

3.1. LEMMA. Suppose $\mathscr{Q}$ is a Σ_0-formula in free variables $v_{i_1},\ldots,v_{i_n}$ and that $\mathscr{M}(v_0)$ is a transitive formula. Then $\vdash_{\mathbf{ZF}}(\bigwedge_{1\leq j\leq n}\mathscr{M}(v_{i_j}))\rightarrow(\mathscr{Q}\leftrightarrow\mathscr{Q}^{(\mathscr{M})})$.

The proof is an easy induction on the number of connectives $\sim$, $\rightarrow$, $\forall$ in $\mathscr{Q}$ and depends on the fact that under the assumptions, $\mathscr{M}(v_i)\rightarrow(v_j\dot{\in}v_i\leftrightarrow\leftrightarrow(\mathscr{M}(v_j)\wedge(v_j\dot{\in}v_i)))$. Therefore relativization of quantifiers to $\mathscr{M}$ is superfluous.

The informal definition of the constructible sets is as follows.

3.2. DEFINITION. The function L is defined on the ordinals by the recursion

$L(0)=0$.

$L(\lambda)=\bigcup_{\xi<\lambda}L(\xi)$ if $\mathrm{Lim}(\lambda)$.

$L(\alpha+1)=$ the set of all subsets of $L(\alpha)$ of the form

$\{x\in L(\alpha)|\mathscr{Q}(x,a_1,\ldots,a_n)\}$ where $a_1,\ldots,a_n\in L(\alpha)$

and $\mathscr{Q}$ is a Σ_0-formula in $n+1$ variables, $n\in\omega$.

x is constructible iff $x\in L(\alpha)$ for some ordinal α.

Note the similarity between L and the generating function V for the partial universes in section 1. The difference is that the subsets of $L(\alpha)$ introduced into $L(\alpha+1)$ have to be defined in terms of sets in $L(\alpha)$.

The computational part of the consistency proof shows that L can be formally defined within **ZF** by a formula of a special form. When this is done, it will be clear that the next lemma can be proved within **ZF**. It is, however, a useful exercise to prove it informally now.

3.3. Lemma. (1) Every set $L(\alpha)$ is transitive and whenever $x \in L(\alpha)$ and $y \in x$, there is $\xi < \alpha$ such that $y \in L(\xi)$. Hence L is increasing with respect to $\subseteq$.

(2) If x is a set of constructible sets, there is an α such that $x \subseteq L(\alpha)$.

(3) If x and y are constructible, then $\{x, y\}$ and $\bigcup x$ are constructible. Indeed, if $x, y \in L(\alpha)$, then $\{x, y\}$ and $\bigcup x$ are in $L(\alpha+1)$.

(4) If x is constructible, then the set of constructible subsets of x is constructible.

(5) For any ordinal α, if $x, y_1, \ldots, y_n$ are constructible and $\mathcal{Q}$ is a Σ_0-formula in $n+2$ variables such that $(\forall u \in x)(\exists! v \in L(\alpha))\, \mathcal{Q}(u, v, y_1, \ldots, y_n)$, and if we let $f`u$ be that unique v for $u \in x$, then the f-image of x is constructible.

Informal Proof. That every $L(\alpha)$ is transitive may be proved by transfinite induction on α. The case where α is a limit number follows from the fact that the union of a set of transitive sets is transitive. Furthermore, if $L(\alpha)$ is transitive and $y \in x \in L(\alpha+1)$, then since $x \subseteq L(\alpha)$, $y = \{z \in L(\alpha) | z \in y\}$ is a set in $L(\alpha+1)$. The rest of (1) follows from the definition.

If x is a set of constructible sets, for $y \in x$ let $g`y$ be the least ordinal $\xi$ such that $y \in L(\xi)$. Then $x \subseteq L(\bigcup_{y \in x} g`y)$. Hence (2).

If x, y are in $L(\alpha)$, then $\{x, y\} = \{z \in L(\alpha) | z = x \vee z = y\} \in L(\alpha+1)$ and $\bigcup x = \{z \in L(\alpha) | (\exists y \in x)\,(z \in y)\} \in L(\alpha+1)$. Hence (3).

If $x \in L(\alpha)$ and y is the set of constructible subsets of x, then $y \subseteq L(\beta)$ for some β by (2). Then $y = \{z \in L(\beta) | z \subseteq x\} \in L(\beta+1)$ since $z \subseteq x$ is a Σ_0-condition. Hence (4).

Under the hypothesis of (5), $f``x = \{v \in L(\alpha) | (\exists u \in x)\, \mathcal{Q}(u, v, y_1, \ldots, y_n)\} = \{v \in L(\beta) | v \in L(\alpha) \wedge (\exists u \in x)\, \mathcal{Q}(u, v, y_1, \ldots, y_n)\} \in L(\beta+1)$ where β is the least ordinal $\xi > \alpha$ such that $x, y_1, \ldots, y_n \in L(\xi)$. Note that $L(\alpha) = \{x \in L(\alpha) | x = x\} \in L(\alpha+1) \subseteq L(\beta)$ by (1), so that the form of $f``x$ admits it to $L(\beta+1)$.

This completes the proof of the lemma. Note that since each $L(\alpha)$ is transitive, it follows from lemma 3.1 that the decision whether or not a given $x \in \mathrm{L}(\alpha)$ is in the set of $\mathrm{L}(\alpha+1)$ determined by $\mathscr{Q}, a_1, \ldots, a_n$, can be made relative to $\mathrm{L}(\alpha)$.

4. The constructible sets form a model of ZF

At this point we need to assume the computation in the appendix showing that L is formally definable within **ZF** and that lemma 3.3 is provable within **ZF**. We do not yet need the Σ_1-definability of L. Let $\mathscr{L}(v_0)$ be the formula $(\exists v_1)(\dot{\mathrm{O}}\mathrm{rd}(v_1) \wedge v_0 \dot{\in} \dot{\mathrm{L}}(v_1))$ so that $\mathscr{L}(v_0)$ formally expresses the constructibility of v_0. We must show that the axioms of **ZF** relativized to $\mathscr{L}$ are theorems of **ZF**.

4.1. DEFINITION. A formula $\mathscr{A}$ in free variables $v_{i_1}, \ldots, v_{i_n}$ is $\mathscr{M}(v_0)$-absolute if $\vdash_{\mathbf{ZF}}(\bigwedge_{1 \le j \le n} \mathscr{M}(v_{i_j})) \rightarrow (\mathscr{A} \leftrightarrow \mathscr{A}^{(\mathscr{M})})$.

An $\mathscr{M}$-absolute formula has for arguments satisfying $\mathscr{M}$, the same meaning relative to $\{x | \mathscr{M}(x)\}$ as it has absolutely. Lemma 3.1 says that a Σ_0-formula is $\mathscr{M}$-absolute for all transitive $\mathscr{M}$, in particular, for $\mathscr{L}$. But suppose that $\mathscr{A}$ is not itself a Σ_0-formula, but can be reduced to a Σ_0-formula with the aid of some of the axioms of **ZF**. Then lemma 4.2 says that $\mathscr{A}$ will be $\mathscr{M}$-absolute for those transitive $\mathscr{M}$ for which the relativizations of the relevant axioms can be proved.

4.2. LEMMA. Suppose $\mathscr{A}$ is a formula such that $\vdash_\Gamma \mathscr{A} \leftrightarrow \mathscr{Q}$, where $\mathscr{Q}$ is a Σ_0-formula and Γ is a set of axioms of **ZF**. Then if $\mathscr{M}$ is a transitive formula and $\vdash_{\mathbf{ZF}} \mathscr{B}^{(\mathscr{M})}$ for all $\mathscr{B} \in \Gamma$, then $\mathscr{A}$ is $\mathscr{M}$-absolute.

PROOF: Suppose that $\mathscr{A}$ has free variables $v_{i_1}, \ldots, v_{i_n}$. Then relativizing the proof of $\mathscr{A} \leftrightarrow \mathscr{Q}$ to $\mathscr{M}$, $(\bigwedge_{1 \le j \le n} \mathscr{M}(v_{i_j})) \vdash_{\mathbf{ZF}} \mathscr{A}^{(\mathscr{M})} \leftrightarrow \mathscr{Q}^{(\mathscr{M})}$. By lemma 3.1, $\mathscr{Q}^{(\mathscr{M})}$ can be replaced by $\mathscr{Q}$, and by the hypothesis, $\mathscr{Q}$ can be replaced by $\mathscr{A}$. Hence $(\mathscr{A} \leftrightarrow \mathscr{A}^{(\mathscr{M})})$ can be deduced and $\mathscr{A}$ is $\mathscr{M}$-absolute.

4.3. THEOREM. $\mathscr{L}(v_0)$ defines a transitive inner model of **ZF**.

PROOF. It is required to prove $\vdash_{\mathbf{ZF}} \mathscr{A}^{(\mathscr{L})}$ for axioms $\mathscr{A}$ of **ZF**. Though the proofs are given informally, it is clear from the work in the appendix that they can be carried out in **ZF**.

The transitivity of $\mathscr{L}$ alone guarantees $\mathscr{A}^{(\mathscr{L})}$ in case $\mathscr{A}$ is the axiom of extensionality or of regularity. The relativized form of the pairing axiom is, after simplification,

$$(\mathscr{L}(v_1) \wedge \mathscr{L}(v_2)) \rightarrow (\exists v_0)(\mathscr{L}(v_0) \wedge (\forall v_3)(v_3 \dot{\in} v_0 \leftrightarrow (v_3 \doteq v_1 \vee v_3 \doteq v_2)).$$

This is precisely lemma 3.3(3) stated in **ZF**. The proof of the relativized union axiom goes the same way. The relativized power set axiom reduces to

$$\mathscr{L}(v_1) \to (\exists v_0)(\mathscr{L}(v_0) \wedge (\forall v_2)(v_2 \dot{\in} v_0 \leftrightarrow v_2 \dot{\subseteq} v_1 \wedge \mathscr{L}(v_2)))$$

using the $\mathscr{L}$-absoluteness of the Σ_0-condition $v_2 \dot{\subseteq} v_1$. This is lemma 3.3(4) stated within **ZF**.

In order to establish the relativized axiom schema of replacement, we first show by induction on the number of occurrences of connectives $\sim$, $\to$, $\forall$, that if $\mathscr{A}$ is any formula in free variables $v_{i_1}, \ldots, v_{i_n}$, having k occurrences of $\forall$,

$$(1)_{\mathscr{A}} \vdash_{\mathbf{ZF}} (\forall \alpha)(\exists \beta_1) \ldots (\exists \beta_k)(\forall v_{i_1} \ldots v_{i_n} \dot{\in} \dot{\mathrm{L}}(\alpha))(\mathscr{A}^{(\mathscr{L})} \leftrightarrow \mathscr{A}^{(\dot{\mathrm{L}}(\beta_1), \ldots, \dot{\mathrm{L}}(\beta_k))})$$

where $\mathscr{A}^{(\dot{\mathrm{L}}(\beta_1), \ldots, \dot{\mathrm{L}}(\beta_k))}$ arises from $\mathscr{A}$ by replacing the j-th quantification $(\forall v_i)(\ldots)$ by $(\forall v_i)(v_i \dot{\in} \dot{\mathrm{L}}(\beta_j) \ldots)$, $j = 1, \ldots, k$. Thus $(1)_{\mathscr{A}}$ says that for arguments in a given $\mathrm{L}(\alpha)$, $\mathscr{A}$ is equivalent to a formula with all of its quantifiers restricted to segments of the constructible hierarchy. To prove $(1)_{\mathscr{A}}$, note that it is trivial for $\mathscr{A}$ of form $(v_{i_1} \dot{\in} v_{i_2})$ or $(v_{i_1} \doteq v_{i_2})$. If $\mathscr{A} = (\sim \mathscr{B})$ and $(1)_{\mathscr{B}}$, then $(1)_{\mathscr{A}}$ using the same bounds $\beta_1, \ldots, \beta_k$ as used for $\mathscr{B}$. Similarly, if $(1)_{\mathscr{B}}$ and $(1)_{\mathscr{C}}$ and $\mathscr{A} = (\mathscr{B} \to \mathscr{C})$, then a list of bounds for quantifiers in $\mathscr{A}$ is obtained by juxtaposing the lists for $\mathscr{B}$ and $\mathscr{C}$. Finally suppose $\mathscr{A} = (\forall v_i)\mathscr{B}$ and $(1)_{\mathscr{B}}$. For any α and $v_{i_1}, \ldots, v_{i_n} \dot{\in} \dot{\mathrm{L}}(\alpha)$, let $\dot{\mathrm{G}}(v_{i_1}, \ldots, v_{i_n})$ be the least $\xi \geq \alpha$ such that $(\exists v_i)(\mathscr{L}(v_i) \wedge \sim \mathscr{B}^{(\mathscr{L})}) \leftrightarrow (\exists v_i)(v_i \dot{\in} \dot{\mathrm{L}}(\xi) \wedge \sim \mathscr{B}^{(\mathscr{L})})$. Let $\delta \doteq \dot{\bigcup} \{\dot{\mathrm{G}}(v_{i_1}, \ldots, v_{i_n}) | v_{i_1}, \ldots, v_{i_n} \dot{\in} \dot{\mathrm{L}}(\alpha)\}$. Then since L is increasing, we can deduce $(\forall v_{i_1}, \ldots, v_{i_n} \dot{\in} \dot{\mathrm{L}}(\alpha))((\exists v_i)(\mathscr{L}(v_i) \wedge \sim \mathscr{B}^{(\mathscr{L})}) \leftrightarrow (\exists v_i)(v_i \dot{\in} \dot{\mathrm{L}}(\delta) \wedge \sim \mathscr{B}^{(\mathscr{L})}))$. Thus $(\forall v_{i_1}, \ldots, v_{i_n} \dot{\in} \dot{\mathrm{L}}(\alpha))(\mathscr{A}^{(\mathscr{L})} \leftrightarrow (\forall v_i)(v_i \dot{\in} \dot{\mathrm{L}}(\delta) \to \mathscr{B}^{(\mathscr{L})}))$. Using $(1)_{\mathscr{B}}$ to obtain bounds $\beta_2, \ldots, \beta_k$ for δ and $\mathscr{B}$, we can deduce $(\forall v_i \dot{\in} \dot{\mathrm{L}}(\delta))(\forall v_{i_1}, \ldots, v_{i_n} \dot{\in} \dot{\mathrm{L}}(\alpha))(\mathscr{B}^{(\mathscr{L})} \leftrightarrow \mathscr{B}^{(\dot{\mathrm{L}}(\beta_2), \ldots, \dot{\mathrm{L}}(\beta_k))})$. Thus $\delta, \beta_2, \ldots, \beta_k$ are bounds for α and $\mathscr{A}$. This completes the proof of $(1)_{\mathscr{A}}$ for formulas $\mathscr{A}$.

After obvious simplifications, the relativized replacement axiom for a formula $\mathscr{A}$ in variables $v_2, v_3, v_{i_1}, \ldots, v_{i_n}$, is $\mathscr{L}(v_1) \wedge (\bigwedge_{1 \leq j \leq n} \mathscr{L}(v_{i_j})) \to [(\forall v_2)(\mathscr{L}(v_2) \wedge v_2 \dot{\in} v_1 \to (\exists! v_3)(\mathscr{L}(v_3) \wedge \mathscr{A}^{(\mathscr{L})})) \to (\exists v_0)(\mathscr{L}(v_0) \wedge \mathscr{C})]$where $\mathscr{C}(v_0)$ reduces to $(\forall v_3)(v_3 \dot{\in} v_0 \leftrightarrow \mathscr{L}(v_3) \wedge (\exists v_2)(v_2 \dot{\in} v_1 \wedge \mathscr{A}^{(\mathscr{L})}))$. Take the first two clauses of the relativized axiom as assumptions on $v_1, v_{i_1}, \ldots, v_{i_n}$. The axiom of replacement yields $(\exists v_0)\mathscr{C}(v_0)$. It remains to show $\mathscr{L}(v_0)$ assuming $\mathscr{C}(v_0)$. Since v_0 is a set of constructible sets, lemma 3.3(2) implies $(\exists \alpha)(v_1 \dot{\in} \dot{\mathrm{L}}(\alpha) \wedge (\bigwedge_{1 \leq j \leq n} v_{i_j} \dot{\in} \dot{\mathrm{L}}(\alpha)) \wedge v_0 \dot{\in} \dot{\mathrm{L}}(\alpha))$. Use $(1)_{\mathscr{A}}$ for α and let $\mathscr{Q}(v_2, v_3, v_{i_1}, \ldots, v_{m_1}, \ldots)$ be $\mathscr{A}^{(v_{m_1}, \ldots, v_{m_k})}$ where the v_{m_j} are new variables.

Then $(\exists\beta_1\ldots\beta_k)(\forall v_2\dot{\in}v_1)(\forall v_3\dot{\in}\dot{\mathrm{L}}(\alpha))(\mathscr{A}^{(\mathscr{L})}\leftrightarrow\mathscr{Q}(v_2, v_3, v_{i_1},\ldots, \dot{\mathrm{L}}(\beta_1),\ldots, \dot{\mathrm{L}}(\beta_k)))$.

Since $\mathscr{Q}$ is a Σ_0-formula and $\mathscr{L}(\dot{\mathrm{L}}(\gamma))$ for all ordinals γ, lemma 3.3(5) applies. Hence $\mathscr{L}(v_0)$.

Finally we must prove the relativized axiom of infinity. The formula $\mathscr{Z}(v_1)$ defining zero is logically equivalent to the Σ_0-formula $(\forall v_2)(v_2\dot{\in}v_1\rightarrow v_2\neq v_2)$ and the formula $(v_2\dot{\cup}\{v_2\})\dot{\in}v_0$ reduces to a Σ_0-formula using only the axioms of extensionality, pairing, and union. Since the relativizations of these axioms to $\mathscr{L}$ have already been proved, the formulas $\mathscr{Z}(v_1)$ and $(v_2\dot{\cup}\{v_2\})\dot{\in}v_0$ are $\mathscr{L}$-absolute by lemma 4.2. Thus the relativized axiom of infinity reduces to $(\exists v_0)(\mathscr{L}(v_0)\wedge\dot{0}\dot{\in}v_0\wedge(\forall v_2)(v_2\dot{\in}v_0\rightarrow(v_2\dot{\cup}\{v_2\})\dot{\in}v_0))$. But this condition can be proved for $v_0\doteq\dot{\mathrm{L}}(\dot{\omega})$ using lemma 3.3(3). This completes the proof.

This technique for proving the relativized replacement schema is due to P. Cohen.

5. Absoluteness and related properties of Σ_1 and Π_1-definable relations

We have already seen that Σ_0-formulas are $\mathscr{M}$-absolute for all transitive $\mathscr{M}$. Following Lévy [2], we call a **ZF**-formula a Σ_1-formula if it has form $(\exists v_i)\,\mathscr{Q}$ where $\mathscr{Q}$ is a Σ_0-formula, and a Π_1-formula if it has form $(\forall v_i)\,\mathscr{Q}$. It is an obvious consequence of the theorem on Σ_0-formulas that the Σ_1-formulas are $\mathscr{M}$-stable for all transitive formulas $\mathscr{M}$, that is, if such a formula holds relative to $\mathscr{M}$ for arguments in $\{x|\mathscr{M}(x)\}$, then it holds for those arguments absolutely.

5.1. LEMMA. Suppose that $\mathscr{A}$ is a Σ_1-formula in free variables $v_{i_1},\ldots, v_{i_n}$, and that $\mathscr{M}$ is a transitive formula. Then $\vdash_{\mathbf{ZF}}(\bigwedge_{1\leq j\leq n}\mathscr{M}(v_{i_j}))\rightarrow(\mathscr{A}^{(\mathscr{M})}\rightarrow\mathscr{A})$.

PROOF. Immediate from lemma 3.1.

5.2. LEMMA. Suppose that $\mathscr{A}$ is a Π_1-formula in free variables $v_{i_1},\ldots, v_{i_n}$, and that $\mathscr{M}$ is a transitive formula. Then $\vdash_{\mathbf{ZF}}(\bigwedge_{1\leq j\leq n}\mathscr{M}(v_{i_j}))\rightarrow(\mathscr{A}\rightarrow\mathscr{A}^{(\mathscr{M})})$.

Lemma 5.2 is the dual of lemma 5.1. Putting the two together, we obtain a very useful absoluteness theorem.

5.3. THEOREM. Suppose that $\mathscr{A}$ is a **ZF**-formula for which there is a Σ_1-formula $\mathscr{B}$ and a Π_1-formula $\mathscr{C}$ such that $\vdash_{\Gamma}(\mathscr{A}\leftrightarrow\mathscr{B})\wedge(\mathscr{A}\leftrightarrow\mathscr{C})$ where Γ is a set of axioms of **ZF**. Then if $\mathscr{M}$ is a transitive formula and $\vdash_{\mathbf{ZF}}\mathscr{D}^{(\mathscr{M})}$ for $\mathscr{D}\in\Gamma$, then $\mathscr{A}$ is $\mathscr{M}$-absolute.

PROOF. Relativizing the proof of $(\mathscr{A}\leftrightarrow\mathscr{B})\wedge(\mathscr{A}\leftrightarrow\mathscr{C})$ to $\mathscr{M}$, we obtain a proof of $(\bigwedge_{1\le j\le n}\mathscr{M}(v_{i_j}))\rightarrow((\mathscr{A}^{(\mathscr{M})}\leftrightarrow\mathscr{B}^{(\mathscr{M})})\wedge(\mathscr{A}^{(\mathscr{M})}\leftrightarrow\mathscr{C}^{(\mathscr{M})}))$ where $v_{i_1},\ldots,v_{i_n}$ is a list of the variables free in $\mathscr{A}$, $\mathscr{B}$ and $\mathscr{C}$. Then from the assumption $(\bigwedge_{1\le j\le n}\mathscr{M}(v_{i_j}))$ there follows a string of implications $(\mathscr{A}\rightarrow\mathscr{C})$, $(\mathscr{C}\rightarrow\mathscr{C}^{(\mathscr{M})})$ by 5.2, $(\mathscr{C}^{(\mathscr{M})}\rightarrow\mathscr{A}^{(\mathscr{M})})$, $(\mathscr{A}^{(\mathscr{M})}\rightarrow\mathscr{B}^{(\mathscr{M})})$, $(\mathscr{B}^{(\mathscr{M})}\rightarrow\mathscr{B})$ by 5.1, $(\mathscr{B}\rightarrow\mathscr{A})$. These together imply $\mathscr{A}\leftrightarrow\mathscr{A}^{(\mathscr{M})}$.

Call a formula a $\Sigma_1^{\mathbf{ZF}}$-formula if it is equivalent to a Σ_1-formula in **ZF**, and a $\Pi_1^{\mathbf{ZF}}$-formula if it is equivalent to a Π_1-formula in **ZF**.

5.4. COROLLARY. A $\Sigma_1^{\mathbf{ZF}}\cap\Pi_1^{\mathbf{ZF}}$-formula is $\mathscr{M}$-absolute in any transitive inner model $\mathscr{M}$ of **ZF**.

It is this simple fact that allows us to bypass the absoluteness calculations for the model of constructible sets. If the defining formula for a set-theoretical relation can be cast into both Σ_1 and Π_1-forms within **ZF**, then that relation is automatically $\mathscr{L}$-absolute. If the defining formula for a set-theoretical function can be cast in Σ_1-form within **ZF**, then the model of constructible sets is automatically closed under that function and the function is $\mathscr{L}$-absolute. For the defining formula $\mathscr{D}_{\mathrm{F}}$ of a function F defines the relation $x_0=\mathrm{F}(x_1,\ldots,x_n)$ and is functional, i.e., $\vdash_{\mathbf{ZF}}(\forall v_1\ldots v_n)(\exists! v_0)\,\mathscr{D}_{\mathrm{F}}(v_0,v_1,\ldots,v_n)$. Then by the lemma in Appendix I $\mathscr{D}_{\mathrm{F}}$ is also a $\Pi_1^{\mathbf{ZF}}$-formula since $\vdash_{\mathbf{ZF}}{\sim}\mathscr{D}_{\mathrm{F}}(v_0,v_1,\ldots,v_n)\leftrightarrow(\exists v_{n+1})({\sim}v_{n+1}\doteq v_0\wedge\mathscr{D}_{\mathrm{F}}(v_{n+1},v_1,\ldots,v_n))$. Hence $\mathscr{D}_{\mathrm{F}}$ is $\mathscr{L}$-absolute and the relativization to $\mathscr{L}$ of the proof that $\mathscr{D}_{\mathrm{F}}$ is functional shows that the model is closed under F.

The Σ_1-formulas have another important property that is used in this consistency proof: that property is their cardinal boundedness. A set x is *hereditarily of power at most* κ if $\bar{\bar{x}}\le\kappa$, $\bar{\bar{y}}\le\kappa$ whenever $y\in x$, $\bar{\bar{z}}\le\kappa$ whenever z is an element of an element of y, and so on. The theorem says that whenever a relation R is definable in **ZF** by a $\Sigma_1^{\mathbf{ZF}}$-formula, κ is an infinite cardinal, $x_1,\ldots,x_n$ are hereditarily of power at most κ, and $(\exists y)\,\mathrm{R}(x_1,\ldots,x_n,y)$, then there is z hereditarily of power at most κ such that $\mathrm{R}(x_1,\ldots,x_n,z)$. The axiom of choice is required for the proof. It follows that a function F defined by a $\Sigma_1^{\mathbf{ZF}}$-formula cannot raise the hereditary cardinality of its arguments. The power-set operation is therefore not $\Sigma_1^{\mathbf{ZF}}$ definable, nor is the operation aleph on the ordinals. It is this theorem plus the Σ_1-definability of L that yields the generalized continuum hypothesis for the model of constructible sets. This theorem in its present form is due to

Lévy and the proof, based on Gödel's original proof of the generalized continuum hypothesis for constructible sets, is found in [2].

5.5. DEFINITION. $\mathrm{TC}(x)=\bigcup_{n<\omega}\mathrm{F}(n,x)$, where $\mathrm{F}(0,x)=x$, $\mathrm{F}(n+1,x)=\bigcup\mathrm{F}(n,x)$. $\mathrm{HC}(x)=\overline{\overline{\mathrm{TC}(x)}}$, the cardinal of $\mathrm{TC}(x)$.

The function $\mathrm{TC}(x)$, the transitive closure of x, gives the smallest transitive set containing x as a subset. The form of the definition shows it to be formally definable in **ZF**; in fact, a glance at the appendix shows it to be Σ_1-definable. The function $\mathrm{HC}(x)$ is definable in **ZF** plus $\mathscr{AC}$.

5.6. LEMMA. Let $\mathscr{Q}$ be a Σ_0-formula in n free variables, let v_k be a variable not in $\mathscr{Q}$ and let $\mathscr{Q}^{(v_k)}$ be the result of restricting all quantifiers to membership in v_k. Then the following can be proved in **ZF**: If a is a set, φ is an $\in$-isomorphism from a onto a transitive set b, then $\mathscr{Q}^{(a)}(x_1,\ldots,x_n)\leftrightarrow\mathscr{Q}(\varphi(x_1),\ldots,\varphi(x_n))$ for all $x_1,\ldots,x_n\in a$. [Formally, for Σ_0-formulas $\mathscr{Q}$ in $v_{i_1},\ldots,v_{i_n}$, $\vdash_{\mathbf{ZF}}(1-1\dot{\mathrm{F}}\mathrm{cn}(v_0)\wedge\mathrm{Tr\dot{a}ns}(\mathrm{Rg}(v_0))\wedge(\forall v_1,v_2)(v_1,v_2\dot{\in}\dot{\mathrm{D}}\mathrm{m}(v_0)\rightarrow(v_1\dot{\in}v_2\leftrightarrow v_0`v_1\dot{\in}v_0`v_2)))\rightarrow(\forall v_{i_1},\ldots,v_{i_n}\dot{\in}\dot{\mathrm{D}}\mathrm{m}(v_0))(\mathscr{Q}^{(\dot{\mathrm{D}}\mathrm{m})(v_0))}(v_{i_1},\ldots,v_{i_n})\leftrightarrow\mathscr{Q}(v_0`v_{i_1},\ldots,v_0`v_{i_n}))$.]

Informal PROOF. The proof is by induction on the number of occurrences of $\sim,\rightarrow,\forall$. It is obvious for formulas $(v_{i_1}\dot{\in}v_{i_2})$, $(v_{i_1}\doteq v_{i_2})$, and the passage from $\mathscr{Q}_1$ and $\mathscr{Q}_2$ to $(\sim\mathscr{Q}_1)$ and $(\mathscr{Q}_1\rightarrow\mathscr{Q}_2)$ is immediate. Suppose $\mathscr{Q}$ is $(\forall v)(v\dot{\in}v_{i_j}\rightarrow\mathscr{Q}_1(v,v_{i_1},\ldots,v_{i_n}))$ and $x_1,\ldots,x_n\in a$. Then if $\sim\mathscr{Q}^{(a)}(x_1,\ldots,x_n)$, there is $u\in a\cap x_j$ such that $\sim\mathscr{Q}_1^{(a)}(u,x_1,\ldots,x_n)$. By the induction hypothesis, $\sim\mathscr{Q}_1(\varphi(u)\,\varphi(x_1),\ldots,\varphi(x_n))$. Thus $\sim\mathscr{Q}(\varphi(x_1),\ldots,\varphi(x_n))$. Conversely, if $\sim\mathscr{Q}(\varphi(x_1),\ldots,\varphi(x_n))$, then since b is transitive, there is $\varphi(u)\in\varphi(x_j)$ such that $\sim\mathscr{Q}_1(\varphi(u),\varphi(x_1),\ldots,\varphi(x_n))$. But then $u\in x_j\cap a$, so $\sim\mathscr{Q}_1^{(a)}(u,x_1,\ldots,x_n)$ by induction hypothesis. Hence $\sim\mathscr{Q}^{(a)}(x_1,\ldots,x_n)$.

5.7. THEOREM (LÉVY). Let $\mathscr{A}$ be a $\Sigma_1^{\mathbf{ZF}}$-formula in $n+1$ free variables. Then the following can be proved in **ZF** plus $\mathscr{AC}$: If κ is an infinite cardinal and $\mathrm{HC}(x_j)\leq\kappa$ for $1\leq j\leq n$, then $(\exists y)\,\mathscr{A}(y,x_1,\ldots,x_n)\leftrightarrow(\exists y)(\mathrm{HC}(y)\leq\kappa\wedge\mathscr{A}(y,x_1,\ldots,x_n))$. [Formally, for **ZF**-formulas in $v_{i_1},\ldots,v_{i_n}$, $\mathscr{AC}\vdash_{\mathbf{ZF}}(\mathrm{C\dot{a}rd}(\kappa)\wedge\kappa\dot{\geqslant}\dot{\omega}\wedge(\bigwedge_{1\leq j\leq n}\dot{\mathrm{H}}\mathrm{C}(v_{i_j})\dot{\leqslant}\kappa))\rightarrow((\exists v_{i_0})\,\mathscr{A}\leftrightarrow(\exists v_{i_0})(\dot{\mathrm{H}}\mathrm{C}(v_{i_0})\dot{\leqslant}\kappa\wedge\mathscr{A}))$.]

PROOF. It suffices to establish the theorem for Σ_0-formulas $\mathscr{Q}$. For suppose $(\mathscr{A}\leftrightarrow(\exists v)\,\mathscr{Q}')$ in **ZF**. Then $((\exists v_{i_0})\,\mathscr{A}\leftrightarrow(\exists v')\,\mathscr{Q})$ in **ZF**, where $\mathscr{Q}$ is $(\exists v_{i_0}\dot{\in}v')(\exists v\dot{\in}v')\,\mathscr{Q}'$. Take $v'=\{v_{i_0},v\}$ to establish the equivalence. Then under assumptions $\mathscr{AC}$, $\mathrm{C\dot{a}rd}(\kappa)$, $\kappa\dot{\geqslant}\dot{\omega}$, it follows that

$(\exists v_{i_0})$ $(\dot{\mathrm{HC}}(v_{i_0}) \dot{\leqslant} \kappa \wedge \mathscr{A}) \leftrightarrow (\exists v')$ $(\dot{\mathrm{HC}}(v') \dot{\leqslant} \kappa \wedge \mathscr{Q})$ in **ZF**. Hence the theorem for $\mathscr{Q}$ yields the theorem for $\mathscr{A}$.

Suppose $\mathscr{Q}$ is a Σ_0-formula in $n+1$ variables, κ is an infinite cardinal, $\mathrm{HC}(x_j) \leq \kappa$, $1 \leq j \leq n$, and $\mathscr{Q}(y, x_1, \ldots, x_n)$. Let $w = \mathrm{TC}(\{y, x_1, \ldots, x_n\})$. Extend the language of **ZF** by adjoining individual constants $\dot{u}$ for $u \in \mathrm{TC}(\{x_1, \ldots, x_n\})$. Let Γ consist of the two statements $(\exists v_{i_0})$ $\mathscr{Q}(v_{i_0}, \dot{x}_1, \ldots, \dot{x}_n)$ and the axiom of extensionality. Then the language has as most κ symbols and by lemma 3.1, $M = \langle w, \in_w, \mathrm{I} \rangle$ is a model of Γ, where $\in_w$ is the membership relation restricted to w and $\mathrm{I}(\dot{u}) = u$ for $u \in \mathrm{TC}(\{x_1, \ldots, x_n\})$. The Löwenheim-Skolem Theorem in the form discussed in section 1 says that there is a substructure $M' = \langle w', \in_{w'}, \mathrm{I} \rangle$ of M having power $\leq \kappa$, which is also a model of Γ.

Let $c = \mathrm{TC}(\{x_1, \ldots, x_n\})$. Since each $u \in c$ is the denotation in M of the constant $\dot{u}$, and since M' is a substructure of M, $c \subseteq w'$. According to the principle of definition by recursion discussed in section 1, the relation $\varphi(x) = \{\varphi(z) | z \in x \cap w'\}$ defines a total set-function. Moreover, $\varphi``w'$ is a transitive set and it can be shown using the induction principle for sets that φ is an $\in$-isomorphism on w' which is the identity on c. For let the property $C(x)$ be defined by $(x \in c \rightarrow \varphi(x) = x) \wedge (x \in w' \rightarrow (\forall y \in w')\, (y \neq x \rightarrow \varphi(y) \neq \varphi(x)))$. Suppose $C(z)$ for all $z \in x$. Then if $x \in c$, it follows that $\varphi(x) = \{\varphi(z) | z \in x \cap w'\} = x$. If $x \in w'$ and $y \neq x$, $y \in w'$, then since the axiom of extensionality holds in M', either there is $z_1 \in w'$, $z_1 \in y - x$ or there is a $z_2 \in w'$, $z_2 \in x - y$. In the first case, $\varphi(z_1) \in \varphi(y)$ but $\varphi(z_1) \notin \varphi(x)$ since the induction hypothesis implies $\varphi(z_1) \neq \varphi(z)$ for all $z \in x \cap w'$. In the second case, $\varphi(z_2) \in \varphi(x)$ but $\varphi(z_2) \notin \varphi(y)$ for the induction hypothesis applied to z_2 says that $\varphi(z_2) \neq \varphi(z)$ for all $z \in y$. Hence $\varphi(y) \neq \varphi(x)$. This completes the inductive proof of $(\forall x)\, \mathrm{C}(x)$.

According to the lemma, $\mathscr{Q}^{(w')}(z, x_1, \ldots, x_n) \leftrightarrow \mathscr{Q}(\varphi(z), x_1, \ldots, x_n)$ where $z \in w'$ is chosen so that z satisfies $\mathscr{Q}(v_{i_0}, \dot{x}_1, \ldots, \dot{x}_n)$ in M'. Since then $\mathscr{Q}^{(w')}(z, x_1, \ldots, x_n)$, we have $\mathscr{Q}(\varphi(z), x_1, \ldots, x_n)$. But $\varphi(z)$ is in $\varphi``w'$, a transitive set of power $\leq \kappa$, so $\mathrm{HC}(\varphi(z)) \leq \kappa$. This completes the proof.

6. The proof of the axiom of choice and the generalized continuum hypothesis for the model of constructible sets

At this point we need the strong form of the result in Appendix II: the Σ_1-definability of the function L generating the constructible sets, regarded as a total set function. So the formula $v_0 \doteq \dot{\mathrm{L}}(v_1)$ is a $\Sigma_1^{\mathbf{ZF}}$-formula and $\vdash_{\mathbf{ZF}} (\forall v_1)(\exists ! v_0)(v_0 \doteq \dot{\mathrm{L}}(v_1))$. Therefore the formulas $v_0 \doteq \dot{\mathrm{L}}(v_1)$ and $v_0 \dot{\in} \dot{\mathrm{L}}(v_1)$ are $\Sigma_1^{\mathbf{ZF}} \cap \Pi_1^{\mathbf{ZF}}$-formulas.

6.1. LEMMA. It can be proved in **ZF** that every ordinal is constructible. (Formally, $\vdash_{\mathbf{ZF}} \dot{\mathrm{Ord}}(v_1) \rightarrow \mathscr{L}(v_1)$.) Moreover, $\{\xi | \xi \in \mathrm{L}(\alpha)\} = \alpha$.

PROOF. The proof is by transfinite induction on ordinals carried out within **ZF**. It goes by formalizing the following informal proof. Let $\mathrm{C}(\alpha)$ be the property $\{\xi | \xi \in \mathrm{L}(\alpha)\} = \alpha$. Obviously $\mathrm{C}(0)$. Assume $\mathrm{C}(\gamma)$ for all $\gamma < \alpha$. If $\mathrm{Lim}(\alpha)$, then $\{\xi | \xi \in \mathrm{L}(\alpha)\} = \bigcup_{\gamma<\alpha} \{\xi | \xi \in \mathrm{L}(\gamma)\} = \bigcup_{\gamma<\alpha} \gamma = \alpha$. If $\alpha = \gamma + 1$, $\xi \in \mathrm{L}(\alpha)$ implies $\xi \subseteq \mathrm{L}(\gamma)$, hence $\xi \leq \gamma$. But $\gamma \subseteq \mathrm{L}(\alpha)$ and $\gamma = \{x \in \mathrm{L}(\gamma) | \mathrm{Ord}(x)\} \in \mathrm{L}(\alpha)$. Therefore in this case as well, $\{\xi | \xi \in \mathrm{L}(\alpha)\} = \gamma \cup \{\gamma\} = \alpha$. Hence $\mathrm{C}(\alpha)$. This completes the proof.

6.2. THEOREM. $\vdash_{\mathbf{ZF}} \mathscr{L}(v_0) \rightarrow \mathscr{L}(v_0)^{(\mathscr{L})}$. Hence IV of section 2.

PROOF. The formula $\mathscr{L}(v_0)$ is $(\exists v_1)(\dot{\mathrm{Ord}}(v_1) \wedge v_0 \dot{\in} \dot{\mathrm{L}}(v_1))$. Since $\dot{\mathrm{Ord}}(v_1)$ is a Σ_0-formula and $v_0 \dot{\in} \dot{\mathrm{L}}(v_1)$ is a $\Sigma_1^{\mathbf{ZF}} \cap \Pi_1^{\mathbf{ZF}}$-formula, both are $\mathscr{L}$-absolute according to corollary 5.4 and lemma 3.1. The relativization of $\mathscr{L}$ to $\mathscr{L}$ reduces to $(\exists v_1)(\dot{\mathrm{Ord}}(v_1) \wedge v_0 \dot{\in} \dot{\mathrm{L}}(v_1) \wedge \mathscr{L}(v_1))$ under the assumption $\mathscr{L}(v_0)$. This in turn reduces to $\mathscr{L}(v_0)$ using the lemma.

It now remains only to prove II′ and III′ of section 2. The first of these, the fact that the axiom of choice follows from the assumption that every set is constructible, is an exercise in ordinal arithmetic. This will be done by defining within **ZF** a function W such that it is provable within **ZF** that for every α, $\mathrm{W}(\alpha)$ is a sequence, not necessarily one-one, whose range is $\mathrm{L}(\alpha)$. This implies that a strong form of the axiom of choice holds for the constructible sets since the concatenation of all the sequences $\mathrm{W}(\alpha)$ gives a **ZF**-definable well-ordering of the entire constructible universe.

6.3. THEOREM. There is a **ZF**-definable function W such that $\vdash_{\mathbf{ZF}} (\forall \alpha)(\dot{\mathrm{Seq}}(\dot{\mathrm{W}}(\alpha)) \wedge \dot{\mathrm{Rg}}(\dot{\mathrm{W}}(\alpha)) \doteq \dot{\mathrm{L}}(\alpha))$.

PROOF. The definition of L taken from Appendix II is

$$\mathrm{L}(0) = 0$$
$$\mathrm{L}(\alpha+1) = \{\mathrm{S}(\mathrm{L}(\alpha), w, z) | w \in \mathrm{L}(\alpha)^{\nearrow \omega}, z \in \Sigma_0\text{-Fmla}\}$$
$$\mathrm{L}(\lambda) = \bigcup_{\xi<\lambda} \mathrm{L}(\xi) \quad \text{if} \quad \mathrm{Lim}(\lambda).$$

The meaning of S is irrelevant to this proof. The set Σ_0-Fmla of Gödel-sets of Σ_0-formulas is obviously denumerable because every element arises from natural numbers by formation of finite sequences. Let s enumerate Σ_0-Fmla in a sequence of length ω. Then $\mathrm{L}(\alpha+1)$ may be rewritten as $\{\mathrm{S}(\mathrm{L}(\alpha), w, s`k) | (w, k) \in (\bigcup_{n<\omega} \mathrm{L}(\alpha)^n) \times \omega\}$.

If a, b are sequences of length α, β respectively, let $a^\frown b$ be their ordinal sum (concatenation) and $a \otimes b$ their ordinal product. Then $\mathrm{Dm}(a^\frown b) = \alpha+\beta$, $\mathrm{Rg}(a^\frown b) = \mathrm{Rg}(a) \cup \mathrm{Rg}(b)$, $\mathrm{Dm}(a \otimes b) = \alpha \cdot \beta$, $\mathrm{Rg}(a \otimes b) = \mathrm{Rg}(a) \times \times \mathrm{Rg}(b)$. If $\langle a_\xi | \xi < \delta \rangle$ is a sequence of sequences a_ξ of length α_ξ, let $\frown_{\xi<\delta} a_\xi$ be their ordinal sum (concatenation). Then $\mathrm{Dm}(\frown_{\xi<\delta} a_\xi) = \Sigma_{\xi<\delta} \alpha_\xi$ and $\mathrm{Rg}(\frown_{\xi<\delta} a_\xi) = \bigcup_{\xi<\delta} \mathrm{Rg}(a_\xi)$. Finally if a is a sequence of length α let $\mathrm{E}(a, n)$ be a sequence of type $\alpha \exp n$ (ordinal exponentiation) enumerating $\mathrm{Rg}(a)^n$. Then each set $\mathrm{L}(\alpha)$ has a natural well-ordering $\mathrm{W}(\alpha)$ of length $\mathrm{P}(\alpha)$ where

$$\mathrm{P}(0) = 0,$$
$$\mathrm{P}(\alpha+1) = (\sum_{n<\omega} \mathrm{P}(\alpha) \exp n) \cdot \omega,$$
$$\mathrm{P}(\lambda) = \sum_{\xi<\lambda} \mathrm{P}(\xi) \quad \text{if} \quad \mathrm{Lim}(\lambda),$$
$$\mathrm{W}(0) = 0,$$
$$\mathrm{W}(\alpha+1) = \langle \mathrm{S}(\mathrm{L}(\alpha), [\mathrm{d}`\mu]_1, \mathrm{s}`[\mathrm{d}`\mu]_2) | \mu < \mathrm{P}(\alpha+1) \rangle \quad \text{where}$$
$$\mathrm{d} = \frown_{n<\omega} \mathrm{E}(\mathrm{W}(\alpha), n) \otimes 1_\omega,\ 1_\omega \text{being the identity sequence of length } \omega,$$
$$\mathrm{W}(\lambda) = \frown_{\xi<\lambda} \mathrm{W}(\xi).$$

(The notation is taken from Appendix I.) The functions appearing in the definition of W are all **ZF**-definable and the theorems needed to prove $\vdash_{\mathbf{ZF}} \dot{\mathrm{R}}\mathrm{g}(\dot{\mathrm{W}}(\alpha)) \doteq \dot{\mathrm{L}}(\alpha)$ are part of the basic development of set theory.

6.4. COROLLARY. $\vdash_{\mathbf{ZF}} (\forall v_0)\, \mathscr{L}(v_0) \rightarrow \mathscr{AC}$. (II′ of section 2.)

PROOF. The following proof can be carried out in **ZF**. Let x be any constructible set. By lemma 3.3 there is an ordinal α such that $x \subseteq \mathrm{L}(\alpha)$ and by the theorem $\mathrm{W}(\alpha)$ well-orders $\mathrm{L}(\alpha)$, that is, $\mathrm{W}(\alpha)$ is a sequence of length $\mathrm{P}(\alpha)$ whose range is $\mathrm{L}(\alpha)$. If we fix an element $y \in x$, then the following sequence has range x: For $\gamma < \mathrm{P}(\alpha)$, $\mathrm{F}(\gamma) = \mathrm{W}(\alpha)`[(\min \xi < \mathrm{P}(\alpha))((\mathrm{W}(\alpha)`\xi) \in x - \mathrm{F}``\gamma)]$ if $x - \mathrm{F}``\gamma \neq 0$, y otherwise. Hence x can be well-ordered.

It now remains only to prove III′ of section 2, that the generalized continuum hypothesis follows from the assumption that every set is constructible. The axiom of choice is now available to us. Let $\approx$ be the relation of cardinal equivalence. Using the axiom of choice we can show that for infinite ordinals α, $\alpha \approx \alpha + \alpha \approx \alpha \cdot \alpha \approx \alpha \exp n$ for all $n < \omega$, and $\alpha \approx \Sigma_{n<\omega} \alpha \exp n$. Therefore transfinite induction on α shows that $\alpha \approx \mathrm{P}(\alpha)$ for infinite α, P being the ordinal function just defined in the proof of 6.3. But since $\mathrm{L}(\alpha)$ has an enumeration of length $\mathrm{P}(\alpha)$ and since $\alpha \subseteq \mathrm{L}(\alpha)$ by lemma 6.1, it follows that $\mathrm{L}(\alpha) \approx \alpha$.

6.5. LEMMA. $\vdash_{\mathbf{ZF}} \mathscr{AC} \wedge \alpha \dot{\geqslant} \dot{\omega} \rightarrow \dot{\mathrm{L}}(\alpha) \dot{\approx} \alpha$.

6.6. THEOREM. $\vdash_{\mathbf{ZF}} ((\forall v_0)\, \mathscr{L}(v_0) \wedge \mathscr{AC}) \rightarrow \mathscr{GCH}$. (III′ of section 2.)

PROOF. The following informal proof can be carried out in **ZF**. Let $\mathscr{P}(\kappa)$ be the power-set of κ, κ^+ be the next cardinal after κ, assuming κ is an infinite cardinal. It is required to show $\mathscr{P}(\kappa) \approx \kappa^+$, but in view of the lemma, it suffices to show $\mathscr{P}(\kappa) \subseteq \mathrm{L}(\kappa^+)$. This follows by Lévy's Theorem 5.7 and the Σ_1-definability of L, Appendix II. For if $x \subseteq \kappa$, then $\bar{\bar{x}} \leq \kappa$ and elements of x are ordinals less than κ, so $\mathrm{HC}(x) \leq \kappa$. According to the theorem, $(\exists \alpha)\,(x \in \mathrm{L}(\alpha)) \leftrightarrow (\exists \alpha)\,(\mathrm{HC}(\alpha) \leq \kappa \wedge x \in \mathrm{L}(\alpha))$, using the fact that the condition $\mathrm{Ord}(y)$ is Σ_0 and $x \in \mathrm{L}(y)$ is $\Sigma_1^{\mathbf{ZF}}$. But assuming the axiom of constructibility, $(\exists \alpha)\,(x \in \mathrm{L}(\alpha))$ holds for x, and for all ordinals α, $\mathrm{HC}(\alpha) \leq \kappa \leftrightarrow \alpha < \kappa^+$. But L increases with respect to $\subseteq$, so it follows that $x \in \mathrm{L}(\kappa^+)$. This completes the proof.

7. Remarks

The proof that L defines a transitive inner model of **ZF** was given so that the same proof works for T, a formula defining the minimal model of Cohen [6].

7.1. DEFINITION. Let T be defined informally by ordinal recursion as $\mathrm{T}(0) = \omega \cup \{\omega\}$

$\mathrm{T}(\alpha)$ is the set of all subsets of $\mathrm{C}(\alpha) = \bigcup_{\xi<\alpha} \mathrm{T}(\xi)$ having one of the forms

(i) $\{x, y\}$ for $x, y \in \mathrm{C}(\alpha)$,

(ii) $\bigcup x$ for $x \in \mathrm{C}(\alpha)$,

(iii) $\{y \in \mathrm{C}(\alpha) | y \subseteq x\}$ for $x \in \mathrm{C}(\alpha)$,

(iv) $\{y \in \mathrm{C}(\alpha) | (\exists z \in x)\ \mathscr{Q}(z, y, \mathrm{T}(\beta_1), \ldots, \mathrm{T}(\beta_k), a_1, \ldots, a_n)\}$ where $\mathscr{Q}$ is a Σ_0-formula, $x, a_1, \ldots, a_n \in \mathrm{C}(\alpha)$, $\beta_1, \ldots, \beta_k < \alpha$, and $(\forall z \in x)\,(\exists! y \in \mathrm{C}(\alpha))\,(\mathscr{Q}(z, y, \mathrm{T}(\beta_1), \ldots, \mathrm{T}(\beta_k), a_1, \ldots, a_n))$.

This definition can be formalized in **ZF** only through the use of coding in order to bring in the infinitely many sets of step (iv). The fourth set of subsets can be defined as $\{\mathrm{S}'(\langle \mathrm{T}(\xi) | \xi < \alpha \rangle, x, w_1, w_2, q) | x \in \mathrm{C}(\alpha), w_1 \in \{\mathrm{T}(\xi) | \xi < \alpha\}^{\nearrow\omega}, w_2 \in \mathrm{C}(\alpha)^{\nearrow\omega}, q \in \Sigma_0\text{-Fmla}\}$ where S′ is defined by cases as $S'(f, x, w_1, w_2, q) = \{y | y \in \bigcup Rg(f) \wedge (\exists z \in x)(\langle z, y\rangle^\frown w_1{}^\frown w_2 \text{ Sat } q)\}$ if $Var(q) \subseteq 2 + Dm(w_1) + Dm(w_2)$ and $(\forall z \in x)(\exists! y \in \bigcup Rg(f))(\langle z, y\rangle^\frown w_1{}^\frown w_2 \text{ Sat} q)$, and is 0 otherwise. Since the satisfaction relation for Σ_0-formulas is $\Sigma_1 \cap \Pi_1$-definable, the definition of $T(\alpha)$ can be put in the form $G(\langle T(\xi) | \xi < \alpha\rangle, \alpha)$, where G is Σ_1-definable. Therefore

7.2. THEOREM. The function T is a Σ_1-definable total function.

The analogue of lemma 3.3 for T is proved in much the same way as it was for L. For example, to show that the $T(\alpha)$ are transitive, proceed by transfinite induction within **ZF**. Assuming $(\forall \xi < \alpha)\, Trans(T(\xi))$, it follows that $Trans(C(\alpha))$ since unions of transitive sets are transitive. Every element of $T(\alpha)$ is a subset of $C(\alpha)$, so to show $Trans(T(\alpha))$ it suffices to show $C(\alpha) \subseteq T(\alpha)$. But $x \in C(\alpha)$ implies $x = \{y \in C(\alpha) | (\exists z \in x)(y = z)\}$. This set has form (iv) with $\mathscr{Q} = (v_0 \doteq v_1)$. Thus $x \in T(\alpha)$. With the aid of the lemmas in Appendix II, this argument can be carried out in **ZF**. The proof that the formula $\mathscr{T}(v_0)$ defines a transitive inner model for **ZF** is so similar to the corresponding proof for $\mathscr{L}$ that we omit it here.

7.3. THEOREM. Let $\mathscr{T}(v_0)$ be the formula $(\exists \alpha)(v_0 \dot{\in} T(\alpha))$. Then $\mathscr{T}(v_0)$ defines a transitive inner model of **ZF**.

The minimal property of $\mathscr{T}$ is that $\{x | \mathscr{T}(x)\}$ is the smallest transitive collection X of sets such that the axioms of **ZF** are satisfied in $\langle X, \in_X\rangle$. This is a semantic condition not expressible in **ZF**. Thus theorem 7.5 and its corollaries are theorems about models of **ZF** and require a stronger metatheory than has been used up to this point. The main consequence is that if $\mathscr{B}$ is a **ZF**-formula such that $\vdash_{ZF} \mathscr{B}^{(\mathscr{T})}$, or $\vdash_{ZF} \mathscr{B}^{(\mathscr{L})}$, then there is no formula $\mathscr{M}(v_0)$ defining a transitive inner model such that $\vdash_{ZF} \sim \mathscr{B}^{(\mathscr{M})}$. Thus the method of transitive inner models will not give a proof of the independence of the axiom of choice or of the continuum hypothesis or of the axiom of constructibility. The proof given here, taken from Cohen [6], uses semantic methods, but such methods are not necessary. It is just that a proof in a weaker metatheory requires more formalization than can be given here. The corresponding result for Von Neumann-Gödel-Bernays set theory was given by Shepherdson [5], but this theory has finitely many axioms so the predicate "the axioms are satisfied in $\langle X, \in_X\rangle$" can be rendered without coding. Thus the notion of complete inner model used there is not equivalent to our notion of definable transitive inner model of **ZF** and the argument given there does not carry over without the use of semantic methods.

Incidentally the formal analogue of the minimal property of $\mathscr{L}$, the fact that $\mathscr{L}$ is the smallest transitive inner model containing the ordinals, is easily seen to be provable in **ZF**. For suppose $\mathscr{M}(v_0)$ defines a transitive inner model. Then relativizing a proof in **ZF** of $(\forall\alpha)(\exists! v_1)(v_1 \doteq \dot{\mathrm{L}}(\alpha))$ and using the fact that $\dot{\mathrm{O}}\mathrm{rd}$ and $\dot{\mathrm{L}}$ are $\mathscr{M}$-absolute, we have $\vdash_{\mathbf{ZF}}(\forall\alpha)(\mathscr{M}(\alpha)\to\mathscr{M}(\dot{\mathrm{L}}(\alpha)))$. Hence $\vdash_{\mathbf{ZF}}(\forall\alpha)\,\mathscr{M}(\alpha)\to(\forall v_0)\,(\mathscr{L}(v_0)\to\mathscr{M}(v_0))$.

The satisfaction sign is needed at this point. If $\mathscr{A}$ is a **ZF**-formula in variables $v_0,\ldots,v_n$, and $x_0,\ldots,x_n$ are sets, then $\models\mathscr{A}(x_0,\ldots,x_n)$ means $(x_0,\ldots,x_n)$ satisfies $\mathscr{A}$, while $\models_{\mathrm{X}}\mathscr{A}(x_0,\ldots,x_n)$ means $(x_0,\ldots,x_n)$ satisfies $\mathscr{A}$ in $\langle \mathrm{X},\in_{\mathrm{X}}\rangle$. The latter notation will only be used when $x_0,\ldots,x_n\in\mathrm{X}$. If $\models_{\mathrm{X}}\mathscr{A}$ for all axioms $\mathscr{A}$ of **ZF**, then of course $\vdash_{\mathbf{ZF}}\mathscr{B}$ implies $\models_{\mathrm{X}}\mathscr{B}$. If, moreover, X is transitive and $\mathscr{B}$ is a $\Sigma_1^{\mathbf{ZF}}\cap\Pi_1^{\mathbf{ZF}}$-formula and $x_1,\ldots,x_n\in\mathrm{X}$, then arguments like those of section 5 show that $\models\mathscr{B}(x_1,\ldots,x_n)$ iff $\models_{\mathrm{X}}\mathscr{B}(x_1,\ldots,x_n)$. If F is a Σ_1-definable total function then X is closed under F.

7.4. Lemma. For formulas $\mathscr{M}(v_0)$ and $\mathscr{A}(v_1,\ldots,v_n)$, if X is a collection of sets, $\mathrm{Y}=\{x\in\mathrm{X}\mid\ \models_{\mathrm{X}}\mathscr{M}(x)\}$, and $x_1,\ldots,x_n\in\mathrm{Y}$, then $\models_{\mathrm{X}}\mathscr{A}^{(\mathscr{M})}(x_1,\ldots,x_n)$ iff $\models_{\mathrm{Y}}\mathscr{A}(x_1,\ldots,x_n)$. Therefore if $\mathscr{M}(v_0)$ defines a transitive inner model of **ZF**, and $\mathrm{Y}=\{x\mid\ \models\mathscr{M}(x)\}$ then $\models_{\mathrm{Y}}\mathscr{A}$ for all axioms of **ZF**.

Proof. This is proved by a trivial induction on $\mathscr{A}$.

7.5. Theorem. Let X be any transitive collection of sets such that $\models_{\mathrm{X}}\mathscr{A}$ for all axioms $\mathscr{A}$ of **ZF**. Then $\bigcup_\alpha \mathrm{T}(\alpha)\subseteq\mathrm{X}$.

Proof. Since T is a Σ_1-definable total function, X is closed under T. If all ordinals are in X then clearly $\bigcup_\alpha\mathrm{T}(\alpha)\subseteq\mathrm{X}$. Suppose then that not all ordinals are in X and $\beta=\bigcup_{\alpha\in\mathrm{X}}\alpha$. Then $\mathrm{C}(\beta)\subseteq\mathrm{X}$ and $\{x\in\mathrm{X}\mid\ \models_{\mathrm{X}}\mathscr{T}(x)\}=\{x\in\mathrm{X}\mid(\exists\alpha\in\mathrm{X})\,(x\in\mathrm{T}(\alpha))\}=\mathrm{C}(\beta)$. Since $\vdash_{\mathbf{ZF}}\mathscr{A}^{(\mathscr{T})}$ for all axioms $\mathscr{A}$ of **ZF**, $\models_{\mathrm{X}}\mathscr{A}^{(\mathscr{T})}$ and by the lemma

(*) $\models_{\mathrm{C}(\beta)}\mathscr{A}$ for all axioms $\mathscr{A}$ of **ZF**.

We go on to show $\mathrm{C}(\beta)=\bigcup_\alpha\mathrm{T}(\alpha)$. Consider $u\in\mathrm{T}(\beta)$. If u arises from $\mathrm{C}(\beta)$ by 7.1 (i), (ii), (iii), then $u\in\mathrm{C}(\beta)$ because (*) can be used for the pairing axiom, union axiom, and power-set axiom respectively. If u arises by (iv) we may assume $u=\mathrm{S}'(\langle\mathrm{T}(\xi)\mid\xi<\beta\rangle, x, w, q)$ where $x\in\mathrm{C}(\beta)$, $w\in\mathrm{C}(\beta)^{\nearrow\omega}$, $q\in\Sigma_0$-Fmla, $\mathrm{Var}(q)\leq 2+\mathrm{Dm}(w)$, $(\forall z\in x)\,(\exists! y\in\mathrm{C}(\beta))\,(\langle z, y\rangle^\frown w \text{ Sat } q)$. The parameters $\mathrm{T}(\xi)$, $\xi<\beta$, are missing because $\mathrm{C}(\beta)$ is closed under the Σ_1-definable function T by (*). Then there is $n<\omega$, $a_1,\ldots,a_n\in\mathrm{C}(\beta)$, such that $w=\langle a_1,\ldots,a_n\rangle$ and there is Σ_0-formula $\mathscr{Q}$ such that $q=\ulcorner\mathscr{Q}\urcorner$, the free variables of $\mathscr{Q}$ are $v_0, v_1, v_2,\ldots, v_{1+n}$, and $(\forall z\in x)\,(\exists! y\in\mathrm{C}(\beta))\,(\models\mathscr{Q}(z, y,$

$a_1,\ldots, a_n)$). But $\models$ may be replaced by $\models_{C(\beta)}$ and by (*) $\models_{C(\beta)}(\forall v_2)(v_2 \dot{\in} v_1 \rightarrow (\exists ! v_3)\mathscr{A}) \rightarrow (\exists v_0)(\forall v_3)(v_3 \dot{\in} v_0 \leftrightarrow (\exists v_2)(v_2 \dot{\in} v_1 \wedge \mathscr{A}))$ where $\mathscr{A}$ is $\mathscr{Q}(v_2, v_3, v_4,\ldots, v_{3+n})$. The antecedent is true in $C(\beta)$ for $(x, a_1,\ldots, a_n)$ and u is the corresponding v_0. Hence $u \in C(\beta)$.

We now have $T(\beta)=C(\beta+1)=C(\beta)$. Consider $u \in T(\beta+1)$. If u arises by (i), (ii), (iii), then u is already in $C(\beta)$. If u arises by (iv), we may assume $u=S'(\langle T(\xi)|\xi<\beta\rangle, x, \langle T(\beta)\rangle, w, q)$ where $x \in C(\beta)$, $w \in C(\beta)^{\nearrow\omega}$, $q \in \Sigma_0$-Fmla, $\mathrm{Var}(q) \subseteq 3+\mathrm{Dm}(w)$, $(\forall z \in x)(\exists ! y \in C(\beta))(\langle z, y, T(\beta)\rangle^\frown w \text{ Sat } q)$. Again there is $n<\omega$, $a_1,\ldots, a_n \in C(\beta)$ such that $w=\langle a_1,\ldots, a_n\rangle$, and there is Σ_0-formula $\mathscr{Q}$ such that $q=\ulcorner\mathscr{Q}\urcorner$, the free variables of $\mathscr{Q}$ are $v_0, v_1, v_2, v_3,\ldots, v_{2+n}$ and $(\forall z \in x)(\exists ! y \in C(\beta))(\models \mathscr{Q}(z, y, T(\beta), a_1,\ldots, a_n))$. Let $\mathscr{A}(v_0, v_1, v_3,\ldots, v_{2+n})$ arise from $\mathscr{Q}$ by treating v_2 as the universe, that is, by replacing $v_i \dot{\in} v_2$, $i \neq 2$, by $v_i \doteq v_i$, replacing $v_2 \dot{\in} v_i$ or $v_2 \doteq v_i$, $i \neq 2$, by $\sim(v_i \doteq v_i)$ and so on. Then for $z, y, a_1,\ldots, a_n \in T(\beta)$, $\models \mathscr{Q}(z, y, T(\beta), a_1,\ldots, a_n)$ iff $\models_{C(\beta)} \mathscr{A}(z, y, a_1,\ldots, a_n)$. Then proceeding as in the previous case, $u \in C(\beta)$. Therefore $T(\beta+1)=T(\beta)=C(\beta)$. An induction on α now shows $T(\alpha)=C(\beta)$ for all $\alpha \geqslant \beta$. Hence $\bigcup_\alpha T(\alpha)=C(\beta)=X$.

7.6. Corollary. Suppose $\mathscr{M}(v_0)$ defines a transitive inner model of **ZF**. Then if $\models \mathscr{B}^{(\mathscr{T})}$ then not $\vdash_{\mathbf{ZF}} \sim \mathscr{B}^{(\mathscr{M})}$.

Proof. If $\vdash_{\mathbf{ZF}} \sim \mathscr{B}^{(\mathscr{M})}$ then by 7.3 and 7.4, $\models_{T_\infty} \sim \mathscr{B}^{(\mathscr{M})}$ where $T_\infty = \bigcup_\alpha T(\alpha)$. Let $Y=\{x \in T_\infty | \models_{T_\infty} \mathscr{M}(x)\}$. By 7.4, $\models_Y \sim \mathscr{B}$ and $\models_Y \mathscr{A}$ for all axioms $\mathscr{A}$ of **ZF**. Since Y is transitive, $T_\infty = Y$ by the theorem. Hence $\models \sim \mathscr{B}^{(\mathscr{T})}$.

Note that if $\vdash_{\mathbf{ZF}}((\forall v_0)\mathscr{L}(v_0)) \rightarrow \mathscr{B}$ then $\models \mathscr{B}^{(\mathscr{T})}$. For we have seen that $\vdash_{\mathbf{ZF}} \mathscr{B}^{(\mathscr{L})}$ and $\vdash_{\mathbf{ZF}} \mathscr{A}^{(\mathscr{L})}$ for all axioms $\mathscr{A}$ of **ZF**. Whence $\models_{T_\infty} \mathscr{B}^{(\mathscr{L})}$ and $\models_{T_\infty} \mathscr{A}^{(\mathscr{L})}$. Using the lemma again, if $Z=\{x \in T_\infty | \models_{T_\infty} \mathscr{L}(x)\}$ then Z is transitive, all axioms of **ZF** are satisfied in Z and $\models_Z \mathscr{B}$. But by the theorem $Z=T_\infty$. Thus $\models \mathscr{B}^{(\mathscr{T})}$. Therefore it is impossible to use the method of inner models as described in section 2 to prove the independence of the axiom of choice or of the generalized continuum hypothesis or even of the axiom of constructibility. The generic models introduced by P. Cohen to give these independence proofs are not inner models.

APPENDIX I

A calculus of Σ_1-definable functions

A set-theoretical relation R, formally introduced into **ZF** by its defining formula $\mathscr{D}_R$, is called Σ_0-definable (Σ_1-definable, Π_1-definable) if $\mathscr{D}_R$ is a $\Sigma_0^{\mathbf{ZF}}$-formula ($\Sigma_1^{\mathbf{ZF}}$-formula, $\Pi_1^{\mathbf{ZF}}$-formula). An n-place set-theoretical function F, formally introduced into **ZF** by its defining formula $\mathscr{D}_F$, is Σ_0-definable (Σ_1-definable, Π_1-definable) if $\mathscr{D}_F$ is a $\Sigma_0^{\mathbf{ZF}}$-formula ($\Sigma_1^{\mathbf{ZF}}$-formula, $\Pi_1^{\mathbf{ZF}}$-formula). Since we have chosen always to assume that set-functions are introduced into **ZF** as total functions, the formula $(\forall v_1, \ldots, v_n)(\exists! v_0)$ $\mathscr{D}_F(v_0, v_1, \ldots, v_n)$ is assumed to be provable in **ZF**. ($\mathscr{D}_F$ defines the relation $y = F(x_1, \ldots, x_n)$.)

The aim of this appendix is to build up a useful supply of Σ_1-definable functions and the fastest way to do this seems to be first to make a list of Σ_0-definable relations and functions, and then to make a list of closure conditions that lead from Σ_1-definable functions to Σ_1-definable functions. For the record, all of the functions listed here are primitive recursive set functions, meaning that they arise from the projections, the constant functions 0 and ω, and the pairing and union and difference, by composition, the bounded comprehension schema appearing below, and the recursion schema found in section 1. The primitive recursive set functions can be shown to be a proper subclass of the Σ_1-definable functions.

The procedure in this section is first to give an informal definition, if necessary, of the relation or function, then to write a **ZF**-formula in Σ_0-form which the reader is expected to see is equivalent in **ZF** to the definition normally given. Thus the starting relations and functions S1–S24 are Σ_0-definable.

S1. $x \subseteq y$. $v_1 \dot{\subseteq} v_2 \leftrightarrow (\forall v_3 \dot{\in} v_1)(v_3 \dot{\in} v_2)$.

S2. $\bigcup x$. $v_0 \doteq \dot{\bigcup} v_1 \leftrightarrow (\forall v_2 \dot{\in} v_0)(\exists v_3 \dot{\in} v_1)(v_2 \dot{\in} v_3) \wedge$ $(\forall v_3 \dot{\in} v_1)(\forall v_2 \dot{\in} v_3)(v_2 \dot{\in} v_0)$.

S3. Tr̊ans(x), meaning x is transitive. Tr̊ans$(v_1) \leftrightarrow (\forall v_2 \dot{\in} v_1)(v_2 \dot{\subseteq} v_1)$.

S4. $\dot{\mathrm{Ord}}(x)$, meaning x is an ordinal. $\dot{\mathrm{Ord}}(v_1) \leftrightarrow \dot{\mathrm{Trans}}(v_1) \wedge (\forall v_2, v_3 \dot{\in} v_1)(v_2 \dot{\in} v_3 \vee v_2 \doteq v_3 \vee v_3 \dot{\in} v_2)$.

S5. 0, the empty set. $v_0 \doteq \dot{0} \leftrightarrow (\forall v_1 \dot{\in} v_0)(\sim v_1 \doteq v_1)$.

S6. The natural number n, $n>0$. $v_0 \doteq \dot{n} \leftrightarrow (\bigwedge_{i<n} i \dot{\in} v_0) \wedge (\forall v_1 \in v_0)(\bigvee_{i<n} v_1 \doteq i)$. Replace $(i \dot{\in} v_0)$ by the Σ_0-formula $(\exists v_1 \dot{\in} v_0)(v_1 \doteq i)$.

S7. $x-y$. $v_0 \doteq v_1 \dot{-} v_2 \leftrightarrow (\forall v_3 \dot{\in} v_0)(v_3 \dot{\in} v_1 \wedge \sim v_3 \dot{\in} v_2) \wedge (\forall v_3 \dot{\in} v_1)(\sim v_3 \dot{\in} v_2 \rightarrow v_3 \dot{\in} v_0)$.

S8. $x \cup y$. $v_0 \doteq v_1 \dot{\cup} v_2 \leftrightarrow (\forall v_3 \dot{\in} v_0)(v_3 \dot{\in} v_1 \vee v_3 \dot{\in} v_2) \wedge (\forall v_3 \dot{\in} v_1)(v_3 \dot{\in} v_0) \wedge (\forall v_3 \dot{\in} v_2)(v_3 \dot{\in} v_0)$.

S9. $x \cap y$. $v_0 \doteq v_1 \dot{\cap} v_2 \leftrightarrow (\forall v_3 \dot{\in} v_0)(v_3 \dot{\in} v_1 \wedge v_3 \dot{\in} v_2) \wedge (\forall v_3 \dot{\in} v_1)(v_3 \dot{\in} v_2 \rightarrow v_3 \dot{\in} v_0)$.

S10. $s(x) = x \cup \{x\}$. $v_0 \doteq \dot{s}(v_1) \leftrightarrow (\forall v_2 \dot{\in} v_0)(v_2 \dot{\in} v_1 \vee v_2 \doteq v_1) \wedge v_1 \dot{\subseteq} v_0 \wedge v_1 \dot{\in} v_0$.

S11. ω, the set of natural numbers, the first transfinite ordinal. $v_0 \doteq \dot{\omega} \leftrightarrow (\dot{0} \dot{\in} v_0) \wedge (\forall v_1 \dot{\in} v_0)(\dot{s}(v_1) \dot{\in} v_0) \wedge (\forall v_1 \dot{\in} v_0)(v_1 \doteq \dot{0} \vee (\exists v_2 \dot{\in} v_1)(v_1 \doteq \doteq \dot{s}(v_2)))$.

S12. $\{x, y\}$. $v_0 \doteq \{v_1, v_2\} \leftrightarrow v_1 \dot{\in} v_0 \wedge v_2 \dot{\in} v_0 \wedge (\forall v_3 \dot{\in} v_0)(v_3 \doteq v_1 \vee v_3 \doteq v_2)$.

S13. (x, y), the ordered pair. $v_0 \doteq (v_1, v_2) \leftrightarrow (\forall v_3 \dot{\in} v_0)(v_3 \doteq \{v_1\} \vee v_3 \doteq \{v_1, v_2\}) \wedge \{v_1\} \dot{\in} v_0 \wedge \{v_1, v_2\} \dot{\in} v_0$. Replace $\{v_1\} \dot{\in} v_0$ by $(\exists v_3 \dot{\in} v_0)(v_3 \doteq \{v_1\})$ and so on.

S14. $\dot{\mathrm{OrdPr}}(x)$, meaning x is an ordered pair. $\dot{\mathrm{OrdPr}}(v_1) \leftrightarrow (\exists v_2, v_3 \dot{\in} \dot{\bigcup} v_1)(v_1 \doteq (v_2, v_3))$. Replace $(\exists v_2, v_3 \dot{\in} \dot{\bigcup} v_1)$ by $(\exists v_4 \dot{\in} v_1)(\exists v_2, v_3 \dot{\in} v_4)$.

S15. $\mathrm{Rel}(x)$, x is a relation. $\dot{\mathrm{Rel}}(v_1) \leftrightarrow (\forall v_2 \dot{\in} v_1)(\dot{\mathrm{OrdPr}}(v_2))$.

S16. $\mathrm{Fcn}(x)$, x is a function. $\dot{\mathrm{Fcn}}(v_1) \leftrightarrow \dot{\mathrm{Rel}}(v_1) \wedge (\forall v_2, v_3, v_4 \dot{\in} \dot{\bigcup} \dot{\bigcup} v_1)((v_2, v_3) \dot{\in} v_1 \wedge (v_2, v_4) \dot{\in} v_1 \rightarrow v_3 \doteq v_4)$. Replace $(\forall v_2, v_3, v_4 \dot{\in} \dot{\bigcup} \dot{\bigcup} v_1)$ by $(\forall v_5, v_6, v_7 \in \dot{\bigcup} v_1)(\forall v_2 \dot{\in} v_5)(\forall v_3 \dot{\in} v_6)(\forall v_4 \dot{\in} v_7)$ and so on.

S17. $[x]_i$, the i-th coordinate of x if $\dot{\mathrm{OrdPr}}(x)$, 0 if not, $i=1, 2$. $v_0 \doteq [v_1]_i \leftrightarrow (\dot{\mathrm{OrdPr}}(v_1) \wedge (\exists v_2 \dot{\in} \dot{\bigcup} v_1)(v_1 \doteq (v_0, v_2))) \vee (\sim \dot{\mathrm{OrdPr}}(v_1) \wedge v_0 \doteq \dot{0})$ for $i=1$.

S18. $\mathrm{Dm}(x)$, the domain of x, the set of first coordinates of ordered pairs in x. $v_0 \doteq \dot{\mathrm{Dm}}(v_1) \leftrightarrow (\forall v_2 \dot{\in} v_0)(\exists v_3 \dot{\in} \dot{\bigcup} \dot{\bigcup} v_1)((v_2, v_3) \dot{\in} v_1) \wedge (\forall v_4 \dot{\in} v_1)(\dot{\mathrm{OrdPr}}(v_4) \rightarrow [v_4]_1 \dot{\in} v_0)$.

S19. $\mathrm{Rg}(x)$, the range of x, the set of second coordinates of ordered pairs in x. Similar to S18.

S20. x‘y, the value of x at y if $\mathrm{Fcn}(x)$, 0 otherwise. $v_0 \doteq v_1 ‘ v_2 \leftrightarrow (\dot{\mathrm{Fcn}}(v_1) \wedge (v_2, v_0) \dot{\in} v_1) \vee (\sim \dot{\mathrm{Fcn}}(v_1) \wedge v_0 \doteq \dot{0})$.

S21. x“y, the x-image of y, the set of second coordinates of ordered pairs in x having first coordinates in y. $v_0 \doteq v_1``v_2 \leftrightarrow (\forall v_3 \dot{\in} v_0)(\exists v_4 \dot{\in} v_2)((v_4, v_3) \dot{\in} v_1) \wedge (\forall v_5 \dot{\in} v_1)(\dot{\text{OrdPr}}(v_5) \wedge [v_5]_1 \dot{\in} v_2 \rightarrow [v_5]_2 \dot{\in} v_0)$.

S22. $\text{Seq}(x)$, x is a sequence, $\text{Fcn}(x) \wedge \text{Ord}(\text{Dm}(x))$. $\dot{\text{Seq}}(v_1) \leftrightarrow \dot{\text{Fcn}}(v_1) \wedge (\forall v_2 \dot{\in} v_1)(\forall v_3 \dot{\in} \dot{\bigcup} v_2)(v_3 \doteq [v_2]_1 \rightarrow (\dot{\text{Ord}}(v_3) \wedge (\forall v_4 \dot{\in} v_3)(v_4 \dot{\in} \dot{\text{Dm}}(v_1))))$. Replace $v_4 \dot{\in} \dot{\text{Dm}}(v_1)$ by $(\exists v_5 \dot{\in} v_1)(v_4 \doteq [v_5]_1)$.

S23. $x \upharpoonright y$, the restriction of x to y, the set of ordered pairs in x with first coordinates in y. $v_0 \doteq v_1 \upharpoonright v_2 \leftrightarrow (\forall v_3 \dot{\in} v_1)(\dot{\text{OrdPr}}(v_3) \wedge [v_3]_1 \dot{\in} v_2 \rightarrow v_3 \dot{\in} v_0) \wedge (\forall v_3 \dot{\in} v_0)(\dot{\text{OrdPr}}(v_3) \wedge [v_3]_1 \dot{\in} v_2)$.

S24. $x \times y$, the Cartesian product. $v_0 \doteq v_1 \times v_2 \leftrightarrow (\forall v_3 \dot{\in} v_0)(\dot{\text{OrdPr}}(v_3) \wedge [v_3]_1 \dot{\in} v_1 \wedge [v_3]_2 \dot{\in} v_2) \wedge (\forall v_4 \dot{\in} v_1)(\forall v_5 \dot{\in} v_2)((v_4, v_5) \dot{\in} v_0)$.

LEMMA. (1) If $\mathscr{A}$ is a $\Sigma_1^{\mathbf{ZF}}$-formula, then so is $(\exists v_i)\, \mathscr{A}$.
(2) If $\mathscr{A}$, $\mathscr{B}$ are $\Sigma_1^{\mathbf{ZF}}$-formulas, then so are $(\mathscr{A} \wedge \mathscr{B})$, $(\mathscr{A} \vee \mathscr{B})$.
(3) If $\mathscr{A}$ is a $\Sigma_1^{\mathbf{ZF}}$-formula, then $\sim\mathscr{A}$ is a $\Pi_1^{\mathbf{ZF}}$-formula.
(4) If $\mathscr{A}$ is a $\Pi_1^{\mathbf{ZF}}$-formula and $\mathscr{B}$ is a $\Sigma_1^{\mathbf{ZF}}$-formula, then $(\mathscr{A} \rightarrow \mathscr{B})$ is a $\Sigma_1^{\mathbf{ZF}}$-formula.
(5) If $\mathscr{A}$ is a $\Sigma_1^{\mathbf{ZF}}$-formula, then so is $(\forall v_i \dot{\in} v_j)\, \mathscr{A}$.

PROOF. This is taken from Lévy [2]. If $j, k \neq i$ and $\mathscr{A} \leftrightarrow (\exists v_j)\mathscr{Q}$ in **ZF**, then $(\exists v_i)\, \mathscr{A} \leftrightarrow (\exists v_k)\mathscr{Q}'$ in **ZF**, where $\mathscr{Q}'$ is $(\exists v_i \dot{\in} v_k)(\exists v_j \dot{\in} v_k)\mathscr{Q}$. Hence (1). Statements (2), (3), (4) are proved by placing quantifiers in prenex position. Statement (5) requires the axiom of regularity. Suppose $k \neq i, j$ and $\mathscr{A} \leftrightarrow (\exists v_k)\, \mathscr{Q}$ in **ZF** where $\mathscr{Q}$ is again assumed to be a Σ_0-formula. Then $(\forall v_i \dot{\in} v_j)\mathscr{A} \leftrightarrow (\forall v_i \dot{\in} v_j)\,(\exists v_k)\mathscr{Q}$ in **ZF**. In order to show that this formula may be cast in Σ_1-form, it suffices to show that there is a $\text{V}(\beta)$ that bounds the v_k for v_i in v_j, where V is the generating function for partial universes discussed in section 1. Recall that V is provably transitive and increasing with respect to $\subseteq$, and $\vdash_{\mathbf{ZF}} (\forall v)(\exists \alpha)(v \dot{\in} \dot{\text{V}}(\alpha))$. Thus in **ZF**,

$$(\forall v_i)(\exists!\, \alpha)\, [(\sim (\exists v_k)\, \mathscr{Q} \wedge \alpha \doteq \dot{0}) \vee (\exists v_k \dot{\in} \dot{\text{V}}(\alpha))\, (\mathscr{Q} \wedge (\forall \xi \in \alpha) \sim (\exists v_k \dot{\in} \dot{\text{V}}(\xi))\, \mathscr{Q})].$$

By replacement, $\vdash_{\mathbf{ZF}} (\exists v')(\forall \alpha)(\alpha \dot{\in} v' \leftrightarrow (\exists v_i \dot{\in} v_j)\, \mathscr{B})$ where $\mathscr{B}$ is the formula in brackets. But then, taking β as $\bigcup v'$, $\vdash_{\mathbf{ZF}} (\exists \beta)(\forall v_i \dot{\in} v_j)\, [(\exists v_k)\, \mathscr{Q} \leftrightarrow (\exists v_k \dot{\in} \dot{\text{V}}(\beta))\, \mathscr{Q}]$. But then $(\forall v_i \dot{\in} v_j)(\exists v_k)\, \mathscr{Q}$ has the equivalent form $(\exists v)(\forall v_i \dot{\in} v_j)(\exists v_k \dot{\in} v)\, \mathscr{Q}$ in **ZF**. Hence (5).

COROLLARY. (1) If F is a Σ_1-definable set-function, then all of the relations $x_0 = \text{F}(x_1, \ldots, x_n)$, $x_0 \in \text{F}(x_1, \ldots, x_n)$, $\text{F}(x_1, \ldots, x_n) \in x_0$, are $\Sigma_1 \cap \Pi_1$-definable.

(2) If R is a $\Sigma_1 \cap \Pi_1$-definable relation, then the characteristic function of R, defined by $C_R(x_1,\ldots,x_n)=0$ if $R(x_1,\ldots,x_n)$, 1 if $\sim R(x_1,\ldots,x_n)$, is a Σ_1-definable function.

PROOF. If $\mathscr{D}_F$ is the $\Sigma_1^{\mathbf{ZF}}$-defining formula of F, then $(\exists v)(\mathscr{D}_F(v, v_1,\ldots, v_n)\wedge(\ldots))$ defines $x_0 \neq F(x_1,\ldots,x_n)$ if we put $v_0 \neq v$ for the dots, defines $x_0 \in F(x_1,\ldots,x_n)$ if we put $v_0 \dot{\in} v$ for the dots, and so on. These are all $\Sigma_1^{\mathbf{ZF}}$-formulas. The function C_R is defined by the $\Sigma_1^{\mathbf{ZF}}$-formula $(v_0 \doteq \dot{0} \wedge \mathscr{D}_R(v_1,\ldots,v_n)) \vee (v_0 \doteq \dot{1} \wedge \sim\mathscr{D}_R(v_1,\ldots,v_n))$.

COROLLARY. If R_1, R_2 are $\Sigma_1 \cap \Pi_1$-definable relations, so are $R_1 \wedge R_2$, $R_1 \vee R_2$, $\sim R_1$, $R_1 \rightarrow R_2$, $(\forall x_i \in x_j)\, R_1$, $(\exists x_i \in x_j)\, R_1$.

COROLLARY (DEFINITION BY CASES). If G_i is a Σ_1-definable function, $i=1,\ldots,m$, if R_i is a Σ_1-definable relation, $i=1,\ldots,m$, and both $(\bigvee_{1\le i\le m} \mathscr{D}_{R_i}(v_1,\ldots,v_n))$ and $(\bigwedge_{1\le i\neq j\le m} \sim(\mathscr{D}_{R_i}(v_1,\ldots,v_n)\wedge \mathscr{D}_{R_j}(v_1,\ldots,v_n)))$ are provable in **ZF**, then F is a Σ_1-definable function, where $F(x_1,\ldots,x_n)= G_i(x_1,\ldots,x_n)$ if $R_i(x_1,\ldots,x_n)$, $i=1,\ldots,m$.

COROLLARY (COMPOSITION). If H is an m-place Σ_1-definable function and G_i an n-place Σ_1-definable function, $i=1,\ldots,m$, then F defined by composition as $F(x_1,\ldots,x_n)=H(G_1(x_1,\ldots,x_n),\ldots,G_m(x_1,\ldots,x_n))$ is Σ_1-definable.

PROOF. If $\mathscr{D}_H$, $\mathscr{D}_{G_i}$ are $\Sigma_1^{\mathbf{ZF}}$-defining formulas for H, $G_1,\ldots,G_m$, then a $\Sigma_1^{\mathbf{ZF}}$-defining formula for F is

$$\mathscr{D}_F(v_0, v_1,\ldots,v_n)\leftrightarrow (\exists v_{n+1}\ldots v_{n+m})\Big(\bigwedge_{1\leqslant i\leqslant m} \mathscr{D}_{G_i}(v_{n+i}, v_1,\ldots,v_n) \wedge \mathscr{D}_H(v_0, v_{n+1},\ldots,v_{n+m})\Big).$$

COROLLARY (COMPREHENSION). If G is an $n+1$-place Σ_1-definable function, H is an n-place Σ_1-definable function and R is an $n+1$-place $\Sigma_1 \cap \Pi_1$-definable relation, then F is an n-place Σ_1-definable function, where $F(x_1,\ldots,x_n)=\{G(z, x_1,\ldots,x_n) \mid z\in H(x_1,\ldots,x_n)\wedge R(z, x_1,\ldots,x_n)\}$.

PROOF. Since we have already shown that the Σ_1-definable functions are closed under composition, it suffices to show that F is Σ_1-definable where $F(x_1,\ldots,x_{n+1})=\{G(z, x_1,\ldots,x_n) \mid z\in x_{n+1}\wedge R(z, x_1,\ldots,x_n)\}$. If $\mathscr{D}_G$ is a $\Sigma_1^{\mathbf{ZF}}$-defining formula for G and $\mathscr{D}_R$ is a $\Sigma_1^{\mathbf{ZF}} \cap \Pi_1^{\mathbf{ZF}}$-defining formula for R, a $\Sigma_1^{\mathbf{ZF}}$-defining formula for F is

$$\mathscr{D}_F(v_0, v_1,\ldots,v_{n+1})\leftrightarrow(\forall v_{n+2}\dot{\in} v_0)(\exists v_{n+3}\dot{\in} v_{n+1})(\mathscr{D}_R(v_{n+3}, v_1,\ldots,v_n)\wedge \mathscr{D}_G(v_{n+2}, v_{n+3}, v_1,\ldots,v_n))\wedge(\forall v_{n+3}\dot{\in} v_{n+1})(\mathscr{D}_R(v_{n+3}, v_1,\ldots,v_n)\rightarrow \rightarrow(\exists v_{n+2}\dot{\in} v_0)\,\mathscr{D}_G(v_{n+2}, v_{n+3}, v_1,\ldots,v_n)).$$

The required condition $(\forall v_1 \dots v_{n+1})(\exists! v_0)\, \mathscr{D}_{\mathrm{F}}$ follows by the Replacement scheme.

COROLLARY (ORDINAL RECURSION). If G is an $n+1$-place Σ_1-definable function and F is defined by ordinal recursion on x_1 as $\mathrm{F}(x_1, \dots, x_n)=0$ if $\sim\mathrm{Ord}(x_1)$, $\mathrm{F}(x_1, \dots, x_n)=\mathrm{G}(\langle \mathrm{F}(\xi, x_2, \dots, x_n) | \xi \in x_1 \rangle, x_1, \dots, x_n)$ if $\mathrm{Ord}(x_1)$, then F is Σ_1-definable.

(Brackets $\langle, \rangle$ are used to write functions, so $\langle \mathrm{F}(\xi, x_2, \dots, x_n) | \xi \in x_1 \rangle$ is that function on x_1 whose value at ξ is $\mathrm{F}(\xi, x_2, \dots, x_n)$.)

PROOF. If $\mathscr{D}_{\mathrm{G}}$ is a $\Sigma_1^{\mathbf{ZF}}$-defining formula for G, then a defining formula for F, $\Sigma_1^{\mathbf{ZF}}$ by the lemma, is $\mathscr{D}_{\mathrm{F}}(v_0, v_1, \dots, v_n) \leftrightarrow (\sim \dot{\mathrm{Ord}}(v_1) \wedge v_0 \doteq \dot{0}) \vee (\dot{\mathrm{Ord}}(v_1) \wedge (\exists v_{n+1})(\dot{\mathrm{Seq}}(v_{n+1}) \wedge \dot{\mathrm{Dm}}(v_{n+1}) \doteq v_1 \wedge \mathscr{D}_{\mathrm{G}}(v_0, v_{n+1}, v_1, \dots, v_n) \wedge (\forall v_{n+2} \dot{\in} v_1)(\mathscr{D}_{\mathrm{G}}(v_{n+1}`v_{n+2}, v_{n+1} \upharpoonright v_{n+2}, v_{n+2}, v_2, \dots, v_n)))$.

An ordinal recursion may appear in the form $\mathrm{F}(\alpha, x_2, \dots, x_n)= \mathrm{G}(\langle \mathrm{F}(\xi, x_2, \dots, x_n) | \xi \in \alpha \rangle, \alpha, x_2, \dots, x_n)$. In this case α is as usual assumed to be an ordinal, and the value of F at $\langle x_1, \dots, x_n \rangle$ where x_1 is not an ordinal, is assumed to be 0. An ordinal recursion may also appear in the form

$$\mathrm{F}(0, x_2, \dots, x_n) = \mathrm{G}_1(x_2, \dots, x_n),$$

$$\mathrm{F}(\alpha + 1, x_2, \dots, x_n) = \mathrm{G}_2(\mathrm{F}(\alpha, x_2, \dots, x_n), \alpha, x_2, \dots, x_n),$$

$$\mathrm{F}(\lambda, x_2, \dots, x_n) = \mathrm{G}_3(\langle \mathrm{F}(\zeta, x_2, \dots, x_n) | \zeta < \lambda \rangle, \lambda, x_2, \dots, x_n) \quad \text{if} \quad \mathrm{Lim}(\lambda).$$

This form reduces to the one above with $\mathrm{G}(y, \alpha, x_2, \dots, x_n)$ defined by cases as $\mathrm{G}_1(x_2, \dots, x_n)$ if $\alpha=0$, $\mathrm{G}_2(y`\bigcup\alpha, \bigcup\alpha, x_2, \dots, x_n)$ if $\bigcup\alpha<\alpha$, $\mathrm{G}_3(y, \alpha, x_2, \dots, x_n)$ if $\bigcup\alpha=\alpha$, $\alpha>0$.

APPENDIX II

The Σ_1-definability of L

The function L generating the constructible sets and introduced informally in section 3, is defined by ordinal recursion in terms of the relation "the $n+1$-tuple $\langle x, a_1, \ldots, a_n \rangle$ satisfies $\mathcal{Q}$", informally written "$\mathcal{Q}(x, a_1, \ldots, a_n)$", where $\mathcal{Q}$ is a Σ_0-formula. It is necessary to go through a coding of Σ_0-formulas in order to express this relation formally in **ZF**. It is in fact a $\Sigma_1 \cap \Pi_1$-definable relation, a fact that is needed in order to establish the Σ_1-definability of L. The computation that follows appears in a somewhat different form in Lévy [2], where it is extended to show that the satisfaction relation for $\Sigma_n \cup \Pi_n$-formulas is $\Sigma_{n+1} \cap \Pi_{n+1}$-definable. An application of the classical undefinability-of-truth argument of Tarski shows that the satisfaction relation for arbitrary **ZF**-formulas is not definable in **ZF**.

The brackets, $\langle, \rangle$, are reserved for functions. The positional notation $\langle x_0, \ldots, x_{n-1} \rangle$ stands for the sequence whose domain is n and whose value at i is x_i. Exponential notation is used here in the cardinal sense, x^y is the set of functions on y into x. The Gödel-set $\ulcorner \mathcal{Q} \urcorner$ of a Σ_0-formula $\mathcal{Q}$ is defined recursively as follows:

Formula	Gödel-set
$(v_i \dot{=} v_j)$	$\langle 0, i, j \rangle$
$(v_i \dot{\in} v_j)$	$\langle 1, i, j \rangle$
$(\sim \mathcal{Q})$	$\langle 2, \ulcorner \mathcal{Q} \urcorner \rangle$
$(\mathcal{Q}_1 \to \mathcal{Q}_2)$	$\langle 3, \ulcorner \mathcal{Q} \urcorner_1, \ulcorner \mathcal{Q}_2 \urcorner \rangle$
$(\forall v_i)(v_i \dot{\in} v_j \to \mathcal{Q})$	$\langle 4, i, j, \ulcorner \mathcal{Q} \urcorner \rangle$

There follows a list of relations and functions involving the coding and ending with L. Each is first described informally, then is cast in terms of the starting functions and relations S1–S24 by means of the closure conditions in Appendix I. Therefore each of the functions is a Σ_1-definable total function and each of the relations is $\Sigma_1 \cap \Pi_1$-definable. Since complete instructions for writing defining formulas in the proper form have been given, it is not necessary to do that here.

T1. $x^{\nearrow\omega}$, the set of finite sequences of elements of x. Note that $x^{\nearrow\omega} = \bigcup\{\mathrm{F}(k, x) | k \in \omega\}$ where F is defined by ordinal recursion as $\mathrm{F}(0, x) = \{0\}$, $\mathrm{F}(\alpha+1, x) = \{y \cup \{(\alpha, v)\} | y \in \mathrm{F}(\alpha, x) \wedge v \in x\}$.

An inductive argument shows that $\mathrm{F}(k, x) = x^k$ for $k \in \omega$. Theorem 5.7 on the cardinal boundedness of Σ_1-definable functions shows that the function x^ω is not Σ_1-definable.

T2. AtFmla, the set of all Gödel-sets of atomic formulas. $\mathrm{AtFmla} = \{x | x \in \omega^{\nearrow\omega} \wedge \mathrm{Dm}(x) = 3 \wedge x`0 \in 2\}$.

Note that this is Σ_1-definable regarded as a 0-place function. Therefore the relations $x \in \mathrm{AtFmla}$, $x = \mathrm{AtFmla}$, are $\Sigma_1 \cap \Pi_1$-definable.

T3. Σ_0-Fmla, the set of all Gödel-sets of Σ_0-formulas. $\Sigma_0\text{-Fmla} = \bigcup\{\mathrm{Fmla}(k) | k \in \omega\}$ where Fmla is defined by ordinal recursion as $\mathrm{Fmla}(0) = \mathrm{AtFmla}$, $\mathrm{Fmla}(\alpha+1) = \mathrm{Fmla}(\alpha) \cup \{\langle 2, x\rangle | x \in \mathrm{Fmla}(\alpha)\} \cup \{\langle 3, x, y\rangle | x, y \in \mathrm{Fmla}(\alpha)\} \cup \{\langle 4, x, y, z\rangle | x, y \in \omega \wedge z \in \mathrm{Fmla}(\alpha)\}$.

T4. $\mathrm{Rk}(x) = (\min k < \omega)\,(\Sigma_0\text{-Fmla}(x) \rightarrow x \in \mathrm{Fmla}(k))$. Let $\mathrm{G}(x) = \{k | k \in \omega \wedge (x \in \Sigma_0\text{-Fmla} \rightarrow x \in \mathrm{Fmla}(k))\}$. Then $\mathrm{Rk}(x) = \bigcap \mathrm{G}(x)$.

The function Rk operates on Gödel-sets of formulas as a rank function, where atomic formulas have rank 0, $\mathrm{rank}(\sim\mathscr{Q}) = \mathrm{rank}(\mathscr{Q})+1$, $\mathrm{rank}(\mathscr{Q}_1 \rightarrow \mathscr{Q}_2) = \max\{\mathrm{rank}(\mathscr{Q}_1), \mathrm{rank}(\mathscr{Q}_2)\}+1$, $\mathrm{rank}((\forall v_i)\,(v_i \dot{\in} v_j \rightarrow \mathscr{Q})) = \mathrm{rank}(\mathscr{Q})+1$.

Lemma. Let $\mathscr{Q}$ be a Σ_0-formula with Gödel-set q, rank r. Then the following are theorems of **ZF**: $(\dot{q} \dot{\in} \dot{\mathrm{Fmla}}(\dot{r}))$, $(\forall v \dot{\in} \dot{r})\,(\dot{q} \dot{\notin} \dot{\mathrm{Fmla}}(v))$, $\dot{\mathrm{Rk}}(\dot{q}) \doteq \dot{r}$.

Proof. This reduces to a list of formal theorems that are properly part of the basic development of **ZF**. For natural numbers i, j, $\vdash_{\mathbf{ZF}} \langle \dot{0}\; i j\rangle \dot{\in} \dot{\mathrm{Fmla}}(\dot{0})$ follows from $\vdash_{\mathbf{ZF}} \langle \dot{0} i j\rangle \dot{\in} \dot{\omega}^{\nearrow\dot{\omega}} \wedge \dot{\mathrm{Dm}}(\langle \dot{0} i j\rangle) \doteq \dot{3} \wedge \langle \dot{0} i j\rangle`\dot{0} \dot{\in} \dot{2}$. Thus if $\mathscr{Q}$ is $(v_i \doteq v_j)$, then since $q = \langle 0\; i\; j\rangle$ and $r = 0$, $\vdash_{\mathbf{ZF}} \dot{q} \dot{\in} \dot{\mathrm{Fmla}}(\dot{r})$ follows from the statement $\dot{q} \doteq \langle \dot{0}\; i\; j\rangle$. Consider the case $\mathscr{Q} = (\mathscr{Q}_1 \rightarrow \mathscr{Q}_2)$ with $q_1\; q_2$ being the Gödel-sets, r_1, r_2 the ranks of $\mathscr{Q}_1$ and $\mathscr{Q}_2$. Then $q = \langle 3\; q_1\; q_2\rangle$ and $r = r_2+1$, assuming $r_1 \leq r_2$. The induction hypothesis gives $\dot{q}_1 \dot{\in} \dot{\mathrm{Fmla}}(\dot{r}_1)$, $\dot{q}_2 \dot{\in} \dot{\mathrm{Fmla}}(\dot{r}_2)$ and the definition of Fmla gives $\dot{\mathrm{Fmla}}(\dot{r}_1) \dot{\subseteq} \dot{\mathrm{Fmla}}(\dot{r}_2)$. Then $\langle \dot{3}\; \dot{q}_1\; \dot{q}_2\rangle \dot{\in} \dot{\mathrm{Fmla}}(\dot{r})$. The result $\vdash_{\mathbf{ZF}} \dot{q} \dot{\in} \dot{\mathrm{Fmla}}(\dot{r})$ follows from $\dot{q} \doteq \langle \dot{3}\; \dot{q}_1\; \dot{q}_2\rangle$. The other cases are similar.

The second statement follows by a similar induction from the provability in **ZF** of $(v \dot{\in} \dot{r}) \rightarrow (\bigvee_{k<r} v \doteq \dot{k})$.

T5. $w\ \mathrm{Sat}_0\ x$, meaning w satisfies $\mathcal{Q}$ if $x = \ulcorner\mathcal{Q}\urcorner$, $\mathcal{Q}$ an atomic formula, $\mathrm{Fcn}(w)$, and $\mathrm{Dm}(w) \subseteq \omega$. $w\ \mathrm{Sat}_0\ x \leftrightarrow (x{'}0 = 0 \wedge w{'}(x{'}1) = w{'}(x{'}2)) \vee (x{'}0 = 1 \wedge w{'}(x{'}1) \in w{'}(x{'}2))$. Note that the assignment corresponding to w is $w{'}i$ for v_i, but that the unintended meaning of ‘ according to S20 gives value 0 to v_i in case $i \notin \mathrm{Dm}(w)$.

T6. $\mathrm{Sa}(0, y) = \{\langle w, x, k\rangle \mid w \in y^{\nearrow\omega} \wedge x \in \mathrm{AtFmla} \wedge k \in 2 \wedge$
$\wedge ((w\ \mathrm{Sat}_0 x \wedge k = 0) \vee (\sim w\ \mathrm{Sat}_0 x \wedge k = 1))\}$.
$\mathrm{Sa}(\alpha+1, y) = \mathrm{Sa}(\alpha, y) \cup \{\langle w, x, k\rangle \mid w \in y^{\nearrow\omega} \wedge x \in \Sigma_0\text{-Fmla} \wedge k \in 2 \wedge$
$\wedge (C_1 \vee C_2 \vee C_3)\}$, where
C_1 is $x = \langle 2, x{'}1\rangle \wedge ((\langle w, x{'}1, 0\rangle \in \mathrm{Sa}(\alpha, y) \wedge k = 1) \vee$
$\vee (\langle w, x{'}1, 1\rangle \in \mathrm{Sa}(\alpha, y) \wedge k = 0))$,
C_2 is $x = \langle 3, x{'}1, x{'}2\rangle \wedge [(\langle w, x{'}1, 0\rangle \in \mathrm{Sa}(\alpha, y) \wedge \langle w, x{'}2, 0\rangle \in$
$\in \mathrm{Sa}(\alpha, y) \wedge k = 0) \vee (\langle w, x{'}1, 0\rangle \in \mathrm{Sa}(\alpha, y) \wedge \langle w, x{'}2, 1\rangle \in \mathrm{Sa}(\alpha, y) \wedge$
$\wedge k = 1) \vee (\langle w, x{'}1, 1\rangle \in \mathrm{Sa}(\alpha, y) \wedge \langle w, x{'}2, 0\rangle \in \mathrm{Sa}(\alpha, y) \wedge k = 0) \vee$
$\vee (\langle w, x{'}1, 1\rangle \in \mathrm{Sa}(\alpha, y) \wedge \langle w, x{'}2, 1\rangle \in \mathrm{Sa}(\alpha, y) \wedge k = 0)]$,
C_3 is $x = \langle 4, x{'}1, x{'}2, x{'}3\rangle \wedge [(\forall z \in w{'}(x{'}2))\ (\langle (w - \{x{'}1, w{'}(x{'}1)\}) \cup$
$\cup \{(x{'}1, z)\}, x{'}3, 0\rangle \in \mathrm{Sa}(\alpha, y) \wedge k = 0) \vee (\exists z \in w{'}(x{'}2))$
$(\langle (w - \{x{'}1, w{'}(x{'}1)\}) \cup \{(x{'}1, z)\}, x{'}3, 1\rangle \in \mathrm{Sa}(\alpha, y) \wedge k = 1)]$.
$\mathrm{Sa}(\lambda, y) = 0$ if $\mathrm{Lim}(\lambda)$.

The meaning of the function Sa, defined by transfinite induction on α, will be clear from the following lemma.

LEMMA. Let $\mathcal{Q}$ be a Σ_0-formula with Gödel-set q, rank r. Then if every variable v_i appearing in $\mathcal{Q}$ has index $i \le n$ and $f \in \omega^{n+1}$, the following are formal theorems of **ZF**: $(\dot{\mathrm{T}}\mathrm{C}(\{v_{f(0)}, \ldots, v_{f(n)}\}) \dot{\subseteq} v \wedge \mathrm{SF}_f(\mathcal{Q})) \rightarrow \langle\langle v_{f(0)}, \ldots, v_{f(n)}\rangle, \dot{q}, \dot{0}\rangle \dot{\in} \dot{\mathrm{S}}\mathrm{a}(\dot{r}, v)$ and $(\dot{\mathrm{T}}\mathrm{C}(\{v_{f(0)}, \ldots, v_{f(n)}\}) \dot{\subseteq} v \wedge \sim \mathrm{SF}_f(\mathcal{Q})) \rightarrow \langle\langle v_{f(0)}, \ldots, v_{f(n)}\rangle, \dot{q}, \dot{1}\rangle \dot{\in} \dot{\mathrm{S}}\mathrm{a}(\dot{r}, v)$, where TC, the transitive closure, is the function defined in Def. 5.5, and $\mathrm{SF}_f(\mathcal{Q})$ is the result of substituting free occurrences of v_i in $\mathcal{Q}$ by $v_{f(i)}$, $i \le n$.

PROOF. This may be proved by induction on the rank of $\mathcal{Q}$. Let t_f be the term $\langle v_{f(0)}, \ldots, v_{f(n)}\rangle$, $\mathcal{A}(t_f, v)$ be the formula $\dot{\mathrm{T}}\mathrm{C}(\{v_{f(0)}, \ldots, v_{f(n)}\}) \dot{\subseteq} v$. If $r = 0$ and $\mathcal{Q} = (v_i \dot{\in} v_j)$, $i, j \le n$, then $q = \langle 1, i, j\rangle$, and from the assumptions $\mathrm{SF}_f\mathcal{Q}$ and $\mathcal{A}(t_f, v)$ can be deduced $\dot{q}{'}\dot{0} \doteq \dot{1}$, $t_f{'}(\dot{q}{'}\dot{1}) \dot{\in} t_f(\dot{q}{'}\dot{2})$, whence $t_f \dot{\mathrm{S}}\mathrm{at}_0 \dot{q}$. Since $t_f \dot{\in} v^{\nearrow\omega} \wedge \dot{q} \dot{\in} \mathrm{AtF\dot{m}la} \wedge \dot{0} \dot{\in} \dot{2}$ is also deducible, it follows $\langle t_f, \dot{q}, \dot{0}\rangle \dot{\in} \dot{\mathrm{S}}\mathrm{a}(\dot{0}, v)$. The case with $\mathrm{SF}_f\mathcal{Q} = \sim(v_{f(i)} \dot{\in} v_{f(j)})$ is similar as are the cases with $\mathcal{Q} = (v_i \doteq v_j)$. Passage over $\sim$ and $\rightarrow$ is immediate. The provability of the inclusion $\dot{\mathrm{S}}\mathrm{a}(\dot{r}_1, v) \subseteq \dot{\mathrm{S}}\mathrm{a}(r_2, v)$ for $r_1 \le r_2$, is needed for the case $\mathcal{Q} = (\mathcal{Q}_1 \rightarrow \mathcal{Q}_2)$.

Suppose $\mathscr{Q}=(\forall v_i)(v_i \dot{\in} v_j \rightarrow \mathscr{Q}_1)$, $i, j \leq n$. Then $r=r_1+1$, $q=\langle 4, i, j, q_1\rangle$, and $\mathrm{SF}_f\mathscr{Q}=(\forall v_i)(v_i \dot{\in} v_{f(j)} \rightarrow \mathrm{SF}_g\mathscr{Q}_1)$, where g is the same as f except that $g(i)=i$. The induction hypothesis on $\mathscr{Q}_1$ says that $(\mathrm{SF}_g\mathscr{Q}_1 \wedge \mathscr{A}(t_g, v)) \rightarrow \langle t_g, \dot{q}_1, \dot{0}\rangle \dot{\in} \dot{\mathrm{S}}\mathrm{a}(\dot{r}_1, v))$ is provable. Hence $\vdash_{\mathbf{ZF}}(\mathrm{SF}_f\mathscr{Q} \wedge (\forall v_i)(v_i \dot{\in} v_{f(j)} \rightarrow \mathscr{A}(t_g, v))) \rightarrow (\forall v_i)(v_i \dot{\in} v_{f(j)} \rightarrow \langle t_g, \dot{q}_1, \dot{0}\rangle \dot{\in} \dot{\mathrm{S}}\mathrm{a}(\dot{r}_1, v))$. The provability of $(\mathrm{SF}_f\mathscr{Q} \wedge \mathscr{A}(t_f, v)) \rightarrow \langle t_f, \dot{q}, \dot{0}\rangle \dot{\in} \dot{\mathrm{S}}\mathrm{a}(\dot{r}, v)$ follows, making use of this list of theorems of **ZF**: $\mathscr{A}(t_f, v) \rightarrow (\forall v_i)(v_i \dot{\in} v_{f(j)} \rightarrow \mathscr{A}(t_g, v))$, $t_f \dot{\in} v^{\nearrow\omega} \wedge \dot{q} \dot{\in} \Sigma_0\text{-}\dot{\mathrm{F}}\mathrm{mla} \wedge \dot{0} \dot{\in} \dot{2}$, $t_f`(\dot{q}`\dot{2}) \doteq v_{f(j)}$, and $\langle t_g, \dot{q}_1, \dot{0}\rangle \doteq \langle (t_f \dot{-} \{(\dot{q}`\dot{1}, t_f`(\dot{q}`\dot{1}))\}) \dot{\cup} \{(\dot{q}`\dot{1}, v_i)\}, \dot{q}`\dot{3}, \dot{0}\rangle$. The other case is similar.

T7. $\mathrm{Var}(x)$, the set of indices of free variables appearing in $\mathscr{Q}$ if $x=\ulcorner\mathscr{Q}\urcorner$. $\mathrm{Var}(x)=\mathrm{Vbl}(\mathrm{Rk}(x))`x$ where Vbl is defined by ordinal recursion as
$\mathrm{Vbl}(0)=\{(x, \{x`1, x`2\}) | x \in \mathrm{Fmla}(0)\}$,
$\mathrm{Vbl}(\alpha+1)=\mathrm{Vbl}(\alpha) \cup \{(\langle 2, x\rangle, \mathrm{Vbl}(\alpha)`x) | x \in \mathrm{Fmla}(\alpha)\} \cup$
$\{(\langle 3, x, y\rangle, \mathrm{Vbl}(\alpha)`x \cup \mathrm{Vbl}(\alpha)`y) | x, y \in \mathrm{Fmla}(\alpha)\} \cup$
$\{(\langle 4, x, y, z\rangle, ((\mathrm{Vbl}(\alpha)`z \dot{-} \{x\}) \cup \{y\}) | x, y \in \omega, z \in \mathrm{Fmla}(\alpha)\}$,
$\mathrm{Vbl}(\lambda)=0$ if $\mathrm{Lim}(\lambda)$.

A comparison with the definition of $\mathrm{Fmla}(\alpha)$ in T3 shows that $\mathrm{Vbl}(r)$ is the set of all ordered pairs $(x, \mathrm{Var}(x))$ where x is the Gödel-set of a Σ_0-formula of rank $\leq r$.

LEMMA. If $\mathscr{Q}$ is a Σ_0-formula, $\ulcorner\mathscr{Q}\urcorner=q$, and the variables appearing free in $\mathscr{Q}$ are $v_{i_0}, \ldots, v_{i_n}$, then $\vdash_{\mathbf{ZF}} \dot{\mathrm{V}}\mathrm{ar}(\dot{q}) \doteq \{\dot{i}_0, \ldots, \dot{i}_n\}$.

PROOF. This reduces to the lemma on T3 plus a list of formal theorems that are properly part of the basic development of **ZF**. First show by ordinary mathematical induction on α carried out in **ZF**, $\alpha \dot{\in} \dot{\omega} \vdash_{\mathbf{ZF}} \dot{\mathrm{F}}\mathrm{cn}\ (\dot{\mathrm{V}}\mathrm{bl}(\alpha))$. Then show by induction on the rank r of $\mathscr{Q}$ that statements $((\dot{q}, \{\dot{i}_0, \ldots, \dot{i}_n\}) \dot{\in} \mathrm{Vbl}(\dot{r}))$ are provable in **ZF**.

LEMMA. $\vdash_{\mathbf{ZF}}(v_3 \dot{\in} \dot{\mathrm{F}}\mathrm{mla}(\alpha) \wedge \dot{\mathrm{V}}\mathrm{bl}(\alpha)`v_3 \subseteq \dot{\mathrm{D}}\mathrm{m}(v_1) \cap \dot{\mathrm{D}}\mathrm{m}(v_2) \wedge v_1 \upharpoonright (\dot{\mathrm{V}}\mathrm{bl}(\alpha)`v_3) = v_2 \upharpoonright (\dot{\mathrm{V}}\mathrm{bl}(\alpha)`v_3)) \rightarrow \sim(\langle v_1, v_3, \dot{0}\rangle \dot{\in} \dot{\mathrm{S}}\mathrm{a}(\alpha, v) \wedge \langle v_2, v_3, \dot{1}\rangle \dot{\in} \dot{\mathrm{S}}\mathrm{a}(\alpha, v))$.

PROOF. This is the formal version of the usual proof that the truth value of a formula depends only on the values assigned to its free variables. It is proved by induction on α carried out in **ZF**.

T8. w Sat x, meaning the assignment $w`i$ to v_i satisfies $\mathscr{Q}$, if $x=\ulcorner\mathscr{Q}\urcorner$, $\mathscr{Q}$ a Σ_0-formula, $\mathrm{Fcn}(w)$, $(\exists n<\omega)(\mathrm{Dm}(w) \subseteq n)$, $\mathrm{Var}(q) \subseteq \mathrm{Dm}(w)$. w Sat $x \leftrightarrow (\exists w' \in \mathrm{TC}(\mathrm{Rg}(w))^{\nearrow\omega})(w' \upharpoonright \mathrm{Dm}(w)=w \wedge \langle w', x, 0\rangle \in \mathrm{Sa}(\mathrm{Rk}(x), \mathrm{TC}(\mathrm{Rg}(w))))$.

THEOREM. If $\mathcal{Q}$ is a Σ_0-formula, $q = \ulcorner \mathcal{Q} \urcorner$, every free variable of $\mathcal{Q}$ has index $\leq n$, and $f \in \omega^{n+1}$, then $\vdash_{\mathbf{ZF}} \mathrm{SF}_f \mathcal{Q} \leftrightarrow \langle v_{f(0)} \ldots v_{f(n)} \rangle \; \dot{\mathrm{S}}\mathrm{at} \; \dot{q}$.

PROOF. Suppose that r is the rank of $\mathcal{Q}$, that every variable of $\mathcal{Q}$ has index $\leq m$, where $m \geqslant n$. Let $g \in \omega^{m+1}$ be f on $n+1$, 0 elsewhere. Then by the preceding lemmas the following are provable in **ZF** where as before, t_f is $\langle v_{f(0)}, \ldots, v_{f(n)} \rangle$ and t_g is $\langle v_{g(0)}, \ldots, v_{g(m)} \rangle$: $\dot{r} \doteq \dot{\mathrm{R}}\mathrm{k}(\dot{q})$, $\dot{\mathrm{R}}\mathrm{g}(t_f) \doteq \{v_{f(0)}, \ldots, v_{f(n)}\}$, $t_g \dot{\in} \dot{\mathrm{T}}\mathrm{C}(\dot{\mathrm{R}}\mathrm{g}(t_f))^{\nearrow\omega}$, $\dot{\mathrm{D}}\mathrm{m}(t_f) \doteq n \dot{+} 1$, $t_g \upharpoonright n \dot{+} 1 \doteq t_f$, $\mathrm{SF}_f \mathcal{Q} \rightarrow \langle t_g, \dot{q}, \dot{0} \rangle \dot{\in} \dot{\mathrm{S}}\mathrm{a}(\dot{r}, \dot{\mathrm{T}}\mathrm{C}(\dot{\mathrm{R}}\mathrm{g}(t_f)))$. Thus $\vdash_{\mathbf{ZF}} \mathrm{SF}_f \mathcal{Q} \rightarrow t_f \; \dot{\mathrm{S}}\mathrm{at} \; \dot{q}$. Also we can prove $\sim \mathrm{SF}_f \mathcal{Q} \rightarrow \langle t_g, \dot{q}, \dot{1} \rangle \dot{\in} \dot{\mathrm{S}}\mathrm{a}(\dot{r}, \dot{\mathrm{T}}\mathrm{C}(\dot{\mathrm{R}}\mathrm{g}(t_f)))$, $\dot{q} \dot{\in} \mathrm{F}\dot{\mathrm{m}}\mathrm{la}(\dot{r})$, $\mathrm{V}\dot{\mathrm{b}}\mathrm{l}(\dot{r})`\dot{q} \dot{\subseteq} n \dot{+} 1$. Therefore the assumption $(v \dot{\in} \dot{\mathrm{T}}\mathrm{C}(\dot{\mathrm{R}}\mathrm{g}(t_f)) \wedge v \upharpoonright n \dot{+} 1 \doteq t_f \wedge \langle v, \dot{q}, \dot{0} \rangle \dot{\in} \dot{\mathrm{S}}\mathrm{a}(\dot{r}, \dot{\mathrm{T}}\mathrm{C}(\dot{\mathrm{R}}\mathrm{g}(t_f)))$ yields $\sim \langle t_g, \dot{q}, \dot{1} \rangle \dot{\in} \dot{\mathrm{S}}\mathrm{a}(\dot{r}, \dot{\mathrm{T}}\mathrm{C}(\dot{\mathrm{R}}\mathrm{g}(t_f)))$ by the preceding lemma. It therefore yields also $\mathrm{SF}_f \mathcal{Q}$. Hence $\vdash_{\mathbf{ZF}} t_f \; \dot{\mathrm{S}}\mathrm{at} \; \dot{q} \rightarrow \mathrm{SF}_f \mathcal{Q}$.

T9. L, the generating function for constructible sets. L is defined by ordinal recursion as

$$\mathrm{L}(x) = 0 \quad \text{if} \quad \sim \mathrm{Ord}(x),$$
$$\mathrm{L}(\lambda) = \bigcup \mathrm{L}(\xi) \quad \text{if} \quad \mathrm{Lim}(\lambda),$$
$$\mathrm{L}(\alpha + 1) = \{\mathrm{S}(\mathrm{L}(\alpha), w, z) | w \in \mathrm{L}(\alpha)^{\nearrow\omega}, z \in \Sigma_0\text{-Fmla}\}, \text{ where } \mathrm{S}(y, w, z) =$$
$$\{x | x \in y \wedge (w \cup \{(\mathrm{Dm}(w), x)\}) \; \mathrm{Sat} \; z\} \text{ if } \mathrm{Var}(z) \subseteq \mathrm{Dm}(w) + 1,$$
0 otherwise.

The precise form of the definition of $\mathrm{L}(\alpha+1)$ is used only in the proofs of lemma 3.3 and lemma 6.1, and in these proofs is used only to show that for some given Σ_0-formula $\mathcal{Q}$, $\{x \in \mathrm{L}(\alpha) | \; \mathcal{Q}(x_0, \ldots, x_{n-1}, x)\} \in \mathrm{L}(\alpha+1)$ where $x_0, \ldots, x_{n-1} \in \mathrm{L}(\alpha)$. Such statements can be proved in **ZF** using the formal definition of L, for suppose $\mathcal{Q}$ has free variables $v_0, \ldots, v_n$, and $q = \ulcorner \mathcal{Q} \urcorner$. Using the string of lemmas in this appendix, the following can be deduced in **ZF** from the assumption $v_0, \ldots, v_{n-1} \dot{\in} \dot{\mathrm{L}}(\alpha)$: $(\dot{q} \dot{\in} \Sigma_0\text{-F}\dot{\mathrm{m}}\mathrm{la})$, $\langle v_0, \ldots, v_{n-1} \rangle \in \dot{\mathrm{L}}(\alpha)^{\nearrow\omega}$, $\dot{\mathrm{S}}(\dot{\mathrm{L}}(\alpha), \langle v_0, \ldots, v_{n-1} \rangle, \dot{q}) \dot{\in} \dot{\mathrm{L}}(\alpha+1)$, $\dot{\mathrm{D}}\mathrm{m}(\langle v_0, \ldots, v_{n-1} \rangle) = \dot{n}$, $\mathrm{V}\dot{\mathrm{a}}\mathrm{r}(\dot{q}) \doteq n \dot{+} 1$, $v \dot{\in} \dot{\mathrm{S}}(\dot{\mathrm{L}}(\alpha), \langle v_0, \ldots, v_{n-1} \rangle, \dot{q}) \leftrightarrow v \dot{\in} \dot{\mathrm{L}}(\alpha) \wedge (\langle v_0, \ldots, v_{n-1} \rangle \cup \{(\dot{n}, v)\}) \; \dot{\mathrm{S}}\mathrm{at} \; \dot{q}$, and finally using T7, $v \dot{\in} \dot{\mathrm{S}}(\dot{\mathrm{L}}(\alpha), \langle v_0, \ldots, v_{n-1} \rangle, \dot{q}) \leftrightarrow v \dot{\in} \dot{\mathrm{L}}(\alpha) \wedge \mathcal{Q}(v_0, \ldots, v_{n-1}, v)$. This is precisely what needed to be proved.

References

[1] K. Gödel, Consistency-proof for the generalized continuum hypothesis, Proc. Nat. Acad. Sci. USA **25** (1939) 220.

[2] A. Lévy, A hierarchy of formulas in set theory, Memoirs Amer. Math. Soc. No. 57 (1965).
[3] P. Suppes, Axiomatic set theory (Van Nostrand, 1960).
[4] E. Mendelson, Introduction to mathematical logic (Van Nostrand, 1964).
[5] J. C. Shepherdson, Inner models for set theory, Part III, J. Symbolic Logic **18** (1953) 145.
[6] P. J. Cohen, A minimal model for set theory, Bull. Amer. Math. Soc. **69** (1963) 537.

EQUIVALENCES BETWEEN GÖDEL'S DEFINITIONS OF CONSTRUCTIBILITY

TH. A. LINDEN *)
Yeshiva University, New York, USA

1. Introduction

Kurt Gödel, in his 1939 paper [1] on the consistency of the continuum hypothesis, defined the class of constructible sets in terms of an ordinal hierarchy M_α. In his 1940 monograph [2], he defined the constructible sets as elements of the range of a special ordinal function $F(\alpha)$. While it is well known that these two definitions are equivalent, it is interesting to investigate the relative locations where sets first occur within these constructions. In this paper I will prove:

THEOREM. For every ordinal α, $M_\alpha \in F(\omega^{\omega^{2\alpha+1}})$ and if α is finite, then $M_\alpha \in F(\omega)$.

From the definition of the function F (see below), it follows that for any limit number β, $F(\beta) = F''(\beta) = \{F(\xi) : \xi < \beta\}$, and this is known to be transitive ([2] p. 38, section 9.5). Thus this theorem includes facts such as: if $x \in M_\alpha$ then there is a $\xi < \omega^{\omega^{2\alpha+1}}$ such that $x = F(\xi)$. Also it is comparatively clear that for ε_γ an ε-number, $F(\varepsilon_\gamma) \subseteq M_{\varepsilon_\gamma}$. Stronger results in this direction would be possible, but considering this much as obvious, we have:

COROLLARY. For all ε-numbers ε_γ, $M_{\varepsilon_\gamma} = F(\varepsilon_\gamma)$.

PROOF. If $x \in M_{\varepsilon_\gamma}$, then for some $\xi < \varepsilon_\gamma$, $x \in M_\xi$ so, assuming the main

---

*) This work was inspired by Prof. Raymond M. Smullyan who suggested the problem and provided many helpful ideas. As originally presented at the Logic Colloquium, the theorem was stated only in the form that $M_{\omega_\gamma} = F(\omega_\gamma)$ for cardinal numbers ω_γ. I am indebted to Profs. M. Machover and D. Scott for suggesting possible extensions of the theorem. The present proof turned out to be a very simple refinement of the proof for cardinal numbers dependent only on the use of lemma 1 which M. Machover called to my attention. I am also indebted to the referee for an important correction. This work was done while the author was supported by a U.S. National Science Foundation Graduate Fellowship.

theorem above, $x \in F(\omega^{\omega^{2\xi+1}})$. But if $\varepsilon_\gamma > \omega$ then $\omega^{\omega^{2\xi+1}} < \varepsilon_\gamma$ so $x \in F''(\varepsilon_\gamma) = F(\varepsilon_\gamma)$. If $\varepsilon_\gamma = \omega$ then ξ is finite so again $x \in F(\varepsilon_\gamma)$.

In particular, this says that for all cardinal numbers ω_γ, $M_{\omega_\gamma} = F(\omega_\gamma)$.

The proof of the main theorem will proceed by transfinite induction. It could be formalized within either of the axiomatic theories ZF or VBG with the axiom of choice.

2. Preliminaries

Extensive use will be made of notation and propositions from Gödel's monograph [2]. References will be given on the first appearance unless the notation is standard. By $\varphi^{(U)}(x_1, \ldots, x_n)$ we mean the result of relativizing all quantifiers in $\varphi(x_1, \ldots, x_n)$ to the set U. We will write $\mathrm{Def}_{\mathrm{R}}(U)$ for the set of all first-order definable finitary relations over the set U; that is, $A \in \mathrm{Def}_{\mathrm{R}}(U)$ iff for some first-order formula $\varphi(x_1, \ldots, x_n)$ with constants from U,

$$A = \{\langle u_1, \ldots, u_n \rangle : u_1, \ldots, u_n \in U \;\&\; \varphi^{(U)}(u_1, \ldots, u_n)\}.$$

Similarly, we will write $\mathrm{Def}(U)$ for the set of all first-order definable subsets of U; that is, $A \in \mathrm{Def}(U)$ iff for some formula $\varphi(x)$ with one free variable and constants in U,

$$A = \{u \in U : \varphi^{(U)}(u)\}.$$

If U is transitive, it is easily seen that $A \in \mathrm{Def}(U)$ if and only if $A \in \mathrm{Def}_{\mathrm{R}}(U)$ and $A \subseteq U$.

Let us recall that the M_α hierarchy is defined in [1] by a transfinite recursion from the equations:

$$\begin{aligned} M_0 &= \emptyset \\ M_{\alpha+1} &= \mathrm{Def}(M_\alpha) \\ M_\beta &= \bigcup_{\alpha<\beta} M_\alpha \quad \text{for } \beta \text{ a limit ordinal}. \end{aligned}$$

To define the function F, we first need the function J (see [2] p. 36, section 9.2.1) which maps ordered triples $\langle i, \alpha, \beta \rangle$ with $i \leq 8$ onto the ordinals and preserves a given well-ordering ([2] p. 36, section 9.2) of the triples.

Then F is defined so that if $J(i, \alpha, \beta)=\gamma$ then:

$$\begin{aligned}
&\text{if} \quad i = 0, F(\gamma) = F''(\gamma) = \{F(\xi) : \xi < \gamma\} \\
&\text{if} \quad i = 1, F(\gamma) = \{F(\alpha), F(\beta)\} \\
&\text{if} \quad i = 2, F(\gamma) = E \cap F(\alpha) \quad \text{where } E \text{ is the } \varepsilon\text{-relation} \\
&\text{if} \quad i = 3, F(\gamma) = F(\alpha) - F(\beta) \\
&\text{if} \quad i = 4, F(\gamma) = F(\alpha) \restriction F(\beta) = F(\alpha) \cap (V \times F(\beta))\ ^{*)} \\
&\text{if} \quad i = 5, F(\gamma) = F(\alpha) \cap \text{Domain}\,(F(\beta)) \\
&\text{if} \quad i = 6, F(\gamma) = F(\alpha) \cap \text{Inverse}\,(F(\beta)) \\
&\text{if} \quad i = 7, F(\gamma) = F(\alpha) \cap \text{Cnv}_2\,(F(\beta))\ ^{**)} \\
&\text{if} \quad i = 8, F(\gamma) = F(\alpha) \cap \text{Cnv}_3\,(F(\beta)).\ ^{**)}
\end{aligned}$$

The following set theoretic characterization†) of first-order definable relations over transitive sets proves quite useful:

PROPOSITION 1. If U is transitive, then $A \in \text{Def}_{\text{R}}(U)$ if and only if there exists a finite sequence $Z_1, \ldots, Z_m = A$ such that each term Z_k of the sequence is obtained in one of the following ways:

(A) there are finite integers p, q, r with $p \leq r$, $q \leq r$ and elements a, b in U such that one of the following holds:

$$\begin{aligned}
&\text{i)} \quad Z_k = \{\langle u_1, \ldots, u_r \rangle : u_1, \ldots, u_r \in U \;\&\; u_p \in u_q\} \\
&\text{ii)} \quad Z_k = \{\langle u_1, \ldots, u_r \rangle : u_1, \ldots, u_r \in U \;\&\; u_p \in a\} \\
&\text{iii)} \quad Z_k = \{\langle u_1, \ldots, u_r \rangle : u_1, \ldots, u_r \in U \;\&\; a \in u_p\} \\
&\text{iv)} \quad Z_k = \{\langle u_1, \ldots, u_r \rangle : u_1, \ldots, u_r \in U \;\&\; a \in b\},
\end{aligned}$$

(B) there are Z_i and Z_j with $i, j < k$ such that $Z_k = Z_i \cap Z_j$,

(C) there is a Z_i with $i < k$ and a finite integer r such that $Z_k = U^r - Z_i$,

(D) there is a Z_i with $i < k$ and there are integers r and p with $p \leq r$ and $Z_k = \{\langle u_1, \ldots, u_{p-1}, u_{p+1}, \ldots, u_r \rangle :$ for some $u_p \in U, \langle u_1, \ldots, u_r \rangle \in Z_i\}$.

---

*) Note that we are following Gödel's notation in which the elements of the domain of a function are the second elements of the ordered pair.

**) Cnv2 and Cnv3 are permutations of ordered triples, see [2] p. 15.

†) This characterization was suggested by Profs. Martin Davis and Raymond M. Smullyan.

PROOF. First, assume $A \in \mathrm{Def}_{\mathrm{R}}(U)$. This half of the proof is by induction on the length of the formula $\varphi(x_1, \ldots, x_n)$ that defines A over U. One can assume that φ is written with $\sim$, $\wedge$ and $\exists$ as the only logical constants. One then proves that for all integers $r \geqslant n$ and all $i_1, \ldots, i_n$ each less than or equal to r, the set of all elements of U^r such that $\varphi^{(U)}(u_{i_1}, \ldots, u_{i_n})$ can be obtained by a suitable sequence providing this can be done for all formulas ψ with fewer logical constants. The obvious details are left to the reader.

Conversely, let $Z_1, \ldots, Z_m$ be a sequence of the prescribed form. We must show that there is a formula defining Z_m. First, by induction it is easily seen that for each $k \leq m$, there is an n such that $Z_k \subseteq U^n$. We will also need the simple fact that if Z_i is definable by a formula $\varphi(x_1, \ldots, x_n)$, then for any integer r there is a formula $\psi(x_1, \ldots, x_r)$ defining $Z_i \cap U^r$. This follows once we note that $\langle u_1, \ldots, u_n \rangle$ is by definition $\langle u_1 \langle u_2, \ldots, \langle u_{n-1}, u_n \rangle \ldots \rangle \rangle$. For if $r \leq n$ then $\langle v_1, \ldots, v_r \rangle \in Z_i \cap U^r$ iff $v_r = \langle u_r, \ldots, u_n \rangle$ and $\varphi^{(U)}(v_1, \ldots, v_{r-1}, u_r, \ldots, u_n)$. Hence we can pick

$$\psi^{(U)}(x_1, \ldots, x_r) = (\exists\, y_r, \ldots, y_n \in U)$$
$$[x_r = \langle y_r, \ldots, y_n \rangle \,\&\, \varphi^{(U)}(x_1, \ldots, x_{r-1}, y_r, \ldots, y_n)].$$

The transitivity of U guarantees the absoluteness of $x_r = \langle y_r, \ldots, y_n \rangle$. Similarly the reader can easily verify that if $n < r$, one would pick

$$\psi^{(U)}(x_1, \ldots, x_n, \ldots, x_r) = (\exists\, y_n \in U)$$
$$[y_n = \langle x_n, \ldots, x_r \rangle \,\&\, \varphi^{(U)}(x_1, \ldots, x_{n-1}, y_n)].$$

From this the result follows by induction on the length of the sequence $Z_1, \ldots, Z_m$. If Z_k is obtained by step (A), then trivially Z_k is defined by one of the formulas $x_p \in x_q$, $x_p \in a$, $a \in x_p$, or $a \in b$ considered as a formula with r free variables.

Suppose $Z_k = Z_i \cap Z_j$ where by induction hypothesis we can assume Z_i is defined by some $\psi_1(x_1, \ldots, x_{n_i})$ and Z_j is defined by $\psi_2(x_1, \ldots, x_{n_j})$. Let $\psi_2'(x_1, \ldots, x_{n_i})$ define $Z_j \cap U^{n_i}$. Then Z_k is defined by $\psi_1 \wedge \psi_2'$.

Suppose $Z_k = U^r - Z_i$ where by induction hypothesis Z_i is defined by $\psi(x_1, \ldots, x_{n_i})$. We know that there is a $\psi'(x_1, \ldots, x_r)$ that defines $U^r \cap Z_i$. Then Z_k is defined by $\sim\psi'(x_1, \ldots, x_r)$.

If Z_k proceeds from Z_i by (D) where we can assume Z_i is defined by $\psi(x_1, \ldots, x_n)$, then Z_k is defined by $(\exists x_p)\psi$. This concludes the induction and the proof.

3. The induction at successor ordinals

We can now begin the proof of the main theorem which proceeds by transfinite induction. The fact that $M_0 \in F(\omega)$ is trivial. For the induction at successor ordinals the following result, employed by Levy in [3] Ch. 1, §4, will be used repeatedly:

LEMMA 1. If α and β are both less than some δ-number ω^{ω^γ}, then $J(i, \alpha, \beta) < \omega^{\omega^\gamma}$.

PROOF. For the mapping P of ordered pairs of ordinals onto the ordinals ([2] p. 29, section 7.9) the following inequalities are easily verified:

$$\begin{aligned} P(\alpha, \beta) &\leqslant \sum_{\gamma \leqslant \max\{\alpha, \beta\}} (\gamma \cdot 2 + 1) \\ &\leqslant (\max\{\alpha, \beta\} \cdot 2 + 1)(\max\{\alpha, \beta\} + 1) \\ &\leqslant (\max\{\alpha, \beta\} \cdot 2 + 1)^2 . \end{aligned}$$

It follows from the definition of J ([2] p. 36, section 9.2.1) that

$$J(i, \alpha, \beta) \leqslant 9(\max\{\alpha, \beta\} \cdot 2 + 1)^2 + 9 .$$

But since numbers of the form ω^{ω^γ} are closed under addition and multiplication (see, for example, Bachmann, Transfinite Zahlen (Springer Verlag, 1955) §15), the conclusion follows immediately.

For the induction at successor ordinals we must show that $M_{\alpha+1} \in F(\omega^{\omega^{2(\alpha+1)+1}})$ on the assumption that $M_\alpha \in F(\omega^{\omega^{2\alpha+1}})$ and that for finite α, $M_{\alpha+1} \in F(\omega)$ on the assumption that $M_\alpha \in F(\omega)$. Our first goal is to show that on the given assumptions, if $A \in \mathrm{Def}_{\mathrm{R}}(M_\alpha)$, then $A \subseteq F(\omega^{\omega^{2\alpha+1}})$ and for finite α, $A \subseteq F(\omega)$.

Throughout the rest of this paper δ will always denote a δ-number; that is, an ordinal of the form ω^{ω^γ} for $\gamma \geq 0$. Also let

$$X \otimes Y = \{\{x, y\} : x \in X \;\&\; y \in Y\} .$$

LEMMA 2. If X, $Y \in F(\delta)$, then there exists an $\eta < \delta$ such that $X \otimes Y \subseteq F(\eta)$.

PROOF. Since X and Y are both elements of $F(\delta)$, there exist $\xi_1 < \delta$ and $\xi_2 < \delta$ such that $X = F(\xi_1)$ and $Y = F(\xi_2)$. Let $\eta = J(0, \xi_1, \xi_2)$, so by lemma 1 $\eta < \delta$. Let $\{x, y\} \in X \otimes Y$. We can assume $x \in X$ and $y \in Y$, so there exist $\xi'_1 < \xi_1$ and $\xi'_2 < \xi_2$ such that $x = F(\xi'_1)$ and $y = F(\xi'_2)$ (see [2] p. 39, section 9.5.2). But then $\{x, y\} = F(J(1, \xi'_1, \xi'_2))$ and $J(1, \xi'_1, \xi'_2) < J(0, \xi_1, \xi_2) = \eta$. So $\{x, y\} \in F(\eta)$ since $F(\eta) = F''(\eta)$.

LEMMA 3. If $X, Y \in F(\delta)$, then $X \times Y \in F(\delta)$.

PROOF. Again let $X = F(\xi_1)$ and $Y = F(\xi_2)$ where $\xi_1, \xi_2 < \delta$. By lemma 2 there exists an $\eta_0 < \delta$ such that $X \otimes Y \subseteq F(\eta_0)$. Since $X \times Y \subseteq (X \otimes X) \otimes \otimes (X \otimes Y)$ another application of lemma 2 gives an $\eta_1 < \delta$ such that $X \times Y \subseteq F(\eta_1)$. Similarly we get an $\eta_2 < \delta$ such that $Y \times X \subseteq F(\eta_2)$. Now let $\eta_3 = J(4, \eta_2, \xi_1)$ so

$$F(\eta_3) = F(\eta_2) \upharpoonright X .$$

Then let $\eta_4 = J(6, \eta_1, \eta_3)$ so

$$F(\eta_4) = F(\eta_1) \cap \text{Inverse}\,(F(\eta_2) \upharpoonright X) .$$

Finally letting $\eta_5 = J(4, \eta_4, \xi_2)$ we have

$$F(\eta_5) = [F(\eta_1) \cap \text{Inverse}\,(F(\eta_2) \upharpoonright X)] \upharpoonright Y = X \times Y .$$

By repeated application of lemma 1 it follows that $\eta_5 < \delta$ and so $X \times Y \in F(\delta)$.

COROLLARY. If $X \in F(\delta)$, then for all finite n, $X^n \in F(\delta)$.

PROOF. By the obvious induction.

LEMMA 4. Let $X, Y \in F(\delta)$. Then all of the following are also in $F(\delta)$:

(a)	$E_X = \{\langle x, y\rangle : x, y \in X \;\&\; x \in y\}$	(e)	$\text{Domain}\,(Y)$
(b)	$X \cap Y$	(f)	$\text{Inverse}\,(Y)$
(c)	$X^n - Y$	(g)	$\text{Cnv}_2\,(Y)$
(d)	$X \times Y$	(h)	$\text{Cnv}_3\,(Y)$.

PROOF. Let $X = F(\xi_1)$, $Y = F(\xi_2)$ where $\xi_1, \xi_2 < \delta$. By lemma 3 there exists a $\xi_1' < \delta$ with $X^2 = F(\xi_1')$. Then setting $\eta = J(2, \xi_1', 0)$, $F(\eta) = E \cap F(\xi_1') = E_X$ and $\eta < \delta$. This proves (a). For (b) set $\eta = J(3, \xi_1, J(3, \xi_1, \xi_2))$ so that $F(\eta) = X - (X - Y) = X \cap Y$. Lemma 3 gives (c) and (d) almost immediately. For the remaining cases, define $J_0(\alpha, \beta) = J(0, \alpha, \beta)$ so that $\theta \in \text{Range}(J_0)$ implies that $F(\theta)$ is transitive (see [2] pp. 37–38, sections 9.3, 9.3.5 and 9.5). We can pick a $\theta \in \text{Range}(J_0)$ with $\xi_2 < \theta < \delta$ so $Y \subseteq F(\theta)$. Then setting $\eta = J(5, \theta, \xi_2)$ we have $F(\eta) = F(\theta) \cap \cap \text{Domain}(F(\xi_2)) = \text{Domain}(Y)$. This proves (e). For (f) pick θ_2 such that $F(\theta_2) = F(\theta)^2$ and set $\eta = J(6, \theta_2, \xi_2)$ and the result follows. For (g) and (h) pick θ_3 such that $F(\theta_3) = F(\theta)^3$ and proceed as above.

We know now that $F(\delta)$ is closed under set construction procedures analogous to Gödel's class existence axioms of group B. The proof of the following proposition is now analogous to part of the proof of the general class existence theorem ([2] pp. 8–11).

PROPOSITION 2. If X is transitive and $X \in F(\delta)$, then $\mathrm{Def}_{\mathrm{R}}(X) \subseteq F(\delta)$.

PROOF. Let $Z_1, \ldots, Z_m = A$ be a finite sequence as in proposition 1. We show by induction on the length of the sequence that for each Z_k there is an $\eta_k < \delta$ such that $Z_k = F(\eta_k)$.

If Z_k proceeds from earlier terms by (B) or (C) of proposition 1, then the result is immediate from lemma 4.

Suppose $Z_k = \{\langle x_1, \ldots, x_n\rangle : x_p \in x_q\}$. (For easier reading I will omit conditions of the form $x_i \in X$; however, they are to be understood in all set abstracts of this proof.) If $p = q$, then $Z_k = \emptyset \in F(\delta)$ trivially. Now by lemma 4a we can get $E_X = \{\langle x_p, x_q\rangle : x_p \in x_q\}$. In view of the closure of $F(\delta)$ under inverses, we can assume $p < q$. If $n = 1$ or $n = 2$ we are finished. If $n > 2$, by lemma 4d we have $E_X \times X$ in $F(\delta)$ and by proper use of parts f, g and h from lemma 4 we can get, for example, $\{\langle x_p \langle x_{q-1}, x_q\rangle\rangle : x_p \in x_q\} \in F(\delta)$. This process can be repeated inductively to get $Z_k \in F(\delta)$. The interested reader will be able to fill in the details by consulting the proof in [2] pp. 9–10.

For $Z_k = \{\langle x_1, \ldots, x_n\rangle : x_p \in a\}$ we proceed similarly getting $a \cap X \in F(\delta)$ by lemma 4b and then building up the n-tuple by lemma 4 parts d, f, g, and h as above. For $Z_k = \{\langle x_1, \ldots, x_n\rangle : a \in x_p\}$ using the closure properties on $F(\delta)$ already proved we can get the following all in $F(\delta)$: $\{a\}$, $\{a\} \times X$, $(\{a\} \times X) \cap E_X$, and $\mathrm{Domain}((\{a\} \times X) \cap E_X) = \{x : a \in x\}$. Then the n-tuple Z_k is built up as above. For $Z_k = \{\langle x_1, \ldots, x_n\rangle : a \in b\}$ either $Z_k = X^n$ or $Z_k = \emptyset$. In either case we know $Z_k \in F(\delta)$.

If Z_k proceeds from an earlier term Z_i by (D), we again use the closure properties of lemma 4 to get

$$\{\langle x_p \langle x_1, \ldots, x_{p-1}, x_{p+1}, \ldots, x_n\rangle\rangle : \langle x_1, \ldots, x_n\rangle \in Z_i\} \in F(\delta)$$

and then taking the domain of this we get $Z_k \in F(\delta)$. This completes the induction for this proposition.

We can now conclude the general proof for the case when α is a finite successor ordinal. From the assumption that $M_\alpha \in F(\delta)$, proposition 2 implies that $M_{\alpha+1} = \mathrm{Def}(M_\alpha) \subseteq F(\omega)$. Since $M_{\alpha+1}$ is finite, we can choose a finite integer k larger than the order of any element of $M_{\dot{\alpha}+1}$. Further, k can be chosen so that $k \in \mathrm{Range}(J_0)$ so $F(k)$ is transitive and thus

$M_{\alpha+1} \subseteq F(k)$. Now since $M_{\alpha+1}$ is finite, it is a definable subset of $F(k)$ and hence by proposition 2 it follows that $M_{\alpha+1} \in F(\omega)$.

In the case where α is infinite, we are assuming $M_\alpha \in F(\omega^{\omega^{2\alpha+1}})$ so proposition 2 does give $M_{\alpha+1} \subseteq F(\omega^{\omega^{2\alpha+1}})$. The approach now is to show that $M_{\alpha+1}$ is itself first-order definable over an appropriate superset of $F(\omega^{\omega^{2\alpha+1}})$. Clearly

$$F(\omega^{\omega^{2\alpha+1}}) \in F(\omega^{\omega^{2\alpha+2}})$$

so by proposition 2 we have

$$\mathrm{Def}_{\mathrm{R}}(F(\omega^{\omega^{2\alpha+1}})) \subseteq F(\omega^{\omega^{2\alpha+2}}).$$

By setting

$$X = M_\alpha, \qquad Y = F(\omega^{\omega^{2\alpha+1}}), \quad \text{and} \quad Z = F(\omega^{\omega^{2\alpha+2}})$$

the following proposition shows that for α infinite, $\mathrm{Def}(M_\alpha)$ is itself first-order definable over $F(\omega^{\omega^{2\alpha+2}})$. Thus by a further application of proposition 2, we have:

$$M_{\alpha+1} \in F(\omega^{\omega^{2\alpha+3}}).$$

The following proposition thus will conclude the induction at successor ordinals for the main theorem.

PROPOSITION 3. Let X be a transitive set with $\omega \subseteq X$. Let Y and Z be transitive sets such that $\mathrm{Def}_{\mathrm{R}}(X) \subseteq Y$ and $\mathrm{Def}_{\mathrm{R}}(Y) \subseteq Z$. Then $\mathrm{Def}(X)$ is first-order definable over Z; that is, $\mathrm{Def}(X) \in \mathrm{Def}(Z)$.

PROOF. The proof rests simply on the fact that the definition of $\mathrm{Def}(X)$ is absolute when relativized to Z. We use the characterization of $\mathrm{Def}_{\mathrm{R}}(X)$ from proposition 1 together with the fact that when X is transitive, $A \in \mathrm{Def}(X)$ if and only if $A \in \mathrm{Def}_{\mathrm{R}}(X)$ and $A \subseteq X$. This characterization of $\mathrm{Def}(X)$ can be written out in purely set theoretic formalism with all except one quantifier bounded to *elements* of Z, beginning roughly as follows:

$$A \in \mathrm{Def}(X) \Leftrightarrow (\exists S)\,[\text{Finite sequence}\,(S) \wedge A \in \mathrm{Range}(S) \wedge A \subseteq X \wedge$$
$$(\exists z \in Y \times Y)\,\{z \in S \Rightarrow (\exists k \in \omega)\,(\exists T \in Y)\,[z = \langle k, T\rangle \ldots .$$

All of the quantifiers implicit in the expression "Finite sequence (S)" can be bounded by either Y or $Y \times X$. This is true since elements of the domain of any S are finite integers and elements of the range are by definition in $\mathrm{Def}_{\mathrm{R}}(X)$ and hence in Y. It is easily checked that all quantifiers implicit in the other expressions can be bounded by either Y or $Y \times Y$.

It follows that when we relativize this formula to Z, the only change is that $\exists S$ changes to $\exists S \in Z$, and to show absoluteness it is only necessary to show that for any S satisfying the formula, we must have $S \in Z$. But this is true since S is a finite subset of $Y \times Y$ and hence S is a definable relation over Y, and hence $S \in Z$. Since all the parameters of the formula with the bounded quantifiers are elements of Z and since $\mathrm{Def}(X) \subseteq Z$, this formula with one free variable does give a first-order definition of $\mathrm{Def}(X)$ over Z; that is, $\mathrm{Def}(X) \in \mathrm{Def}(Z)$.

4. The induction at limit ordinals

To conclude the main proof we need only carry through the induction for limit ordinals. Let β be a limit ordinal. We can assume that for all $\alpha < \beta$, $M_\alpha \in F(\omega^{\omega^{2\alpha+1}})$ and we show that $M_\beta \in F(\omega^{\omega\beta+1})$. Clearly $M_\beta \subseteq F(\omega^{\omega\beta})$ since if $x \in M_\beta$, then there exists an $\alpha < \beta$ with $x \in M_\alpha$ and $M_\alpha \in F(\omega^{\omega^{2\alpha+1}}) \subseteq$ $\subseteq F(\omega^{\omega\beta})$ and the conclusion follows from the transitivity of $F(\omega^{\omega\beta})$.

Proposition 4. From the above assumption it follows that $\beta \in F(\omega^{\omega\beta+1})$.

Proof*. Clearly $\beta \subseteq F(\omega^{\omega\beta})$. Now Raphael Robinson's definition of "x is an ordinal" as "x is transitive and ε-connected" is known to be absolute when relativized to any transitive set. Hence this formula for "x is an ordinal" defines over $F(\omega^{\omega\beta})$ a certain set of ordinals B with $\beta \subseteq B$. By proposition 2, $B \in F(\omega^{\omega\beta+1})$. Now either $\beta = B$ or B contains an ordinal γ with $\beta \leq \gamma$. In any case the transitivity of $F(\omega^{\omega\beta+1})$ gives $\beta \in F(\omega^{\omega\beta+1})$.

Definition 1. Let f_γ denote the function with domain γ such that for each $\xi \in \gamma, f_\gamma(\xi) = M_\xi$.

The transfinite recursion theorem guarantees that for each ordinal γ there exists a unique function f_γ.

Definition 2. Let $\mathcal{M}_\beta(f)$ be the collection of all functions of the form f_γ for some $\gamma < \beta$.

An explicit formula defining the collection $\mathcal{M}_\beta(f)$ could be written out along the following lines:

$$\begin{aligned} f \in \mathcal{M}_\beta(f) \Leftrightarrow \mathrm{Function}(f) \wedge (\exists \gamma \in \beta) & \\ & [\mathrm{Domain}(f) = \gamma \wedge \gamma \neq 0 \Leftrightarrow \langle 0, 0 \rangle \in f \wedge \\ & (\forall \sigma \in \gamma)\,[\sigma + 1 < \gamma \Leftrightarrow f(\sigma + 1) = \mathrm{Def}(f(\sigma))] \wedge \\ & (\forall \tau \in \gamma)\,[\mathrm{Limit\ ordinal}(\tau) \Rightarrow f(\tau) = \bigcup_{\sigma < \tau} f(\sigma)]] \end{aligned}$$

*) This is also proved in [3] in essentially the same manner.

where an expression like $f(\sigma+1)=\mathrm{Def}(f(\sigma))$ is to be understood as a short way of writing

$$(\forall A)\,[\langle\sigma, A\rangle \in f \Leftrightarrow \langle\sigma+1, \mathrm{Def}(A)\rangle \in f].$$

PROPOSITION 5. For all ordinals γ, $f_\gamma \in M_{\gamma+3}$.

PROOF. The proof is by transfinite induction. Clearly $f_0 \in M_3$. At successor ordinals $\gamma+1$ we notice that

$$x \in f_{\gamma+1} \Leftrightarrow x \in f_\gamma \vee x = \langle\gamma, M_\gamma\rangle.$$

By induction hypothesis $f_\gamma \in M_{\gamma+3}$. Further we can rewrite this definition with all quantifiers bounded by elements of $M_{\gamma+3}$ as follows

$$x \in f_{\gamma+1} \Leftrightarrow x \in f_\gamma \vee (\forall z \in M_{\gamma+2})\,[z \in x \Leftrightarrow [z = \{\gamma\} \vee z = \{\gamma, M_\gamma\}]].$$

All constants in this formula are in $M_{\gamma+3}$ and the formula is clearly absolute when relativized to $M_{\gamma+3}$. Hence $f_{\gamma+1} \in M_{\gamma+4}$.

For γ a limit ordinal we clearly have $f_\gamma \subseteq M_\gamma$ and we will show that f_γ can be defined over $M_{\gamma+1}$. We have the following formula for f_γ

$$x \in f_\gamma \Leftrightarrow (\exists g \in M_\gamma)\, \mathscr{M}_\gamma(g) \wedge x \in g.$$

The quantifier $\exists g$ can be bounded by M_γ since by induction hypothesis we know that if g is of the form f_ξ for some $\xi<\gamma$ then $g \in M_{\xi+3} \subseteq M_\gamma$. A brief glance at the formula defining $\mathscr{M}_\gamma(g)$ will convince one that all quantifiers that appear in this formula can also be bounded by M_γ without changing the extension of the formula. Note that proposition 3 can be used to show that all the quantifiers implicit in $g(\sigma+1)=\mathrm{Def}(g(\sigma))$ can be so bounded. It thus follows that this formula is absolute when relativized to $M_{\gamma+1}$ and hence $f_\gamma \in M_{\gamma+2} \subseteq M_{\gamma+3}$. This completes the induction.

PROPOSITION 6. $M_\beta \in F(\omega^{\omega^{\beta+1}})$ for β a limit ordinal.

PROOF. By proposition 4 we know that $\beta \in F(\omega^{\omega^{\beta+1}})$ so there is a $\xi<\omega^{\omega^{\beta+1}}$ with $\beta=F(\xi)$. Now clearly we can pick an ordinal θ in the range of J_0 with $\xi<\theta<\omega^{\omega^{\beta+1}}$ and $\omega^{\omega^\beta}<\theta$. Let $Y=F(\omega^{\omega^\beta})$. We know that $M_\beta \subseteq Y$, $Y \in F(\theta)$, $\beta \in F(\theta)$ and $F(\theta)$ is transitive. We show that M_β is definable by a formula with parameters in $F(\theta)$ which is absolute when relativized to $F(\theta)$. It will then follow by proposition 2 that $M_\beta \in F(\omega^{\omega^{\beta+1}})$.

Now the following formula defines M_β:

$$x \in M_\beta \Leftrightarrow (\exists f \in Y)\,[\mathscr{M}_\beta(f) \wedge (\exists y \in Y)\,[x \in y \wedge y \in \mathrm{Range}(f)]]\,.$$

The quantifier $\exists f$ can be bounded by Y since proposition 5 guarantees that any function satisfying $\mathscr{M}_\beta(f)$ will be an element of M_β and hence of Y. And the formulas for $\mathscr{M}_\beta(f)$ and Range(f) can be written with all quantifiers bounded by Y. Thus this formula is absolute when relativized to $F(\theta)$ and hence M_β is definable over $F(\theta)$. Thus $M_\beta \in F(\omega^{\omega^{\beta+1}})$.

This completes the transfinite induction and proves the original theorem.

References

[1] K. Gödel, Consistency proof for the generalized continuum hypothesis, Proc. Nat. Acad. Sci. **25** (1939) 220.

[2] K. Gödel, The consistency of the continuum hypothesis (Princeton University Press, Princeton, 1940).

[3] A. Levy and M. Machover, in preparation.

[4] W. Sierpinski, Cardinal and ordinal numbers (Warsaw, 1958).

CONCRETE MODELS OF SET THEORY

R. B. JENSEN
Universität Bonn, W. Germany

These notes are intended as an introductory exposition of Cohen's forcing method, and were originally written to accompany a series of lectures given in Oberwolfach during the spring of 1965. In their present form they incorporate numerous suggestions from the participants of that meeting – in particular from Prof. G. H. Müller – for which the author wishes to express his deepest gratitude.

The classical method of demonstrating that a statement $\mathfrak{A}$ is consistent with the axioms of set theory is the method of "inner models": One shows that to each model M satisfying the theory there is a uniformly definable submodel $N \subset M$ which also satisfies $\mathfrak{A}$. A typical application of the method is the well-known proof that the axiom of foundation is consistent with the remaining axioms of set theory. By a much deeper application Gödel succeeded in showing consistency of the axiom of choice and the general continuum hypothesis with the axioms of set theory; he demonstrated that each model M of set theory contains a "constructible" inner model $L \subset M$ satisfying these two axioms. By its very success, however, Gödel's investigation revealed a new impass in axiomatic set theory. Using Gödel's methods it was shown (independently by Shepherdson and Cohen) that there exists a model M of set theory which is minimal in the sense that for every inner model $N \subset M$ we have $N = M$. Thus if $\mathfrak{A}$ has been proved consistent by the method of inner models, the consistency of $\neg \mathfrak{A}$ cannot be proved by the same method. The independence of the axiom of choice and the continuum hypothesis required a new approach. In 1963 Paul Cohen devised a method of *extending* a given countable model M of set theory to a larger model $N \supset M$. He did this by adding in a controlled manner certain new "generic" sets A and defining N as the closure of M and the new sets A under the "constructible" operations used by Gödel to obtain the model L. Cohen used his method to construct models N which violate the axiom of choice and the continuum hypothesis. Since then the method has been successfully applied to an astonishing variety of independence problems.

This paper gives a fairly general account of Cohen's basic method and closes with a proof of the independence of the continuum hypothesis as a typical application. The plan of the paper is as follows: sections 1–3 are devoted to preliminaries. Section 1 describes the formal system of Zermelo-Fraenkel set theory (ZF) and introduces the basic notations. Section 2 specifies the metalinguistic framework of the investigation and describes an arithmetisation of the object language. Section 3 introduces the class of *concrete* models, which are the only models dealt with in the paper. Section 4 describes the notion of *constructible closure* and contains a proof that every constructibly closed inner model of a concrete ZF model M is a ZF model. The ramified language used in section 4 is taken from [2] and [6] and is based according to [2] on a suggestion of D. Scott. Section 5 then introduces the notions of *forcing* and *generic model.* By a straightforward modification of the arguments of section 4 it is shown that every generic model is a ZF model. Section 6 applies the methods developed in section 5 to an independence problem. It is shown that each of a class of axioms which violate the general continuum hypothesis is consistent. The result is due to Solovay.

1. The system ZF

In this section we describe a formalised system of Zermelo-Fraenkel set theory (ZF). The formulae of ZF are composed of the following primitive symbols:

(1) set variables: $v_0, v_1, \cdots, v_n, \cdots,$

(2) predicates: ε, $\equiv$,

(3) the abstraction operator: E,

(4) sentential connectives: N, K,

(5) the universal quantifier: Δ.

The letters '$\mathfrak{x}$', '$\mathfrak{y}$', '$\mathfrak{z}$', $\cdots$ will stand for set variables. We define the set of *formulae* of ZF by the following recursion:

(i) $\mathfrak{x} \varepsilon \mathfrak{y}$, $\mathfrak{x} \equiv \mathfrak{y}$ are formulae,

(ii) if $\mathfrak{A}$ is a formula, then so is $\mathfrak{x} \varepsilon E \mathfrak{y} \mathfrak{A}$.

(iii) if $\mathfrak{A}, \mathfrak{B}$ are formulae, then so are $N\mathfrak{A}$, $K\mathfrak{A}\mathfrak{B}$, $\Delta\mathfrak{x}\,\mathfrak{A}$.

We call the formulae (i) *atomic formulae.* The letters '$\mathfrak{A}$', '$\mathfrak{B}$', '$\mathfrak{G}$', ... will be used to stand for formulae. For the sake of perspicuity we employ the following abbreviations:

$$[\mathfrak{x}|\mathfrak{A}] =_{\mathrm{Df}} E\mathfrak{x}\mathfrak{A}$$
$$\neg\mathfrak{A} =_{\mathrm{Df}} N\mathfrak{A}$$
$$(\mathfrak{A} \wedge \mathfrak{B}) =_{\mathrm{Df}} K\mathfrak{A}\mathfrak{B}.$$

The further abbreviations: $(\mathfrak{A} \vee \mathfrak{B})$, $(\mathfrak{A} \rightarrow \mathfrak{B})$, $(\mathfrak{A} \leftrightarrow \mathfrak{B})$, $\nabla\mathfrak{x}\,\mathfrak{A}$ may be introduced by the customary definitions.

The usual rules and axioms of first order predicate logic with identity hold in ZF. In addition we have Church's *conversion principle*:

$$\mathfrak{x}\,\varepsilon\,[\mathfrak{x}|\mathfrak{A}] \leftrightarrow \mathfrak{A}.$$

Our first specifically set theoretical axiom is the *principle of extensionality*:

$$\varDelta\mathfrak{x}(\mathfrak{x}\,\varepsilon\,\mathfrak{y} \leftrightarrow \mathfrak{x}\,\varepsilon\,\mathfrak{z}) \rightarrow \mathfrak{y} \equiv \mathfrak{z}.$$

Expressions of the form $[\mathfrak{x}|\mathfrak{A}]$ are called *abstraction terms*; we refer to abstraction terms and variables jointly as *class terms* (or more briefly as *terms*). Let the letters 's', 't', ... stand for class terms. If at least one of s, t is an abstraction term, then we take '$s \equiv t$' as denoting the formula which expresses extensional equality; that is we set*:

$$s \equiv t =_{\mathrm{Df}} \varDelta\mathfrak{x}(\mathfrak{x}\,\varepsilon\,s \leftrightarrow \mathfrak{x}\,\varepsilon\,t). \tag{1}$$

If s is an abstraction term we set:

$$s\,\varepsilon\,t =_{\mathrm{Df}} \varDelta\mathfrak{x}(\mathfrak{x} \equiv s \wedge \mathfrak{x}\,\varepsilon\,t). \tag{2}$$

We use (1), (2) to define the "substitution" $\mathfrak{A}(\mathfrak{x}/t)$ of all free occurrences of $\mathfrak{x}$ by free occurrences of t in $\mathfrak{A}$.** If we can do so without confusion, we write: $\mathfrak{A}(t)$ for $\mathfrak{A}(\mathfrak{x}/t)$.

By A1 we obtain:

$$s \equiv t \rightarrow \cdot\mathfrak{A}(s) \leftrightarrow \mathfrak{A}(t),$$

whence in particular follows:

$$\varDelta\mathfrak{x}\mathfrak{A} \wedge \nabla\mathfrak{y}\,\mathfrak{y} \equiv t \cdot \rightarrow \mathfrak{A}(\mathfrak{x}/t).$$

* All definitions are extensions of the *metalanguage*; the object language remains unchanged.

** $\mathfrak{A}(\mathfrak{x}/t)$ is the formula which we obtain by first actually replacing the free occurrences of $\mathfrak{x}$ by t and then using (1), (2) to eliminate the subformulae of the form $\mathfrak{y} \equiv t$, $t \equiv \mathfrak{y}$, $t\varepsilon\mathfrak{y}$. It may be necessary to reletter the bound variables before carrying out the initial replacement.

In the usual manner we define the notations: $t \subset s$ (inclusion); $(t \cup s)$, $\cup\, t$ (union); $(t \cap s)$, $\cap\, t$ (intersection); $\bar{t}$ (complement); $(t - s)$ (class difference); $\emptyset$ (empty class); V (universal class). The formula $t \varepsilon V$ says that t is a set, for obviously we have:

$$t \varepsilon V \leftrightarrow \nabla \mathfrak{x}\, \mathfrak{x} \equiv t .$$

We further define:

$$\mathfrak{P} t =_{\mathrm{Df}} [\mathfrak{x} | \mathfrak{x} \subset t] \qquad \text{(power class)},$$
$$[t] =_{\mathrm{Df}} [\mathfrak{x} | \mathfrak{x} \equiv t] \qquad \text{(singleton)},$$
$$[t_1, \ldots, t_n] =_{\mathrm{Df}} [t_1] \cup \ldots \cup [t_n] .$$

Ordered n-tuples are defined by Kuratowski's method:

$$\langle t \rangle =_{\mathrm{Df}} t ,$$
$$\langle t, s_1, \ldots, s_n \rangle =_{\mathrm{Df}} [[t], [t, \langle s_1, \ldots, s_n \rangle]] .$$

For convenience we shall often write:

$$t s_1 \ldots s_n =_{\mathrm{Df}} \langle s_1, \ldots, s_n \rangle \, \varepsilon\, t .$$

We introduce a somewhat more flexible notation for class abstraction by the definition:

$$[t \underset{\mathfrak{x}_1 \ldots \mathfrak{x}_n}{|} \mathfrak{A}] =_{\mathrm{Df}} [\mathfrak{y} | \nabla \mathfrak{x}_1 \ldots \mathfrak{x}_n (\mathfrak{y} \equiv t \wedge \mathfrak{A})] .$$

As a rule we omit the list of variables under the vertical stroke, leaving it to be inferred from the context. We also write:

$$\bigcup_{\mathfrak{A}} t =_{\mathrm{Df}} \bigcup [t | \mathfrak{A}] \,;\; \bigcap_{\mathfrak{A}} t =_{\mathrm{Df}} \bigcap [t | \mathfrak{A}] \,;$$
$$[\mathfrak{x}_1 \ldots \mathfrak{x}_n | \mathfrak{A}] =_{\mathrm{Df}} [\langle \mathfrak{x}_1, \ldots, \mathfrak{x}_n \rangle | \mathfrak{A}] .$$

If R is a class term, we define:

$\mathrm{Rel}(R)$	$=_{\mathrm{Df}} R \equiv [\mathfrak{x}\mathfrak{y} | R\mathfrak{x}\mathfrak{y}]$	("R is a relation"),
$R''t$	$=_{\mathrm{Df}} [\mathfrak{y} | \nabla \mathfrak{x} (R\, \mathfrak{y}\mathfrak{x} \wedge \mathfrak{x}\, \varepsilon\, t)]$	("the R image of t"),
$R \upharpoonright t$	$=_{\mathrm{Df}} [\mathfrak{y}\mathfrak{x} | R\, \mathfrak{y}\mathfrak{x} \wedge \mathfrak{x}\, \varepsilon\, t]$	("R restricted to t"),
R^{-1}	$=_{\mathrm{Df}} [\mathfrak{x}\mathfrak{y} | R\, \mathfrak{y}\mathfrak{x}]$	("the inverse of R"),
$D(R)$	$=_{\mathrm{Df}} R^{-1}{}''V$	("the domain of R"),
$W(R)$	$=_{\mathrm{Df}} R''V$	("the codomain of R").

We wish to define *descriptions* (ι-terms) in such a way that:

$$\iota \mathfrak{x} \mathfrak{A} \equiv \begin{cases} \mathfrak{x} & \text{if } [\mathfrak{x}] \equiv [\mathfrak{x} | \mathfrak{A}] \\ V & \text{otherwise} . \end{cases}$$

(Thus in particular "$\iota\mathfrak{x}\mathfrak{A}$ exists" is expressed by: $\iota\mathfrak{x}\mathfrak{A}\,\varepsilon\, V$.)
The following definition proves adequate:

$$\iota\mathfrak{x}\mathfrak{A} =_{\mathrm{Df}} \cap [\mathfrak{x}|[\mathfrak{x}] \equiv [\mathfrak{x}|\mathfrak{A}]].$$

If F is a class term we define:

$$F(t_1, \ldots, t_n) =_{\mathrm{Df}} \iota\mathfrak{y}F\mathfrak{y}t_1 \ldots t_n,$$
$$\mathrm{Func}(F) =_{\mathrm{Df}} \mathrm{Rel}(F) \wedge D(F) \equiv [\mathfrak{x}|F(\mathfrak{x})\,\varepsilon\, V] \qquad (\text{"}F \text{ is a function"}).$$

We define an abstraction operator for functions by:

$$\langle t|\mathfrak{A}\rangle_{\mathfrak{x}_1 \ldots \mathfrak{x}_n} =_{\mathrm{Df}} [\langle t, \mathfrak{x}_1, \ldots, \mathfrak{x}_n\rangle|\mathfrak{A}]_{\mathfrak{x}_1 \ldots \mathfrak{x}_n}.$$

As before, we shall generally suppress the list of variables under the vertical stroke; we then think of the omitted variables as standing in the order of their first occurrences in t. For $F = \langle t|\mathfrak{x}\mathfrak{A}\rangle$ we have:

$$\mathrm{Func}(F)\,;\ D(F) = [\mathfrak{x}|t\,\varepsilon\, V \wedge \mathfrak{A}]\,;\ W(F) \equiv [t|\mathfrak{A}]_{\mathfrak{x}}\,;\ \mathfrak{x}\,\varepsilon\, D(F) \rightarrow F(\mathfrak{x}) \equiv t.$$

Finally we define the class of *ordinal numbers* by:

$$On =_{\mathrm{Df}} [\mathfrak{x}|\ \cup\mathfrak{x} \subset \mathfrak{x} \wedge \mathrm{connex}(\mathfrak{x})],$$

setting:

$$\mathrm{connex}(\mathfrak{x}) =_{\mathrm{Df}} \Delta\mathfrak{y}\mathfrak{z}(\mathfrak{y}, \mathfrak{z}\,\varepsilon\,\mathfrak{x} \rightarrow \cdot\, \mathfrak{y} \equiv \mathfrak{z} \vee \mathfrak{y}\,\varepsilon\,\mathfrak{z} \vee \mathfrak{z}\,\varepsilon\,\mathfrak{y}).$$

Using our abbreviations, we can now state the remaining ZF axioms in a concise form:

A2. $[\mathfrak{x}, \mathfrak{y}]\,\varepsilon\, V$ (axiom of pairing),
A3. $\cup\mathfrak{x}\,\varepsilon\, V$ (axiom of union),
A4. $\mathfrak{P}\mathfrak{x}\,\varepsilon\, V$ (power set axiom),
A5. $\mathrm{Func}(F) \rightarrow F''\mathfrak{x}\,\varepsilon\, V$, where F is any class term (axiom of replacement),
A6. $\nabla\delta(\emptyset\,\varepsilon\,\delta \wedge \Delta\mathfrak{x}(\mathfrak{x}\,\varepsilon\,\delta \rightarrow \mathfrak{x} \cup [\mathfrak{x}]\,\varepsilon\,\delta))$ (axiom of infinity),
A7. $\mathfrak{x} \equiv \emptyset \vee \nabla\mathfrak{y}(\mathfrak{y}\,\varepsilon\,\mathfrak{x} \wedge \mathfrak{y} \cap \mathfrak{x} \equiv \emptyset)$ (axiom of regularity).

A relation R is called *well-founded* (Found(R)) iff every non-empty set has a minimal element with respect to R. Formally we define:

$$\mathrm{Found}(R) =_{\mathrm{Df}} \mathrm{Rel}(R) \wedge \Delta\mathfrak{x}(\mathfrak{x} \equiv \emptyset \vee \nabla\mathfrak{y}(\mathfrak{y}\,\varepsilon\,\mathfrak{x} \wedge R''[\mathfrak{y}] \cap \mathfrak{x} \equiv \emptyset)),$$

R being an arbitrary class term. Obviously A7 could have been written as:

Found $([\mathfrak{x}\,\mathfrak{y} \mid \mathfrak{x}\,\varepsilon\,\mathfrak{y}])$. We use the notion of well-foundedness in stating the following *recursion theorem*, which justifies the use of recursive definitions in set theory:

THEOREM. Let R, G be class terms. There exists a class term F such that from the assumptions:

$$\text{Found}(R),\ \text{Func}(G),\ D(G) \equiv V,\ \varLambda\mathfrak{x}\, R''[\mathfrak{x}]\,\varepsilon\, V$$

follow:

$$\text{Func}(F),\ D(F) \equiv V,\ \varLambda\mathfrak{x}\, F(\mathfrak{x}) \equiv G(\mathfrak{x}, F \upharpoonright R''\{\mathfrak{x}\}).$$

In particular there is a class term rn such that the following statement holds:

$$\varLambda\mathfrak{x}\,\text{rn}(\mathfrak{x}) \equiv \bigcup_{\mathfrak{y}\varepsilon\mathfrak{x}} \text{rn}(\mathfrak{y}) \cup [\text{rn}(\mathfrak{y})]\,; \tag{*}$$

"rn$(\mathfrak{x})$" is read "rank of $\mathfrak{x}$". By (*) follows: $\varLambda\mathfrak{x}\ \text{rn}(\mathfrak{x})\,\varepsilon\, On$. Moreover we can derive the statement which says that for every $\mathfrak{x}$, rn$(\mathfrak{x})$ is the smallest ordinal larger than every rn$(\mathfrak{y})$ for $\mathfrak{y}\,\varepsilon\,\mathfrak{x}$.

In the course of this paper we shall extend the basic ZF formalism in various directions. In particular we shall frequently adopt new predicates and set constants. The atomic formulae of the extended language then have the form: $u \varepsilon u'$, $u \equiv u'$, $Pu_1 \ldots u_n$, where P is a predicate and u, u', $u_1, \ldots, u_n$ are variables and set constants. We refer to ε, $\equiv$ as *logical predicates* in order to distinguish them from the new predicates.

2. The metalanguage

Our metalanguage is English enriched by a number of logical and mathematical signs. However, we shall admit only such arguments as can be formalised within the language of ZF (adopting further axioms as the need arises – such as the assumption that ZF possesses a model). The set variables of the metalanguage are 'u', 'v', 'w', 'x', 'y', 'z', ... From time to time we shall introduce specialized variables (in fact we have already done so in section 1). In particular we employ 'α', 'β', 'γ', 'δ',... as variables for ordinal numbers. The quantifiers of the metalanguage are '$\wedge$', '$\vee$',* the negation sign is '$\sim$'; our binary sentential connectives

* We also write:

$$\wedge x\colon \in y \ldots x \ldots \leftrightarrow_{\text{Df}} \wedge x\,(x \in y \rightarrow \ldots x \ldots);$$

similarly for $\wedge x\colon \subset y$, $\wedge x\colon = y$, ... etc.

are '$\wedge$', '$\vee$', '$\rightarrow$', '$\leftrightarrow$'*. In forming class abstraction terms we use the customary curly brackets $\{|\}$ rather than the square ones; for singleton x we write $\{x\}$ instead of $[x]$. Our set membership and identity predicates are '$\in$', '$=$' rather than 'ε', '$\equiv$'. In general, however, economy enjoins us to employ the same notation on two linguistic levels. Thus '$\mathfrak{P}u$' may denote the power set of u, or it may denote the expression $[\mathfrak{x} \mid \mathfrak{x} \subset u]$ (u being a term of the object language). In order to prevent confusion we put a dot into the notation when it is used to refer to the object language. Thus we write '$t \dot{\subset} s$', '$\dot{\mathfrak{P}} t$', '$\dot{\langle} t,s \rangle$' rather than '$t \subset s$', '$\mathfrak{P} t$', '$\langle t,s \rangle$' as before. Of course we shall suppress the dots whenever the context permits.

Having resolved to admit only set theoretical notions in our metalanguage, we must find some way to interpret symbols and strings of symbols as sets. A natural method is to identify strings of symbols with *finite sequences* (i.e. functions z such that $\emptyset \neq D(z) \in \omega$). If z, w are strings of symbols in this sense, and if $D(z) = n$, $D(w) = m$, then we define their concatenation zw by:

$$D(zw) = n + m\,;\ (zw)_i = \begin{cases} z_i & \text{if } i < n \\ w_{i-n} & \text{otherwise}. \end{cases}$$

Strings of symbols form a free semigroup with respect to concatenation; its free generators have the form $\{\langle x, 0 \rangle\}$. We specify the primitive signs of ZF as follows:

$$\begin{aligned} v_i &= \{\langle\langle i, 1\rangle, 0\rangle\} \\ N &= \{\langle\langle 0, 2\rangle, 0\rangle\} \\ K &= \{\langle\langle 1, 2\rangle, 0\rangle\} \\ E &= \{\langle\langle 2, 2\rangle, 0\rangle\} \\ \Delta &= \{\langle\langle 3, 2\rangle, 0\rangle\} \\ \varepsilon &= \{\langle\langle 4, 2\rangle, 0\rangle\} \\ \equiv &= \{\langle\langle 5, 2\rangle, 0\rangle\}. \end{aligned}$$

(This specification ensures that the expressions of the ZF language occur in every concrete model of ZF.) From time to time we shall introduce further primitive symbols (e.g. constants, predicates), generally without specifying

* This does not give rise to confusion, since the bracketing tells us whether these signs are used as metalinguistic sentential connectives or as components of terms referring to the object language.

their form. We shall, however, reserve the signs $\boldsymbol{x} =_{\mathrm{Df}} \{\langle\langle x,0\rangle, 0\rangle\}$ as constants; $\boldsymbol{x}$ will be used as a name for x.

3. Concrete models

Extend ZF by adopting a (possibly empty) set of additional constants and predicates. By a *concrete model* for the so extended language we mean a pair $M = \langle U, \Omega\rangle$ such that:

(i) U is a non-empty transitive set,

(ii) Ω is a function defined on the non-logical predicates and constants such that:

$$\Omega(Q) \subset U^n \quad \text{if } Q \text{ is an } n\text{-place predicate,}$$
$$\Omega(c) \in U \quad \text{if } c \text{ is a constant.}$$

We also write: $U_M =_{\mathrm{Df}} U$; $M(b) =_{\mathrm{Df}} \Omega(b)$.

Now let us adjoin the further constants $\{\boldsymbol{x} \mid x \in U\}$ and extend the model by setting: $M(\boldsymbol{x}) =_{\mathrm{Df}} x$ if $x \in U$. The *M-truth* of a statement $\mathfrak{A}$ may then be defined by the following recursion:

$$\models_M c\, \varepsilon\, c' \leftrightarrow M(c) \in M(c')$$
$$\models_M c \equiv c' \leftrightarrow M(c) = M(c')$$
$$\models_M Q c_1 \ldots c_n \leftrightarrow M(Q) \ni \langle M(c_1), \ldots, M(c_n)\rangle$$
$$\models_M (\mathfrak{A} \wedge \mathfrak{B}) \leftrightarrow \cdot \models_M \mathfrak{A} \wedge \models_M \mathfrak{B}$$
$$\models_M \neg \mathfrak{A} \leftrightarrow \sim \models_M \mathfrak{A}$$
$$\models_M \Delta \mathfrak{x} \mathfrak{A} \leftrightarrow \bigwedge x : \in U \models_M \mathfrak{A}(\boldsymbol{x})$$
$$\models_M c\, \varepsilon\, [\mathfrak{x} | \mathfrak{A}] \leftrightarrow \models_M \mathfrak{A}(c).$$

We define a valuation $M(t)$ of the class terms by:

$$M([\mathfrak{x} | \mathfrak{A}]) =_{\mathrm{Df}} \{x | x \in U \wedge \models_M \mathfrak{A}(\boldsymbol{x})\}.$$

If $\mathfrak{A}$ is a formula with the free variables $\mathfrak{x}_1, \ldots, \mathfrak{x}_n$, then we call $\mathfrak{A}$ *M-valid* ($\models_M \mathfrak{A}$) if $\models_M \Delta \mathfrak{x}_1 \ldots \mathfrak{x}_n \mathfrak{A}$. If A is a set of formulae, we call M a *model* of A iff every $\mathfrak{A} \in A$ is M-valid. From now on we make the following assumptions: *There exists a concrete model for the axioms of* ZF (A1–A7). This assumption will be sufficient for all of the arguments in this paper.

We call a class $A \subset U_M$ *definable in M* (or *M-definable*) if there is a class term t such that $A = M(t)$. In particular every $x \in U_M$ is M-definable. The major tool for proving definability in concrete ZF-models is the recursion theorem, which for this purpose is best stated in the following form: Let R be an M-definable well-founded relation and let $R''\{x\} \in U_M$ for every $x \in U_M$. If g is an M-definable function such that: $D(g) = U_M$, then there exists an M-definable function f such that: $D(f) = U_M^2$ and $\bigwedge x :\in U_M\, f(x, y) = g(x, y, \langle f(z, y) | Rzx \rangle)$.

Virtually all proofs of definability can be obtained by iterated applications of this principle, starting with a few easily checked "absoluteness" theorems; e.g.

$$M([\mathbf{x}]) = \{x\}$$
$$M(\langle \mathbf{x}_1, \ldots, \mathbf{x}_n \rangle) = \langle x_1, \ldots, x_n \rangle$$

and, writing $A = M(\dot{A})$, $B = M(\dot{B})$, $R = M(\dot{R})$:

$M(\dot{A} \cap \dot{B}) = A \cap B$ (similarly for $\cup, -$)

$\models_M \mathrm{Rel}(\dot{R}) \leftrightarrow R$ is a relation

$M(\dot{R}''\dot{A}) = R''A$ (similarly for $R \upharpoonright A$, R^{-1}, $D(R)$, $W(R)$)

$\models_M \mathrm{Func}(\dot{R}) \leftrightarrow R$ is a function

and so on. The basic principle behind all of these absoluteness theorems is the absoluteness of bounded quantifications; i.e.

$$\models_M \Lambda \mathfrak{x} (\mathfrak{x} \,\varepsilon\, \dot{A} \to \mathfrak{A}) \leftrightarrow \bigwedge x :\in A \models_M \mathfrak{A}(\mathbf{x}).$$

Since, however, not all notations of set theory are absolute with respect to ZF-models, we shall use several notations less often in their absolute meaning than *relativised to a concrete model M*. The relativisation is indicated by writing 'M' as index; thus we write:

$$On_M =_{\mathrm{Df}} U_M \cap On$$
$$\mathfrak{P}_M x \quad \text{or} \quad (\mathfrak{P}x)_M =_{\mathrm{Df}} U_M \cap \mathfrak{P}x,$$

whence follows: $On_M = M(\dot{O}n)$, $\mathfrak{P}_M x = M(\mathfrak{P}\mathbf{x})$ for $x \in U_M$. We say that $x, y \in U_M$ are *of equal cardinality with respect to M* $(x \sim_M y)$, when a function $f \in U_M$ exists which maps x onto y in 1–1 fashion. $\bar{\bar{x}}^M$ is the least $\alpha \in On_M$ such that $x \sim_M \alpha$. $\langle (\aleph_\nu)_M \,|\, \nu \in On_M \rangle$ is the enumeration of the $\bar{\bar{\alpha}}^M$ in their natural order. Such notations as: $(2^{\aleph_\nu})_M$, $(\prod_{\nu<\alpha} \aleph_{\varphi_\nu})_M$ are to be defined analogously. In contexts where no confusion can arise, we may suppress the relativisation indices. Occasionally we write the words 'in M' after a formula of the metalanguage to indicate that the expressions occurring in it are used relatively to M. For example we write:

$$\aleph_\alpha = \overline{\overline{\mathfrak{P}x}} \quad \text{in } M$$

rather than:

$$(\aleph_\alpha)_M = \overline{\overline{\mathfrak{P}_M x}}^M .$$

In order to construct models by the forcing method we shall need the existence of countable concrete ZF models. This is guaranteed by the following lemma, which is a form of the Löwenheim-Skolem theorem:

THEOREM 1. Let M be a concrete model of ZF with at most countably many additional predicates and constants. Then there exists a countable concrete model M_0 such that $\models_{M_0}\mathfrak{A}\leftrightarrow\models_M\mathfrak{A}$ for all statements $\mathfrak{A}$.

PROOF.* Set $\Delta^0\mathfrak{x}\mathfrak{A}=_{\mathrm{Df}}\Delta\mathfrak{x}\,(\mathfrak{x}\,\varepsilon\,\dot{O}n\rightarrow\mathfrak{A})$ for formulae $\mathfrak{A}$. If t is an abstraction term without free variables let $\alpha(t)$ be the least $\alpha\in On\cap M(t)$; if no such α exists set: $\alpha(t)=_{\mathrm{Df}}0$. Let On_0 be the set of all $\alpha(t)$. We extend the formalism by adopting the countably many new constants $\{\boldsymbol{\alpha}|\alpha\in On_0\}$. $\boldsymbol{\alpha}$ denotes α. In addition we add a countable set K of further new constants. Let S be the set of all statements in the so extended language which are derivable from M-valid formulae by means of first order predicate logic. We then have:

$$\begin{aligned}&\Delta^0\mathfrak{x}\mathfrak{A}\in S\leftrightarrow\bigwedge\alpha{:}\in On_0\;\mathfrak{A}(\boldsymbol{\alpha})\in S\,,\\&\Delta\mathfrak{x}\mathfrak{A}\in S\leftrightarrow\bigwedge K{:}\in K\;\mathfrak{A}(k)\in S\,.\end{aligned}\qquad(*)$$

By a theorem of Sikorski (see [3]) we can extend S to a maximal consistent set $S'\supset S$ which also satisfies (*). Now consider the abstract model $\tilde{M}=\langle\tilde{U},\varepsilon',\simeq,\tilde{\Omega}\rangle$ obtained by taking $\tilde{U}$ as the collection of all constants of our extended formalism and defining:

$$\begin{aligned}&k\,\varepsilon'\,k'\leftrightarrow_{\mathrm{Df}}k\,\varepsilon\,k'\in S'\\&k\simeq k'\leftrightarrow_{\mathrm{Df}}k\equiv k'\in S'\\&\tilde{\Omega}(Q)=_{\mathrm{Df}}\{k_1\ldots k_n|Qk_1\ldots k_n\in S'\}\\&\tilde{\Omega}(k)=_{\mathrm{Df}}k\quad\text{for}\quad k\in\tilde{U}\,.\end{aligned}$$

Using (*) we obtain by induction on the length of $\mathfrak{A}$:

$$\models_{\tilde{M}}\mathfrak{A}\leftrightarrow\mathfrak{A}\in S'.$$

It remains to convert $\tilde{M}$ into a concrete model. By (*) there exists to every $k\in\tilde{U}$ exactly one $\rho=\rho(k)$ such that $\rho\in On_0$ and $\models_{\tilde{M}}\boldsymbol{\rho}\equiv\dot{r}n(k)$. Since M is a ZF model we may conclude:

$$k\,\varepsilon'\,k'\rightarrow\rho(k)<\rho(k').$$

* A more direct proof could be given using the axiom of choice.

Thus ε' is a well founded relation. By the recursion theorem we may define:

$$h(k) =_{\mathrm{Df}} \{h(k') | k' \varepsilon' k\},$$

whence follows:

$$h(k') \in h(k) \leftrightarrow k' \varepsilon' k, \qquad (**)$$
$$h(k') = h(k) \leftrightarrow k' \simeq k.$$

We define the concrete model M_0 by:

$$U_{M_0} =_{\mathrm{Df}} h'' \tilde{U}$$
$$M_0(Q) =_{\mathrm{Df}} \{\langle h(k_1), \ldots, h(k_n)\rangle | \models_{\tilde{M}} Q k_1 \ldots k_n\}$$
$$M_0(\boldsymbol{k}) =_{\mathrm{Df}} h(k).$$

By (**) we obtain at once:

$$\models_{M_0} \mathfrak{A} \leftrightarrow \models_{\tilde{M}} \mathfrak{A}.$$

4. Inner models

Suppose M is a concrete model in which all the ZF axioms hold. The following question suggests itself: Do there exist concrete ZF models N different * from M but possessing the same ordinals (i.e. $On_N = On_M$)? The answer to this question was not known until Cohen's discovery of the forcing method in 1963. However, Gödel in 1938 was able to establish the following fact: Among the concrete ZF models N such that $On_N = On_M$ there exists a smallest model. This smallest model, which we label $L(=\langle L, \emptyset\rangle)$, is called the *constructible model.* Gödel's procedure was first to define a hierarchy $\langle L_\nu | \nu \in On_M\rangle$ by:

$$L_0 =_{\mathrm{Df}} \emptyset\,;\; L_{\nu+1} =_{\mathrm{Df}} \mathrm{Def}(L_\nu)\,;$$
$$L_\lambda =_{\mathrm{Df}} \bigcup_{\nu<\lambda} L_\nu \quad \text{if } \lambda \text{ is a limit ordinal}$$

(where $\mathrm{Def}(X)$ is the set of $Y \subset X$ definable in the model $\langle X, \emptyset\rangle$), and then to set:

$$L =_{\mathrm{Df}} \bigcup_{\nu \in On_M} L_\nu.$$

The minimality of L follows by the fact that the hierarchy $\langle L_\nu | \nu \in On_M\rangle$ is definable in every concrete ZF model containing the ordinals of M.

* i.e. $U_N \neq U_M$; it is obvious that models $N = \langle U_N, \Omega_N\rangle$ exist such that $\Omega_N \neq \Omega_M$.

The difficult step is to verify that L is a model of the ZF axioms. In this section we shall carry out such a verification in a more general setting.

We begin by generalizing the construction of L. We extend the ZF language by adding a (possibly empty) collection of new predicates, which we suppose to form a set in M. Let $\langle U^0, \Omega\rangle$ be a concrete model for the so extended language; we suppose, moreover, that U^0, Ω are M-definable* and that $On_M \subset U^0 \subset U_M$. We do not assume $\langle U^0, \Omega\rangle$ to be a model of the ZF axioms; in fact the only axioms which are certain to hold are the axiom of extensionality A1 (since U^0 is transitive), the axiom of infinity A6 (since $\omega \in U^0$), and the axiom of regularity A7 (since the $\in$ relation is well founded). We wish to extend U^0 in a canonical manner (i.e. without reference to M) to a $U \supset U^0$ such that $N = \langle U, \Omega\rangle$ is a ZF model. We do this essentially by repeating Gödel's construction of L; that is we construct a hierarchy $\langle U_\nu | \nu \in On_M\rangle$ and set:

$$U =_{\mathrm{Df}} \bigcup_{\nu \in On_M} U_\nu .$$

In defining the hierarchy U_ν we modify the definition of L_ν in two respects: (i) each element of U^0 is injected at the level of its rank; (ii) U_ν contains all subsets of U_ν which are definable in $\langle U_\nu, \Omega_\nu\rangle, \Omega_\nu$ being the suitable restriction of Ω (i.e. $\Omega_\nu(Q) =_{\mathrm{Df}} \Omega(Q) \cap U_\nu^n$ for n-ary predicates Q).

Our "official" definition of U will be given in a somewhat different fashion. We shall first describe a canonical system of notations for the elements of U and then use this system in defining U. One arrives at such a system of notations by thinking of the U_α as levels of a ramified theory of types: First let the variables $\mathfrak{x}^0$ range over U_0; then the elements of U_1 are denoted by terms of the form:

$$[\mathfrak{x}^0 | \mathfrak{A}]$$

and

$$x \quad \text{for} \quad x \in U, \quad \mathrm{rn}(x) < 1 .$$

Add variables $\mathfrak{x}^1$ ranging over U_1; then the elements of U_2 are denoted by

$$[\mathfrak{x}^1 | \mathfrak{A}]$$

and

$$x \quad \text{for} \quad x \in U, \quad \mathrm{rn}(x) < 2$$

* More precisely: $\{\langle x, Q\rangle \mid x \in \Omega(Q)\}$ is M-definable.

and so on. In the following we shall carry out this program systematically; in place of indexed variables, however, we use indexed quantifiers Δ_α and indexed abstraction terms E_α. Let ZF_0 be the ZF language extended by the set of predicates $(D(\Omega))$ mentioned at the outset and by the constants $\{\boldsymbol{x} \mid x \in U^0\}$. We now construct a *ramified language* (RL) containing in addition to the symbols of ZF_0 the following primitive signs:

(1) bounded quantifiers Δ_α for each $\alpha \in On_M$,

(2) bounded abstraction operators E_α for each $\alpha \in On_M$.

The variables $\mathfrak{x}, \mathfrak{y}, \ldots$ will of course range over elements of U; for the sake of convenience we also add:

(3) countably many new variables $\mathfrak{x}^0, \mathfrak{y}^0, \ldots,$ which will range over elements of U^0. We suppose the new variables to form a countable set in M. We also suppose the functions $\langle \Delta_\alpha | \alpha \in On_M \rangle$, $\langle E_\alpha | \alpha \in On_M \rangle$ to be M-definable. The *formulae* and *set constants* of RL are defined simultaneously by the following recursion:

(i) $Qt_1 \cdots t_n$ is a formula, where Q is a predicate of ZF_0 and each t_i is either one of the variables $\mathfrak{x}^0$ or a set constant of the form $\boldsymbol{x} (x \in U^0)$.

(ii) $t \varepsilon t'$, $t \equiv t'$ are formulae, where t, t' are variables or set constants.

(iii) If $\mathfrak{A}, \mathfrak{B}$ are formulae, then so are $(\mathfrak{A} \wedge \mathfrak{B})$, $\neg \mathfrak{A}$, $\Delta \mathfrak{x} \mathfrak{A}$, $\Delta \mathfrak{x}^0 \mathfrak{A}$, $\Delta_\alpha \mathfrak{x} \mathfrak{A}$, $\Delta_\alpha \mathfrak{x}^0 \mathfrak{A}$.

(iv) If $\mathfrak{A}$ is a formula and t is a variable or set constant, then $t \varepsilon [\mathfrak{x} | \mathfrak{A}]$ is a formula.

Formulae in which no unbounded quantifiers occur are called *bounded.*

(v) $\boldsymbol{x}$ is a set constant if $x \in U^0$.

(vi) If $\Delta_\alpha \mathfrak{x} \mathfrak{A}$ is a bounded statement and if (a) $\alpha > \beta$ whenever E_β occurs in $\mathfrak{A}$ or $\beta = \mathrm{rn}(x)$ and $\boldsymbol{x}$ occurs in $\mathfrak{A}$ and (b) $\alpha \geq \beta$ whenever Δ_β occurs in $\mathfrak{A}$, then $E_\alpha \mathfrak{x} \mathfrak{A}$ is a set constant.

Set constants of the form $E_\alpha \mathfrak{x} \mathfrak{A}$ are called *bounded abstraction terms.* Let T be the class of all RL set constants and T^0 the class of all RL set constants of the form $\boldsymbol{x}$. We define a *rank function* ρ on T by:

$$\rho(\boldsymbol{x}) =_{\mathrm{Df}} \mathrm{rn}(x) ; \; \rho(E_\alpha \mathfrak{x} \mathfrak{A}) =_{\mathrm{Df}} \alpha$$

and set:

$$T_\alpha =_{\mathrm{Df}} \{t | t \in T \wedge \rho(t) < \alpha\}$$
$$T_\alpha^0 =_{\mathrm{Df}} \{\boldsymbol{x} | x \in U^0 \wedge \rho(\boldsymbol{x}) < \alpha\}.$$

The notion of truth for RL statements ($\models_N^*$) and the valuation of the set constants ($\langle N(t)|t \in T\rangle$) are defined simultaneously by the following recursion:

$$\begin{aligned}
&\vDash_N^* Q\boldsymbol{x}_1 \ldots \boldsymbol{x}_n \leftrightarrow \Omega(Q)\, x_1 \ldots x_n\,, && (^*)\\
&\vDash_N^* t\,\varepsilon\, t' \leftrightarrow N(t) \in N(t')\,,\\
&\vDash_N^* t \equiv t' \leftrightarrow N(t) = N(t')\,,\\
&\vDash_N^* (\mathfrak{A} \wedge \mathfrak{B}) \leftrightarrow \vDash_N^* \mathfrak{A} \wedge \vDash_N^* \mathfrak{B}\,,\\
&\vDash_N^* \neg\mathfrak{A} \leftrightarrow \sim \vDash_N^* \mathfrak{A}\,,\\
&\vDash_N^* \Delta_\alpha \mathfrak{x}^0 \mathfrak{A} \leftrightarrow \bigwedge t{:}\in T_\alpha^0 \vDash_N^* \mathfrak{A}(t)\,,\\
&\vDash_N^* \Delta_\alpha \mathfrak{x}\, \mathfrak{A} \leftrightarrow \bigwedge t{:}\in T_\alpha \vDash_N^* \mathfrak{A}(t)
\end{aligned}$$

(analogously for $\Delta\mathfrak{x}^0, \Delta\mathfrak{x}$),

$$\begin{aligned}
&\vDash_N^* t\,\varepsilon\,[\mathfrak{x}|\mathfrak{A}] \leftrightarrow \vDash_N^* \mathfrak{A}(t)\,,\\
&N(\boldsymbol{x}) \quad = x\,,\\
&N(E_\alpha \mathfrak{x}\mathfrak{A}) = \{N(t)|t \in T_\alpha \wedge \vDash_N^* \mathfrak{A}(t)\}\,.
\end{aligned}$$

In addition we set:

$$N([\mathfrak{x}|\mathfrak{A}]) =_{\mathrm{Df}} \{N(t)|t \in T \wedge \vDash_N \mathfrak{A}(t)\}\,.$$

It remains to be shown that (*) is truly a definition; i.e. we must show that there is just one set $\{U|\vDash_N^* \mathfrak{A}\}$ and one function $\langle N(t)|t \in T\rangle$ satisfying (*).

To this end we assign an ordinal $\gamma(b)$ to each b which is either a set constant or a statement of RL:*

$$\gamma(b) = On_M \cdot q + \omega\alpha + r$$

where

q = the number of occurrences of Δ,

α = the least ordinal such that:
  $\alpha > \beta$ whenever E_β occurs in b or $\beta = \rho(\boldsymbol{x})$ and $\boldsymbol{x}$ occurs in b
  $\alpha \geq \beta$ whenever Δ_β occurs in b,

r = the number of occurrences of logical signs (*not* counting the occurrences within terms of the form $E_\beta \mathfrak{x}\mathfrak{B}$ where $\beta < \alpha$).

If we set:

$$N(\mathfrak{A}) = \begin{cases} 1 & \text{if } \vDash_N^* \mathfrak{A} \\ 0 & \text{otherwise} \end{cases}$$

for RL statements $\mathfrak{A}$, then the definition (*) can be written in the form:

$$N(b) = G(b, N \upharpoonright \gamma^{-1}{}''\gamma(b))\,.$$

* On_M is of course the smallest ordinal not contained in M.

By the recursion theorem, however, there exists precisely one such N, which was to be shown. This result holds in a still stronger version: The function γ restricted to set constants and bounded statements is certainly M-definable, as is the restriction of G to U_M. Thus, by the recursion theorem, the function N restricted to set constants and bounded statements is M-definable. Let Fml_n be the set of formulae containing at most n unbounded quantifiers. A straightforward argument yields:

LEMMA 1. The function $\langle N(t) | t \in T \rangle$ is M-definable, as is each of the classes $\{\mathfrak{A} | \mathfrak{A} \in \mathrm{Fml}_n \wedge \models_N^* \mathfrak{A}\}$ for $n < \omega$. We now define the model $N = \langle U, \Omega \rangle$ and the hierarchy $\langle U_\alpha | \alpha \in On_M \rangle$ by setting:

$$U =_{\mathrm{Df}} \{N(t) | t \in T\} \; ; \; U_\alpha =_{\mathrm{Df}} \{N(t) | t \in T_\alpha\} .$$

One may verify that for ZF_0 statements $\mathfrak{A}$:

$$\models_N^* \mathfrak{A} \leftrightarrow \models_N \mathfrak{A} .$$

Thus the star may be omitted from '$\models_N^*$' without risk of confusion. We now turn to the proof of the main result of this section:

THEOREM 2. N is a model of all the ZF axioms.

We have already established that A1, A6, A7 are N-valid. Since pairs and unions can be described by bounded abstraction terms, we have:

LEMMA 3. The axiom of pairing (A2) and the axiom of union (A3) are N-valid.

PROOF. We must show that U is closed under $\{,\}$ and $\cup$. Let $s_0, s_1 \in T_\beta$. Let $t = E_\beta \mathfrak{x} (\mathfrak{x} \equiv s_0 \vee \mathfrak{x} \equiv s_1)$; then $N(t) = \{N(s_0), N(s_1)\}$. Let $t = E_\beta \mathfrak{x} \; \nabla_\beta \mathfrak{y} (\mathfrak{x} \varepsilon \mathfrak{y} \wedge \mathfrak{y} \varepsilon s_0)$; then $N(t) = \cup N(s_0)$.

In order to prove the N-validity of the replacement axiom (A5) and the power set axiom (A4), we must make use of lemma 1. The proof of the replacement axiom will proceed in several stages, beginning with the following *relativization lemma*:

LEMMA 4. Let $\nabla \mathfrak{y} \mathfrak{A} = \nabla \mathfrak{y} \mathfrak{A}(\mathfrak{x}_1, \ldots, \mathfrak{x}_n)$ be an RL formula containing at most the n free variables $\mathfrak{x}_1, \ldots, \mathfrak{x}_n$. For each $\alpha \in On_M$ there exists a $\beta \in On_M$ such that:

$$\models_N \nabla \mathfrak{y} \mathfrak{A}(t_1, \ldots, t_n) \leftrightarrow \nabla_\beta \mathfrak{y} \mathfrak{A}(t_1, \ldots, t_n)$$

for all $t_1, \ldots, t_n \in T_\beta$.

PROOF. Set:

$$\sigma(t_1, \ldots, t_n) =_{\mathrm{Df}} \mu\beta \vDash_N \nabla_\beta \mathfrak{y} \mathfrak{A}(t_1, \ldots, t_n).\ ^*$$

By lemma 1 the relation

$$\{\beta t_1 \ldots t_n | \vDash_N \nabla_\beta \mathfrak{y} \mathfrak{A}(t_1, \ldots, t_n)\}$$

is M-definable. Hence, so is σ. Since M is a ZF model and $T_\alpha \in U_M$, there must be a $\beta \geq \alpha$ in M such that:

$$\beta > \sup\{\sigma(t_1, \ldots, t_n) | t_1, \ldots, t_n \in T_\alpha\}.$$

β obviously has the required property.

By iterated applications of lemma 4 we obtain:

LEMMA 5. Let $\mathfrak{A} = \mathfrak{A}(\mathfrak{x}_1, \ldots, \mathfrak{x}_n)$ be an RL formula with at most the n free variables $\mathfrak{x}_1, \ldots, \mathfrak{x}_n$. For each $\alpha \in On_M$ there exists a bounded RL formula $\mathfrak{A}_\alpha$ such that:

$$\vDash_N \mathfrak{A}(t_1, \ldots, t_n) \leftrightarrow \mathfrak{A}_\alpha(t_1, \ldots, t_n)$$

for $t_1, \ldots, t_n \in T_\alpha$.

PROOF (by induction on the length of $\mathfrak{A}$). For bounded $\mathfrak{A}$ the assertion is trivial. If the assertion holds for $\mathfrak{A}$ and $\mathfrak{B}$, then obviously it holds for $(\mathfrak{A} \wedge \mathfrak{B})$ and $\neg\mathfrak{A}$. Now let the assertion be proven for $\mathfrak{A}(\mathfrak{y}, \mathfrak{x}_1, \ldots, \mathfrak{x}_n)$. We wish to show that it holds for $\Delta\mathfrak{y}\mathfrak{A}$. By lemma 4 and the induction hypothesis there is a $\beta \in On_M$ such that $\beta \geq \alpha$ and:

$$\begin{aligned}\vDash_N \Delta\mathfrak{y}\mathfrak{A}(\mathfrak{y}, t_1, \ldots, t_n) &\leftrightarrow \Delta_\beta \mathfrak{y}\, \mathfrak{A}(\mathfrak{y}, t_1, \ldots, t_n) \\ &\leftrightarrow \Delta_\beta \mathfrak{y} \mathfrak{A}_\beta(\mathfrak{y}, t_1, \ldots, t_n)\end{aligned}$$

for all $t_1, \ldots, t_n \in T_\alpha$. But $\Delta_\beta \mathfrak{y} \mathfrak{A}_\beta$ is bounded.

The proof is analogous for $\Delta\mathfrak{y}^{\mathrm{o}}\mathfrak{A}$, $\Delta_\gamma\mathfrak{y}\mathfrak{A}$ and $\Delta_\gamma\mathfrak{y}^{\mathrm{o}}\mathfrak{A}$.

Using lemma 5 we show that the axiom of separation holds in N:

LEMMA 6. Let A be an (unbounded) abstraction term without free variables. For each $s \in T$ there exists a $t \in T$ such that: $\vDash_N t \equiv s \cap A$.

PROOF. Let $\rho(s) = \alpha$, $A = [\mathfrak{x} | \mathfrak{A}]$. Let $\mathfrak{A}_\alpha$ be as in lemma 5. If we set: $t =_{\mathrm{Df}} E_\beta \mathfrak{x}(\mathfrak{x} \varepsilon s \wedge \mathfrak{A}_\alpha)$ for a sufficiently large β, then the conclusion follows at once.

* $\mu\beta \ldots \beta \ldots =_{\mathrm{Df}}$ the smallest β such that $\ldots \beta \ldots$, if such a β exists; otherwise $\mu\beta \ldots \beta \ldots =_{\mathrm{Df}} 0$.

We now show that the replacement axiom holds in N:

LEMMA 7. Let F be an (unbounded) abstraction term without free variables. For each $s \in T$ there is a $t \in T$ such that:

$$\models_N \mathrm{Func}(F) \to t \equiv F''s\,.$$

PROOF. Let $\rho(s)=\alpha$. By the relativization lemma there is a $\beta \in On_M$, $\beta \geq \alpha$ such that:

$$\models_N \nabla \mathfrak{y} F \mathfrak{y} t \leftrightarrow \nabla_\beta \mathfrak{y} F \mathfrak{y} t$$

for $t \in T_\alpha$. Setting $\dot{U}_\beta =_{\mathrm{Df}} E_\beta \mathfrak{x}\, \mathfrak{x} \equiv \mathfrak{x}$ we obtain:

$$\models_N \mathrm{Func}(F) \to F''s \equiv \dot{U}_\beta \cap F''s\,.$$

By lemma 6 however there is a $t \in T$ such that:

$$\models_N t \equiv \dot{U}_\beta \cap F''s\,.$$

All that remains to be shown is the N-validity of the power set axiom. By lemma 6 it is sufficient to prove:

LEMMA 8. For each $\alpha \in On_M$ there is a $\beta \in On_M$ such that:

$$\models_N \mathfrak{P} \dot{U}_\alpha \subset \dot{U}_\beta\,.$$

PROOF. Obviously $U_\alpha = N(\dot{U}_\alpha)$. If we set:

$$\pi(x) =_{\mathrm{Df}} \mu\beta x \in U_\beta \quad \text{for} \quad x \in U,$$

then π is M-definable by lemma 1. Since $\mathfrak{P}_N U_\alpha$ is a set of M, it follows that $\beta =_{\mathrm{Df}} \sup \pi'' \mathfrak{P}_N U_\alpha$ is an ordinal of M. The conclusion follows by:

$$\mathfrak{P}_N U_\alpha \subset U_\beta\,.$$

We close this section with an observation which will prove useful in connection with the forcing method. We chose to define the truth notion for RL ($\models_N$) simultaneously with the valuation $\langle N(t) | t \in T \rangle$. We could equally well have introduced the truth notion directly by the definition:

(a) $\models_N Q\boldsymbol{x}_1 \ldots \boldsymbol{x}_n \leftrightarrow \Omega(Q) x_1 \ldots x_n$.
(b) $\models_N \boldsymbol{x} \varepsilon \boldsymbol{z} \leftrightarrow x \in z$, if $\rho(\boldsymbol{x}) < \rho(\boldsymbol{z})$.
(c) $\models_N t \varepsilon \boldsymbol{x} \leftrightarrow \models_N \nabla_\beta \mathfrak{y}^0 (\mathfrak{y}^0 \equiv t \wedge \mathfrak{y}^0 \varepsilon \boldsymbol{x})$,
if $\rho(t) < \beta = \rho(\boldsymbol{x})$, $t \notin T^0$.
(d) $\models_N t \varepsilon E_\alpha \mathfrak{x}\, \mathfrak{A} \leftrightarrow \models_N \mathfrak{A}(t)$, if $\rho(t) < \alpha$.

(e) $\models_N t\varepsilon t' \leftrightarrow \models_N \nabla_\beta \mathfrak{x}\,(\mathfrak{x}\equiv t \wedge \mathfrak{x}\varepsilon t')$,
if $\beta=\rho(t')\leq\rho(t)$.

(f) $\models_N t\equiv t' \leftrightarrow \models_N \nabla_\beta \mathfrak{x}(\mathfrak{x}\varepsilon t \leftrightarrow \mathfrak{x}\varepsilon t')$,
if $\beta=\max(\rho(t),\rho(t'))$.

(g) $\models_N t\varepsilon[\mathfrak{x}|\mathfrak{A}] \leftrightarrow \models_N \mathfrak{A}(t)$.

(h) $\models_N(\mathfrak{A}\wedge\mathfrak{B}) \leftrightarrow \cdot \models_N \mathfrak{A} \wedge \models_N \mathfrak{B}$.

(i) $\models_N \Delta\,\mathfrak{x}\,\mathfrak{A} \leftrightarrow \bigwedge t{:}\in T \models_N \mathfrak{A}(t)$
(analogously for $\Delta_\alpha \mathfrak{x}$, $\Delta\,\mathfrak{x}^0$, $\Delta_\alpha \mathfrak{x}^0$).

(j) $\models_N \neg\,\mathfrak{A} \leftrightarrow \sim\, \models_N \mathfrak{A}$.

That $\models_N$ satisfies (a)–(j) is obvious. We must still show, however, that $\models_N$ is uniquely defined by (a)–(j). We do this by assigning to every statement $\mathfrak{A}$ a set $\Theta\mathfrak{A}$ such that (a)–(j) may be written in the form:

$$N(\mathfrak{A}) = G(\mathfrak{A}, N \upharpoonright \Theta\mathfrak{A}) \qquad (**)$$

(N being the characteristic function of $\models_N$). We then prove that $\{\mathfrak{B}\mathfrak{A}\,|\,\mathfrak{B}\in\Theta\mathfrak{A}\}$ is a well-founded relation. The uniqueness of $\models_N$ follows easily. $\Theta\mathfrak{A}$ is defined by cases parallel to (a)–(j). If $\mathfrak{A}$ is $Q\boldsymbol{x}_1\ldots\boldsymbol{x}_n$ or if $\mathfrak{A}$ is $\boldsymbol{x}\varepsilon\boldsymbol{z}$ and $\rho(\boldsymbol{x})<\rho(\boldsymbol{z})$, we set: $\Theta\mathfrak{A}=_{\mathrm{Df}}\emptyset$. In cases (c)–(g) we have an equivalence of the form:

$$\models_N \mathfrak{A} \leftrightarrow \models_N \tilde{\mathfrak{A}}\,.$$

We then set: $\Theta\mathfrak{A}=_{\mathrm{Df}}\{\tilde{\mathfrak{A}}\}$. In the remaining cases we define:

$$\Theta(\mathfrak{A}\wedge\mathfrak{B}) =_{\mathrm{Df}} \{\mathfrak{A},\mathfrak{B}\}$$
$$\Theta\Delta\mathfrak{x}\mathfrak{A} =_{\mathrm{Df}} \{\mathfrak{A}(t)|t\in T\}$$

(analogously for $\Delta_\alpha\mathfrak{x}$, $\Delta\mathfrak{x}^0$, $\Delta_\alpha\mathfrak{x}^0$)

$$\Theta\,\neg\,\mathfrak{A} =_{\mathrm{Df}} \{\mathfrak{A}\}\,.$$

It is clear that (a)–(j) can be given the form (**). Cases (c)–(i) can be written concisely as:

$$\models_N \mathfrak{A} \leftrightarrow \bigwedge \mathfrak{B}{:}\in\Theta\mathfrak{A} \models_N \mathfrak{B}\,.$$

Henceforth we shall refer to (a), (b) as the *initial cases*, (c)–(i) as the *middle cases*, and to (j) as the *negation case*. It remains only to be checked that $\{\mathfrak{B}\mathfrak{A}\,|\,\mathfrak{B}\in\Theta\mathfrak{A}\}$ is a well-founded relation. This is a consequence of the following assertion, which the reader may easily verify: To each $\mathfrak{A}$ there is an n such that no sequence of formulae $\mathfrak{A}=\mathfrak{B}_0,\ldots,\mathfrak{B}_n$ satisfies the conditions:

$$\mathfrak{B}_{i+1} \in \Theta \mathfrak{B}_i \quad \text{and} \quad \rho(\mathfrak{B}_{i+1}) \geq \rho(\mathfrak{A}) \quad \text{for} \quad i < n .$$

This completes the proof that (a)–(j) form a definition. We define the *grade* ($\mathrm{gr}(\mathfrak{A})$) of a statement $\mathfrak{A}$ by:

$$\mathrm{gr}(\mathfrak{A}) =_{\mathrm{Df}} \sup\{\mathrm{gr}(\mathfrak{B}) + 1 | \mathfrak{B} \in \Theta \mathfrak{A}\} .$$

For bounded $\mathfrak{A}$ there follows: $\mathrm{gr}(\mathfrak{A}) \in On_M$.

5. Generic models

As in section 4 we suppose M to be a concrete ZF model and U^0 to be an M-definable transitive collection of sets such that $On_M \subset U^0 \subset U_M$. In addition we assume that M is countable. As in section 4 let us extend the ZF language by adjoining a collection of new predicates which form a set in M. Again we suppose $\langle U^0, \Omega \rangle$ to be a concrete model of the so extended language, but *we no longer assume that* Ω *is* M*-definable.* Ignoring this difficulty for the moment, we introduce the ramified language RL, the truth notion $\models_N$, the valuation $\langle N(t) | t \in T \rangle$ and the model $N = \langle U, \Omega \rangle$ exactly as in section 4. We then pose the question: Are there conditions less restrictive than the M-definability of Ω which will ensure that the ZF axioms hold in N? Cohen needed such conditions in order to construct a model N such that $U_N \supset U_M$, $U_N \neq U_M$ and $On_N = On_M$. His N was to be the constructible closure of $\langle U_M, A \rangle$, where A is a subset of ω which is not a set of M. Obviously not every choice of A will yield a ZF model; for example, A might encode a well-ordering of type On_M or even an enumeration of M itself. The problem is to prevent too much of the structure of M from reappearing in A. Cohen's solution was to choose his A in such a manner that the truth value of every statement about A is determined by a finite amount of information. As a result, A can contain only finite bits of information about M (thus e.g. every set of M which is a subset of A is finite).

The first step in carrying out this – as yet very sketchy – programme is to provide a formal version of the notion "determined by a finite amount of information". We shall do this in a more general setting. By a *basic statement* of RL let us understand a statement of the form $Q\boldsymbol{x}_1 \ldots \boldsymbol{x}_n$ or $\neg Q\boldsymbol{x}_1 \ldots \boldsymbol{x}_n$. We write: $(\neg \mathfrak{A})' =_{\mathrm{Df}} \mathfrak{A}$ and $\mathfrak{A}' =_{\mathrm{Df}} \neg \mathfrak{A}$ if $\mathfrak{A}$ is a non-negated basic statement. Now let a set Cond of "conditions" be given; we suppose Cond to be a set of M and that $\emptyset \in$ Cond. The letters 'P',... will be used to stand for conditions. We think of the conditions as embodying pieces of information about a possible predicate assignment Ω (in Cohen's case about A). If $P \subset P'$, then P' contains at least as much information as P. The information in the conditions is "decoded" by a relation $\Vdash_0$ holding between conditions and basic statements such that:

(i) $\sim (P \Vdash_0 \mathfrak{A} \wedge P \Vdash_0 \mathfrak{A}')$,
(ii) $P \subset P' \wedge P \Vdash_0 \mathfrak{A} \cdot \rightarrow P' \Vdash_0 \mathfrak{A}$,
(iii) $P \Vdash_0 \mathfrak{A} \vee \bigvee P' \supset P \; P' \Vdash_0 \mathfrak{A}'$.

(i), (ii) are obvious consequences of the conception of conditions as pieces of information. (iii) says that the information contained in the conditions is in a certain sense complete. The principle behind (iii) might be stated as follows: The information contained in the conditions must be sufficient to eventually decide every basic statement $\mathfrak{A}$. Thus if no extension of P forces us to accept $\mathfrak{A}'$, then P forces us to accept $\mathfrak{A}$. Using (i)–(iii) as a guide, we now extend $\Vdash_0$ to the *forcing relation** $\Vdash$ between conditions and arbitrary statements of RL. In the initial cases we set:

$$P \Vdash Q\boldsymbol{x}_1 \dots \boldsymbol{x}_n \leftrightarrow P \Vdash_0 Q\boldsymbol{x}_1 \dots \boldsymbol{x}_n$$

$$P \Vdash \boldsymbol{x} \,\varepsilon\, \boldsymbol{z} \leftrightarrow x \in z\,.$$

In the middle cases** we set:

$$P \Vdash \mathfrak{A} \leftrightarrow \bigwedge \mathfrak{B} : \in \Theta\mathfrak{A} \; P \Vdash \mathfrak{B}\,,$$

and in the negation case:

$$P \Vdash \neg \mathfrak{A} \leftrightarrow \bigwedge P' \supset P \sim P' \Vdash \mathfrak{A}\,.$$

The essential clause of the definition is the negation case. It ensures that $\Vdash$ satisfies the same completeness condition as $\Vdash_0$ (i.e. for every statement $\mathfrak{A}$, either $\mathfrak{A}$ or $\neg\mathfrak{A}$ is eventually forced).

* $\Vdash$ is also known as the "weak" forcing relation in contradistinction to the "strong" forcing relation used by Cohen in his original paper. If $\Vdash^*$ is the strong forcing relation, then $\Vdash$ may be defined in terms of $\Vdash^*$ by:

$$P \Vdash \mathfrak{A} \leftrightarrow \bigwedge P' : \supset P \sim P' \Vdash^* \neg \mathfrak{A}.$$

** cf. section 4, p. 57 for the definition of middle cases.

Now let us return, briefly, to Cohen's construction, described at the outset. Cohen's conditions were consistent finite sets of basic statements $\boldsymbol{An}$, $\neg \boldsymbol{An}$ for $n<\omega$. The relation $\Vdash_0$ was defined by:

$$P \Vdash_0 \mathfrak{A} \leftrightarrow \mathfrak{A} \in P \quad \text{if} \quad \mathfrak{A} \text{ is } A\boldsymbol{n} \text{ or } \neg A\boldsymbol{n},$$
$$P \Vdash_0 \neg A\boldsymbol{x} \quad \text{if} \quad x \notin \omega .$$

These conditions are the "finite bits of information" alluded to earlier. The phrase "$\mathfrak{A}$ is determined by the finite amount of information P" can now be rendered formally by: $P \Vdash \mathfrak{A}$.

If we set: $F(\mathfrak{A}) =_{\mathrm{Df}} \{P \mid P \Vdash \mathfrak{A}\}$, then we can write the above definition in the form:

$$F(\mathfrak{A}) = G(\mathfrak{A}, F \upharpoonright \Theta \mathfrak{A}) ;$$

hence $\Vdash$ is uniquely defined. The well-founded relation $\{\mathfrak{B}\mathfrak{A} \mid \mathfrak{B} \in \Theta \mathfrak{A}\}$ is obviously M-definable. If $\mathfrak{A}$ is bounded, then $\Theta \mathfrak{A}$ is a set of M. $G \upharpoonright U_M$ is also M-definable. By the recursion theorem the restriction of F to bounded statements is also M-definable. A straightforward argument then yields:

LEMMA 1. $\Vdash \upharpoonright \mathrm{Fml}_n$ is M-definable for every $n<\omega$.*

We now prove the analogues of (i)–(iii) for the relation $\Vdash$. By the definition of $\Vdash$ there follows immediately:

LEMMA 2a. $\sim (P \Vdash \mathfrak{A} \wedge P \Vdash \neg \mathfrak{A})$.

By induction on the grade of $\mathfrak{A}$ ($\mathrm{gr}(\mathfrak{A})$) we obtain:

LEMMA 2b. $P \subset P' \wedge P \Vdash \mathfrak{A} \cdot \rightarrow P' \Vdash \mathfrak{A}$.

PROOF. Let the theorem be proven for all $\mathfrak{B}$ such that $\mathrm{gr}(\mathfrak{B}) < \mathrm{gr}(\mathfrak{A})$. Suppose that $P' \supset P$. In the initial cases, the theorem is trivial if $\mathfrak{A} = \boldsymbol{x} \varepsilon \boldsymbol{z}$ and follows by (ii) if $\mathfrak{A} = Q\boldsymbol{x}_1 \cdots \boldsymbol{x}_n$. In the middle cases we have:

$$\begin{aligned} P \Vdash \mathfrak{A} &\rightarrow \bigwedge \mathfrak{B} : \in \Theta \mathfrak{A} \ P \Vdash \mathfrak{B} \\ &\rightarrow \bigwedge \mathfrak{B} : \in \Theta \mathfrak{A} \ P' \Vdash \mathfrak{B} \\ &\rightarrow P' \Vdash \mathfrak{A}, \end{aligned}$$

and in the negation case:

$$\begin{aligned} P \Vdash \neg \mathfrak{B} &\rightarrow \bigwedge P'' : \supset P \sim P'' \Vdash \mathfrak{B} \\ &\rightarrow \bigwedge P'' : \supset P' \sim P'' \Vdash \mathfrak{B} \\ &\rightarrow P' \Vdash \neg \mathfrak{B} . \end{aligned}$$

* $\mathrm{Fml}_n =_{\mathrm{Df}}$ the set of formulae containing $\leq n$ unbounded quantifiers.

A similar induction yields:

LEMMA 2c. $P \Vdash \mathfrak{A} \vee \bigvee P' : \supset P\, P' \Vdash \neg \mathfrak{A}$.

PROOF. Let the theorem be proven for all $\mathfrak{B}$ such that gr $(\mathfrak{B}) <$ gr $(\mathfrak{A})$. In the initial cases the theorem is trivial if $\mathfrak{A} = x\varepsilon z$ and follows by (iii) if $\mathfrak{A} = Qx_1 \cdots x_n$ In the middle cases we have:

$$\begin{aligned} \sim P \Vdash \mathfrak{A} &\to \bigvee \mathfrak{B} : \in \Theta\mathfrak{A} \sim P \Vdash \mathfrak{B} \\ &\to \bigvee \mathfrak{B} : \in \Theta\mathfrak{A} \bigvee P' : \supset P\, P' \Vdash \neg \mathfrak{B} \\ &\to \bigvee \mathfrak{B} : \in \Theta\mathfrak{A} \bigvee P' : \supset P \bigwedge P'' : \supset P' \sim P'' \Vdash \mathfrak{B} \\ &\to \bigvee P' : \supset P \bigwedge P'' : \supset P' \sim P'' \Vdash \mathfrak{A} \\ &\to \bigvee P' : \supset P\, P' \Vdash \neg \mathfrak{A}. \end{aligned}$$

In the negation case we have:

$$\begin{aligned} \sim P \Vdash \neg \mathfrak{B} &\to \bigvee P' : \supset P\, P' \Vdash \mathfrak{B} \\ &\to \bigvee P' : \supset P \bigwedge P'' : \supset P' \sim P'' \Vdash \neg \mathfrak{B} \\ &\to \bigvee P' : \supset P\, P' \Vdash \neg\neg \mathfrak{B}. \end{aligned}$$

Lemmata 2a–2c are jointly equivalent to:

LEMMA 2d. $P \Vdash \mathfrak{A} \leftrightarrow \bigwedge P' : \supset P \sim P' \Vdash \neg \mathfrak{A}$.

Now let us set:

$$P < N \leftrightarrow_{\mathrm{Df}} \bigwedge \mathfrak{A} (P \Vdash \mathfrak{A} \to \models_N \mathfrak{A})$$

for concrete models $N = \langle U, \Omega \rangle$ such that N is the constructible closure of $\langle U^0, \Omega \rangle$. We then obtain the following *completeness theorem*:

THEOREM 3. $P \Vdash \mathfrak{A} \leftrightarrow \bigwedge N : > P \models_N \mathfrak{A}$.

In the direction $(\to)$ the theorem is of course trivial. By lemma 2 the completeness theorem is equivalent to:

LEMMA 4. For every P there is an N such that $P < N$.

PROOF. We have assumed M to be countable. Thus there is an enumeration $\langle \mathfrak{A}_i | i < \omega \rangle$ of all RL statements. We define a sequence of conditions $\langle P_i | i < \omega \rangle$ by:

$$P_0 =_{\mathrm{Df}} P;\ P_{i+1} =_{\mathrm{Df}} \begin{cases} P_i & \text{if } P_i \Vdash \mathfrak{A}_i \\ P' & \text{otherwise} \end{cases}$$

for a $P' \supset P$ such that $P' \Vdash \neg \mathfrak{A}_i$; in the middle cases we choose P' in such a way that:

$$\bigvee \mathfrak{B} : \in \Theta\mathfrak{A}_i P' \Vdash \neg \mathfrak{B}.$$

If we now set:

$$\Vdash^* \mathfrak{A} \leftrightarrow_{\mathrm{Df}} \bigvee i P_i \Vdash \mathfrak{A},$$

we obtain:

$$\Vdash^* \boldsymbol{x}\, \varepsilon\, \boldsymbol{z} \leftrightarrow x \in z,$$

in the middle cases,

$$\Vdash^* \mathfrak{A} \leftrightarrow \bigwedge \mathfrak{B} : \in \Theta \mathfrak{A} \Vdash^* \mathfrak{B},$$

$$\Vdash^* \neg \mathfrak{A} \leftrightarrow \sim \Vdash^* \mathfrak{A}.$$

Define the predicate assignment Ω by:

$$\Omega(Q) =_{\mathrm{Df}} \{x_1 \dots x_n \mid \Vdash^* Q \boldsymbol{x}_1 \dots \boldsymbol{x}_n\}.$$

If $N = \langle U, \Omega \rangle$ is the constructible closure of $\langle U^0, \Omega \rangle$, we obtain by induction on $\mathrm{gr}(\mathfrak{A})$:

$$\models_N \mathfrak{A} \leftrightarrow \Vdash^* \mathfrak{A}.$$

In particular $P_i < N$ for each i.

We have actually proved more than we had asserted. Let us call a model N *generic* ($N \in \mathrm{Gn}$), if

$$\models_N \mathfrak{A} \leftrightarrow \bigvee P : < N \; P \Vdash \mathfrak{A}$$

for every RL statement $\mathfrak{A}$. Our construction shows that for every P a generic model N exists such that $P < N$. Thus the completeness theorem can be written in the form:

THEOREM 3*. $P \Vdash \mathfrak{A} \leftrightarrow \bigwedge N : \in \mathrm{Gn}(P < N \to \models_N \mathfrak{A})$.

The question which we posed at the outset, whether conditions less restrictive than the M-definability of Ω will ensure that N is a ZF model, can now be answered in the affirmative:

THEOREM 5. Every generic N is a ZF model.

In the following we suppose N to be a generic model. Since the proof of section 4, lemma 3 did not use the M-definability of Ω, we have at once:

LEMMA 6. N is a model of all ZF axioms other than the axiom of replacement and the power set axiom.

The verification of the axiom of replacement proceeds almost exactly as in section 4. We first prove the *relativisation lemma*:

LEMMA 7. Let $\nabla \mathfrak{y} \mathfrak{A} = \nabla \mathfrak{y} \mathfrak{A}(\mathfrak{x}_1, \dots, \mathfrak{x}_n)$ be an RL formula containing at most the n free variables $\mathfrak{x}_1, \dots, \mathfrak{x}_n$. For each $\alpha \in On_M$ there exists a $\beta \in On_M$ such that:

$$\Vdash \nabla \mathfrak{y} \mathfrak{A}(t_1, \dots, t_n) \leftrightarrow \nabla_\beta \mathfrak{y} \mathfrak{A}(t_1, \dots, t_n)$$

for all $t_1, \dots, t_n \in T_\alpha$.

PROOF. Set:

$$\sigma(P, t_1, \ldots, t_n) =_{\mathrm{Df}} \mu\beta \; P \Vdash \nabla_\beta \mathfrak{y} \mathfrak{A}(t_1, \ldots, t_n).$$

By lemma 1 the relation

$$\{P\beta t_1 \ldots t_n | P \Vdash \nabla_\beta \mathfrak{y} \mathfrak{A}(t_1, \ldots, t_n)\}$$

is M-definable. Hence so is σ. Since M is a ZF model and Cond is a set of M, there must be a $\beta \geq \alpha$ in M such that:

$$\beta > \sup\{\sigma(P, t_1, \ldots, t_n) | P \in \mathrm{Cond} \wedge t_1, \ldots, t_n \in T_\alpha\}.$$

β has the required property; i.e.

$$\models_N \nabla \mathfrak{x} \mathfrak{A}(t_1, \ldots, t_n) \rightarrow \models_N \nabla_\beta \mathfrak{x} \mathfrak{A}(t_1, \ldots, t_n)$$

whenever N is generic and $t_1, \ldots, t_n \in T_\alpha$. For if $\models_N \nabla \mathfrak{x} \mathfrak{A}(t_1 \ldots, t_n)$ then there is a smallest ordinal γ such that $\models_N \nabla_\gamma \mathfrak{x} \mathfrak{A}(t_1, \ldots, t_n)$. There must then be a $P < N$ such that $P \Vdash \nabla_\gamma \mathfrak{x} \mathfrak{A}(t_1, \ldots, t_n)$, γ being the smallest ordinal with this property. By the definition of β there follows: $\gamma < \beta$.

The proofs of the next three lemmata will be omitted since they are word for word like the proofs of the corresponding lemmata 5–7 of section 4 (reading '$\Vdash$' for '$\models_N$' and using the completeness theorem at the appropriate places).

LEMMA 8. Let $\mathfrak{A} = \mathfrak{A}(\mathfrak{x}_1, \ldots, \mathfrak{x}_n)$ be an RL formula with at most the n free variables $\mathfrak{x}_1, \ldots, \mathfrak{x}_n$. For each $\alpha \in On_M$ there exists a bounded RL formula $\mathfrak{A}_\alpha$ such that:

$$\Vdash \mathfrak{A}(t_1, \ldots, t_n) \leftrightarrow \mathfrak{A}_\alpha(t_1, \ldots, t_n)$$

for $t_1, \ldots, t_n \in T_\alpha$.

LEMMA 9. Let A be an (unbounded) abstraction term without free variables. For each $s \in T$ there is a $t \in T$ such that:

$$\Vdash t \equiv s \cap A.$$

LEMMA 10. Let F be an (unbounded) abstraction term without free variables. For each $s \in T$ there is a $t \in T$ such that:

$$\Vdash \mathrm{Func}(F) \rightarrow t \equiv F''s.$$

Thus every generic N is a model of the replacement axiom. All that remains is the verification of the power set axiom. This, again, is closely analogous to the verification in section 4. By lemma 9 it suffices to prove:

LEMMA 11. For each $\alpha \in On_M$ there is a $\beta \in On_M$ such that $\Vdash \mathfrak{P}\dot{U}_\alpha \subset \dot{U}_\beta$.*

PROOF. Set: $\eta_t =_{\mathrm{Df}} \{\langle P, s\rangle | s \in T_\alpha \wedge P \Vdash s\varepsilon t\}$ for $t \in T$.
Since $N(\dot{U}_\alpha) = U_\alpha = N'' T_\alpha$ in every generic N, we have by the completeness theorem:

$$\eta_t = \eta_{t'} \rightarrow \Vdash \dot{U}_\alpha \cap t \equiv \dot{U}_\alpha \cap t' . \tag{1}$$

If we set: $\pi(x) =_{\mathrm{Df}} \mu\beta x \in \eta'' T_\beta$ for $x \in U_M$, then π is M-definable by lemma 1. Hence there is a $\beta \in On_M$ such that $\beta > \sup \pi'' \eta'' T$. By (1) we have:

$$\bigwedge t : \in T \bigvee t' : \in T_\beta \Vdash \dot{U}_\alpha \cap t \equiv \dot{U}_\alpha \cap t' .$$

Assuming (without loss of generality) that β is a limit ordinal we can easily show that

$$\bigwedge t : \in T \bigvee t' : \in T_\beta \Vdash \dot{U}_\alpha \cap t \equiv t' .$$

Thus $\mathfrak{P}_N U_\alpha \subset U_\beta$ in every generic N. By the completeness theorem there follows: $\Vdash \mathfrak{P}\dot{U}_\alpha \subset \dot{U}_\beta$.

6. Alternatives to the continuum hypothesis

Let M be a countable concrete model for the axioms of ZF, the axiom of choice and the general continuum hypothesis. In this section we shall use the apparatus developed in section 5 to prove:

THEOREM 1.** Let $\gamma < \gamma' \in On_M$ and let $\aleph_\gamma$ be regular in M.† Then there exists a concrete model N for the ZF axioms and the axiom of choice such that:

(i) $U_M \subset U_N$,
(ii) $On_M = On_N$,
(iii) $(\aleph_\nu)_M = (\aleph_\nu)_N$ for all $\nu \in On_M$,
(iv) $\aleph_{\gamma'} \leq 2^{\aleph_\gamma}$ in N,
(v) $2^{\aleph_\nu} = \aleph_{\nu+1}$ for $\nu < \gamma$ in N.

It follows, of course, that the continuum hypothesis is not derivable from the ZF axioms and the axiom of choice.

We shall construct the extended model by "generically" adjoining to

* $\dot{U}_\alpha =_{\mathrm{Df}} E_\alpha \mathfrak{x}\, \mathfrak{x} \equiv \mathfrak{x}$.

** This result was first proved by R. M. Solovay.

† The case $\gamma = 0$ is not excluded.

M a sequence $a = \langle a_\nu | \nu < \aleph_{\gamma'} \rangle$ of subsets of $\aleph_\gamma$. We first extend the ZF language by adjoining a new two place predicate $\dot{A}$. Our new model N is to be the constructible closure of $\langle U_M, A \rangle$, where A is the relation assigned to $\dot{A}$. Thus our basic statements have the form $\boldsymbol{Axz}$, $\neg \boldsymbol{Axz}$ $(x, z \in U_M)$. We call P a *condition* ($P \in \text{Cond}$) if P is a consistent set (in M) of basic statements of the form:

$$\boldsymbol{A\nu\kappa}, \neg \boldsymbol{A\nu\kappa} \ (\nu < \aleph_{\gamma'}, \kappa < \aleph_\gamma \text{ in } M) \qquad (^*)$$

such that $\overline{\overline{P}} < \aleph_\gamma$ in M. The relation $\Vdash_0$ between conditions and basic statements is defined by:

$$P \Vdash_0 \mathfrak{A} \leftrightarrow \mathfrak{A} \in P \quad \text{if } \mathfrak{A} \text{ has the form } (^*),$$
$$P \Vdash_0 \neg \boldsymbol{Axz} \quad \text{otherwise}.$$

The forcing relation $\Vdash$ and the class of generic models Gn are then defined as in section 5. Every generic N is a ZF model and trivially satisfies conditions (i), (ii) of theorem 1. However, we must still show that the axiom of choice holds in N.

LEMMA 2. If $N \in \text{Gn}$, then the axiom of choice is valid in N.

PROOF. Let $N = \langle U_N, A \rangle$ be generic. N is the constructible closure of $\langle U_M, A \rangle$ (i.e. $U_N = N'' T$). U_M and A are obviously N-definable. By section 4, lemma 1 there follows:

$$\langle N(t) | t \in T \rangle \text{ is } N\text{-definable}. \qquad (1)$$

Let $x \subset U_\alpha$ $(= N'' T_\alpha)$. We must show that U_N contains a well-ordering of x. Let $\Gamma \in U_M$ be a well-ordering of T_α. For $y \in U_\alpha$ let $\tilde{y}$ be the first $t \in T_\alpha$ (in the ordering Γ) such that $y = N(t)$. The function $\langle \tilde{y} | y \in x \rangle$ is N-definable by (1); hence so is the well-ordering:

$$\{zw | z, w \in x \wedge \Gamma \tilde{z} \tilde{w}\}.$$

Suppose that B is a set of conditions which is totally ordered by $\subset$. If $\overline{\overline{B}} < \aleph_\gamma$, then $\cup B$ is a condition. This principle underlies the following lemma:

LEMMA 3. Let $\delta < \aleph_\gamma$ and $N \in \text{Gn}$. If f is an N-definable mapping of δ into U_M, then $f \in U_M$.

PROOF. Let $f = N(\dot{f})$, where $\dot{f} \in T$. Since N is generic there is a $P < N$ such that:

$$P \Vdash (\text{Func}(\dot{f}) \wedge D(\dot{f}) \equiv \boldsymbol{\delta} \wedge W(\dot{f}) \subset \dot{U}_M)$$

(where $\dot{U}_M =_{\mathrm{Df}} [\mathfrak{x} | \nabla \mathfrak{x}^0\ \mathfrak{x} \equiv \mathfrak{x}^0]$). Let P' be any condition such that $P' \supset P$. Using the axiom of choice in M we construct an M-definable sequence $\langle P_\nu | \nu \leq \delta \rangle$ such that:

$$P_0 = P';\ P_{\nu+1} \supset P_\nu \quad \text{and} \quad \bigvee x : \in U_M\ P_{\nu+1} \Vdash \dot{f}(\boldsymbol{\nu}) \equiv \boldsymbol{x};$$

$P_\lambda = \bigcup_{\nu<\lambda} P_\nu$ if λ is a limit ordinal.

Set $F =_{\mathrm{Df}} \{x\nu | \nu < \delta \wedge P_\delta \Vdash \dot{f}(\boldsymbol{\nu}) \equiv \boldsymbol{x}\}$.

In every $N \in \mathrm{Gn}$ such that $P_\delta < N$ we have: $N(\dot{f}) = F \in U_M$. By the completeness theorem we have: $P_\delta \vDash \dot{f}\ \varepsilon\ \dot{U}_M$, hence $\sim P' \Vdash \dot{f} \not\varepsilon\ \dot{U}_M$. Since $P' \supset P$ was arbitrary, we have: $P \Vdash \dot{f}\ \varepsilon\ \dot{U}_M$.

Two consequences of lemma 3 are:

$$(\aleph_\nu)_M = (\aleph_\nu)_N \quad \text{for} \quad \nu < \gamma$$
$$(2^{\aleph_\nu})_M = (2^{\aleph_\nu})_N \quad \text{for} \quad \nu < \gamma.$$

Thus theorem 1 (v) is proven. Before we can show that the first of these equations holds for all $\nu \in On_M$, we must prove a further lemma:

LEMMA 4.* If B is a set of conditions in M, then there exists a set $B' \subset B$ in M such that:

(i) $\overline{\overline{B'}} \leq \aleph_\gamma$ in M,

(ii) for each $P \in B$ there is a $P' \in B'$ which is compatible with P (i.e. $P \cup P'$ is a condition).

PROOF. Let σ be an M-definable function such that:

$$P \subset \sigma(P) \in B \quad \text{if} \quad \bigvee P' : \supset P\ P' \in B$$

$\sigma(P)$ otherwise undefined.

For $C \subset \mathrm{Cond}$ put:

$$C^* =_{\mathrm{Df}} \bigcup_{P \in C} \{\mathfrak{A} | \mathfrak{A} \text{ or } \mathfrak{A}' \in P\}.$$

We define a sequence $B_\nu \subset \mathrm{Cond.}\ (\nu \leq \aleph_\gamma)$ by:

$$B_0 =_{\mathrm{Df}} \emptyset;\ B_{\nu+1} =_{\mathrm{Df}} \{\sigma(P) | P \subset B_\nu^*\};$$
$$B_\lambda =_{\mathrm{Df}} \bigcup_{\nu<\lambda} B_\nu$$

if λ is a limit number.

* In the case $\gamma = 0$ the elements of Cond correspond to basic open sets in the Cantor space 2^I, where $I = \aleph_\gamma \times \aleph_{\gamma'}$. Lemma 4 then merely restates the fact that 2^I satisfies the countable chain condition.

Clearly $\langle B_\nu | \nu \leq \aleph_\gamma \rangle$ is a set of M. Moreover $\bar{\bar{B}}_\nu \leq \aleph_\gamma$ in M for $\nu \leq \aleph_\gamma$, for by the regularity of $\aleph_\gamma$ and the continuum hypothesis (which holds in M) we have:

$$\overline{\overline{\{P|P \subset C\}}} \leq \sum_{\nu<\gamma} 2^{\aleph_\nu} = \aleph_\gamma \quad \text{for} \quad \bar{\bar{C}} \leq \aleph_\gamma .$$

We set: $B' =_{\mathrm{Df}} B_{\aleph_\gamma}$. We must show that B' satisfies condition (ii).

Let $P \in B$. Set: $P' =_{\mathrm{Df}} \sigma(P \cap B'^*)$. By the regularity of $\aleph_\gamma$ there is a $\nu < \aleph_\gamma$ such that: $P \cap B'^* = P \cap B^*$, hence $P' = \sigma(P \cup B_\nu^*) \in B'$. If $P \cup P'$ were not a condition, there would be an $\mathfrak{A}$ such that $\mathfrak{A} \in P$ and $\mathfrak{A}' \in P'$. But $\mathfrak{A}' \in P'$ however implies: $\mathfrak{A} \in B'^*$, hence $\mathfrak{A} \in P \cap B'^* \subset P'$, which would be a contradiction.

THEOREM 1 (iii) now follows from:

LEMMA 5. If N is generic and $\alpha \leq \beta \in On_M$, then:

$$\bar{\bar{\alpha}}^N = \bar{\bar{\beta}}^N \rightarrow \bar{\bar{\alpha}}^M = \bar{\bar{\beta}}^M .$$

PROOF. For $\alpha < \aleph_\gamma$ the conclusion follows by lemma 3. Now let $\aleph_\gamma \leq \alpha \leq \beta$ and $\bar{\bar{\alpha}}^N = \bar{\bar{\beta}}^N$. There is then an f: $\alpha \leftrightarrow \beta$ and an $\mathring{f} \in T$ such that $f = N(\mathring{f})$. Since N is generic, there is a $P' < N$ such that:

$$P' \Vdash (\mathrm{Func}(\mathring{f}) \wedge D(\mathring{f}) \equiv \boldsymbol{\alpha} \wedge W(\mathring{f}) \equiv \boldsymbol{\beta}).$$

If we set:

$$b_\nu =_{\mathrm{Df}} \{\kappa | \bigvee P : \supset P' \; P \Vdash \mathring{f}(\boldsymbol{\nu}) \equiv \boldsymbol{\kappa}\},$$

we obtain: $\beta = \bigcup_{\nu<\alpha} b_\nu$. Thus it suffices to prove that $\bar{\bar{b}}_\nu \leq \aleph_\gamma$ in M. Set:

$$B =_{\mathrm{Df}} \{P | P \supset P' \wedge \bigvee \kappa \, P \Vdash \mathring{f}(\boldsymbol{\nu}) \equiv \boldsymbol{\kappa}\}.$$

By lemma 4 there is a $B' \subset B$ such that $\bar{\bar{B}}' \leq \aleph_\gamma$ in M and

$$\bigvee P' : \in B' \; P \cup P' \in \mathrm{Cond}$$

for each $P \in B$. By this follows:

$$b_\nu =_{\mathrm{Df}} \{\kappa | \bigvee P : \in B' \; P \Vdash \mathring{f}(\boldsymbol{\nu}) \equiv \boldsymbol{\kappa}\};$$

hence $\bar{\bar{b}}_\nu \leq \aleph_\gamma$ in M.

All that remains is the proof that $\aleph_{\gamma''} \leq 2_{\aleph_\nu}$ in N, but this is almost trivial. If we set:

$$a_\nu =_{\mathrm{Df}} \{\kappa | \Vdash_N A \boldsymbol{\nu} \boldsymbol{\kappa}\};$$

then $a = \langle a_\nu | \nu < \aleph_{\gamma'} \rangle$ is an N-definable mapping of $\aleph_{\gamma'}$ onto a subset of $\mathfrak{P}_N \aleph_\gamma$. We need only show that a is $1-1$. If it were not, then there would be $\nu < \nu' < \aleph_{\gamma'}$ such that $a_\nu = a_{\nu'}$. Since N is generic there would be a $P < N$ such that

$$\bigwedge \kappa \, P \Vdash (A\nu\kappa \leftrightarrow A\nu'\kappa).$$

However, since $\overline{\overline{P}} < \aleph_\gamma$ in M, there exists a $\kappa < \aleph_\gamma$ such that $A\tau\kappa, \neg A\tau\kappa \notin P$ for all τ. Thus $P' =_{\mathrm{Df}} P \cup \{A\nu\kappa, \neg A\nu'\kappa\}$ is a condition such that

$$P \subset P', \; P' \Vdash (A\nu\kappa \not\leftrightarrow A\nu'\kappa),$$

which contradicts the assumption. This completes the proof of theorem 1.

It is natural to ask whether we can sharpen the inequality (iv) of theorem 1 to: $2^{\aleph_\gamma} = \aleph_{\gamma'}$ in N. In certain cases this is known to be impossible. The (generalized) theorem of König says that if $\aleph_{\gamma'}$ is cofinal with an $\alpha \le \aleph_\gamma$, then $\aleph_{\gamma'} < \aleph_{\gamma'}^{\aleph_\gamma}$. Thus we cannot have $2^{\aleph_\gamma} = \aleph_{\gamma'}$, since this would yield:

$$\aleph_{\gamma'} = 2^{\aleph_\gamma} = (2^{\aleph_\gamma})^{\aleph_\gamma} = \aleph_{\gamma'}^{\aleph_\gamma}.$$

We can prove the following results, however:

THEOREM 6.* Let N be generic. If $\aleph_{\gamma'}$ is not cofinal (in M) with an $\alpha \le \aleph_\gamma$, then

$$2^{\aleph_\gamma} = \aleph_{\gamma'} \quad \text{in } N.$$

Otherwise:

$$2^{\aleph_\gamma} = \aleph_{\gamma'+1} \quad \text{in } N.$$

Since the general continuum hypothesis holds in M, theorem 2 is equivalent to

$$2^{\aleph_\gamma} \le (\aleph_{\gamma'}^{\aleph_\gamma})_M \quad \text{in } N \tag{**}$$

by König's theorem and theorem 1 (iv).

Before proving (**) some preliminary steps are necessary. If $a \subset \aleph_{\gamma'}$, we let '$P_a$' denote the set of $A\nu\iota, \neg A\nu\iota \in P$ such that $\nu \in a$. Let S be the set of $a \subset \aleph_{\gamma'}$ such that $\overline{\overline{a}} \le \aleph_\gamma$ in M.

LEMMA 7. Let $\mathfrak{A}$ be a statement of RL. Then there is an $a \in S$ such that:

$$\bigwedge P (P \Vdash \mathfrak{A} \leftrightarrow P_a \Vdash \mathfrak{A}).$$

PROOF. Set: $B =_{\mathrm{Df}} \{P | P \Vdash \mathfrak{A} \text{ or } P \Vdash \neg \mathfrak{A}\}$. By lemma 4 there is a $B' \subset B$

* This result was first proved by R. M. Solovay.

such that $\bar{\bar{B}}' \leq \aleph_\gamma$ in M and:

$$\bigwedge P :\in B \bigvee P' :\in B' \; P \cup P' \in \text{Cond}. \tag{1}$$

Let a be the set of ν such that $A\nu\iota$ or $\neg A\nu\iota \in \bigcup B$ for some ι. Now let $P \Vdash \mathfrak{A}$. We wish to show that $P_a \Vdash \mathfrak{A}$. If $P' \in B'$ and $P' \cup P_a \in \text{Cond}$, then

$$P' \cup P = (P' \cup P_a) \cup (P - P_a) \in \text{Cond}.$$

Hence there can be no $P' \in B'$ such that $P' \Vdash \neg \mathfrak{A}$ and $P' \cup P_a \in \text{Cond}$. By (1) it follows that there is no $P'' \supset P_a$ such that $P'' \Vdash \neg \mathfrak{A}$; thus $P_a \Vdash \mathfrak{A}$.

For each $a \in S$ let T_a be the class of all $t \in T$ such that:

$$\bigwedge \nu : < \aleph_\gamma \bigwedge P \, (P \Vdash \boldsymbol{\nu} \, \varepsilon \, t \leftrightarrow P_a \Vdash \boldsymbol{\nu} \, \varepsilon \, t).$$

An obvious consequence of lemma 7 is:

$$T = \bigcup_{a \in S} T_a.$$

If we set: $\tilde{N}(t) =_{\text{Df}} \aleph_\gamma \cap N(t)$, then we get:

$$\mathfrak{P}_N \aleph_\gamma = \tilde{N}'' T = \bigcup_{a \in S} \tilde{N}'' T_a. \tag{2}$$

Set: $Q_a =_{\text{Df}} \tilde{N}'' T_a$. Q_a is a set of N and the function $\langle Q_a | a \in S \rangle$ is N-definable.

Since $\bar{\bar{S}} = (\aleph_{\gamma'}^{\aleph_\gamma})_M$ in N, it suffices to show

$$\bar{\bar{Q}}_a \leq (2^{\aleph_\gamma})_M \quad \text{in } N \tag{3}$$

for $a \in S$, for by (3) there follows:

$$2^{\aleph_\gamma} \leq (\aleph_{\gamma'}^{\aleph_\gamma})_M \cdot (2^{\aleph_\gamma})_M = (\aleph_{\gamma'}^{\aleph_\gamma})_M \quad \text{in } N.$$

In order to prove (3) we first define for each $t \in T_a$:

$$\eta_t^a = \{\langle P_a, \nu \rangle | \nu < \aleph_\gamma \wedge P_a \Vdash \boldsymbol{\nu} \, \varepsilon \, \boldsymbol{t}\}.$$

Thus:

$$t, t' \in T_a \wedge \eta_t^a = \eta_{t'}^a \cdot \rightarrow \tilde{N}(t) = \tilde{N}(t').$$

Let f be the mapping of $\{\eta_t^a | t \in T_a\}$ onto Q_a defined by: $f(\eta_t^a) = \tilde{N}(t)$. f is N-definable by section 4, lemma 1. Thus:

$$\bar{\bar{Q}}_a \leq \overline{\overline{\{\eta_t^a | t \in T_a\}}} \quad \text{in } N.$$

We have, however:

$$\{\eta_t^a | t \in T_a\} \subset \mathfrak{P}_M(\mathrm{Cond}_a \times \aleph_\gamma),$$

Cond_a being the set of all P_a. By the continuum hypothesis of M and the regularity of $\aleph_\gamma$ follows: $\overline{\overline{\mathrm{Cond}_a}} = \aleph_\gamma$ in M, hence:

$$\overline{\overline{\{\eta_t^a | t \in T_a\}}} \leq 2^{\aleph_\gamma} \quad \text{in } M,$$

which was to be proved.

References

[1] P. J. Cohen, The independence of the continuum hypothesis, Proc. Nat. Acad. Sci. U.S. **50** (1963) 1143 and **51** (1964) 105.

[2] S. Feferman, Some applications of the notions of forcing and generic sets, in: Fund. Math. **56** (1965) 325.

[3] K. Gödel, The consistency of the continuum hypothesis (Princeton, 1940).

[4] Rasiowa-Sikorski, A proof of the completeness theorem of Gödel, Fund. Math. **37** (1950) 193.

[5] R. Solovay, Measurable cardinals and the continuum hypothesis, Inst. for Advanced Study, Princeton, N.J. (mimeographed).

[6] W. B. Easton, Powers of regular cardinals, dissertation, Princeton 1964.

INDEPENDENCE OF THE AXIOM OF CHOICE FROM VARIANTS OF THE GENERALIZED CONTINUUM HYPOTHESIS

J. DERRICK and F. R. DRAKE
University of Leeds, England

1. Introduction

Since Cantor first introduced the continuum hypothesis the problem of well-ordering the power set of a given set has been the subject of continuous discussion. This problem can be refined to two apparently separate questions:

(a) for which sets can the power set be well-ordered; and

(b) for any set, what is the least upper bound of well-orderings of subsets of its power set.

As usual the answers to these questions will depend on the axiom system that is chosen. For instance, the axiom of choice for sets (axiom VI of Fraenkel and Bar-Hillel [1]) gives a blanket answer to question (a), since (taken with e.g. axioms I–V of [1]) it implies that every set can be well-ordered. The generalized continuum hypothesis gives the same sort of answer to (b) (again assuming e.g. axioms I–V of [1]), and indeed also gives the same answer to (a) since it implies the axiom of choice.

The results of Cohen in [2] on the independence of the axiom of choice and the generalized continuum hypothesis immediately lead one to ask what other answers to (a) and (b) are possible and also to what extent the answers are independent of each other.

In [3] Easton went a long way towards giving a complete description of all possible answers to (b) for the power sets of sets that can be well-ordered. But each of these answers is given under the assumption that the answer to (a) is that every set can be well-ordered. In this work we set ourselves the task of determining what are the possible answers to (a), and whether our choice of answer to (a) is independent of the choice for (b) and vice-versa. We find a wide choice of possible answers to (a) and prove that they are independent of the choice of answer to (b).

The lemmas in this paper are given in model theoretic form, and no attempt is made here to give any translation into syntactic forms, in order to provide relative consistency proofs. The authors plan a further paper which will discuss these syntactic questions, and also further strengthening of the model theoretic results.

2. A *transitive model* of Zermelo-Fraenkel set theory (ZF) plus the axiom of choice (AC) is a transitive set M such that axioms $\mathrm{I_b}$, II–IX of [1] hold in M when $\in$ is interpreted as membership restricted to M. Let α, $\beta, \ldots$ denote ordinals, $\mathscr{P}(x)$ denote the power set (i.e. set of all subsets) of x and $\mathscr{P}_\kappa(x)$ denote the set of all subsets of x of cardinal $<\kappa$ (a cardinal). Let $\bar{\bar{x}}$ denote the cardinality of the set x. Hartog's aleph function is defined by $\aleph(x)$ is the least ordinal which is not similar to a subset of x. $\aleph^{(K)}(x)$ is the value of Hartog's aleph function in any model K.

THEOREM. Let M be a denumerable transitive model of ZF + AC and let κ be any regular infinite cardinal of M such that $\mathscr{P}_\kappa(\kappa)=\kappa$. Then there is a transitive model N of ZF which is an extension of M and in which 2.1–2.4 below hold.

2.1. AC holds for sets of cardinality $<\kappa$.

2.2. The prime ideal theorem fails for $\mathscr{P}(\kappa)$.

2.3. $2^{\aleph_\alpha}$ in $N = 2^{\aleph_\alpha}$ in M if $\aleph_\alpha < \kappa$.

2.4. $\aleph^{(N)}[\mathscr{P}(\aleph_\alpha)] = \aleph^{(M)}[\mathscr{P}(\aleph_\alpha)]$.

In fact for 2.2 we show that N has no prime ideal over $\mathscr{P}(\kappa)$ extending $\mathscr{P}_\kappa(\kappa)$.

In the terminology of section 1, 2.1 and 2.2 give some possible answers to question (a), that the axiom of choice may hold "up to κ and not beyond".

2.3 and 2.4 then give some possible answers to question (b) for each answer to question (a).

Note that if $2^{\aleph_\alpha} = \aleph_{\alpha+1}$ in M, then 2.4 yields a weaker variant, $\aleph(2^{\aleph_\alpha}) = \aleph_{\alpha+2}$ in N, of the Generalized Continuum Hypothesis, and the axiom of choice cannot be deduced from this in ZF.

Sections 3 and 4 of this paper give an outline of the proof of this theorem. Section 3 outlines the particular form of the forcing argument that we shall use, and in this paper we shall only give the main points, leaving the reader to refer to e.g. [2] and [3], and also Lévy [4] and

Feferman [5] for the details. We stress only where our method differs from all of these. We also rely on these references for the proof that N is a model of ZF. Section 4 then gives in detail the lemmas needed to prove that N satisfies 2.1–2.4.

3. The proof of the theorem consists in forming the model N by adding generic subsets of κ to M, the number of these generic subsets also being κ. The set representing the entire sequence will not be added, although the subsequence of any given length $\alpha<\kappa$ will be added.

The idea of 'generic' was introduced by Cohen [2], and so were the ideas needed to show that the result of adding generic sets to M is still a model of ZF. However we shall follow the modifications introduced in Feferman [5] (there attributed to Scott) and use a ramified language to obtain the model N. The actual method used will be closest to Lévy [4], and in the sequel this will facilitate the translation of the results into syntactic forms.

We give here only the main points, and points where the treatment differs from others in the literature. The main difference is in the treatment of the predicate A in definition 3.1. If a_β is a generic subset of κ which is to be added, then $A(\boldsymbol{\alpha},\boldsymbol{\beta})$ will represent $\alpha\in a_\beta$. In the treatment of Feferman [5], a denumerable sequence of generic subsets of ω is added in order to make the prime ideal theorem fail for $\mathscr{P}(\omega)$. Different predicates $S_1, S_2, \ldots$ are used to represent these generic subsets; in a formula of Feferman's language L, it is possible to refer to any finite number of them, but not to all at once. If the relation $x\in S_n$ were to be represented with both x and n as variables, then a restriction on the quantification of n would be needed to prevent a formula of the ramified language from refering to all the generic sets at once (otherwise the axiom of choice would still hold). Restriction of n to finite rank would achieve this: and the natural generalization to our own case, when considering the independence of the axiom of choice at higher cardinalities, is the restriction on the term occuring in the second place of the predicate A to be of rank $< \kappa$.

3.1. Definition. The language L has two two-place predicates ε, A; logical constants &, $\neg$, $\exists$; abstraction operator $\wedge$; ranked variables $x^\alpha, y^\alpha, \ldots$ for each ordinal α of M; unranked variables $x, y, \ldots$; and an individual constant $\boldsymbol{m}$ for each set $m \in M$.

Abstraction terms and ranked formulae are defined in the usual way, with the restriction that the second place of A must always be occupied by a term of rank less than κ:

3.11. If u, v are set constants, ranked variables, or abstraction terms, and w is a set constant, ranked variable, or abstraction term of rank $< \kappa$, then

$$u \in v \quad \text{and} \quad A(u, w)$$

are ranked formulae.

In the definition of abstraction terms we have the usual restrictions, plus one extra (3.125) to ensure that if A appears in an abstraction term, then the rank of that term is at least κ:

3.12. If $\Phi(x^\alpha)$ is a ranked formula such that:

3.121. no free variables occur other than x^α;

3.122. if $\boldsymbol{m}$ occurs in Φ then rank $\boldsymbol{m} < \alpha$;*

3.123. if $\hat{y}^\beta \Psi(y^\beta)$ occurs in Φ then $\beta < \alpha$;

3.124. if $(\exists y^\beta)\, \Psi\,(y^\beta)$ occurs in Φ then $\beta \leq \alpha$; and

3.125. if $\alpha \leq \kappa$ then Φ does not contain A:

then $\hat{x}^\alpha\, \Phi(x^\alpha)$ is an abstraction term of rank α.

The definition of ranked and unranked formulae now proceeds in the usual way. For convenience we assume (as is usual) that all the formulae and terms of L are sets of M, and that the functions represented by the connectives, etc., are all available in M.

3.2. Definition. A condition is a set of M which is a function from a subset of $\kappa \times \kappa$, of cardinality in $M < \kappa$, into 2.

We shall use $p, q, p', \ldots$ as variables for conditions; heuristically if $p(\alpha, \beta) = 0$ then p includes the condition $\alpha \in a_\beta$; if $p(\alpha, \beta) = 1$, the condition $\alpha \notin a_\beta$. This is effected by 3.31 below.

3.3. Definition. Condition p forces formula Φ ($p \Vdash \Phi$) is defined just as usual: the definition contains the clause

3.31. $p \Vdash A(u, v)$ if, for some ordinals α, $\beta < \kappa$, with $\alpha \leq$ rank u, $\beta \leq$ rank v, $p \Vdash u \cong \alpha$, $p \Vdash v \cong \beta$, and $p(\alpha, \beta) = 0$.**

As in [4] lemma 23, we get a formula of ZF, $\Pi(x, y)$, such that

* Here rank $\boldsymbol{m}$ = type of m (as a set) is the level in the cumulative type hierarchy at which m appears: this type is also sometimes referred to as "rank", e.g. in [3].

** $u \cong v$ is the ranked formula $(\forall x^\gamma)\,(x^\gamma \in u \leftrightarrow x^\gamma \in v)$ where $\gamma = \max$ (rank u, rank v).

3.32. If $a,b \varepsilon M$, $M \models \Pi(a,b)$ if and only if a is a condition, b is a ranked formula of L, and $a \Vdash b$.

Also, as in [4] lemma 26, for each term Φ of ZF which is an unranked formula of L with free variables $x_1, \ldots, x_n$, we get a formula $\Pi_\Phi(a_1, \ldots, a_n, a)$ of ZF such that

3.33. If $a_1, \ldots, a_n, a \in M$, and $a_1, \ldots, a_n$ are terms of L, then $M \models \Pi_\Phi(a_1, \ldots, a_n, a)$ if and only if a is a condition and $a \Vdash \Phi(a_1, \ldots, a_n)$.

We note that Π and Π_Φ can be taken to be formulae of L; if the ranks of a, b, $a_1, \ldots, a_n$ are bounded, then Π and Π_Φ can be taken to be ranked formulae.

3.4. Definition. A function P from $\kappa \times \kappa$ into 2 is generic if, for every formula $B(x)$ of the language which contains the predicate $\in$ and constants for all sets of M, and which is such that every condition p has an extension p' (i.e. $p \subseteq p'$) such that $M \models B(p')$, there is a subset $p'' \subset P$ which is a condition such that $M \models B(p'')$.

We shall write $P \Vdash \Phi$ for a formula Φ of L if, for some condition $p \subseteq P$, $p \Vdash \Phi$; and the standard properties of generic sets will follow, e.g. (using here the fact that M is denumerable):

3.41. Any condition p can be extended to a generic P.

3.5. Definition. Assuming P is generic, we define $\mathrm{val}_P(u) = \{\mathrm{val}_P(v) | v$ is a term, rank $v <$ rank u, and $P \Vdash v \in u\}$ and $N_P = \{\mathrm{val}_P(u) | u$ is a term of $L\}$.

The suffix P will normally be omitted: we assume that one fixed, generic P has been chosen from now on.

We have now defined the set N which will be the required transitive model for ZF: in the usual way we deduce for sentences Φ of L:

$$N \models \Phi \quad \text{if and only if} \quad P \Vdash \Phi,$$

and if Φ is an axiom of ZF,

$$N \models \Phi.$$

(The proofs given in Cohen [2], Easton [3] are suggested for all axioms except the power set axiom; for this the argument of Solovay as given in Lévy [4] or Cohen [6] is probably better.)

We note also that N is an extension of M, and that ordinals of N are ordinals of M. For the proofs in section 4 we shall need the following lemmas, which are similar to lemmas 25, 26 of [3]:

3.61. The set of formulae of L obtained by substituting into a formula $\Phi(x)$, a set of M of constant terms, of cardinality $<\kappa$, are all decided* by a single condition $p' \subset P$, which can be taken as extending any given condition $p \subset P$.

(This needs only that κ is a regular cardinal of M and that P is generic.)

3.62. Any set of formulae, formed as in 3.61, of cardinality $\aleph_\alpha$ in M, can each be decided by at least one of a set (of M) of at most $\aleph_\alpha$ conditions, which are such that every condition is compatible with at least one of these conditions.

(Here we simply use 3.61 and the hypothesis that $\overline{\overline{\mathscr{P}_\kappa(\kappa)}}=\kappa$,** in M, so that there are only κ conditions in all; we give here the form in which this is needed for 3.63 and in section 4.)

3.63. Confinality is absolute in the extension from M to N, and hence initial ordinals are absolute in the extension (from 3.62 as in [3]).

4. The following lemmas show that the model N constructed in 3.5 satisfies 2.1–2.4.

4.1. If $h \in N$ is a function on $\alpha<\kappa$, then there is a function $f \in N$ on α such that

$$(\wedge\, \beta<\alpha)(h(\beta) \neq \emptyset \to f(\beta) \in h(\beta))\,;$$

i.e. f is a choice function for h.

PROOF. Since $h \in N$, h must be val(u) for a term u of the form $\hat{x}^\alpha \hat{y}^\gamma k(x^\alpha, y^\gamma)$; let us write $H(z,x)$ for

$$(\exists\, y^\gamma)(k(x,y^\gamma)\,\&\, z \in y^\gamma)$$

so that $H(z,x)$ is a ranked formula representing $z \in h(x)$. Now if $h(\theta) \neq \emptyset$, for an ordinal $\theta<\alpha$, then $P \Vdash H(t,\boldsymbol{\theta})$ for some term t; by the forcing definition this must hold for a term t of rank $<\gamma$.

Consider the α formulae $(\exists z^\gamma) H(z^\gamma, \boldsymbol{\theta})$ for $\theta<\alpha$. Since by hypothesis $\alpha<\kappa$, and since $\alpha \in M$ so that this set of formulae form a set of M, we can apply 3.61 and find a condition $p_0 \subset P$ such that p_0 decides each of these formulae; indeed since $p_0 \subset P$, we have

$$p_0 \Vdash (\exists\, z^\gamma)\, H(z^\gamma, \boldsymbol{\theta}) \quad \text{if and only if} \quad h(\theta) \neq \emptyset\,.$$

* p decides Φ if $p \Vdash \Phi$ or $p \Vdash \neg\, \Phi$.

** We shall only use the notation $\overline{\overline{x}}$ for the cardinality of a set x which is in M. Since the axiom of choice holds in M, this can be taken to be an initial ordinal in the usual way, and by 3.63 it will be immaterial whether this cardinality is computed in M or in N.

Now M is assumed to satisfy the axiom of choice; so the set of terms of rank $<\gamma$ is well-ordered by a relation g in M. We can therefore write a ranked formula $\Pi(z,t)$ which expresses the fact that z is the first term (under g) of rank $<\gamma$ such that $p_0 \Vdash H(z,t)$: $\Pi(z,t)$ would have the form

$$p_0 \Vdash H(z,t) \,\&\, (\forall\, y^\gamma)(\langle y^\gamma, z\rangle \in \boldsymbol{g} \rightarrow \neg\,(p_0 \Vdash H(y^\gamma, t)))$$

where we have used 3.33 in order to write $p_0 \Vdash H(z,t)$ as a ranked formula, with z,t as free variables. $\Pi(z,t)$ will have only two free variables, and so we can write the term v:

$$\hat{x}^\alpha \hat{y}^\gamma\,(x^\alpha \in \boldsymbol{\alpha} \,\&\, \Pi(y^\gamma, x^\alpha)),$$

where $\hat{x}^\alpha \hat{y}^\gamma \Phi$ is short for

$$\hat{z}^\delta\,(\exists\, x^\alpha)(\exists\, y^\gamma)(z^\delta \cong \langle x^\alpha, y^\gamma\rangle \,\&\, \Phi),$$

where δ is the least ordinal such that this is a well-formed term under 3.12.

Now let $f = \mathrm{val}(v)$; then f is a function in N defined on α which is a choice function for h. For $\langle x,y\rangle \in f$ iff $x = \mathrm{val}(w)$, $y = \mathrm{val}(w')$ for terms w, w' such that rank $w<\alpha$, rank $w'<\gamma$, and

(a) $P \Vdash w \cong \boldsymbol{\beta}$ for some $\beta < \alpha$, and

(b) $P \Vdash \Pi(w', w)$.

Hence w', w are terms such that $p_0 \Vdash H(w', w)$, so that $\mathrm{val}(w') \in h(\beta)$; and the second clause of Π ensures that f is a function, since g is assumed to be a well-ordering of the terms with rank $<\gamma$.

4.2. In N, the power set $\mathscr{P}(\kappa)$ has no prime ideal extending $\mathscr{P}_\kappa(\kappa)$.

Proof is by an application of the methods of Feferman [5]; we use the notation of Lévy [4] which uses these methods.

If $r \in M$, $r \subseteq \kappa \times \kappa$, then r defines a transformation; and the properties as in [4] will carry through in the present context. We define:

$$[r, Q] = \{\langle \alpha, \beta, i\rangle | \langle \alpha, \beta, i\rangle \in Q \,\&\, \langle \alpha, \beta\rangle \notin r \cdot \vee \cdot \langle \alpha, \beta, 1-i\rangle \in Q \,\&\, \langle \alpha, \beta\rangle \in r\}$$

for any Q which is a function on a subset of $\kappa \times \kappa$ into 2.

For a formula or term X, $[r, X]$ is the result of replacing each occurrence of $A(u,v)$ in X, where u, v are terms, by

$$[r,u]\in\boldsymbol{\kappa}\,\&\,[r,v]\in\boldsymbol{\kappa}\,\&\,(A([r,u],[r,v])\leftrightarrow\neg\,\langle[r,u],[r,v]\rangle\in\boldsymbol{r}),$$

where $[r,x]$ is x if x is a variable, and $\langle[r,u],[r,v]\rangle\in\boldsymbol{r}$ stands for:

$$(\exists x^\kappa)(x^\kappa\in\boldsymbol{r}\,\&\,(\forall y^\kappa)(y^\kappa\in x^\kappa\leftrightarrow(\forall z^\kappa)(z^\kappa\in y^\kappa\leftrightarrow z^\kappa\cong[r,u])\vee$$
$$\vee(\forall z^\kappa)(z^\kappa\in y^\kappa\leftrightarrow\cdot z^\kappa\cong[r,u]\vee z^\kappa\cong[r,v])))$$

and $z^\kappa\cong[r,u]$ is $(\forall t^\kappa)(t^\kappa\in z^\kappa\leftrightarrow t^\kappa\in[r,u])$.

This maintains the rank even when A occurs, so that rank $[r, X]=$ rank X, and in the usual way we have: if P is generic, so is $[r,P]$; and

4.21. $p\Vdash\Phi\leftrightarrow[r,p]\Vdash[r,\Phi]$.

Now suppose $\Phi(x)$ defines a prime ideal of $\mathscr{P}(\kappa)$ containing $\mathscr{P}_\kappa(\kappa)$ in N, where $\Phi(x)$ is a ranked formula of L. Then $A(u,v)$ can occur in Φ only with rank v bounded by some $\alpha<\kappa$ in each instance; put $\sigma=\max\alpha$ for all such occurrences. $\sigma<\kappa$ since there are only finitely many such occurrences. Let u be the term $\hat{x}^{\kappa+1}A(x^{\kappa+1},\boldsymbol{\sigma+1})$. Then $a_{\sigma+1}=\text{val}(u)$ is in N, and $a_{\sigma+1}\subseteq\kappa$, so either $a_{\sigma+1}$ or $\kappa-a_{\sigma+1}$ is in the ideal. Suppose $a_{\sigma+1}$ is in the ideal; then for some condition $p\subset P$,

$$p\Vdash\Phi(u).$$

Now $\bar{p}<\kappa$, so $\langle\alpha,\sigma+1,i\rangle\in p$ only for $\alpha<\beta$, for some $\beta<\kappa$, since κ is regular in M. Take r as

$$\{\langle\gamma,\sigma+1\rangle|\beta\leq\gamma<\kappa\},$$

then $r\in M$, and $[r,p]=p$ by the definition of β, so by 4.21,

$$p\Vdash[r,\Phi(u)].$$

Now $[r,\Phi(u)]\leftrightarrow\Phi([r,u])$ is valid in N by the definition of σ, so val$([r,u])$ is in the ideal. But val$([r,u])$ is

$$[(\kappa-\beta)\cap(\kappa-a_{\sigma+1})]\cup(a_{\sigma+1}\cap\beta),$$

and this contradicts the assumption that Φ defines a prime ideal containing $\mathscr{P}_\kappa(\kappa)$, since $\beta<\kappa$. Similarly we get a contradiction from the assumption that $\kappa-a_{\sigma+1}$ is in the ideal.

4.3. If $\aleph_\alpha<\kappa$, then N has no new subsets of $\aleph_\alpha$; i.e. $\mathscr{P}(\aleph_\alpha)$ is absolute in the extension.

PROOF. We use 3.61: suppose u is a term such that

$$\mathrm{val}(u) \subseteq \aleph_\alpha .$$

Then the set of $\aleph_\alpha$ formulae:

$$\boldsymbol{\beta} \in u, \quad \text{for} \quad \beta < \aleph_\alpha ,$$

are all decided by a single condition $p_0 \subset P$. Hence $\mathrm{val}(u) = \{\beta | p_0 \Vdash \boldsymbol{\beta} \in u \;\&\; \beta < \aleph_\alpha\} \in M$.

4.31. COROLLARY

$$2^{\aleph_\alpha} \text{ in } N = 2^{\aleph_\alpha} \text{ in } M, \text{ if } \quad \aleph_\alpha < \kappa .$$

(Since cardinals are preserved in the extension.)

4.4. Suppose x is a set of M with $\bar{\bar{x}} \geq \kappa$; $s \in N$; and in N, $s \subseteq \mathscr{P}(x)$ and $s \sim \aleph_\alpha$ for some initial ordinal $\aleph_\alpha$ (where $s \sim \theta$ is an abbreviation for: $(\exists f)(f$ is a $1-1$ mapping of s onto $\theta))$.
Then there is a set $s' \in M$, such that in M,

$$s' \subseteq \mathscr{P}(x) \quad \text{and} \quad s' \sim \aleph_\alpha .$$

PROOF. We adapt the argument of Solovay referred to in 3.5 and used in [3], [4] and [6]. We can suppose we are given a ranked formula $F(x, y)$ of L such that $P \Vdash F(\boldsymbol{\delta}, \boldsymbol{m})$ if and only if $\delta < \aleph_\alpha$ and $m \in f(\delta)$, where $f : \aleph_\alpha \to s$ is a $1-1$ onto mapping which exists by the hypothesis. We can use terms of the form $\boldsymbol{m}$ since we have assumed that $x \in M$; so if $y \in N$ and $y \in x$, then $y \in M$.

Now we define the function H in M by:
$\mathscr{D}(H) = \mathscr{P}_M(Sc \times x)$, where Sc is the set of all conditions, and if $T \subseteq Sc \times x$ is a set of M such that

$$T = \{\langle p, m\rangle | p \Vdash F(\boldsymbol{\delta}, \boldsymbol{m}) \quad \text{and} \quad m \in x\},$$

then $H(T) = \delta$; otherwise $H(T) = \emptyset$.
Now $Sc \times x$ has cardinality $\kappa . \bar{\bar{x}} = \bar{\bar{x}}$, since $\overline{\overline{Sc}} = \kappa$ and by hypothesis $\bar{\bar{x}} \geq \kappa$. The function H is defined in M, and its range includes $\aleph_\alpha$ by the properties of f in N. Hence by the axiom of choice in M we can find the required s' in M.

4.41. COROLLARY.

$$\aleph^{(N)}[\mathscr{P}(\aleph_\alpha)] = \aleph^{(M)}[\mathscr{P}(\aleph_\alpha)],$$

where $\aleph$ *is Hartog's aleph function; i.e.* 2.4 *holds in* N.

Added in proof: The requirement that $\overline{\overline{\mathscr{P}_\kappa(\kappa)}}=\kappa$ in the theorem can be dispensed with if we lay down in 3.2 that conditions must be constructible sets of M (in the Gödel sense); all our proofs can be adapted to this case.

References

[1] A. A. Fraenkel and Y. Bar-Hillel, Foundations of set theory (North-Holland Publ. Co., Amsterdam, 1958).

[2] P. J. Cohen, The independence of the continuum hypothesis, I and II. Proc. Nat. Acad. Sci. U.S.A. **50** (1963) 1143–1148, and **51** (1964) 105–110.

[3] W. B. Easton, Powers of regular cardinals, Ph. D. Thesis, Princeton 1964.

[4] A. Lévy, Definability in axiomatic set theory I. Proc. 1964 Intern. Conf. for Logic, Methodology and Philosophy of Science, ed. Y. Bar-Hillel (North-Holland Publ. Co., Amsterdam, 1965).

[5] S. Feferman, Some applications of the notions of forcing and generic sets, Fundamenta Mathematicae **56** (1965) 325–345.

[6] P. J. Cohen, Independence results in set theory, in: The theory of models, eds. J. W. Addison, L. Henkin and A. Tarski (North-Holland Publ. Co., Amsterdam, 1965).

ULTRAPRODUCTS AND OTHER METHODS OF CONSTRUCTING MODELS

C. C. CHANG
University of California, Los Angeles, USA

(Notes by I. W. Harrison and A. B. Slomson)

In these lectures we are going to discuss various methods of constructing models. In general we are concerned with this question from two points of view, the metamathematical and the algebraic. When we are metamathematically motivated we are interested in constructing structures that satisfy conditions laid down in some specific language. In this area we are concerned with such results as the Extended Completeness Theorem and the Compactness Theorem. Algebraic considerations lead us to consider such constructions as forming submodels, direct products, homomorphic images or unions of chains of previously given structures. There are also occasions when we are concerned with more specific constructions as, for example, when we consider models of set theory.

1. Constructions of models satisfying prescribed conditions

We will confine our attention to models of two valued logics, that is of logics in which every statement is either true or false. We want to investigate the construction of models that satisfy certain prescribed conditions. Before we can begin our investigation we have to make clear precisely what language we have available in which to express conditions. Exactly what language we are using affects the results we obtain. The Compactness Theorem, for example, is not true for sentences expressed in the English language.

The language that we mostly use is basically the first order predicate calculus with identity. The number of predicate and function symbols and individual constants that we have will depend on the nature of the structures that we have in mind. The structures that we consider as models for the sentences of our language are *relational systems*. By a relational system A, we mean an ordered quadruple

$$\mathsf{A} = \langle A, \mathscr{R}, \mathscr{F}, c \rangle$$

where A is a non-empty set, $\mathscr{R}$ is a sequence of finitary relations defined on A, $\mathscr{F}$ is a sequence of finitary functions defined on A and c is a sequence of elements of A. We call the elements in c *specified* elements of A.

The language we use to make statements about structures like A, then, will be the first order predicate calculus with identity, formulated in the usual way with a countable sequence $v_0, v_1, \ldots, v_n, \ldots$ of individual variables, the logical connectives $\neg$, $\wedge$, the quantifier $\exists$ and the identity symbol $\equiv$. We also have a sequence $\boldsymbol{\mathscr{R}}$ of predicate letters corresponding to the sequence $\mathscr{R}$ of relations, a sequence $\boldsymbol{\mathscr{F}}$ of function symbols corresponding to $\mathscr{F}$ and a sequence $\boldsymbol{c}$ of individual constants corresponding to c. The connectives $\vee$, $\rightarrow$, $\leftrightarrow$ and the quantifier $\forall$ are introduced for abbreviation in the usual way. Let us call such a language L.

We have logical axioms for L, including axioms for identity, formulated in the usual way. We assume that it is understood what is meant by a (well-formed) *formula*, by a *term* and by *free* and *bound* occurrences of variables. A formula which contains only bound occurrences of variables is called a *sentence*. We assume also that the notions of *proof*, *theorem* and *consistent set of sentences* are all known. (The reader can find these notions explained precisely in any standard text, e.g. [1].) All the notions we have just mentioned are of a syntactical character. We can now relate them to semantic notions, i.e. to our intended interpretation of our language.

We adopt the usual convention of writing $\tau(v_0, \ldots, v_n)$ if all the free variables occurring in the term τ can be found in the list $v_0, \ldots, v_n$ and, similarly, we write $\varphi(v_0, \ldots, v_n)$ if all the free variables occurring in the formula φ can be found in the list $v_0, \ldots, v_n$.

We are now able to say what we mean by the *value* $\tau_{\mathsf{A}}[x_0, \ldots, x_n]$ of the term $\tau(v_0, \ldots, v_n)$ in A with respect to the elements $x_0, \ldots, x_n$ of A. We define this by recursion on the number of function symbols in τ in the usual way. Similarly, by recursion, we can define what we mean by saying that the formula $\varphi(v_0, \ldots, v_n)$ *holds* in A with respect to the elements $x_0, \ldots, x_n$. Details of these definitions can be found, for example, in [2].

If $\varphi(v_0, \ldots, v_n)$ holds in A with respect to the elements $x_0, \ldots, x_n$ of A then we write

$$\mathsf{A} \models \varphi[x_0, \ldots, x_n].$$

If φ is a sentence then φ contains no free variables and so we simply have that either A satisfies φ, i.e. $\mathsf{A} \models \varphi$, or A does not satisfy φ. If A satisfies a sentence φ then we say that A is a *model* of φ. We say that A is a model of a collection of sentences Σ if A is a model of each sentence in Σ.

If Σ, Δ are collections of sentences and φ is any sentence we write $\Sigma \models \varphi$ if every model of Σ is also a model of φ, and $\Sigma \models \Delta$ if every model of Σ is also a model of Δ. As well as these semantic relations between collections of sentences we can also consider the syntactic relations: $\Sigma \vdash \varphi$, φ is a consequence of Σ and $\Sigma \vdash \Delta$, each sentence of Δ is a consequence of Σ. The relation between the semantic and the syntactical notions is given by the Extended Completeness Theorem (Gödel, Henkin et al.) which tells us that:

$$\models \varphi \Leftrightarrow \vdash \varphi$$

$$\Sigma \models \Delta \Leftrightarrow \Sigma \vdash \Delta$$

and Σ has a model $\Leftrightarrow$ Σ is consistent.

In the case of second and higher order languages the situation is not nearly so pleasant. The construction of models is much more difficult and indeed no general result is known. However by enriching our first order language in various ways we can specify more complicated conditions than is possible in ordinary first order logic and yet still be able to apply general methods of constructing models. The following list gives some idea of the various ways of enriching our language that have been considered.

1. Infinite conjunctions and disjunctions of ordinary first order sentences are allowed. That is, we have sentences of the form

$$\bigvee_{i \in I} \sigma_i \quad \text{or} \quad \bigwedge_{i \in I} \sigma_i$$

where the σ_i are sentences of ordinary first order logic and I is an arbitrary index set. Using these infinitary sentences we can define the various sorts of elementary classes, that is, the classes EC_Δ, EC_Σ, $EC_{\Delta\Sigma}$ and $EC_{\Sigma\Delta}$. For further references see, for example, Hanf [3] and Karp [4].

2. Sentences can be formed by putting one quantifier outside an infinite conjunction or disjunction of ordinary first order formulas. That is we have sentences of the form

$$(\exists v_0) \bigwedge_{i \in I} \varphi_i(v_0); \quad (\forall v_0) \bigvee_{i \in I} \varphi_i(v_0); \quad \text{etc.}$$

where the $\varphi_i(v_0)$ are formulas of ordinary first order logic. Using such sentences we can obtain models which realize certain types of elements and omit others. See, for example, Morley [53].

3. Sentences like

$$(\forall v_0)(\exists v_1) \bigwedge_{i \in I} \bigvee_{j \in J} \varphi_{ij}(v_0, v_1)$$

with infinite conjunctions and disjunctions but only finitely many quantifiers are allowed. Such languages have been studied, for example, by Dana Scott [52], Lopez-Escobar and Malitz.

4. Infinite quantifiers as well as infinite conjunctions and disjunctions are allowed so that we have, for example, sentences like

$$(\forall v_0, v_1, \ldots)(\exists w_0, w_1, \ldots) \bigwedge_i \bigvee_j \Sigma_{ij}(v_0, v_1, \ldots; w_0, w_1, \ldots).$$

Such languages have been considered by, among others, Henkin [5] and Karp [4].

5. Weak second order languages in which the variables are restricted to ranging over finite sets (instead of all sets) or finite sequences of elements have been investigated by Tarski [6].

6. Quantifiers of the form $\exists^{\geq \alpha} v_0$, "there are at least α" are included. These quantifiers can be prefixed to infinite conjunctions and disjunctions of formulas. Such languages have been considered especially with relation to generalisations of the Löwenheim-Skolem theorem for pairs of cardinals by Craig [7], Craig and Hanf [8], Fuhrken [9], Keisler [10] and Vaught [11].

7. Quantifiers are allowed to range over relations, e.g. $(\exists! R)\Sigma(R)$, $(\exists^{\geq \alpha} R)\Sigma(R)$ are sentences of the language. Using such languages we can study such things as the theory of definability, Beth's theorem [12, 13] and its applications, models with a great number of (or very few) automorphisms and the concept of categoricity [15].

Despite the wide range covered by the examples above we will see that the ultraproduct construction which we will shortly describe can be used in studying many of them, particularly 1, 2, 6 and 7. Thus this method of constructing models provides a link between various aspects of the subject.

Given a structure $\mathsf{A}=\langle A, \mathscr{R}, \mathscr{F}, c\rangle$, by the *domain* of A, which we denote by $|\mathsf{A}|$, we mean the set A. We write $|X|$ for the cardinal of the set X. The cardinal of a structure A is the cardinal of its domain, i.e. $|A|=\|\mathsf{A}\|$. By a *theory* Γ, we mean a consistent set of sentences of the language which is closed under deduction, i.e. whenever $\Gamma\vdash\sigma$ then $\sigma\in\Gamma$. Given a theory Γ we write $M(\Gamma)$ for the collection of all models of Γ. For a sentence σ we write $M(\sigma)$ for $M(\{\sigma\})$.

An *elementary class* K is a class of models which are the models of some theory. If K is an elementary class we write $K\in \mathrm{EC}_\Delta$. Thus $K\in\mathrm{EC}_\Delta$ if for some theory Γ, $K=M(\Gamma)$.

Given a model A we can *expand* it by adding more relations, functions or specified elements and we can *reduce* it by reducing the number of relations etc. Correspondingly we can make changes to the language L. For example if $\mathsf{A}=\langle A, \mathscr{R}, \mathscr{F}, c\rangle$ is a model, $\mathscr{R}'$ is a sequence of new relations defined on A, $\mathscr{F}'$ is a sequence of new functions defined on A and c' is a new sequence of elements of A, we can form the expansion

$$\mathsf{A}' = \langle A, \mathscr{R}*\mathscr{R}', \mathscr{F}*\mathscr{F}', c*c'\rangle$$

of A. Here $\mathscr{R}*\mathscr{R}'$ denotes the concatenation of the sequences $\mathscr{R}$ and $\mathscr{R}'$, i.e. the sequence obtained by writing the sequence $\mathscr{R}'$ after the sequence $\mathscr{R}$, and similarly for $\mathscr{F}*\mathscr{F}'$ and $c*c'$. We will often denote this expansion of A by $(\mathsf{A}, \mathscr{R}', \mathscr{F}', c')$. Corresponding to this expansion of A we expand the language L to $(L, \boldsymbol{\mathscr{R}}', \boldsymbol{\mathscr{F}}', \boldsymbol{c}')$ by adding the sequence $\boldsymbol{\mathscr{R}}'$ of predicate letters, the sequence $\boldsymbol{\mathscr{F}}'$ of function letters and the sequence $\boldsymbol{c}'$ of individual constants.

In a similar way we can define the inverse process of reduction. We say that A' is a reduction of A if A is an expansion of A'. Also the language L' is said to be a reduction of L if L is an expansion of L'.

We call expansions and reductions *simple* if they are obtained by adding or removing just specified elements (from models) or individual constants (from languages). When we are making simple expansions and reductions it is clear that as far as the language is concerned all that matters is the order type of the sequence of individual constants that is removed or added. Exactly what symbols are used is irrelevant. Thus we will denote by L_μ the language obtained from L by adjoining a μ-termed sequence of individual constants. L_μ is therefore a simple expansion of L.

A collection K of models is called a *pseudo-elementary class* if K is the class of all reductions of the models of some elementary class in an expansion L' of the language L. If K is a pseudo-elementary class we write $K \in \mathrm{PC}_\Delta$. Thus $K \in \mathrm{PC}_\Delta$ if there is some expansion L' of L and some theory Γ of L' such that $K = \{\mathsf{A} : \mathsf{A}' \in M(\Gamma)\}$ where A is the reduction of A' obtained by dropping the relations, functions and specified elements corresponding to the predicate letters, function letters and individual constants that were added to L to obtain L'.

We now consider the various relations that might hold between two structures $\mathsf{A} = \langle A, \mathscr{R}, \mathscr{F}, c\rangle$ and $\mathsf{B} = \langle B, \mathscr{S}, \mathscr{G}, d\rangle$ of the language L. A is said to be a *submodel* of B and we write $\mathsf{A} \subseteq \mathsf{B}$ if $A \subseteq B$ and the relations of $\mathscr{R}$ are the restrictions of the corresponding relations of $\mathscr{S}$ to A and similarly for the functions of $\mathscr{F}$, and c is the sequence d.

A is said to be an *elementary submodel* of B, and we write $\mathsf{A} \prec \mathsf{B}$ if $\mathsf{A} \subseteq \mathsf{B}$ and whenever $\varphi(v_0, \ldots, v_n)$ is a formula of L and $x_0, \ldots, x_n$ are elements of A then

$$\mathsf{A} \models \varphi[x_0, \ldots, x_n] \Leftrightarrow \mathsf{B} \models \varphi[x_0, \ldots, x_n].$$

A is said to be elementarily equivalent to B and we write $\mathsf{A} \equiv \mathsf{B}$ if, for any sentence σ of L,

$$\mathsf{A} \models \sigma \Leftrightarrow \mathsf{B} \models \sigma;$$

that is, if all sentences which hold in A hold in B and *vice versa.* These last two notions are due to Tarski (see [2]).

It is clear from the definitions that the relations $\equiv$ and $\prec$ have the following properties:

1. If $\mathsf{A} \prec \mathsf{B}$ then $\mathsf{A} \equiv \mathsf{B}$.
2. If $\mathsf{A} \prec \mathsf{B}$ and $\mathsf{B} \prec \mathsf{C}$ then $\mathsf{A} \prec \mathsf{C}$, so $\prec$ is a transitive relation.
3. $\equiv$ is an equivalence relation.

We also have the following results:

THEOREM (Tarski and Vaught [2]). If $\{\mathsf{A}_i : i \in I\}$ is a collection of models which is linearly ordered by the relation $\prec$, then for each $i \in I$,

$$\mathsf{A}_i \prec \mathsf{A} = \bigcup_{i \in I} \mathsf{A}_i.$$

THEOREM (Tarski, see Tarski and Vaught [2]). If $\mathsf{A} \subseteq \mathsf{B}$ and for all formulas $\varphi(v_0, \ldots, v_n)$ of L and all $x_1, \ldots, x_n$ in A whenever $\mathsf{B} \models (\exists v_0) \varphi[x_1, \ldots, x_n]$ there is some x_0 in A such that $\mathsf{B} \models \varphi[x_0, x_1, \ldots, x_n]$ then $\mathsf{A} \prec \mathsf{B}$.

This last result gives a useful test for determining whether some submodel is an elementary submodel of another model.

We say that A is *isomorphically embeddable* in B (or just *embeddable* in B) if A is isomorphic to a subsystem B' of B. If h is an isomorphism between A and $\mathsf{B}' \subseteq \mathsf{B}$, h is an *embedding* of A into B. If A is isomorphic to an elementary subsystem B' of B we say A is *elementarily embeddable* in B. An embedding h which maps A onto an elementary subsystem of B is called an *elementary embedding*.

Let A be a structure with domain A. A sequence $a \in A^\alpha$, where α is some ordinal, is called an *enumeration* of A if each element of A occurs at least once in the sequence a. Now suppose that $a \in A^\alpha$ is a fixed enumeration of A. We extend the language L to L_α by adding an α-termed sequence of individual constants. The set of all sentences of L_α which hold in the structure (A, a) is called the *a-elementary diagram* of A. The *a-diagram* of A is the set which consists of all the atomic sentences of L_α which hold in (A, a) together with the negations of all atomic formulas of L_α which do not hold in (A, a). These two concepts are due to Henkin [16] and Robinson [17]. The following two results show that the condition that A be embeddable or elementarily embeddable in B can be expressed in terms of a semantic condition on the diagrams of A. Suppose A is a structure with domain A and B is a structure with domain B. Let $a \in A^\alpha$ be an enumeration of A and let Δ be the a-elementary diagram of A and Σ the a-diagram of A then

i) A is embeddable in B iff there is some $b \in B^\alpha$, not necessarily an enumeration of B, such that $(\mathsf{B}, b) \models \Sigma$, and

ii) A is elementarily embeddable in B iff there is some $b \in B^\alpha$ such that $(\mathsf{B}, b) \models \Delta$. Again b is not necessarily an enumeration of B.

2. The ultraproduct construction

In this section for ease of exposition we will consider relational systems with a single binary relation and a single two place function and one distinguished element. It is easily seen that all our results carry over to arbitrary relational systems.

Suppose that for each $i \in I$, $\mathsf{A}_i = \langle A_i, R_i, F_i, c_i \rangle$ is a relational system and that D is an ultrafilter on I, that is, D is a collection of subsets of I which is a filter on I and such that for each $X \subseteq I$ either X or $I - X$ is in D, but not both. We denote the cartesian product of the sets A_i by $\prod_{i \in I} A_i$, or, more usually, when there can be no confusion about the index set by ΠA_i.

The relation $\sim_D$ is defined on ΠA_i by

$$f \sim_D g \Leftrightarrow \{i \in I : f(i) = g(i)\} \in D,$$

where $f(i)$ is the i-th coordinate of the element $f \in \Pi A_i$. It is easy to verify that because D is an ultrafilter and $\sim_D$ is an equivalence relation on ΠA_i. (In fact it is sufficient for D to be a filter.) We denote the equivalence class to which the element f belongs by $f^{\sim D}$, or, more usually, when there is no ambiguity about which ultrafilter is intended, by $f^{\sim}$. Let $A = \{f^{\sim} : f \in \Pi A_i\}$ be the collection of equivalence classes of elements of ΠA_i. We are going to define a relational system with domain A.

If for $i \in I$, $x_i \in A_i$, we denote by $\lambda i \in I x_i$ the element x in ΠA_i whose i-th coordinate is x_i; when there is no confusion about the index set we write simply $\lambda i x_i$ for this element.

The relation R is defined on A by

$$R(f^{\sim}, g^{\sim}) \Leftrightarrow \{i \in I : R_i(f(i), g(i))\} \in D,$$

the function F is defined on A by

$$F(f^{\sim}, g^{\sim}) = (\lambda i F_i(f(i), g(i)))^{\sim}$$

and the element c by

$$c = (\lambda i c_i)^{\sim}.$$

It can easily be seen that R, F and c are all well-defined and so $\mathsf{A} = \langle A, R, F, c \rangle$ is a model with domain A. A is called the *ultraproduct* of the A_i modulo D and is denoted by D-prod $\lambda i \mathsf{A}_i$. If all the A_i are equal to A' say we write simply D-prod A' which we call the *ultrapower* of A' modulo D. (Some writers use instead the notations

$$\prod_{i \in I} \mathsf{A}_i / D \quad \text{and} \quad \mathsf{A}'^I / D$$

for the ultraproduct and ultrapower respectively.) This notion is implicit in Łoš [18].

The ultraproduct D-prod $\lambda i \mathsf{A}_i$, like its factors, is a relational system with a single binary relation and a single two place function and one distinguished element. It follows, therefore, that we can use exactly the same language L to make statements about the ultraproduct as we use to make statements about the factors. The following fundamental result relates the semantic properties of the ultraproduct to those of its factors.

FUNDAMENTAL LEMMA ON ULTRAPRODUCTS (Łoš's Theorem [18])

i) For each term $\tau(v_0, \ldots, v_n)$ and all $f_0^{\sim}, \ldots, f_n^{\sim}$ in A

$$\tau_{\mathsf{A}}[f_0^{\sim}, \ldots, f_n^{\sim}] = (\lambda i \tau_{\mathsf{A}_i}[f_0(i), \ldots, f_n(i)])^{\sim}.$$

ii) For each formula $\varphi(v_0, \ldots, v_n)$ and all $f_0^{\sim}, \ldots, f_n^{\sim}$ in A

$$\mathsf{A} \models \varphi[f_0^{\sim}, \ldots, f_n^{\sim}] \Leftrightarrow \{i \in I : \mathsf{A}_i \models \varphi[f_0(i), \ldots, f_n(i)]\} \in D.$$

iii) For each sentence σ

$$\mathsf{A} \models \sigma \Leftrightarrow \{i \in I : \mathsf{A}_i \models \sigma\} \in D.$$

i) is proved by induction on the number of function letters in τ, ii) by induction on the number of logical symbols ($\neg$, $\wedge$, $\exists$) in φ and iii) is an immediate consequence of ii). For the details see, for example, Frayne, Morel and Scott [19].

The lemma gives us precise information about the first order properties of an ultraproduct as compared with those of its factors. The result has many consequences which we now list.

1. Every elementary class is closed under the formation of ultraproducts. That is, if $K \in \mathrm{EC}_\Delta$ and for each $i \in I$, $\mathsf{A}_i \in K$ then D-prod $\lambda i \mathsf{A}_i \in K$. This follows as an immediate consequence of iii) and the definition of EC_Δ. In a similar way we have

2. Every pseudo-elementary class is closed under the formation of ultraproducts.

3. The map $d: |\mathsf{A}| \to |D\text{-prod } \lambda i \mathsf{A}|$ defined by

$$d(x) = \lambda i x^{\sim}$$

is an elementary embedding of A into the ultrapower D-prod A.

4. THE COMPACTNESS THEOREM. If Σ is a set of sentences of L and every finite subset Δ of Σ has a model A_Δ then Σ itself has a model. Indeed there is an ultraproduct of the models A_Δ which is a model of Σ.

PROOF. Let $I=S_\omega(\Sigma)$ be the set of all finite subsets of Σ. Then, by hypothesis, each $\Delta\in I$ has a model A_Δ.

For each $\Delta\in I$ let $\hat{\Delta}=\{\Delta'\in S_\omega(\Sigma):\Delta\subseteq\Delta'\}$. Clearly $\hat{\Delta}\subseteq S_\omega(\Sigma)$. Now let $E=\{\hat{\Delta}:\Delta\in S_\omega(\Sigma)\}$; we show that E has the finite intersection property. In fact, this is immediate since $\Delta_1\cup\ldots\cup\Delta_k\in\hat{\Delta}_1\cap\ldots\cap\hat{\Delta}_k$. Hence E can be extended to an ultrafilter D on I. We will show that $\mathsf{A}=D$-prod $\lambda\Delta\mathsf{A}_\Delta$ is a model of Σ.

Suppose $\varphi\in\Sigma$, then $\{\varphi\}\in S_\omega(\Sigma)$, say $\{\varphi\}=\Delta$. Hence $\hat{\Delta}\in E$ and so $\hat{\Delta}\in \mathrm{D}$. Now if $\Delta'\in\hat{\Delta}$ then $\Delta\subseteq\Delta'$ and so $\varphi\in\Delta'$ whence $\mathsf{A}_{\Delta'}\models\varphi$. Therefore $\{\Delta':\mathsf{A}_{\Delta'}\models\varphi\}\supseteq\hat{\Delta}$ and so $\{\Delta':\mathsf{A}_{\Delta'}\models\varphi\}\in D$. But then it follows from the lemma that $\mathsf{A}\models\varphi$.

This completes the proof.

5. $\mathsf{A}\equiv\mathsf{B}$ iff A is elementarily embeddable in some ultrapower of B. This is just a special case of

6. Let K be some collection of models and let K^* be the set of sentences which hold in all the models in K then

$\mathsf{A}\in M(K^*)$ iff A is elementarily embeddable in some ultraproduct of members of K. (Note that $M(K^*)=\bigcap\{L:K\subseteq L\in \mathrm{EC}_\Delta\}$.)

PROOF. Clearly if A is elementarily embeddable in some ultraproduct of elements of K then $\mathsf{A}\in M(K^*)$.

Conversely suppose that $\mathsf{A}\in M(K^*)$. Let $a\in A^\alpha$ be an enumeration of A. Let Σ be the a-elementary diagram of A. We show that each finite subset of Σ is satisfiable in some member of K.

Let $\Delta=\{\varphi_1,\ldots,\varphi_n\}$ be a finite subset of Σ, then $\varphi=\varphi_1\wedge\ldots\wedge\varphi_n$ is a sentence of L_α. Suppose that φ is $\varphi(d_1,\ldots,d_m)$ where $d_1,\ldots,d_m$ are all the constants of L_α occurring in φ which are not constants of L. Let $\psi=(\forall v_1,\ldots,v_m)\neg\varphi(v_1,\ldots,v_m)$; ψ is a sentence of L. If no $\mathsf{B}\in K$ satisfies φ then for all $\mathsf{B}\in K$, $\mathsf{B}\models\psi$ and so $\psi\in K^*$. But $\mathsf{A}\in M(K^*)$ and hence $\mathsf{A}\models\psi$ and this contradicts the fact that $(\mathsf{A},a)\models\varphi(d_1,\ldots,d_m)$.

Thus for each finite subset Δ of Σ there is some $\mathsf{B}_\Delta\in K$ in which Δ is satisfiable. Then, exactly as in the proof of the Compactness Theorem, we can find an ultraproduct B of the models B_Δ in which Σ is satisfiable. Since Σ is satisfiable in B, A is elementarily embeddable in B.

7. Let K be a collection of models. Then $K\in\mathrm{EC}_\Delta$ iff K is closed under

i) isomorphism

ii) the formation of elementary submodels

iii) the formation of ultraproducts.

PROOF. Clearly if $K \in \mathrm{EC}_\Delta$ then K has the required closure properties. Conversely suppose that K is closed under i), ii) and iii). Let $K' = M(K^*)$, where K^* is the set of sentences which hold in each model in K. Then $K' \in \mathrm{EC}_\Delta$ and obviously $K \subseteq K'$ so it is sufficient to prove that $K' \subseteq K$.

Suppose $\mathsf{A} \in K'$, then by the previous result A is elementarily embeddable in some ultraproduct B of elements of K, i.e. A is isomorphic to some elementary submodel B' of B. By iii) $\mathsf{B} \in K$ and hence by i) and ii) $\mathsf{A} \in K$. So $K' \subseteq K$ and the proof is complete.

This characterization of elementary classes is due to D. Scott.

Notice that if K has the closure properties listed above then it is also the case that

ii′) $\bar{K}$, the complement of K, is closed under the formation of ultrapowers.

For suppose $\mathsf{A} \in \bar{K}$. If D-prod $\mathsf{A} \in K$, since A is elementarily embeddable in its ultrapowers it would follow from i), ii) and iii) that $\mathsf{A} \in K$. Hence D-prod $\mathsf{A} \in \bar{K}$ also. Keisler has shown that if we assume the Generalized Continuum Hypothesis we can replace ii) by ii′) in the above theorem. We discuss this result later.

8. If D is a principal ultrafilter on I then there is some j in I such that D-prod $\lambda i \mathsf{A}_i$ is isomorphic to A_j.

In this case there is some $j \in I$ such that $D = \{X \subseteq I : j \in X\}$, it is easily seen that the map h: $|D\text{-prod } \lambda i \mathsf{A}_i| \to |\mathsf{A}_j|$ defined by $h((\lambda i x_i)^\sim) = x_j$ is an isomorphism.

In particular when I is finite all ultrafilters on I are principal and we get nothing new by forming the ultraproduct. Because of this result from now on we will consider only the cases where D is non-principal and a fortiori I is infinite.

INTERESTING ULTRAFILTERS

We have just seen that in the case of principal ultrafilters the ultraproduct is always isomorphic to one of the factors and so such ultrafilters do not lead to any exciting results. We are now going to consider various properties that ultrafilters can have which lead to interesting results. We shall still be making use of our Fundamental Lemma and so our remarks about interesting ultrafilters will be interspersed with further consequences of the lemma.

(i) *ω-incomplete ultrafilters*

An ultrafilter D on I is said to be *ω-incomplete* if there is a countable set of elements of D whose intersection is the empty set. The question that naturally arises is that of whether all non-principal ultrafilters are ω-incomplete. The question has been partially answered by Scott who showed that, assuming the Axiom of Constructibility, i.e. $V=L$ in the sense of Gödel [20], then all non-principal ultrafilters are necessarily ω-incomplete [21].

(ii) *Uniform ultrafilters*

An ultrafilter D on I is said to be *uniform* if all the sets in D have the same cardinal as I [19]. A consequence of our main lemma shows that as far as constructing different ultraproducts is concerned we need only consider uniform ultrafilters, as follows:

9. Let D be an ultrafilter on I and $\{\mathsf{A}_i : i \in I\}$ a collection of models, and let α be the least cardinal of the sets in D. Then there is a subset J of I of cardinal α and a uniform ultrafilter E on J such that D-prod $\lambda i \in I \mathsf{A}_i$ is isomorphic to E-prod $\lambda j \in J \mathsf{A}_j$.

PROOF. Let J be any subset of D of cardinal α and let $E = \{J \cap X : X \in D\}$. Clearly E is a uniform ultrafilter on J and since $X \in D$ iff $J \cap X \in E$ the result follows immediately.

(iii) *Regular ultrafilters*

Given any infinite set I, the set $S_\omega(I)$ of all finite subsets of I has the same cardinal as I. Hence there is a one-one map from I onto $S_\omega(I)$. An ultrafilter D on I is said to be *regular* if there is a one-one map f from I onto $S_\omega(I)$ such that for each $j \in I$, $\hat{j} \in D$, where $\hat{j} = \{i \in I : j \in f(i)\}$ [22].

The following two results connect the different sorts of ultrafilters that we have just described.

1. If D is a regular ultrafilter on I then D is uniform and ω-incomplete.

2. If I is a countable set then the sets of non-principal ultrafilters, ω-incomplete ultrafilters, uniform ultrafilters and regular ultrafilters all coincide.

CARDINALITY OF ULTRAPRODUCTS

We are now going to discuss the question of how the cardinal of an ultraproduct depends on the cardinals of its factors, the cardinal of the index set and the nature of the ultrafilter. In fact, for simplicity, we consider only ultrapowers. It will be seen that the classification of interesting ultrafilters that we began above is very relevant to our present discussion.

Let A be any set, I an index set and D an ultrafilter on I. Then we have the following results:

i) $|A| \leq |D\text{-prod } A| \leq |A^I|$.
Obvious and legendary.

ii) If $|A| = |I|$ and D is uniform then $|A| < |D\text{-prod } A|$.
Frayne, Morel and Scott [19] p. 206.

iii) If γ is a cardinal $|D\text{-prod } A|^\gamma \leq |D\text{-prod } (A^\gamma)|$.
Keisler [22].

iv) If A is infinite and D is ω-incomplete then $|D\text{-prod } A| = |D\text{-prod } A|^\omega$.
Keisler [22].

v) If A is infinite and D is regular then $|D\text{-prod } A| = |A^I|$.

We prove this last result as an example:

Proof. We already know from i) that $|D\text{-prod } A| \leq |A^I|$. Let B be the set of all sequences $b \in A^\omega$ which are eventually constant. Since A is infinite $|A| = |B|$ and so it will be sufficient to prove that $|A^I| \leq |D\text{-prod } B|$; we will prove this by constructing a one-one function from A^I into D-prod B.

Since D is regular there is a one-one map φ from I onto $S_\omega(I)$ such that for each $j \in I$, $\hat{\jmath} = \{i \in I : j \in \varphi(i)\} \in D$.

Let I be linearly ordered in some manner and let a_0 be some fixed element of A. Suppose $f \in A^I$; we construct a corresponding element $f' \in B^I$ as follows:

f' is to be a function from I to B. For $i \in I$, $\varphi(i)$ is a finite subset of I, say it is $\{i_0, i_1, \ldots, i_k\}$ where the elements are arranged according to the order induced by the linear ordering of I. Then we let $f'(i)$ be the sequence

$$\langle f(i_0), f(i_1), \ldots, f(i_k), a_0, a_0, \ldots, a_0, \ldots \rangle$$

and so $f'(i) \in B$, whence $f' \in B^I$. We define the map $H: A^I \to D\text{-prod } B^I$ by $H(f) = (f')^\sim$. It remains only to show that H is one-one.

Suppose $f \neq g$, for $f, g \in A^I$. Then for some $i_0 \in I$, $f(i_0) \neq g(i_0)$. Suppose $i \in I$ and $i_0 \in \varphi(i)$, say $\varphi(i) = \{i'_0, \ldots, i_0, \ldots, i'_k\}$, then

$$f'(i) = \langle f(i'_0), \ldots, f(i_0), \ldots, f(i'_k), a_0, a_0, \ldots, a_0, \ldots \rangle$$

and
$$g'(i) = \langle g(i'_0), \ldots, g(i_0), \ldots, g(i'_k), a_0, a_0, \ldots, a_0, \ldots\rangle$$
and therefore $f'(i) \neq g'(i)$. Hence $\hat{\imath}_0 = \{i \in I : i_0 \in \varphi(i)\} \subseteq \{i \in I : f'(i) \neq g'(i)\}$. But $\hat{\imath}_0 \in D$, hence $\{i \in I : f'(i) \neq g'(i)\} \in D$ and so $(f')^{\sim} \neq (g')^{\sim}$, i.e. $H(f) \neq$ $\neq H(g)$.

This completes the proof.

We conclude the discussion of the cardinality of ultrapowers by listing some open problems in this field.

1. Is every uniform ultrafilter regular?
2. Is (v) above true if we replace "regular" by "uniform"?
3. If D is a uniform ultrafilter on I, A an infinite set and $|A| < |I|$ is it true that $|A| < |D\text{-prod } A|$?
4. If D is a uniform ultrafilter on I and I is infinite is $|I| < |D\text{-prod } \omega|$?

In particular, when $I = \omega_1$, the first uncountable ordinal, and D is uniform over ω_1, do we have $\omega_1 < |D\text{-prod } \omega|$? (It is known, however, that if the axioms of Zermelo-Fraenkel set theory are consistent then they are consistent with ω_1 being less than $|D\text{-prod } \omega|$ for all uniform ultrafilters D on ω_1.)

5. If D is uniform on ω_2 does D have an ω_1 descending sequence with an empty intersection?

(The answer is known to be "yes" under the assumption that $2^{\omega_1} = \omega_2$, Chang [54].)

Saturated models and ultraproducts

The notion of a saturated model is a natural extension of Hausdorff's idea of an η_α-set, which we now describe. If S is a totally ordered set and A, B are subsets of S we write $A < B$ if for all $a \in A$ and $b \in B$, $a < b$. Similarly for $c \in S$, we write $A < c < B$ if for all $a \in A$ and $b \in B$, $a < c < b$.

Suppose that α is an ordinal and S is a totally ordered set of cardinal ω_α. We say that S is an *η_α-set* if whenever A and B are subsets of S of cardinal $< \omega_\alpha$ such that $A < B$, there is some $c \in S$ such that $A < c < B$. For example, the rationals with the natural ordering form an η_0-set, whereas even assuming the Continuum Hypothesis, the reals are not an η_1-set with the natural ordering.

We have the following results about η_α-sets [23].

1. *Existence*. If $2^\alpha = \alpha^+$ then η_{α^+}-sets exist. In particular, if $2^\omega = \omega_1$, there is an η_1-set.

2. *Uniqueness.* If S and T are η_α-sets then S and T are order isomorphic.

3. *Universality.* If S is an η_α-set and T is an ordered set of cardinal $\leq \omega_\alpha$ then T can be order isomorphically embedded in S.

It is natural to enquire whether we can find models which have analogous properties in the class of models to those which η_α-sets have in the class of ordered sets. It turns out that it is the saturated models which have these properties so we will now explain what saturated models are.

Let A be a model and let F be a set of formulas which contain at most the one free variable v_0. We say that F is *simultaneously satisfiable* in A if there is some element $a_0 \in |\mathsf{A}|$ such that for all $\varphi(v_0) \in F$, $\mathsf{A} \models \varphi[a_0]$. F is said to be *finitely satisfiable* in A if each finite subset of F is simultaneously satisfiable in A. (For simplicity we shall assume in what follows that L is a countable language.)

If A is a model of cardinal β we say that A is *saturated* if for each ordinal $\alpha < \beta$ and each sequence $a \in |\mathsf{A}|^\alpha$, any set of formulas of L which contain at most the one free variable v_0 and which is finitely satisfiable in (A, a) is also simultaneously satisfiable in (A, a).

We have the following results about saturated relational systems.

1. *Existence.* If $2^\alpha = \alpha^+$, for all infinite models A of power $\leq \alpha^+$ there is a saturated model B of power α^+ such that $\mathsf{A} \prec \mathsf{B}$.

2. *Uniqueness.* If A and B are elementarily equivalent saturated relational systems of the same cardinality then they are isomorphic.

3. *Universality.* If B is elementarily equivalent to a saturated relational system A and $\|\mathsf{B}\| \leq \|\mathsf{A}\|$, than B is elementarily embeddable in A.

These three results are due to Morley and Vaught [24]. They show that given any complete theory Γ, then the saturated models in $M(\Gamma)$ play an exactly analogous rôle to that which the η_α-sets play in the class of all ordered sets.

A natural question to ask is whether saturated models can be obtained by the ultraproduct construction. This question has been answered by Keisler [25, 26] who showed that

THEOREM. If $2^\alpha = \alpha^+$ and A is an infinite model of power $\leq \alpha^+$ then there is an ultrafilter D over α such that D-prod A is a saturated model of cardinal α^+.

We shall soon describe the sort of ultrafilters that give rise to saturated ultraproducts. Meanwhile we notice two important consequences of

Keisler's result above. The first is an immediate consequence of 2 and the theorem above.

THEOREM. Assuming the Generalized Continuum Hypothesis, two models A and B are elementarily equivalent iff they have isomorphic ultrapowers.

This result was first proved by Keisler [27] without using saturated models. Later Keisler [25] pointed out that it is a corollary of his result above. This last result can be used to improve our earlier characterization of elementary classes, as follows:

THEOREM. Let K be a class of models, then $K \in EC_\Delta$ iff

i) K is closed under isomorphism,

ii) $\bar{K}$ is closed under ultrapowers and

iii) K is closed under ultraproducts.

PROOF. We have already remarked that one way round is trivial. Suppose then that K has the properties i), ii), iii). We shall show that $K \in EC_\Delta$.

Let $K' = M(K^*)$, clearly $K' \in EC_\Delta$ and $K \subseteq K'$, so it is sufficient to prove that $K' \subseteq K$.

Suppose $A \in K'$. Then, by a previous result, A is isomorphic to an elementary submodel of an ultraproduct of elements of K and this ultraproduct is itself in K.

Hence $A \equiv B$ for some $B \in K$. By the previous theorem A and B have isomorphic ultrapowers A$'$ and B$'$. $B' \in K$ and so $A' \in K$. It follows that $A \in K$ or else by ii) $A' \in \bar{K}$. This proves the result.

GOOD ULTRAFILTERS

We are now going to describe the sort of ultrafilters that give rise to saturated ultraproducts.

Let I be some set and let α be the cardinal of I. We denote by $S_{\bar{\omega}}(\alpha)$ the set of all co-finite subsets of α, that is $S_{\bar{\omega}}(\alpha) = \{X : X \subseteq \alpha \text{ and } \alpha - X \text{ is finite}\}$. Suppose that f is a map from $S_{\bar{\omega}}(\alpha)$ to $S(I)$, the set of all subsets of I. We say that f is a *monotone* function if whenever $u \subseteq v$ then $f(u) \subseteq f(v)$. f is said to be *multiplicative* if $f(u \cap v) = f(u) \cap f(v)$ for all u, v in $S_{\bar{\omega}}(\alpha)$. If $g : S_{\bar{\omega}}(\alpha) \rightarrow S(I)$ is another such map we write $f \leq g$ if $f(u) \subseteq g(u)$ for all $u \in S_{\bar{\omega}}(\alpha)$.

An ultrafilter D on I is said to be *good* if for every monotone function $f : S_{\bar{\omega}}(\alpha) \rightarrow D$ there is a multiplicative function $g : S_{\bar{\omega}}(\alpha) \rightarrow D$ such that $g \leq f$. This notion is due to Keisler [26].

We have the following results about good ultrafilters:

1. If $|I|=\alpha$ and $2^\alpha=\alpha^+$ then there is a good ω-incomplete ultrafilter on I.

2. If $2^\alpha=\alpha^+$ and A is an infinite model of cardinal $\leq\alpha^+$ and D is any good ω-incomplete ultrafilter on I then D-prod A is a saturated model of cardinal α^+.

3. If $|I|=\omega$, then the notions of being a non-principal ultrafilter, an ω-incomplete ultrafilter, a regular ultrafilter, a uniform ultrafilter and a good ultrafilter on I all coincide.

Assuming the Continuum Hypothesis the results 2 and 3 above give us the

THEOREM. If $\omega\leq\|\mathsf{A}\|\leq\omega_1$ and D is a non-principal ultrafilter on ω then D-prod A is a saturated model of cardinal ω_1.

It is known that if D is a good ω-incomplete ultrafilter on I then D is regular. Assuming the Generalized Continuum Hypothesis the converse is not true.

The following lemma is the key to the result that good ultrafilters exist as well as the result that there exists a regular ω-incomplete ultrafilter which is not good.

LEMMA (Keisler [27]). Let α be an infinite cardinal and $F=\{X_\xi:\xi<\alpha\}$ be a family of sets each of cardinal α. Then there is a family $F'=\{Y_\xi:\xi<\alpha\}$ of sets each of cardinal α such that for $\xi<\alpha$, $Y_\xi\subseteq X_\xi$ and for $\xi\neq\eta$, $Y_\xi\cap Y_\eta=\emptyset$.

3. Essential and inessential applications of ultraproducts

We are now going to list various applications of the ultraproduct construction, some of which we have already mentioned. We classify as "essential" all those applications which prove results which have not been obtained by other methods. Applications to results which can be proved without using the ultraproduct construction we classify as "inessential". Of course, it might always turn out that applications we now regard as essential prove later to be inessential.

INESSENTIAL APPLICATIONS

1. Compactness Theorem (for first order predicate logic): Morel, Scott and Tarski [28].

2. The Completeness of Real Closed Fields: Kochen [41].

An ordered field is said to be *real-closed* if every positive element is a square and each polynomial of odd degree has a zero in the field.

The proof that the theory of such fields is complete runs as follows. Suppose A and B are real closed fields of cardinal ω. Let D be a non-principal ultrafilter on ω then, assuming the Continuum Hypothesis, the ultraproducts D-prod A and D-prod B, considered as ordered sets, are η_1-sets. By a result of Erdös, Gillman and Hendrickson [32] any two real closed fields which are η_α-sets with respect to their ordering are isomorphic. Hence D-prod A is isomorphic to D-prod B, from which we may conclude that $A \equiv B$. By the Löwenheim-Skolem Theorem, this shows that any two real-closed fields are elementarily equivalent. It follows that the theory of such fields is complete.

The axioms for a real closed field can be written down recursively and so they form a recursive set. If a theory is recursively axiomatizable the theorems of the theory, that is the logical consequences of the axioms, form a recursively enumerable set. Similarly the refutable sentences, that is the negations of the theorems, also form a recursively enumerable set. But if a theory is complete every sentence is either a theorem or is refutable. Hence for a recursively axiomatizable complete theory the set of theorems and its complement are both recursively enumerable. It follows then that for such a theory the set of theorems forms a recursive set, that is, such a theory is decidable. In particular we may conclude that the theory of real closed fields is decidable. One can show that the use of the Continuum Hypotheses in this argument is inessential.

Ax and Kochen have also proved that the theory of a p-adic number field is decidable using similar methods [29, 30, 31].

3. The first inaccessible cardinal is not measurable.

A cardinal α is said to be *regular* if whenever $\gamma < \alpha$ and for each

$$\xi < \gamma, \beta_\xi < \alpha \quad \text{then} \quad \sum_{\xi < \gamma} \beta_\xi < \alpha .$$

A regular cardinal $\theta > \omega$ is said to be *inaccessible* if whenever $\beta < \theta$ then $2^\beta < \theta$.

A cardinal $\kappa > \omega$ is said to be *measurable* if there is a non-principal ultrafilter D on κ which is β-complete for each $\beta < \kappa$. We have the following result [3, 33, 34]:

THEOREM. The first inaccessible cardinal is not measurable.

We shall sketch the proof of this theorem.

Suppose that θ is the first inaccessible cardinal and that θ is in fact measurable. Then there is a non-principal ultrafilter D on θ which is β-complete for each $\beta<\theta$.

Consider the model $\Theta=\langle\theta, \leq\rangle$, that is the model whose domain is the set of ordinals less than θ with the natural ordering $\leq$. $\leq$ is of course a well-ordering of θ. Let D-prod $\Theta=\langle\theta', \leq'\rangle$. Since D is countably complete $\leq'$ is a well-ordering of θ'. We know that there is an elementary embedding d: $\Theta\to D$-prod Θ. The element $\langle 0, 1, 2, \ldots\rangle^{\sim}$ is not in $d(\theta)$ and is in fact bigger than any element of $d(\theta)$. Hence the ordinal of θ' with the ordering $\leq'$ is greater than θ. Hence there is some $\varphi\in\theta'$ such that if $\varphi'=\{\psi\in\theta':\psi\leq'\varphi\}$ then $\langle\varphi', \leq'\rangle$ has the ordinal θ. Since $\varphi\in D$-prod Θ, there is some function $f:\theta\to\theta$ such that $\varphi=f^{\sim}$.

Let $X_1=\{\xi<\theta:f(\xi)=0 \text{ or } f(\xi)=\omega\}$

$X_2=\{\xi<\theta:f(\xi) \text{ is accessible from below by cardinal sums}\}$

$X_3=\{\xi<\theta:f(\xi)\leq 2^{\eta} \text{ for some } \eta<f(\xi)\}$.

Since no $\xi<\theta$ is inaccessible $X_1\cup X_2\cup X_3=\theta$ and hence one of these sets is in D. But this implies that $f^{\sim}$ is not inaccessible which contradicts the choice of f.

This completes our outline of the proof.

4. The Axiom of Constructibility ($V=L$, in the sense of Gödel [20]) is inconsistent with the hypothesis that there is a measurable cardinal.

We sketch a proof of this result which is due to Scott [21]. We suppose that L is the universe of constructible sets and $\kappa>\omega$ is a measurable cardinal. Then there is some non-principal ultrafilter D on κ which is β-complete for each $\beta<\kappa$. Then we can show that $\langle L,\in\rangle$ is not isomorphic to D-prod$\langle L,\in\rangle$ but that if $D\in L$ then $\langle L,\in\rangle$ is isomorphic to D-prod $\langle L,\in\rangle$. Hence $D\in V-L$ which contradicts that $V=L$.

5. The existence of saturated models. (See our previous remarks above.)

ESSENTIAL APPLICATIONS

1. Given a model A we can ask whether there is an elementary extension B of A which has the same cardinal as A but which is not equal to A. In particular we shall say a cardinal α has the property P, $P(\alpha)$, if for all models A of cardinal α, there is a model B of cardinal α such that $\mathsf{A}\prec\mathsf{B}$, but $\mathsf{A}\neq\mathsf{B}$, and we shall ask which cardinals have the property P.

If the language with which we are dealing is countable then an easy application of the Löwenheim-Skolem theorem shows that all infinite cardinals have the property P. However for larger languages we shall not be able to use this theorem.

If $\alpha=\alpha^{\omega}$ then α has the property P. For suppose $\|\mathsf{A}\|=\alpha$ and let D be a non-principal ultrafilter on ω. Then D-prod A has cardinal β, where $\alpha\leq\beta\leq\alpha^{\omega}$, and hence $\beta=\alpha$. Clearly D-prod A is a proper elementary extension of A. The essential application of ultraproducts occurs here.

Conversely it has been shown by Rabin that, assuming the Generalized Continuum Hypothesis and that α is less than the first inaccessible cardinal, if $P(\alpha)$, then $\alpha=\alpha^{\omega}$. Also, it has been shown by Keisler that if α is less than the first measurable cardinal and $P(\alpha)$ then $\alpha=\alpha^{\omega}$. Keisler's proof uses limit ultrapowers but this use is not essential since the result has been obtained without them by Chang. For further references see [35, 36, 37].

The following similar problem has been raised by B. Jónsson. We shall say that a cardinal α has the property Q, $Q(\alpha)$, if there is a model A of cardinal α all of whose proper elementary sub-models are of smaller cardinal. The question then arises as to which cardinals have the property Q.

It is known that $Q(\omega_1)$ and, assuming that $V=L$, each cardinal $\alpha>\omega$ has the property Q. This last result is an unpublished result of Keisler's. Just recently (added Dec. 27, 1965), Erdös-Hajnal and (later) Chang have found independent proofs of the fact that every non-limit infinite cardinal has the property Q (GCH). Furthermore, it has been shown that exceedingly large limit cardinals (e.g. α is measurable, say) do not have the property Q. Hence the assumption that $V=L$ in Keisler's result appears to be justified.

2. *Pairs of cardinals*

Suppose that L is a language with models of the form $\mathsf{A}=\langle A,\mathscr{U},\ldots\rangle$ where $\mathscr{U}$ is a singulary relation on A. Corresponding to this relation the language L will have a singulary predicate letter P. We let U be the set of all those elements of A which have the propery $\mathscr{U}$, that is

$$U=\{a\in A:\mathsf{A}\models P[a]\}.$$

Now let Γ be a theory of the language L and let α and β be cardinals. We say that Γ *admits* the pair of cardinals $\langle\alpha,\beta\rangle$ if there is a model A

of Γ such that A has cardinal α and U has cardinal β. The question that naturally arises is: if Γ admits the pair $\langle\alpha, \beta\rangle$ which other pairs does it admit?

If β is a cardinal we define the cardinal $\beth_n(\beta)$ recursively by

$$\beth_0(\beta) = \beta \quad \text{and} \quad \beth_{n+1}(\beta) = 2^{\beth_n(\beta)}$$

(here $\beth$ is the second letter of the Hebrew alphabet, 'beth').

We have the following answers to the question we have just raised:

i) For each n there is some theory Γ such that if Γ admits $\langle\alpha, \beta\rangle$ then $\alpha \leq \beth_n(\beta)$ (R. M. Robinson, see [38]).

ii) If α and β are distinct infinite cardinals and Γ admits $\langle\alpha, \beta\rangle$ then Γ admits $\langle\omega_1, \omega\rangle$ (Vaught, see [24]).

iii) Assuming the Generalized Continuum Hypothesis, if Γ admits $\langle\alpha, \beta\rangle$ then Γ admits all pairs $\langle\gamma, \delta\rangle$ with $\beta \leq \delta \leq \gamma \leq \alpha$ (Chang and Keisler [39]). This result uses the ultrapower construction essentially.

iv) Assuming the Generalized Continuum Hypothesis, if α and β are distinct infinite cardinals and Γ admits $\langle\alpha, \beta\rangle$ then Γ admits $\langle\delta^+, \delta\rangle$ for each regular cardinal δ (Chang [51]).

v) If for each n Γ admits some pair $\langle\beth_n(\beta), \beta\rangle$ with $\beta \geq \omega$, then Γ admits all pairs $\langle\alpha, \beta\rangle$ with $\alpha \geq \beta \geq \omega$ (Vaught [40]).

The following questions are still unanswered:

a) Is iv) true with "singular" in place of "regular"?

b) Is iv) true without the assumption of the Generalized Continuum Hypothesis?

3. The Compactness Theorem for languages enriched with quantifiers of the form $\exists^{\geq\alpha}$, "there are at least α".

We say that the cardinal β is *small* relative to α if $\gamma_\tau < \alpha$ for $\tau < \beta$ implies $\prod_{\tau<\beta} \gamma_\tau < \alpha$. The following result about enriched languages with quantifiers of the form $\exists^{\geq\alpha}$ has been proved by Fuhrken [9].

THEOREM. If β is small relative to α and Σ is a set of sentences of this language of cardinal β which is finitely satisfiable then Σ is simultaneously satisfiable.

4. Throughout this section we shall assume that the Generalized Continuum Hypothesis is true.

If A is a model we let $G(\mathsf{A})$ be the group of all automorphisms of A. We consider the problem of whether there is some model A such that given any model B which is elementarily equivalent to A and whose cardinal is not bigger than that of A then the group $G(\mathsf{B})$ can be isomorphically embedded in $G(\mathsf{A})$.

The answer turns out to be "yes", and since we have already seen that saturated models have a certain universality property it is not surprising that the result is

THEOREM. Let A be a saturated model of cardinal α^+, then if $\mathsf{A} \equiv \mathsf{B}$ and $\|\mathsf{B}\| \leq \|\mathsf{A}\|$, $G(\mathsf{B})$ can be isomorphically embedded in $G(\mathsf{A})$.

PROOF. Let $\langle G_\xi : \xi < \gamma \rangle$ be a sequence consisting of all the automorphisms of B. Each G_ξ is a binary relation on $|\mathsf{B}|$. If we extend our language L to L_G by adjoining a sequence $\langle G_\xi : \xi < \gamma \rangle$ of binary predicate letters we can make statements about these relations. Indeed we can write down sentences of L_G which say that each G_ξ is an automorphism and which describe how the group $\{G_\xi : \xi < \gamma\}$ behaves.

Now let D be a good ultrafilter on α and consider the model D-prod $(\mathsf{B}, \langle G_\xi : \xi < \gamma \rangle) = (D\text{-prod } \mathsf{B}, \langle G'_\xi : \xi < \gamma \rangle)$, where each G'_ξ is a binary relation on the domain of D-prod B. Since the ultrapower is elementarily equivalent to $(\mathsf{B}, \langle G_\xi : \xi < \gamma \rangle)$ with respect to the language L_G, because of our remarks above about what we can say in L_G, it follows that each G'_ξ is an automorphism of D-prod B and that $\{G'_\xi : \xi < \gamma\}$ is in fact a group of automorphisms which is isomorphic to $\{G_\xi : \xi < \gamma\}$. But since D is a good ultrafilter D-prod B is saturated and hence isomorphic to A. Therefore $\{G_\xi : \xi < \gamma\}$ is isomorphic to a group of automorphisms of A. That is $G(\mathsf{B})$ can be isomorphically embedded in $G(\mathsf{A})$.

5. Let Γ be a complete theory of arithmetic, i.e. some complete extension of the usual axioms for formal arithmetic, and let A be a model of Γ. For each a $\in |\mathsf{A}|$ let $|a| = |\{b \in |\mathsf{A}| : b < a\}|$ where $<$ is the usual 'less than' relation of arithmetic. We let $N(\mathsf{A}) = \{|a| > \omega : a \in |\mathsf{A}|\}$.

Suppose now that C is a non-empty set of infinite cardinals with the following properties

i) The supremum of any non-empty set of cardinals from C is also in C.
ii) If $\alpha \in C$ then $|\{\beta \in C : \beta < \alpha\}| < \alpha$.

Then clearly the supremum of C exists and is in C, say it is γ.
We have the following result [50].

THEOREM. There is some model A of Γ which is γ^+-universal and of cardinal γ^+ such that $N(\mathsf{A}) = \{\alpha^+ : \alpha \in C\}$.

Here by γ^+-universal we mean that if $\mathsf{B} \equiv \mathsf{A}$ and $\|\mathsf{B}\| \leq \gamma^+$ then B is elementarily embeddable in A.

4. Generalizations and specializations of the ultraproduct construction

Three main generalizations of the ultraproduct construction have been considered in recent years. These are the ultralimit construction of Kochen [41] and two constructions due to Keisler, limit ultrapowers [36] and limit ultraproducts [10].

A number of specializations of this construction have also been investigated, among others by Cleave, Fraïssé, Keisler, MacDowell-Specker and Skolem.

Generalizations

We recall first a result due to Frayne. Let A and B be any two models, then $\mathsf{A} \equiv \mathsf{B}$ iff A can be elementarily embedded in some ultrapower of B (Frayne and Scott [42]). We have already remarked that Keisler has proved the stronger result that $\mathsf{A} \equiv \mathsf{B}$ if A and B have isomorphic ultrapowers, but that this result depends on the Generalized Continuum Hypothesis. Kochen's ultralimit construction enables us to obtain a similar result without the use of this hypothesis.

We have already seen that a model A is elementarily embeddable in an ultrapower D-prod A. Hence we can regard an ultrapower D-prod A, up to isomorphism, as an elementary extension of A. Suppose, in general, that $\{\mathsf{A}_n : n < \omega\}$ is a collection of relational systems and that for $m < n < \omega$, $\mathsf{A}_m \prec \mathsf{A}_n$. Then we can form the union $\mathsf{A}_\omega = \bigcup \mathsf{A}_n$ of this chain. By the result of Tarski that we mentioned earlier for each $n < \omega$, $\mathsf{A}_n \prec \mathsf{A}_\omega$ (Tarski and Vaught [2]). We call A_ω the *direct limit* of the chain $\{\mathsf{A}_n : n < \omega\}$. In particular if for each $n < \omega$, A_{n+1} is, up to isomorphism, an ultrapower of A_n, we call A_ω an *ultralimit* of A_0. Kochen's result is that given any two models A_0, B_0, $\mathsf{A}_0 \equiv \mathsf{B}_0$ iff there are chains $\{\mathsf{A}_n : n < \omega\}$, $\{\mathsf{B}_n : n < \omega\}$ such that for each $n < \omega$, A_{n+1}, B_{n+1} are, up to isomorphism, ultrapowers of A_n, B_n respectively, and such that the ultralimits of these chains are isomorphic [41].

We have already defined the notion of a pseudo-elementary class and we recall that we write $K \in \mathrm{PC}_\Delta$ if K is a pseudo-elementary class. Further we had the following results about elementary classes.

Ai) $\mathsf{B} \in \bigcap \{L : \mathsf{A} \in L \in \mathrm{EC}_\Delta\}$ iff B is elementarily embeddable in an ultrapower of A.

Aii) $\mathsf{B} \in \bigcap\{L : K \subseteq L \in \mathrm{EC}_\Delta\}$ iff B is elementarily embeddable in an ultraproduct of elements of K.

Using the limit ultrapower and ultraproduct constructions Keisler has obtained the following similar results about PC_Δ.

Bi) $\mathsf{B} \in \bigcap\{L : \mathsf{A} \in L \in \mathrm{PC}_\Delta\}$ iff B is isomorphic to a limit ultrapower of A.

Bii) $\mathsf{B} \in \bigcap\{L : K \subseteq L \in \mathrm{PC}_\Delta\}$ iff B is isomorphic to a limit ultraproduct of elements of K (Keisler [10, 36]).

We write $K \in \bigcap \mathrm{PC}_\Delta$ if $K = \bigcap_{i \in I} K_i$ with $K_i \in \mathrm{PC}_\Delta$. From the results above we can obtain the following characterization of $\bigcap \mathrm{PC}_\Delta$.

$K \in \bigcap \mathrm{PC}_\Delta$ iff K is closed under isomorphism and the formation of limit ultraproducts.

It remains an open question to give useful characterizations of PC and PC_Δ.

In this context we remark that an application of ultralimits is the following due to Park:

If $K \in \mathrm{EC}_\Delta$ then K is closed under descending chain intersections iff K is closed under ascending chain unions and the intersection of two elementary submodels [43].

As far as we can see at this moment this result of Park is another essential application of the ultraproduct construction.

Specializations

1. A non-standard model of arithmetic.

Let $\mathcal{N} = \langle \omega, +, \cdot, \leq, 0 \rangle$ be the standard model of arithmetic. Let $\mathscr{F}$ be the set of all arithmetically definable functions of one variable, so $\mathscr{F} \subseteq \omega^\omega$. Clearly $\mathscr{F}$ has the following properties:

i) every constant function is in $\mathscr{F}$,

ii) the identity function id, where for $n \in \omega$, $\mathrm{id}(n) = n$, is in $\mathscr{F}$,

iii) if $\Phi(v_0, v_1, \ldots, v_n)$ is a formula with free variables $v_0, \ldots, v_n$ and $f_1, \ldots, f_n$ are all functions in $\mathscr{F}$, then there is some function g in $\mathscr{F}$ such that

$$\mathcal{N} \models (\forall v)((\exists v_0) \Phi(v_0, f_1(v), \ldots, f_n(v)) \rightarrow \Phi(g(v), f_1(v), \ldots, f_n(v))).$$

If A is a relational system and $B \subseteq |\mathsf{A}|$, the restriction of A to B which we denote by $\mathsf{A}|B$ is the relational system whose domain is B and whose relations and functions are those of A restricted to B. Let D be a non-principal ultrafilter on ω. As usual we can define an equivalence relation $\sim$ on ω^ω by putting $f \sim g$ if $\{n \in \omega : f(n) = g(n)\} \in D$. Let $\mathscr{F}^\sim$ be the set of equivalence classes of elements of $\mathscr{F}$ under this relation. Let $\mathscr{N}' = (D\text{-prod } \mathscr{N}) | \mathscr{F}^\sim$.

We know that $\mathscr{N} \equiv D$-prod $\mathscr{N}$; this can be proved by induction on the number of logical symbols in the formulas of our language. An exactly similar proof shows that $\mathscr{N} \equiv \mathscr{N}'$ since condition iii) ensures that the induction step for the existential quantifier works. In fact we know that $\mathscr{N}$ is elementarily embeddable in D-prod $\mathscr{N}$; in an exactly similar way we know that $\mathscr{N}$ is elementarily embeddable in $\mathscr{N}'$, since $\mathscr{F}$ satisfies condition i).

It follows from condition ii) that $\mathscr{N}'$ is a proper elementary extension of $\mathscr{N}$. Let $\varphi : \mathscr{N} \to \mathscr{N}'$ be the elemetary embedding which maps each $n \in \omega$ onto $c_n^\sim$, where $c_n \subseteq \omega^\omega$ is the constant function which has the value n everywhere. Then $\mathrm{id}^\sim \in |\mathscr{N}'| - \varphi(|\mathscr{N}|)$. Indeed $\mathrm{id}^\sim$ is greater than any $c_n^\sim$ in $\varphi(|\mathscr{N}|)$ because $\mathrm{id}^\sim > c_n^\sim$ if $X_n = \{k \in \omega : \mathrm{id}(k) > c_n(k)\} \in D$. But $X_n = \{k \in \omega : k > n\}$ and hence is the complement of a finite set. Since D is non-principal it contains no finite sets and hence it contains X_n. Therefore $\mathrm{id}^\sim > c_n^\sim$.

Finally we notice that $\mathscr{N}'$ is countable since $\mathscr{F}$ and hence $\mathscr{F}^\sim$ is certainly countable. Thus we have constructed a countable non-standard model of arithmetic. This construction is due to Skolem in the 1930's (see e.g. [44]).

2. Realizing and omitting types.

A *type* is a set of formulas which contain just one free variable, the same variable for each formula. Sometimes we shall also insist that types are closed under the formation of conjunctions.

We shall denote a type T by $\{t(v)\}$, and a family of types U by $\mathscr{U}$. We say that A *realizes* T if there is some $a \in |\mathsf{A}|$ such that for all $t(v) \in T$, $\mathsf{A} \models t[a]$, i.e. if some element of $|\mathsf{A}|$ satisfies all the formulas of T.

We say that A *omits* U if for all $a \in |\mathsf{A}|$ there is some $u \in U$ such that not $\mathsf{A} \models u[a]$, i.e. if no element of $|\mathsf{A}|$ satisfies all the formulas of U.

We see that Skolem's construction described above gives a model which realizes a certain type, namely the type $T = \{n < v\}_{n \in \omega}$. We now give some similar results:

a) THEOREM (McDowell-Specker [45]). (We give a watered down version here.)

Every countable model of Peano arithmetic has a proper extension in which all the new elements occur after the old ones in the natural ordering. We call such an extension an *end extension.*

PROOF. Let $\mathsf{A}=\langle A,+,\cdot,\leq,0\rangle$ be a countable model of Peano arithmetic. We extend our language so that it contains a constant $\boldsymbol{a}$ for each $a\in A$.

The type that we want to realize is $T=\{\boldsymbol{a}<v\}_{a\in A}$. In order to get an end extension we want to omit the family of types $\mathscr{U}=\{U_a\}_{a\in A}$ where for each $a\in A$, $U_a=\{\neg(v<\boldsymbol{a}\rightarrow v=\boldsymbol{b})\}_{b\in A}$, that is $U_a=\{v<\boldsymbol{a}\wedge v\neq\boldsymbol{b}\}_{b\in A}$. Hence U_a is realized if there is some new element less than a. So each U_a is omitted if there are no new elements less than the original ones, i.e. if the extension we get is an end extension.

We let $\mathscr{F}$ be the set of all definable functions with parameters in A. Thus $\mathscr{F}\subseteq A^A$ and as in the Skolem construction before we have

i) the constant functions are in $\mathscr{F}$

ii) the identity function, id, is in $\mathscr{F}$

iii) if $\Phi(v_0, v_1,\ldots, v_n)$ is a formula with free variables $v_0,v_1,\ldots,v_n$ and $f_1,\ldots,f_n\in\mathscr{F}$, then there is some $g\in\mathscr{F}$ such that

$$(\forall v)((\exists v_0)\Phi(v_0,f_1(v),\ldots,f_n(v))\rightarrow\Phi(g(v),f_1(v),\ldots,f_n(v)))$$

holds in A under the interpretation of a for $\boldsymbol{a}$.

As in the previous construction these conditions are sufficient to ensure that we get a proper elementary extension which realizes the type T when we form an ultrapower of A. In order to ensure that at the same time we omit all the types of $\mathscr{U}$ we have to choose our ultrafilter D rather more carefully. We set about making this choice in the following way.

Since $\mathscr{F}$ and $\mathscr{U}$ are both countable so is their cartesian product $\mathscr{F}\times\mathscr{U}$. Hence we can arrange the elements of $\mathscr{F}\times\mathscr{U}$ in a sequence of order type ω.

We shall show that we can construct a sequence of sets $\langle X_n\rangle_{n\in\omega}$ such that

(i) $A=X_0\supseteq X_1\supseteq\ldots\supseteq X_n\supseteq\ldots$,

(ii) each X_n is *cofinal* in A, i.e. contains arbitrarily large elements of A,

(iii) if $\langle f,U_a\rangle$ is the n-th pair of the enumeration of $\mathscr{F}\times\mathscr{U}$ then there is some $b\in A$ such that for all $x\in X_{n+1}$,
$f(x)<a\Rightarrow f(x)=b$.

Suppose that we have constructed $X_0,\ldots,X_n$ which satisfy these conditions. Let $\langle f,U_a\rangle$ be the n-th pair in the enumeration of $\mathscr{F}\times\mathscr{U}$. Either $f(x)<a$ for only finitely many elements of X_n or for arbitrarily large elements of X_n. In the first case we take $X_{n+1}=\{x\in X_n : f(x)\geq a\}$. In the

second case f must be constant on a set which contains arbitrarily large elements of X_n. We take X_{n+1} to be this set, say $f(x)=b$ for $x \in X_{n+1}$. Then it is clear that $X_0,\dots,X_n,X_{n+1}$ also satisfy the three conditions above. Hence by induction we can find a sequence $\langle X_n \rangle_{n\in\omega}$ which satisfies the conditions (i)–(iii) above.

Let $E=\{X_n : n\in\omega\}$. Cleary E has the finite intersection property and so can be extended to an ultrafilter D on A. Let $\mathsf{A}'=(D\text{-prod } \mathsf{A})|\mathscr{F}^{\sim}$, then certainly A', is, up to isomorphism, a proper elementary extension of A which realizes the type T; we show that it also omits the types in $\mathscr{U}$.

Suppose $f^{\sim} \in |\mathsf{A}'|$ and $f^{\sim} < c_a^{\sim}$ for some $a \in A$. Then we show that $f^{\sim} = c_b^{\sim}$ for some b which is in A. That is the only elements less than $c_a^{\sim}$ are old elements.

Since $f^{\sim} < c_a^{\sim}$, $\{i\in A : f(i) < c_a(i)\} = \{i \in A : f(i) < a\} \in D$. Now for some $n<\omega$, $\langle f, U_a\rangle$ is the n-th pair of the enumeration: of $\mathscr{F}\times\mathscr{U}$. $X_{n+1} \cap \{i\in A : f(i)<a\}\in D$. But $X_{n+1} \cap \{i\in A : f(i)<a\} \subseteq \{i\in A : f(i)=b\} \in D$ and so $f^{\sim} = c_b^{\sim}$. This completes the proof.

Note: this theorem can also be proved without the hypothesis that A is countable.

(b) Let $\mathsf{A}=\langle A,\in\rangle$ be a countable model of Zermelo-Fraenkel set theory (ZF) together with the Axiom of Choice (AC), and let α be a cardinal in A. We say that an elementary extension of A leaves α *fixed* if it contains no new elements less than α.

THEOREM (Keisler). There is an elementary extension B of A which leaves α fixed but which realizes the type $T=\{\boldsymbol{\xi} < v < \boldsymbol{\alpha}^+\}_{\xi<\alpha^+}$, where $\boldsymbol{\xi}$, $\boldsymbol{\alpha}^+$ are the constants of our language corresponding to ξ, α^+ respectively. That is B contains a new element less than α^+ which is greater than any element of A which is less than α^+.

PROOF. We want to find an elementary extension of A which realizes the type $T=\{\boldsymbol{\xi}<v<\boldsymbol{\alpha}^+\}_{\xi<\alpha^+}$ but which omits the single type $U = \{v<\boldsymbol{\alpha} \wedge v \neq \boldsymbol{\xi}\}_{\xi<\alpha}$.

Let $\mathscr{F}$ be the set of all functions in A with domain α^+. Then $\mathscr{F}\subseteq A^{\alpha^+}$. Clearly $\mathscr{F}$ satisfies conditions (i) and (ii), and, since the Axiom of Choice holds in A, also condition (iii) of the theorem above.

If we take D to be an ultrafilter on α^+ it will therefore follow that $(D\text{-prod } \mathsf{A})\ |\mathscr{F}^{\sim}$ is, up to isomorphism, an elementary extension of A which realizes T. It is only necessary to choose D so that the type U is omitted. We do this as follows.

$\mathscr{F}$ is countable and hence can be enumerated as a sequence $\langle f_n \rangle_{n\in\omega}$. We show that we can construct a sequence of sets $\langle X_n \rangle_{n\in\omega}$ such that
(i) $\alpha^+ = X_0 \supseteq X_1 \supseteq \ldots \supseteq X_n \supseteq \ldots$,
(ii) each X_n is a set of cardinal α^+ in A,
(iii) for each $n\in\omega$ there is some $b\in A$ such that for all $x\in X_{n+1}$,
$f_n(x)<\alpha \Rightarrow f_n(x)=b$.

Suppose that we have constructed $X_0,\ldots,X_n$. Either there are α^+ (in A) elements of X_n for which $f_n(x)<\alpha$ or not. If there are then there is some subset of X_n of cardinal α^+ in A on which f_n has some constant value b. Let this subset be X_{n+1}. Otherwise there is a subset of X_n or cardinal α^+ in A on which $f_n \geq \alpha$. Let this set be X_{n+1}.

In either case $X_0,\ldots,X_n,X_{n+1}$ satisfies (i)–(iii). Hence we can find a sequence $\langle X_n \rangle_{n\in\omega}$ satisfying these conditions. Let $E=\{X_n : n\in\omega\}$. Then exactly as in the previous theorem E has the finite intersection property and hence can be extended to an ultrafilter D on α^+. It is easily seen that $\mathsf{B}=(D\text{-prod }\mathsf{A})|\mathscr{F}^{\sim}$ is, up to isomorphism, the desired elementary extension of A.

In a similar way the following result can be obtained.

THEOREM (Keisler). If A is a countable model of ZF together with $V=L$ then there is a proper elementary extension of A which leaves all the ordinals of A fixed, i.e. a proper elementary end extension.

Morley has improved these last results by showing that the assumptions AC and $V=L$ can be dropped. We shall deal with these improvements in the next section.

Incidentally, we remark that using ideas contained in the last two results, Keisler has improved the two cardinal theorem of Vaught (i.e. if Γ admits $\langle \alpha,\beta \rangle$ with $\alpha\neq\beta$ then Γ admits $\langle \omega_1,\omega \rangle$). Using this improvement Keisler has obtained a simple proof of the

UPWARD MORLEY THEOREM. If Γ is ω_1-categorical, Γ is β-categorical for all $\beta\geq\omega_1$. (Γ is said to be α-categorical if all models of Γ of cardinal α are isomorphic.)

5. Refinements of the completeness theorem

We shall see in this section how some of the earlier results in 4 can be proved without the (specialized) ultraproduct construction.

Let L be a countable language. For simplicity we shall assume that L

has no function or constant symbols and has just one binary predicate letter P. Let the individual variables of L be $\{v_n : n \in \omega\}$.

We have the following fundamental result:

THE EXTENDED COMPLETENESS THEOREM. If Γ is a consistent set of sentences of L then Γ has a model.

PROOF. Let F be the set of all formulas of L. We define the relation $\sim$ on F by putting $\varphi \sim \psi$ if $\Gamma \vdash \varphi \leftrightarrow \psi$. $\sim$ is clearly an equivalence relation on F. Let $\varphi^{\sim}$ be the equivalence class to which an element $\varphi \in F$ belongs and let B be the set of all equivalence classes of elements of F.

We define the relation $\leq$ on B by putting

$$\varphi^{\sim} \leq \psi^{\sim} \Leftrightarrow \Gamma \vdash \varphi \rightarrow \psi ;$$

$\leq$ is easily seen to be a well defined partial ordering of B. With this partial ordering B is in fact a Boolean Algebra, B_{Γ}. The meet and join operators of this Boolean Algebra $\bigwedge$, $\bigvee$ satisfy

$$\varphi^{\sim} \bigwedge \psi^{\sim} = (\varphi \wedge \psi)^{\sim}, \quad \varphi^{\sim} \bigvee \psi^{\sim} = (\varphi \vee \psi)^{\sim} .$$

The complement operator $*$ satisfies

$$\varphi^{\sim} * = (\neg \varphi)^{\sim}$$

the unit element 1 is given by

$$\varphi^{\sim} = 1 \Leftrightarrow \Gamma \vdash \varphi$$

and the zero element 0 by

$$\varphi^{\sim} = 0 \Leftrightarrow \Gamma \vdash \neg \varphi .$$

All these facts can easily be checked. Since Γ is consistent B_{Γ} has at least two elements.

Suppose that φ is a formula in F. Let $\varphi(v_k/v_p)$ be the formula obtained from φ by first replacing all bound occurrences of v_p in φ by v_j, the first variable of the sequence $\langle v_n : n \in \omega \rangle$ not already occurring in φ, and then replacing all free occurrences of v_k by v_p. Then

$$\bigvee_{p \in \omega} \varphi(v_k/v_p)^{\sim} = (\exists v_k) \varphi(v_k)^{\sim} .$$

Suppose that we have a collection of joins

$$\{\bigvee_{j\in J_i} y_{ji} = z_i : i\in I\}$$

where the y_{ji} and z_i are elements of B_Γ. We say that an ultrafilter D in B_Γ *preserves* these joins if for each $i\in I$

$$z_i \in D \quad \text{iff for some} \quad j\in J_i,\, y_{ji}\in D\,.$$

We use the following

LEMMA. In any Boolean Algebra B, given a countable number of joins

$$\{\bigvee_{j\in J_n} y_{jn} = z_n : n\in\omega\}$$

there is an ultrafilter D in B which preserves them all.

For a proof, due to Tarski, of this lemma see [46].

Since F is countable there are only countably many joins

$$\bigvee_{p\in\omega} \varphi(v_k|v_p)^\sim = (\exists\, v_k)\,\varphi(v_k)^\sim$$

hence there are ultrafilters D in B_Γ which preserve them all. We call such an ultrafilter a Q-ultrafilter. Let D be such an ultrafilter.

We now define a model A_D of Γ.

If v_i, v_j are variables we put $v_i \sim v_j$ iff $(v_i \equiv v_j)^\sim \in D$. This defines an equivalence relation on $V=\{v_n : n\in\omega\}$. Let the equivalence class to which v_i belongs be $v_i^\sim$. Let $A=\{v_i^\sim : i\in\omega\}$. We define the relation R on A by

$$\langle v_i^\sim, v_j^\sim\rangle \in R \quad \text{iff} \quad P(v_i, v_j)^\sim \in D\,.$$

Clearly this relation is well defined. We let A_D be the model $\langle A, R\rangle$, and we claim that A_D is a model of Γ.

In fact we have for any formula $\varphi(v_0,\dots,v_n)$ with free variables $v_0,\dots,v_n$

$$\mathsf{A}_D \models \varphi[v_{i_0}^\sim, \dots, v_{i_n}^\sim] \quad \text{iff} \quad \varphi(v_{i_0}, \dots, v_{i_n})^\sim \in D\,.$$

We can prove this by induction on the number of logical symbols in φ. The only non-trivial step is that for the existential quantifier and that works since D is a Q-ultrafilter.

In particular for a sentence σ

$$\mathsf{A}_D \models \sigma \quad \text{iff} \quad \sigma^\sim \in D\,.$$

Now for any $\sigma \in \Gamma$, $\Gamma \vdash \sigma$, hence $\sigma^{\sim} = 1 \in D$. So $\mathsf{A}_D \models \sigma$. Thus A_D is a model of Γ and the theorem is proved.

This theorem is due to, among others, Gödel, Malcev, Henkin, and Hasenjäger. The proof we have given here is due to Rasiowa and Sikorski [47] with improvements noted by Tarski and Feferman.

In the above proof we took D to be any Q-ultrafilter in B_Γ and we saw that this was sufficient to ensure that A_D was a model of Γ. If we had been more particular in our choice of D we could have arranged for A_D to have other properties as well as being a model of Γ. We shall be doing this to obtain the next result.

THEOREM (Engeler [48]). Let Γ be a complete theory of a countable language and U a type. Then the following two conditions are equivalent
i) Γ has a model which omits U,
ii) for each formula $\varphi(v)$ of L there is some $u(v) \in U$ such that

$$\Gamma \vdash (\exists v)\varphi(v) \rightarrow (\exists v)(\varphi(v) \wedge \neg u(v)).$$

PROOF. i)$\Rightarrow$ii). This is an immediate consequence of Γ being complete. Since if ii) does not hold then for all $u(v)$ in U

$$\Gamma \vdash (\exists v)\varphi(v) \wedge \neg(\exists v)(\varphi(v) \wedge \neg u(v)),$$

hence with $v = v$ as $\varphi(v)$

$$\Gamma \vdash \neg(\exists v)(v = v \wedge \neg u(v))$$

but $\Gamma \vdash (\forall v)(v = v)$ and so $\Gamma \vdash (\forall v)u(v)$. But then every model of Γ realizes U and this contradicts i).

ii)$\Rightarrow$i). Suppose ii) is true. We form the Boolean Algebra B_Γ as in the proof of the previous theorem. We show that in B_Γ for each variable v

$$\bigvee_{u \in U} \neg u(v)^{\sim} = 1. \qquad [\Xi]$$

Suppose that for some v, $[\Xi]$ does not hold. Then there is some formula φ such that for each $u \in U$,

$$\neg u(v)^{\sim} \leq \varphi^{\sim} < 1$$

and hence

$$\Gamma \vdash \neg u(v) \rightarrow \varphi$$

whence

$$\Gamma \vdash (\forall v)(\neg \varphi \rightarrow u(v)).$$

We may suppose that v is the only free variable in φ.
Since Γ is complete and $\varphi^{\sim} \neq 1$, $\Gamma \vdash (\exists v) \neg \varphi(v)$.
Therefore by ii), for some $u \in U$

$$\Gamma \vdash (\exists v)(\neg \varphi \wedge \neg u(v)),$$

i.e.

$$\Gamma \vdash \neg (\forall v)(\neg \varphi \rightarrow u(v)),$$

which is a contradiction. Thus $[\Xi]$ holds for each variable v.

There are only countably many such joins $[\Xi]$. Hence by the lemma we had before we can find a Q-ultrafilter D which preserves all the joins $[\Xi]$. We construct the model A_D as before. Since D is a Q-ultrafilter A_D is a model of Γ. Since D preserves the joins $[\Xi]$ for each variable v there is some $u \in U$ such that $\neg u(v)^{\sim} \in D$ and hence such that $\mathsf{A}_D \models \neg u[v^{\sim}]$. Thus A_D omits U.

Note that this theorem is false for uncountable languages and non-complete Γ. Essentially the same result was proved also by Svenonius [49], Ehrenfeucht, Ryll-Nardzewski, and Vaught using the Henkin completeness proof construction.

The next result deals with the case where Γ is not complete.

THEOREM. Let Γ be a set of sentences of a countable language and U some type. Then the following two conditions are equivalent:

i) For all sentences σ, if $\Gamma \cup \{\sigma\}$ is consistent then $\Gamma \cup \{\sigma\}$ has a model which omits U.

ii) For all sentences σ, if $\Gamma \cup \{\sigma\}$ is consistent then for each formula $\varphi(v)$ there is some $u(v)$ in U such that

$$\Gamma \cup \{\sigma\} \cup \{(\exists v)\varphi(v) \rightarrow (\exists v)(\varphi(v) \wedge \neg u(v))\}$$

is also consistent.

PROOF. As in the previous theorem i) $\Rightarrow$ ii) is easy.

Suppose then that ii) holds. Let σ be a sentence such that $\Gamma \cup \{\sigma\}$ is consistent. We shall show that $\Gamma \cup \{\sigma\}$ has a model which omits U.

Let $\{\varphi_n : n \in \omega\}$ be an enumeration of the formulas of L. We shall construct a sequence $\langle u_n(v) : n \in \omega \rangle$ of formulas of U, such that, if, for each $n \in \omega$, $\sigma_n = (\exists v)\varphi_n(v) \rightarrow (\exists v)(\varphi_n(v) \wedge \neg u_n(v))$ then $\Gamma \cup \{\sigma\} \cup \{\sigma_n : n \in \omega\}$ is consistent.

It follows immediately from ii) that there is some $u_0(v)$ in U such that

$\Gamma \cup \{\sigma\} \cup \{\sigma_0\}$ is consistent. Suppose that we have constructed a sequence $\langle u_n : n<k \rangle$ such that $\Gamma \cup \{\sigma\} \cup \{\sigma_n : n<k\}$ is consistent. Then $\Gamma \cup \{\tau\}$ is consistent, where $\tau = \sigma \wedge \sigma_1 \wedge \ldots \wedge \sigma_{k-1}$. Hence by ii) there is some $u_k(v)$ in U such that $\Gamma \cup \{\tau\} \cup \{\sigma_k\}$ is consistent. Hence $\Gamma \cup \{\sigma\} \cup \{\sigma_n : n \leq k\}$ is consistent. Therefore by induction we can define a sequence $\langle u_n(v) : n \in \omega \rangle$ such that, for each $k<\omega$, $\Gamma \cup \{\sigma\} \cup \{\sigma_n : n \leq k\}$ is consistent. It follows that $\Delta = \Gamma \cup \{\sigma\} \cup \{\sigma_n : n \in \omega\}$ is consistent since each finite subset of it is.

We can therefore deduce from Lindenbaum's Theorem that Δ has a complete consistent extension Σ. By the way that Σ has been constructed, for each formula φ of L there is some $u(v)$ in U such that

$$\sigma_\varphi = (\exists v)\, \varphi(v) \rightarrow (\exists v)(\varphi(v) \wedge \neg u(v)) \in \Sigma$$

and *a fortiori* that $\Sigma \vdash \sigma_\varphi$.

Hence, from the previous theorem, Σ has a model A which omits U. Since $\Gamma \cup \{\sigma\} \subseteq \Delta \subseteq \Sigma$, A is a model of $\Gamma \cup \{\sigma\}$ which omits U.

This concludes the proof.

The following theorem is an unpublished result of Keisler which was motivated by a proof due to Morley and slightly simplified by Chang.

If Γ is a complete theory and T is a type we call a formula $\theta(v)$ a *T-formula* if $\Gamma \cup T \cup \{\theta(v)\}$ is consistent.

THEOREM. If Γ is a complete theory of a countable language, T is a type which is closed under conjunction and U is another type the following two conditions are equivalent.

i) For each T-formula $\theta(v)$ there is a model A of Γ which realizes $T \cup \{\theta(v)\}$ and omits U.

ii) For each T-formula $\theta(v)$ and each formula $\varphi(v,w)$ there is a formula $u(w) \in U$ such that for any $t(v) \in T$

$$\Gamma \vdash (\exists v)(t(v) \wedge \theta(v) \wedge ((\exists w)\, \varphi(v,w) \rightarrow (\exists w)(\varphi(v,w) \wedge \neg u(w)))).$$

PROOF. Again the implication i) $\Rightarrow$ ii) is easy.

Now suppose that ii) holds. We adjoin a constant c to the language L to obtain the language L_1.

Let $T_c = \{\theta(c) : \theta$ is a formula in $T\}$. The set of conditions $\Gamma \cup T_c$ is not necessarily complete in the language L_1. We can easily show that condition ii) implies condition ii) of the previous theorem phrased in the language L_1. Whence $\Gamma \cup T_c$ will have a model omitting U. This model obviously realizes T.

This theorem shows that some of the earlier results obtained by specializations of the ultraproduct construction can be obtained directly from the completeness theorem. This last theorem can easily be generalized to the case where $\mathscr{U}$ is a countable family of types U and each U is to be omitted. As an example of an application consider a countable model $\mathsf{A}=\langle A,\in\rangle$ of ZF. Let α be a cardinal in A. Put $T=\{\xi<v<\boldsymbol{a}^+\}_{\xi<\alpha^+}$ and $U=\{\neg(v<\boldsymbol{a}\rightarrow v=\boldsymbol{\eta})\}_{\eta<\alpha}$.

Then we can find a proper elementary extension of A which realizes T and omits U. This follows because the a-elementary diagram of A is a complete theory Γ and we can check that Γ satisfies the second condition of the previous theorem. Hence Γ has a model which leaves α fixed but which increases α^+.

Extensions of all of these results to non-countable languages can all be given in some form (for a start see the abstract [14]), however none of them so far lead to any significant applications. For instance, for non-countable models of ZF (or ZF+AC or ZF+$V=L$) it is not known whether there exist proper elementary end extensions.

These lecture notes would not have appeared were it not for the efforts of Ian Harrison and Alan Slomson, to whom I wish to extend my thanks. All the credit for these notes should go to them. Among the debits, I think that many references given during the lectures and in the notes are not as complete and accurate as can be desired; I would like to take this opportunity to apologise for any omissions and possible errors. Special thanks are due to H. J. Keisler who made available to me a preprint of his excellent survey article [50] and as the reader will notice, a large part of these lectures is organised along the lines of that survey. Finally, I wish to give thanks to the organisers of the Leicester Summer School for making these lectures possible and, in particular, to the editor of this volume John Crossley, without whose unstinting effort and encouragement the preparation and publication of these notes would not have been possible.

References

[1] E. Mendelson, Introduction to Mathematical Logic (Van Nostrand, Princeton, 1964).

[2] A. Tarski and R. Vaught, Arithmetical Extensions of Relational Systems, Comp. Math. **13** (1957) 81–102.

[3] W. Hanf, Imcompleteness in Languages with Infinitely Long Expressions, Fund. Math. **53** (1964) 309–323.

[4] C. Karp, Languages with Expressions of Infinite Length (North-Holland Publ. Co., Amsterdam, 1964).

[5] L. Henkin, Some Remarks on Infinitely Long Formulas, in Infinitistic Methods, Proc. Symp. on the Foundations of Mathematics, Warsaw, September 1959 (Pergamon Press, Oxford and Panstowe Wydawnictwo Naukowe, Warsaw, 1961) 167–183.

[6] A. Tarski, Some Model Theoretic Results concerning Weak Second Order Logic, Notices Amer. Math. Soc. **6** (1958) 673.

[7] W. Craig, Relative Characterizability and Generalized Existential Quantifiers, Notices Amer. Math. Soc. **9** (1962) 153.

[8] W. Craig and W. Hanf, On Relative Characterizability in a Language, Notices Amer. Math. Soc. **9** (1962) 152–153.

[9] G. Fuhrken, Skolem-type Normal Forms for First Order Languages with a Generalized Quantifier, Fund. Math. **54** (1964) 291–302.

[10] H. J. Keisler, Limit Ultraproducts, J. Symbolic Logic **30** (1965) 212–234.

[11] R. Vaught, The Completeness of Logic with the added quantifier 'there are uncountably many', Fund. Math. **54** (1964) 303–304.

[12] E. W. Beth, On Padoa's Method in the Theory of Definition, Indag. Math. **56** (1953) 330–339.

[13] C. C. Chang, Some New Results in Definability, Bull. Amer. Math. Soc. **70** (1964) 808–813.

[14] C. C. Chang, On the Formula 'there exists x such that $f(x)$ for all $f \in F$', Notices Amer. Math. Soc. **11** (1964) 587.

[15] M. Morley, Categoricity in Power, Trans. Amer. Math. Soc. **114** (1965) 514–538.

[16] L. Henkin, Some Interconnections between Modern Algebra and Mathematical Logic, Trans. Amer. Math. Soc. **74** (1953) 410–427.

[17] A. Robinson, Introduction to Model Theory and to the Metamathematics of Algebra (North-Holland Publ. Co., Amsterdam, 1963).

[18] J. Łoš, Quelque remarques, théorèmes et problèmes sur les classes définissable d'algèbres, in: Mathematical Interpretations of Formal Systems (North-Holland Publ. Co., Amsterdam, 1955) 98–113.

[19] T. Frayne, A. Morel and D. Scott, Reduced Direct Products, Fund. Math. **51** (1962) 195–228.

[20] K. Gödel, The Consistency of the Axiom of Choice and of the Generalized Continuum Hypothesis with the Axioms of Set Theory (Princeton University Press, Princeton, 1940; latest reprint 1964).

[21] D. Scott, Measurable Cardinals and Constructible Sets, Bull. Acad. Polon. Sci. Ser. Sci. Math. Astronom. Phys. **9** (1961) 521–524.

[22] H. J. Keisler, On Cardinalities of Ultraproducts, Bull. Amer. Math. Soc. **70** (1964) 644–647.

[23] F. Hausdorff, Grundzüge der Mengenlehre (Leipzig, 1914; reprinted by Chelsea Books, New York, 1949).

[24] M. Morley and R. Vaught, Homogeneous Universal Models, Math. Scand. **11** (1962) 37–57.

[25] H. J. Keisler, Ultraproducts and Saturated Models, Indag. Math. **26** (1964) 178–186.

[26] H. J. Keisler, Good Ideals in Fields of Sets, Ann. of Math. **79** (1964) 338–359.

[27] H. J. Keisler, Ultraproducts and Elementary Classes, Indag. Math. **23** (1961) 477–495.

[28] A. Morel, D. Scott and A. Tarski, Reduced Products and the Compactness Theorem, Notices Amer. Math. Soc. **5** (1958) 674–675.

[29] J. Ax and S. Kochen, Diophantine Problems over Local Fields I, Amer. J. Math. **57** (1965) 605–630.

[30] J. Ax and S. Kochen, Diophantine Problems over Local Fields II, A Complete Set of Axioms for *p*-adic Number Theory, Amer. J. Math. **57** (1965) 631–648.

[31] J. Ax and S. Kochen, Diophantine Problems over Local Fields III, to appear in Ann. of Math. (1967).

[32] P. Erdös, L. Gillman and M. Hendrickson, An Isomorphism Theorem for Real Closed Fields, Ann. of Math. **61** (1955) 542–554.

[33] H. J. Keisler, Some Applications of the Theory of Models to Set Theory, in: Logic, Methodology and Philosophy of Science, eds. E. Nagel, P. Suppes and A. Tarski (Stanford University Press, Stanford, 1962) 80–86.

[34] A. Tarski, Some Problems and Results revelant to the Foundations of Set Theory, in: Logic, Methodology and Philosophy of Science, eds. E. Nagel, P. Suppes and A. Tarski (Stanford University Press, Stanford, 1962) 125–135.

[35] C. C. Chang, A Simple Proof of the Rabin-Keisler Theorem, Bull. Amer. Math. Soc. **71** (1965) 642–643.

[36] H. J. Keisler, Limit Ultrapowers, Trans. Amer. Math. Soc. **107** (1963) 382–408.

[37] M. Rabin, Arithmetical Extensions with Prescribed Cardinality, Indag. Math. **21** (1959) 439–446.

[38] R. Vaught, Models of Complete Theories, Bull. Amer. Math. Soc. **69** (1963) 299–313.

[39] C. C. Chang and H. J. Keisler, Applications of Ultraproducts of Pairs of Cardinals to the Theory of Models, Pacific J. of Math. **12** (1962) 835–845.

[40] R. Vaught, A Löwenheim-Skolem Theorem for Cardinals far apart, in: Proc. of the Model Theory Symposium, Berkeley, 1963 (1965) 390–401.

[41] S. Kochen, Ultraproducts in the Theory of Models, Ann. of Math. **74** (1961) 221–261.

[42] T. Frayne and D. Scott, Model Theoretic Properties of Ultraproducts, Notices Amer. Math. Soc. **5** (1958) 675.

[43] D. Park, Ph. D. Thesis, M.I.T. (1964).

[44] T. Skolem, Peano's Axioms and Models of Arithmetic, in: Mathematical Interpretations of Formal Systems (North-Holland Publ. Co., Amsterdam, 1955).

[45] R. MacDowell and E. Specker, Modelle der Arithmetik, in Infinitistic Methods, Proc. Symp. on the Foundations of Mathematics, Warsaw, September 1959 (Pergamon Press, Oxford and Panstowe Wydawnictwo Naukowe, Warsaw, 1961) 257–263.

[46] S. Feferman, Review of Rasiowa and Sikorski [47], J. Symbolic Logic **19** (1952) 72.

[47] H. Rasiowa and R. Sikorski, A Proof of the Completeness Theorem of Gödel, Fund. Math. **37** (1950) 193–200.

[48] E. Engeler, Unendliche Formeln in der Modelltheorie, Zeitschr. f. Math. Logik und Grundlagen d. Math. **7** (1961) 154–160.

[49] L. Svenonius, On Minimal Models of First Order Systems, Theoria **26** (1960) 44–52.

[50] H. J. Keisler, A Survey of Ultraproducts, in: Proc. of the 1964 Intern. Congress for Logic, Methodology and Philosophy of Science, Jerusalem, Israel, ed. Y. Bar-Hillel (North-Holland Publ. Co., Amsterdam, 1965) 112–126.

[51] C. C. Chang, A Note on the two Cardinal Problem, Proc. Amer. Math. Soc. **16** (1965) 1148–1155.

[52] D. Scott, Logic with Denumerably Long Formulas and Finite Strings of Quantifiers, in: Proc. of Model Theory Symposium, Berkeley 1963 (1965) 329–341.

[53] M. Morley, Omitting Classes of Elements, in: Proc. of Model Theory Symposium, Berkeley 1963 (1965) 265–273.

[54] C. C. Chang, Descendingly Incomplete Ultrafilters, Trans. Amer. Math. Soc. **126** (1967) 108–118.

UNIFORM EXTENSION OPERATORS FOR MODELS AND THEIR APPLICATIONS*

HAIM GAIFMAN
Hebrew University, Jerusalem, Israel

1. Introduction

A uniform extension operator is one which operates on models and yields, for every model in its domain, a proper elementary extension of it. The extensions are constructed in a "uniform way" with respect to all models in the domain of the operator, an expression which will be given a precise definition in 3. At this point let us consider any infinite cardinal α and a fixed non-principal ultrafilter $\mathscr{F}$ in the algebra of all subsets of α. The operator which extends every model M to its ultrapower $M^\alpha/\mathscr{F}$ is such an operator. Let $f(\ldots,\ldots)$ be a function symbol with a sequence of α empty places and let us agree to write $f(x_0, x_1, \ldots, x_\lambda, \ldots)$ instead of the sequence $\langle x_0, x_1, \ldots, x_\lambda, \ldots\rangle_{\lambda<\alpha}$. Then $M^\alpha/\mathscr{F}$ can be described as the model obtained by adding to M all terms of the form $f(x_0, x_1, \ldots, x_\lambda, \ldots)$, where the x_λ's are members of M, and defining the relations (including the equality relation, if the language of M contains it) in the usual way.

In general a uniform extension operator will be based on a fixed set, Ω of function symbols and, for every model in its domain, the elements added to the model will be just all the terms obtained by sticking its members into the empty places of the function symbols.

If all the function symbols in Ω have finitely many places then the operator is said to be a local extension operator. In this case every added element depends, so to speak, on finitely many of the original elements.

*) The results described here were obtained while the author was working under U.S. Office of Naval Research, Information Systems branch contract N62558–3882, NR049–130.

Sometimes the function symbols will denote Skolem functions, but it need not be always so.

Let us now give a very simple example of a local extension operator.

Consider the theory of a dense linear ordering without first and last elements. Operate on models of this theory in the following way. Given $\langle A, <\rangle$ extend it by forming a disjoint replica of it and placing the replica after the original system. In this case the operator is based on a one-place function symbol, $f(\ )$, which is used in forming the replica. If $M=\langle A, <\rangle$ then $O(M)=\langle A_1, <_1\rangle$ where $A_1=A\cup\{f(x)|x\in A\}$ and $<_1$ is defined by: If $a, b\in A$ and $a<b$ then $a<_1 b$ and $f(a)<_1 f(b)$, and $a<_1 f(b)$ for all $a, b\in A$. It is easily proven that M is an elementary submodel of $O(M)$. Notice, however, that the sets A and $\{f(x)|x\in A\}$ should be disjoint. Consequently no member of A should be of the form $f(a)$ where $a\in A$. This is no serious handicap since f can be chosen to be any one-place function symbol. For a fixed f, the domain of O will be restricted to those models in whose elements f does not occur.

Another simple example concerning the same theory is of an operator based on an infinite set of zero-place function symbols, where a zero-place function symbol is regarded as a constant. This set is ordered by a fixed dense linear ordering, without first or last elements. Given any model of the theory extend it by placing this fixed system after it. Again one should require that none of the symbols on which the operator is based occurs in the models of its domain.

Uniform extension operators are used to construct models with "nice" structural properties. Thus, one has a very simple proof of the Ehrenfeucht-Mostowski theorem concerning the existence of models with many automorphisms [1]. This theorem states that for every theory having infinite models and every ordered set there is a model of the theory whose set of elements contains the given set, so that every automorphism of the ordered set can be extended to an automorphism of the model. The original proof uses Ramsey's theorem. Here we give a very simple construction of the required model, using iterations of uniform extension operators. Once the existence of the operator is established the building of the model is fully constructive and one sees clearly what the automorphisms are. The existence of the uniform extension operator, as well as that of a local extension operator, boils down to the existence of an ultrafilter in the algebra of all subsets of the natural numbers.

Other results which are presented here concern models of Peano's arithmetic. It was shown by Macdowell and Specker [2], that every model of Peano's arithmetic (by which we mean the usual first order theory) posseses an elementary end extension, where an end extension is one in which every new element is bigger, in the natural ordering, than every old element. It was shown later by the author [3] that every model of Peano's arithmetic possesses an end extension which is also minimal, i.e. does not properly include any other proper elementary extension of the model. The proof of this result is not presented here, but use is made of the fact that such a minimal end extension is achieved by means of a local extension operator. By iterating this operator the following is proved: For every model, M, of Peano's arithmetic, and every ordered set, K, there exists an end-extension of M, say N, in which the added segment of elements embeds K, so that every automorphism of K has a unique extension to an automorphism of N which leaves every point of M fixed. Moreover the automorphisms of N over M are exactly those which are induced in this manner by the automorphisms of K. A weaker result of this kind which was unknown to the author was proved earlier by Ehrenfeucht [4]. It states that for every ordered set K there is a model, containing K as a subset, whose automorphisms are exactly those induced by the automorphisms of K.

Further results concerning the structure of the models obtained by iterating minimal end extension operators, as well as the existence of 2^α non-isomorphic models which embed, in the above mentioned way, any fixed order type of cardinality α, are proved as well.

As we said, iterations of uniform extension operators play the central part in the method presented here. It is of major importance that for every uniform extension operator O one can define in a natural way O^η (the ηth power of O) not only where η is a natural number or an ordinal, but also where η is any order type.

2. Conventions and notations

"Models" and "relational systems" are synonymous; what is meant is a system of the form $\langle A; R_0, \ldots, R_i, \ldots, c_0, \ldots, c_j, \ldots \rangle$ where $R_0, \ldots, R_i, \ldots$ are finitary relations over A and $c_0, \ldots, c_j, \ldots$ are distinguished members of A. There is no restriction on the numbers of relations and distinguished elements.

If $M = \langle A; R_0, \ldots, R_i, \ldots, c_0, \ldots, c_j, \ldots \rangle$ then $|M| = A$.

The language of M is the first order language whose predicates and individual constants are the names of the relations and distinguished members of M.

If the language of M contains an equality symbol then we shall assume that, unless otherwise stated, this equality is interpreted in M as an equivalence relation which is also a congruence relation with respect to the other relations of the model. This is done for the technical convenience of the presentation and makes, of course, no difference. We could have interpreted equality as the identity relation on the members of the model and presented the method with the same results. If $a, b \in |M|$ then "$M \models a \approx b$" means that the equality relation of this model holds between a and b. If it is clear which model is meant we shall write just $a \approx b$.

A submodel M' of M is a model in which $|M'| \subseteq |M|$, all distinguished members belong to M', and the relations are just the restrictions to M' of the corresponding relations of M. M' is a proper submodel if there is an element $a \in |M|$ so that $a \not\approx b$ for all $b \in |M'|$.

If $\varphi(v_1, \ldots, v_n)$ is a formula in the language of M and $a_1, \ldots, a_n \in M$ then "$M \models \varphi(a_1, \ldots, a_n)$" means that $\varphi(a_1, \ldots, a_n)$ is satisfied in M.

"$M \prec N$" means that M is an elementary submodel of N. We shall speak also of elementary extensions as well as proper elementary submodels, or extensions. The meanings are self-explanatory.

"$T \vdash \varphi$" means that φ is a theorem in the theory T.

We shall make ample use of function symbols with any number of arguments. These are extralinguistic symbols, with each one of which is associated an indexed set of empty places. For notational convenience we shall assume that the empty places are well-ordered, although this is not essential, and we shall write the function symbol as $f(\ldots, \ldots)$, or simply f. If $a_0, a_1, \ldots, a_\lambda, \ldots$ are individuals then $f(a_0, a_1, \ldots, a_\lambda, \ldots)$ (i.e. the term obtained by putting these individuals in the empty places of the function symbol) is regarded as an individual. We include also function symbols with 0 places and these are to be regarded as individuals.

One may form composite function symbols by placing in some of the empty places of a given function symbol other function symbols, thus getting symbols such as $f(\dots g(\dots,\dots),\dots)$ etc. Composition of function symbols is assumed to be associative, thus $f[\dots, g(\dots, h(\dots,\dots),\dots),\dots]$ is identified with $f(\dots, g[\dots, h(\dots,\dots),\dots],\dots)$, where in the first case g is composed with h, and f is composed with the resulting symbol, and in the second case the order of the operations is reversed.

We define "occurs in" by saying that every function symbol occurs in itself and that f and g, as well as any function symbol which occurs in them, occur in $f(\dots, g(\dots,\dots),\dots)$. A function symbol is primitive if no other function symbol besides itself occurs in it. We assume that all the function symbols are obtained from the primitive ones by iterative compositions, i.e. the class of all function symbols is the smallest containing the primitive ones, such that if $\{g_\lambda(\dots,\dots)\}_\lambda$ is a subset of it and $f(\dots,\dots)$ is a primitive function symbol then $f(\dots, g_\lambda(\dots,\dots),\dots, g_{\lambda'}(\dots,\dots),\dots)$ belongs to it.

We distinguish between individuals of the form $f(a_0,\dots, a_\lambda,\dots)$ (where f is a function symbol) and, so called, primitive individuals, which are not of this form. We assume that every individual is either primitive or is of the form $f(a_0,\dots, a_\lambda,\dots)$ where the a_λ's are primitive. If $b_\lambda = g_\lambda(a_{\lambda,0}, a_{\lambda,1},\dots)$ then we identify $f(b_0,\dots, b_\lambda,\dots)$ with $f^*(a_{0,0},\dots, a_{\lambda,0},\dots,\dots)$ where $f^* = f(g_0(\dots),\dots, g_\lambda(\dots),\dots)$.

If $a = f(a_0,\dots, a_\lambda,\dots)$ then we say that every function symbol which occurs in f occurs in a.

Two elements, either of which may be an individual or a function symbol, are said to be *separated* if no function symbol occurs in both (i.e. the respective primitive function symbols which go into their construction are different). Two *sets* are *separated* if every member of the one is separated from every member of the other.

Ω with or without subscripts (superscripts) will always denote a set of function symbols. If A is a set of individuals then

$\Omega(A) = \{f(a_0,\dots, a_\lambda,\dots) \mid f \in \Omega;\ a_0,\dots, a_\lambda,\dots, \in A\}$

($\Omega(A)$ includes also as members all 0-place function symbols of Ω).

3. Definition of uniform extension operators, and their existence

DEFINITION. A *u.e.o. (uniform extension operator)* O based on a set of function symbols Ω is an operator, whose domain, $D(O)$, consists of a non-empty class of models, and which has the following properties.

(I) For every $M \in D(O)$, $|M|$ is separated from Ω, $O(M)$ is a model whose set of elements is $M \cup \Omega(|M|)$, and it is a proper elementary extension of M.

(II) If M_1, $M_2 \in D(O)$ and τ is an isomorphism of M_1 onto M_2 then $\hat{\tau}$ is an isomorphism of $O(M_1)$ onto $O(M_2)$, where $\hat{\tau}$ is defined by:

$$\hat{\tau}(a) = \tau(a) \quad \text{for} \quad a \in |M_1|$$
$$\hat{\tau}(f(a_0, \ldots, a_\lambda, \ldots)) = f(\tau(a_0), \ldots, \tau(a_\lambda), \ldots)$$

for $f \in \Omega$ and $a_0, \ldots, a_\lambda, \ldots \in |M_1|$.

(III) If M, $N \in D(O)$ and $M \prec N$ then $O(M) \prec O(N)$.

(IV) If M, $N \in D(O)$, $M \prec N$ and $a \in |O(M)|$ is such that $O(N) \models a \not\approx b$ for all $b \in |M|$, then also $O(N) \models a \not\approx b$ for all $b \in |N|$.

All these requirements are natural, this is obvious for (I)–(III). (IV) is natural as well: it means that those elements of $O(M)$ which are really new (i.e. are not identified with any element of M) should be also new with respect to the bigger model N.

Thus, the property of being a new element should be preserved if one passes from a given model to an elementary extension of it.

DEFINITION. A *l.e.o. (local extension operator)* is a u.e.o. based on a set of function symbols all of which have finitely many places.

Local extension operators satisfy, besides conditions (I)–(IV), the following important property:

(V) If O is a l.e.o, $\{M_i\}_{i \in I}$ is a family of models from $D(O)$ which is directed under elementary inclusion (i.e. for every $i, j \in I$ there exists $k \in I$ such that M_i, $M_j \prec M_k$) and $\bigcup_{i \in I} M_i \in D(O)$ then:

$$O(\bigcup_{i \in I} M_i) = \bigcup_{i \in I} O(M_i).$$

Note that for any u.e.o. O we have $\bigcup_{i \in I} O(M_i) \prec O(\bigcup_{i \in I} M_i)$; the M_i's being directed under elementary inclusion, each of them is an elementary submodel of $\bigcup_{i \in I} M_i$, hence. by (III), the $O(M_i)$ are similarly directed and each is an elementary submodel of $O(\bigcup_{i \in I} M_i)$. If O is known to be a local operator, as well, then every member of $O(\bigcup_{i \in I} M_i)$ is of the form $f(a_1, \ldots, a_n)$ where n is finite; as $a_1, \ldots, a_n$ will all belong to some M_i, $f(a_1, \ldots, a_n)$ will belong to $O(M_i)$. Consequently the equality takes place. For general u.e.o.'s (V) is not true, as will be clear later. Actually, for l.e.o.'s, the following stronger condition is satisfied, as can be easily seen:

(V*) The same as (V), except that the requirement that the $\{M_i\}_{i\in I}$ be directed under elementary inclusion is replaced by the following weaker one: Each M_i is an elementary submodel of $\bigcup_{i\in I} M_i$ and, for every finite set A of elements of $\bigcup_{i\in I} M_i$, there exists $i\in I$ such that $A\subseteq|M_i|$.

THEOREM 1. Let α be an infinite cardinal and $\mathscr{F}$ a non-principal ultrafilter in the algebra of all subsets of α. Let f be a function symbol with α places. Then the operator $M\to M^\alpha/\mathscr{F}$, which is defined for all infinite models M in which M is separated from f, is a u.e.o. based on $\{f\}$.

PROOF. Regard any sequence $\langle a_0,\ldots, a_\lambda,\ldots\rangle_{\lambda<\alpha}$ as a new individual $f(a_0,\ldots, a_\lambda,\ldots)$. Given any M consider $|M|\cup\Omega(|M|)$ where $\Omega=\{f\}$. Define on it the relations (including equality) as in the well-known definition of an ultrapower. It is easily seen that (I)–(IV) hold. Q.E.D.

Simple examples of l.e.o's are given in the introduction. The theorem which follows guarantees the existence of l.e.o's, and its proof, which is quite constructive, provides an additional example of such an operator.

We say that a formula $\varphi(v)$, with one free variable v, defines a constant of the theory T if $T\vdash\exists!v\varphi(v)$. ($\exists!v=$there exists exactly one v.) A theory T has at least $\aleph_0$ different constants if there are $\aleph_0$ formulas $\varphi_i(v)$, $i=1, 2,\ldots$ defining constants of T so that $T\vdash\forall v\varphi_i(v)\to\sim\varphi_j(v)$ whenever $i\neq j$. Given a formula $\varphi(v_1,\ldots, v_n, u)$, with the free variables $v_1,\ldots, v_n, u$, we say that $\psi(v_1,\ldots, v_n,u)$ defines within T a Skolem function corresponding to φ if $T\vdash\exists!u\,\psi(v_1,\ldots, v_n, u)$ and $T\vdash\exists u\,\varphi(v_1,\ldots, v_n, u)\to\exists u(\varphi(v_1,\ldots, v_n, u)\wedge\psi(v_1,\ldots, v_n, u))$ (provability of a formula means provability of its universal closure). All Skolem functions are defined within T if for every given formula there is another one defining a Skolem function which corresponds to it. The intuitive meaning of these concepts is obvious.

THEOREM 2. Let T be any theory having at least $\aleph_0$ different constants and such that all Skolem functions are defined within it. For every formula $\varphi(v_1,\ldots, v_n, u)$ of T with free variables $v_1,\ldots, v_n, u$, $n\geq 1$, such that $T\vdash\exists!u\,\varphi(v_1,\ldots, v_n, u)$, let $f_\varphi(\ldots)$ be a function symbol with $n-1$ places ($f_\varphi\neq f_\psi$ if $\varphi\neq\psi$). Let Ω be the set of all these function symbols, together with one additional 0-place function symbol, c. Then there is a l.e.o, O, based on Ω whose domain consists of all models of T, M, in which $|M|$ is separated from Ω.

PROOF. Let $\mathscr{F}$ be a non-principal ultrafilter in the algebra of all subsets of the natural numbers. Once $\mathscr{F}$ is granted the proof is fully constructive.

Let $\varphi_0, \varphi_1, \ldots, \varphi_n, \ldots$ be the formulas which define $\aleph_0$ different constants of T. Fix once and for all their ordering. For every formula $\varphi(v_1, \ldots, v_n, u)$ let $\psi_\varphi(v_1, \ldots, v_n, u)$ be a formula which defines a Skolem function corresponding to it. Fix the mapping $\varphi \to \psi_\varphi$.

Now consider any model M of T. This model will have the elements $a_0, a_1, \ldots, a_n, \ldots$ which are defined within it by $\varphi_0, \varphi_1, \ldots, \varphi_n, \ldots$, respectively. (Actually, because $\approx$ is not interpreted as the identity of the model the elements $a_0, a_1, \ldots, a_n, \ldots$ are not uniquely determined but have to be chosen from the equivalence classes of $\approx$. The way of choosing them makes, however, no difference, moreover the use of the axiom of choice here is inessential and can be avoided altogether if one is willing to use a more cumbersome technique.) Consider the ultrapower $M^\omega/\mathscr{F}$ ($\omega =$ set of natural numbers). Its members are sequences of length ω of members of M. Among these there will be the member $\langle a_0, a_1, \ldots, a_n, \ldots \rangle$, which is not identified with any of the original members of M. Take M together with this element and take the closure under the Skolem functions which are defined by all the formulas of the form ψ_φ. This way one gets an elementary submodel of the ultrapower which properly includes M. It is this last model which will be $O(M)$. Note that it is enough to consider the set of all values of the Skolem functions where the arguments range over $|M| \cup \{\langle a_0, a_1, \ldots, a_n, \ldots \rangle\}$. This will be already closed under further applications of Skolem functions, because if g_i is the function defined by the formula $\psi_i(v_1, \ldots, v_{n_i}, u)$, $i = 1, \ldots, k$ and h is the function defined by $\psi_0(v_1, \ldots, v_k, u)$ then $h(g_1(\ ), \ldots, g_k(\ ))$ is the function defined by: $\exists u_1 \ldots \exists u_k [\psi_1(v_1, \ldots, v_{n_1}, u_1) \wedge \psi_2(v_1, \ldots, u_2) \wedge \ldots \wedge \psi_0(u_1, \ldots, u_k, u)]$. (Remember that $T \vdash \exists! u\, \psi_i(v_1, \ldots, u)$.)

Having made this general explanation we shall now show precisely how O is defined so as to be a l.e.o.. c will always be the new element $\langle a_0, a_1, \ldots, a_n, \ldots \rangle$. Applying Skolem functions to elements of M will yield elements of M; hence the additional elements will arise only when Skolem functions are applied to c or to c together with some old elements of M. In every formula $\varphi(v_1, \ldots, v_n, u)$ such that $T \vdash \exists! u\, \varphi(v_1, \ldots, v_n, u)$, we shall always substitute c in the place which corresponds to v_1, while $v_2, \ldots, v_n$ will be left for elements of M. With this stipulation the function is actually of $n-1$ arguments which range over $|M|$. This explains why f_φ is a function symbol with $n-1$ places. The following definition should now be clear.

Let M be such that $|M|$ is separated from Ω.

$O(M)$ is the model whose set of elements is $|M| \cup \Omega(|M|)$, whose distinguished elements are the same as those of M, and whose relations are determined according to the following rule.

Let P be a k-place predicate in the language of M. Let $b_1, \ldots b_k \in |O(M)|$. If $b_i \in |M|$ put $b_{i,j} = b_i$ for $j = 0, 1, \ldots, n, \ldots$, if $b_i = c$ put $b_{i,j} = a_j$, $j = 0, 1, \ldots$, and if $b_i = f_\varphi(d_1, \ldots, d_{n-1})$ let $b_{i,j}$ be the unique element $x \in |M|$ satisfying $M \models \varphi(a_j, d_1 \ldots, d_{n-1}, x)$. Then $O(M) \models P(b_1, \ldots, b_k)$ iff $\{j | M \models P(b_{1,j}, \ldots, b_{k,j})\}$ is a member of the ultrafilter $\mathscr{F}$.

We leave the reader to check that O satisfies all the requirements of a l.e.o.; this is straightforward. Q.E.D.

Note that the cardinality of $|O(M)|$ in this construction is $\mathrm{Max}(\alpha, \beta)$ where α = cardinality of $|M|$ and β is the number of constants of the language of M.

If T is a theory having infinite models then one can enlarge its language by adding to it $\aleph_0$ different individual constants and new predicates, which will define all the Skolem functions, together with axioms which ensure the inequality of any two different new constants and the required properties of the predicates. Thus one gets a theory T^* to which the theorem is applicable. Moreover, every infinite model of T can be made into a model of T^* by adding new relations and distinguished elements in a suitable way and without adding any new members to the model. As we shall see u.e.o.'s will be used to construct models having certain properties (such as "many" automorphisms) and for these purposes it does not matter whether one starts from T or T^*. Any model of T^* turns out, after deleting the additional distinguished members and relations, to be a model of T having the same properties. However, the question whether the theorem remains true without any stipulations on T is of interest in itself and we do not know the answer. The theory of dense linear ordering without first and last elements does not satisfy the stipulations made in the theorem, but still, as the examples in the introduction show, the theorem holds for it.

4. Iterations of u.e.o.'s

Let O_i be u.e.o.'s based, respectively, on Ω_i, $i = 1,2$. By $O_2 \circ O_1$ we mean the operator whose domain consists of those M's for which $O_1(M) \in D(O_2)$

and which is defined by:

$$O_2 \circ O_1(M) = O_2(O_1(M)).$$

Note that in order for $D(O_2 \circ O_1)$ to be non empty, Ω_2 and Ω_1 must be separated.

If $M \in D(O_2 \circ O_1)$ then

$$|O_2 \circ O_1(M)| = |O_2(O_1(M))| = |O_1(M)| \cup \Omega_2(|O_1(M)|) =$$
$$= |M| \cup \Omega_1(|M|) \cup \Omega_2(|M| \cup \Omega_1(|M|)).$$

This motivates the following definition.

Definition. If Ω_i, $i=1,2$ are sets of function symbols then $\Omega_2 \circ \Omega_1 = \Omega_1 \cup \{f(\ldots, g(\ldots,\ldots),\ldots) \mid f \in \Omega_2, g \in \Omega_1\}$. Here $f(\ldots, g(\ldots,\ldots),\ldots)$ ranges over all function symbols obtained through placing, in some, possibly none, of the empty places of function symbols of Ω_2, function symbols of Ω_1.

In particular $\Omega_2 \circ \Omega_1$ includes Ω_1 and Ω_2 as subsets. It follows that $|O_2 \circ O_1(M)| = |M| \cup \Omega_2 \circ \Omega_1(|M|)$.

Proposition 1. If O_i are u.e.o.'s based on Ω_i, $i=1,2$ and if $D(O_2 \circ O_1)$ is non-empty, then $O_2 \circ O_1$ is a u.e.o. based on $\Omega_2 \circ \Omega_1$.

Proof. We have shown that $O_2 \circ O_1$ is based on $\Omega_2 \circ \Omega_1$. The rest of the properties follow easily, we pause only for the proof of (IV). Assume $M, N \in D(O_2 \circ O_1)$ and $M \prec N$. Let $a \in |O_2 \circ O_1(M)|$ be such that $a \not\approx b$ for all $b \in |M|$. If for some $a' \in |O_1(M)|$ we have $a \approx a'$ then $a' \not\approx b$ for all $b \in |M|$, hence, by applying (IV) to O_1, we have $a' \not\approx b$, for all $b \in |N|$, and therefore the same holds for a. If $a \not\approx b$ for all $b \in |O_1(M)|$ then, since by (III) $O_1(M) \prec O_1(N)$, we have, by applying (IV) to O_2, $a \not\approx b$ for all $b \in |O_1(N)|$ and, a fortiori, for all $b \in |N|$. Q.E.D.

Consider now operators O_i based on Ω_i where $i=1,\ldots,n$ and the Ω_i are separated. One can form $O_n \circ \ldots \circ O_1$ which will be based on $\Omega_n \circ \ldots \circ \Omega_1$ (we omit the brackets since the operation $\circ$ whether applied to operators or to the sets of function symbols is, obviously, associative). Assume now that for every $i \neq j$ if $M \in D(O_i)$ and $|M|$ is separated from Ω_j then M, as well as $O_i(M)$, belong to $D(O_j)$.

Proposition 2. Under the above assumptions and if $1 \leq i_1 < i_2 < \ldots < i_k \leq n$ then

$$O_{i_k} \circ O_{i_{k-1}} \circ \ldots \circ O_{i_1}(M) \prec O_n \circ \ldots \circ O_1(M)$$

for all $M \in D(O_n \circ \ldots \circ O_1)$.

PROOF. It is clear that, by our assumptions, if $M \in D(O_n \circ \ldots \circ O_1)$ then also $M \in D(O_{i_k} \circ \ldots \circ O_{i_1})$. The claim is proved by induction on n. For $n=1$ it is obvious. Assume it holds for $n-1$. If $i_k \leq n-1$ then we have $O_{i_k} \circ \ldots \circ O_{i_1}(M) \prec O_{n-1} \circ \ldots \circ O_1(M)$, but (by (I)) $O_{n-1} \circ \ldots \circ O_1(M) \prec O_n \circ \ldots \circ O_1(M)$. If $i_k = n$ then $O_{i_{k-1}} \circ \ldots \circ O_{i_1}(M) \prec O_{n-1} \circ \ldots \circ O_1(M)$, hence (by (III)) $O_n \circ O_{i_{k-1}} \circ \ldots \circ O_{i_1}(M) \prec O_n \circ \ldots \circ O_1(M)$. Q.E.D.

Now let $I = \langle I, < \rangle$ be an ordered set. For every $i \in I$ let O_i be a u.e.o. based on Ω_i so that, for every $i \neq j$, Ω_i and Ω_j are separated and if $M \in D(O_i)$ and $|M|$ is separated from Ω_j then $M, O_i(M) \in D(O_j)$. Under these conditions we define:

$$\prod_{i \in I} O_i(M) = \bigcup_{i_n > i_{n-1} > \ldots > i_1} O_{i_n} \circ O_{i_{n-1}} \circ \ldots \circ O_{i_1}(M)$$

where the union on the right-hand side is taken over all finite sequences of members of I which are decreasing in the order of I. From proposition 2 it follows that the system of all models of the form $O_{i_n} \circ \ldots \circ O_{i_1}(M)$ where $i_n > \ldots > i_1$ is directed by elementary inclusion, $\prec$ (the model which corresponds to a finite subset is an elementary submodel of that which corresponds to a bigger finite subset, and therefore the system is directed just as the finite subsets are under inclusion). Consequently the union on the right-hand side is an elementary extension of M. If we define

$$\prod_{i \in I} \Omega_i = \bigcup_{i_n > \ldots > i_1} \Omega_{i_n} \circ \ldots \circ \Omega_{i_1}$$

we get:

PROPOSITION 3. $\prod_{i \in I} O_i$ is a u.e.o which is based on $\prod_{i \in I} \Omega_i$.

PROOF. By straightforward verification. Each of the required properties holds for every $O_{i_n} \circ \ldots \circ O_{i_1}$ and consequently holds in the union of all $O_{i_n} \circ \ldots \circ O_{i_1}(M)$. Q.E.D.

We also have

PROPOSITION 4. If I_1 is a subset of I with the same ordering then $\prod_{i \in I_1} O_i(M) \prec \prod_{i \in I} O_i(M)$, and the left-hand side is a proper submodel if $I_1 \neq I$.

PROOF. The right-hand side is obtained by taking a union over a bigger directed system hence it is an elementary extension of the left-hand side. Its being proper in the case $I_1 \neq I$ follows from (IV): for the detailed argument see proposition 6 and theorems 3 and 4. Q.E.D.

Observe the following: If I is well ordered, say $I = \alpha$, then one can give another natural definition of $\prod_{\lambda<\alpha} O_\lambda$. This is by transfinite induction on α:

$$\prod_{\lambda<\alpha+1} O_\lambda = O_\alpha \circ \prod_{\lambda<\alpha} O_\lambda$$

and for limit ordinals:

$$\prod_{\lambda<\alpha} O_\lambda(M) = \bigcup_{\mu<\alpha} \prod_{\lambda<\mu} O_\lambda(M).$$

This definition coincides with the general one if α is finite or $\alpha=\omega$. For $\alpha>\omega$ it will coincide with the general definition if all the operators O_λ, where $\lambda\geq\omega$, are local extension operators; it will not coincide if in some Ω_λ, where $\lambda\geq\omega$, there is an infinitary function symbol. To see what happens assume that $g_i\in\Omega_i$, for $i<\omega$, and let $f\in\Omega_\omega$ be with infinitely many places. Operating with O_ω on $\prod_{\lambda<\omega} O_\lambda(M)$ will get us, among others, individuals of the form $f(g_0(a_0,\ldots), g_1(b_0,\ldots),\ldots, g_n(c_0,\ldots),\ldots)$, where $a_0,\ldots$ $b_0,\ldots, c_0,\ldots$ are members of $|M|$. No such individual is a member of any of the models $O_\omega \circ O_n \circ \ldots \circ O_1(M)$. In the case of l.e.o.'s such a situation cannot arise and it is obvious that both definitions coincide. In general the model obtained by our given definition will be an elementary submodel of the one obtained by using the definition by transfinite induction which, by the way, also yields a u.e.o.. For instance, in the case of ultrapowers the definition by induction yields the so-called limit ultrapowers; for $\alpha=\omega$ these will coincide with the general definition but for ordinals $>\omega$ the limit ultrapowers are proper elementary extensions of the models $\prod_{\lambda<\alpha} O_\lambda(M)$.

Proposition 5. Let $\{I_j\}_{j\in J}$ be disjoint ordered sets where J is an ordered set. Assume that O_i is a l.e.o. for all $i\in\bigcup_{j\in J} I_j$. Let $\sum_{j\in J} I_j$ be the ordered set consisting of $\bigcup_{j\in J} I_j$ with the ordering defined in the usual way (definition of summation of ordered types). Then:

$$\prod_{j\in J}\prod_{i\in I_j} O_i = \prod_{i\in K} O_i \quad \text{where} \quad K=\sum_{j\in J} I_j$$

provided that both sides have meaning.

Proof. By straightforward verification, using the condition (V) which l.e.o.'s satisfy.

Note that the proposition is not true for general u.e.o., as the discussion preceding it clearly indicates.

PROPOSITION 6. Let O_i be a u.e.o. based on Ω_i, $i \in I$, where $I = \langle I, < \rangle$ is an ordered set and all the conditions in the definition of $\prod_{i \in I} O_i$ are satisfied. Let $M \in D(\prod_{i \in I} O_i)$. For every finite subset I_1 of I define M_{I_1} as the set of all a's in $|\prod_{i \in I} O_i(M)|$ for which there exists $b \in |\prod_{i \in I_1} O_i(M)|$ such that $a \approx b$; if $I_1 = \emptyset$ then M_{I_1} consists of all a's for which there exists $b \in |M|$ such that $a \approx b$. Then $a \in M_{I_1} \cap M_{I_2}$ implies that $a \in M_{I_3}$, where $I_3 = \{i \mid i \in I_1 \text{ and } i \leq i^*\}$ and $i^* =$ maximal element of $I_1 \cap I_2$ (under the ordering of I). If $I_1 \cap I_2 = \emptyset$ then $I_3 = \emptyset$. (Since I_1 and I_2 play symmetric roles the same will hold if we put $I_3 = \{i \mid i \in I_2 \text{ and } i \leq i^*\}$.)

PROOF. Let i_1 be the maximal element of I_1 and i_2 the maximal element of I_2. We will show that if $i_1 > i_2$ then $a \in M_{J_1}$ where $J_1 = I_1 - \{i_1\}$. Similarly if $i_2 > i_1$ then $a \in M_{J_2}$ where $J_2 = I_2 - \{i_2\}$. In this way we continue to chop off the maximal elements of I_1 or I_2 until we get two sets having the same maximal elements. The set obtained in this way from I_1 will be I_3. In case $I_1 \cap I_2 = \emptyset$ we will get $I_3 = \emptyset$.

Assume $i_1 > i_2$ and let $J_1 = I_1 - \{i_1\}$ and $K = J_1 \cup I_2$. Put

$$M_1 = \prod_{i \in J_1} O_i(M), \qquad M_2 = \prod_{i \in K} O_1(M).$$

Then $M_1 \prec M_2$ and, since $i_1 \notin K$, both are in $D(O_{i_1})$. Within the model $O_{i_1}(M_2)$ we have: $a \in |O_{i_1}(M_1)|$ and $a \approx b$ for some $b \in |M_2|$, consequently, by (IV), $a \approx b$ for some $b \in |M_1|$. Hence $a \in M_{J_1}$. Q.E.D.

THEOREM 3. Let $a \in |\prod_{i \in I} O_i(M)|$ and assume $a \not\approx b$ for all $b \in |M|$. Consider all i's for which there are $i_{k-1}, \ldots, i_1$ such that $i = i_k > i_{k-1} > \ldots > i_1$ and $a \approx b$ for some b in $|O_{i_k} \circ \ldots \circ O_{i_1}(M)|$. Then, among all these, there is a minimal one (with respect to the ordering of I). The minimal one also has the property that it belongs to every subset, I_1, of I, for which there exists $b \in \prod_{i \in I_1} O_i(M)$ satisfying $a \approx b$.

PROOF. Let $a \in |O_{i_n} \circ \ldots \circ O_{i_1}(M)|$. Let j be the smallest number such that there exists b in $|O_{i_j} \circ \ldots \circ O_{i_1}(M)|$ satisfying $a \approx b$. By proposition 6 i_j is the required minimal element. Proposition 6 implies also the additional property. Q.E.D.

DEFINITION. Let I be an ordered set and O_i be u.e.o.'s as i ranges over I. For convenience we assume $0 \notin I$. If $M \in D(\prod_{i \in I} O_i)$ then $M(0, I)$ is the set of all $a \in |\prod_{i \in I} O_i(M)|$ for which there exists $b \in |M|$ such that $a \approx b$. For every $i \in I$, $M(i, I)$ is the set of all $a \in |\prod_{i \in I} O_i(M)|$ for which i is the minimal element of I such that $a \approx b \in O_i \circ O_{i_{k-1}} \circ \ldots \circ O_{i_1}(M)$, for some b and some $i_1 < \ldots < i_{k-1} < i$.

We will write $M(i)$ instead of $M(i, I)$ in cases where it is clear what I is meant.

THEOREM 4. For every $M \in D(\prod_{i \in I} O_i)$ we have $|\prod_{i \in I} O_i(M)| = M(0, I) \cup \bigcup_{i \in I} M(i, I)$. This is a decomposition into mutually disjoint non-empty sets. We also have: $a \in |M(i, I)|$ and $a \approx b$ imply $b \in |M(i, I)|$, for all $i \in \{0\} \cup I$. If $I_1 \subseteq I$ then $M(i, I_1) \subseteq M(i, I)$ and if I_1 is an initial segment of I then for every $a \in M(i, I)$ there exists $b \in M(i, I_1)$, such that $a \approx b$.

PROOF. It is obvious that we have here a decomposition of $|\prod_{i \in I} O_i(M)|$ into mutually disjoint sets. None of these is empty because for every O_i there exists $a \in |O_i(M)|$ so that $a \not\approx b$ for all $b \in |M|$ (remember that the extensions are always proper). Such an a will belong to $M(i, I)$. The rest of the assertions follow immediately from the definition of $M(i, I)$ and from theorem 3. Q.E.D.

Note also that if M, $N \in D(\prod_{i \in I} O_i)$ and $M \prec N$ then $M(i, I) \subseteq N(i, I)$ for all $i \in I \cup \{0\}$. This can be established using, again, (IV) in a similar way.

5. Iterations of the same operator and Ehrenfeucht-Mostowski's theorem

Our aim is to form products $\prod_{i \in I} O_i$ where all the O_i's are the same operator. Strictly speaking this is impossible since the O_i's must be based on separated sets of function symbols. We overcome this difficulty by forming different replicas of the same set of function symbols. In this way we get replicas of the same operator.

Let Ω be any set of function symbols. By a replica of Ω we mean a set of function symbols, Ω_i, where i is a one-to-one mapping of Ω onto Ω_i, $i: f \to f_i$, so that the sequence of empty places of f_i has the same order type as that of f. Obviously, if Ω_i is a replica of Ω then, in a natural way, Ω is a replica of Ω_i and therefore we speak about them as being replicas of each other.

DEFINITION. Let Ω_1, Ω_2 be replicas of each other. For every $f_1 \in \Omega_1$ let f_2 be the corresponding symbol in Ω_2. Let O_1, O_2 be two u.e.o.'s based on Ω_1, Ω_2 respectively. We will say that O_1 and O_2 are replicas of each other, or replicas of the same operator, if the following holds.

(i) If $M_i \in D(O_i)$, $i=1,2$ and τ is an isomorphism of M_1 onto M_2, then τ can be extended to an isomorphism $\hat{\tau}$ of $O_1(M_1)$ onto $O_2(M_2)$ by putting:

$$\hat{\tau}(f_1(a_0, \ldots, a_\lambda, \ldots)) = f_2(\tau(a_0), \ldots, \tau(a_\lambda), \ldots)$$

for every $f_1 \in \Omega_1$; $a_0, \ldots, a_\lambda, \ldots \in |M_1|$.

(ii) If $M \in D(O_i)$ and Ω_j is separated from $|M|$ then $M \in D(O_j)$, $i, j=1,2$.

(iii) If $M \in D(O_i)$ and Ω_j is separated from $O_i(M)$ then $O_i(M) \in D(O_j)$, $i, j=1,2$.

Requirements (i), (ii) are obviously the natural ones to make. (iii) guarantees the possibility of reapplying a second replica after applying the first, provided that they are based on separated sets of symbols.

O_i, where $i \in I$, are said to be replicas of each other, or replicas of the same operator, if O_i and O_j are replicas of each other for all $i, j \in I$.

Assume now that O is based on Ω and that $D(O)$ consists of all models of some theory T whose sets of members are separated from Ω. Let Ω_i be any replica of Ω. Then one can define a replica O_i of O in the following way. Given any model M of T in which $|M|$ is separated from Ω_i, let M' be an isomorphic model so that $|M'|$ is separated from Ω and let τ be the isomorphism of M onto M'. Then $O_i(M)$ is defined by making $\hat{\tau}$ an isomorphism which extends τ, where $\hat{\tau}$ is defined by:

$$\hat{\tau}(f(a_0, \ldots, a_\lambda, \ldots)) = f_i(\tau(a_0), \ldots, \tau(a_\lambda), \ldots), \quad f \in \Omega; a_0, \ldots \in |M'|.$$

It is easily seen that $O_i(M)$ does not depend on the choice of M' and τ (by (ii)). It is also obvious that O_i is a replica of O, whose domain consists of all models M of T in which $|M|$ is separated from Ω_i. Together with theorems 1 and 2 these considerations yield the following results:

THEOREM 1*. Let T be any theory having infinite models and let $\Omega = \{f\}$, where f is a function symbol with $\aleph_0$ places. Then if, for all $i \in I$, Ω_i is a replica of Ω, there are u.e.o.'s O_i, $i \in I$, based on the Ω_i's, respectively, which are all replicas of each other, such that $D(O_i)$=class of all infinite models of T whose sets of elements are separated from Ω_i.

THEOREM 2*. If all Skolem functions can be defined in T and it has at least $\aleph_0$ different definable individual constants, then there is a set Ω of finitary symbols, whose cardinality is that of the set of all formulas of T, so that if Ω_i, $i \in I$, are replicas of Ω there are l.e.o.'s O_i based on the Ω_i, respectively and having the properties mentioned in theorem 1*.

Notice that if Ω_i is a replica of Ω'_i, $i=1,\ldots,n$ then also $\Omega_n\circ\ldots\circ\Omega_1$ is, in a natural way, a replica of $\Omega'_n\circ\ldots\circ\Omega'_i$. If O_i is a replica of O'_i, $i=1,\ldots,n$ then also $O_n\circ\ldots\circ O_1$ is a replica of $O'_n\circ\ldots\circ O'_1$, and for every model M, which is in both domains, there is a natural isomorphism of $O_n\circ\ldots\circ O_1(M)$ onto $O'_n\circ\ldots\circ O'_1(M)$. The effect of the isomorphism is to replace every $f_i\in\Omega_i$ by its corresponding $f'_i\in\Omega'_i$.

It follows easily that if $I=\langle I, <\rangle$ is order isomorphic to $I'=\langle I', <'\rangle$, where the isomorphism is $i\to i'$, and if $O_{i'}$ is a replica of O_i, for all $i\in I$, then also $\prod_{i'\in I'}O_{i'}$ is a replica of $\prod_{i\in I}O_i$. For every model M, which is in the domain of both, the mapping obtained through replacing every $f_i\in\Omega_i$ by the corresponding $f_{i'}\in\Omega_{i'}$ is an isomorphism of $\prod_{i\in I}O_i(M)$ onto $\prod_{i'\in I'}O_{i'}(M)$. If we take $I'=I$ and the mapping $i\to i'$ to be an automorphism of I we get the model whose existence is claimed by the Ehrenfeucht-Mostowski theorem. This theorem claims the following:

Let I be any set and $<$ an ordering on it. Let T be any theory with infinite models. There is a model N of T containing I as a subset so that every automorphism of $\langle I, <\rangle$ can be extended to an automorphism of N.

In order to get N just take any infinite model M of T, and let $\{O_i\}_{i\in I}$ be a system of replicas of a u.e.o., so that their respective sets of symbols are separated from $|M|$ and from each other. Put $N=\prod_{i\in I}O_i(M)$. Every automorphism of I will induce an automorphism of N. Pick any element $a(i_0)$ in $O_{i_0}(M)$ such that $a(i_0)\not\approx b$ for all $b\in|M|$. By replacing every function symbol occurring in $a(i_0)$ by its corresponding symbol of the ith replica one gets the corresponding $a(i)$, as i varies over I. It is easily seen that $a(i)\not\approx a(j)$ if $i\neq j$ (this follows of course from proposition 6, or theorems 3 or 4, but it follows as easily directly from (IV)). If τ is an automorphism of I and τ^* the induced automorphism of N then $\tau^*(a(i))=a(\tau(i))$. Hence by identifying every $i\in I$ with $a(i)$ we get the Ehrenfeucht-Mostowski theorem.

If we use theorem 2 which guarantees the existence of l.e.o.'s we can construct such a model whose cardinality will be $\mathrm{Max}(\alpha, \beta)$ where $\alpha=$ cardinality of the set of formulas of the theory and $\beta=$cardinality of I. As we remarked before, one gets a theory to which theorem 2 is applicable by extending the language, if neccessary, so that all Skolem functions and $\aleph_0$ different individual constants would be definable within it.

Note that in order to prove this theorem one actually uses only theorem

1*, which itself relies on theorem 1, in addition to the basic definitions of a u.e.o. and the construction of $\prod_{i\in I} O_i$.

The exact relationships between the models which are constructed in the original proof by Ehrenfeucht and Mostowski, which uses Ramsey's theorem, and those which are constructed using possible u.e.o.'s, have still to be sorted out.

Assume that O is a l.e.o. and has replicas $\{O_i\}_{i\in I}$ based on separated sets of symbols, where $I=\langle I, <\rangle$. $\prod_{i\in I} O_i$, up to a replica, depends only on O and the order type of I. Denoting it by O^ξ where ξ is the order type of I we get, using proposition 5,

$$\prod_{i\in I} O^{\lambda_i} = O^\xi$$

(where $\xi = \sum_{i\in I} \lambda_i$, order type summation) and in particular:

$$(O^\lambda)^\xi = O^{\lambda\cdot\xi}.$$

Theorem 4 together with theorem 2 and the construction described in this section imply the next theorem. It is simpler to formulate it for models in which equality is interpreted as the real identity of the model, hence we assume that we have already identified every a and b such that $a \approx b$.

THEOREM 5. Let M be any infinite model. For any ordered set I there is a proper elementary extension $M(I)$ of M having the following properties:

(1) $M(I) = |M| \cup \bigcup_{i\in I} M(i, I)$, where the right-hand side is a union of pairwise disjoint non-empty sets.

(2) If $I' \subseteq I$ and the ordering of I' is the restriction of that of I then $M(I') \prec M(I)$ and $M(i, I') \subseteq M(i, I)$ for all $i \in I'$. If I' is an initial segment of I then $M(i, I') = M(i, I)$. If $I \neq I'$ then $M(I') \neq M(I)$.

(3) If $I_1, I_2 \subseteq I$ (and their orderings are the restrictions of the ordering of I) and τ is an isomorphism of I_1 onto I_2 then there is an induced isomorphism τ^* of $M(I_1)$ onto $M(I_2)$ so that $\tau^*(M(i, I_1)) = M(\tau(i), I_2)$ for all $i \in I_1$, $\tau^*(a) = a$ for all $a \in |M|$.

(4) Let τ be an isomorphism of I_1 onto I_2. If $J_1 \supseteq I_1$, $J_2 \supseteq I_2$ and σ is an isomorphism of J_1 onto J_2 which extends τ, then σ^* extends τ^*.

(5) $(\tau^{-1})^* = (\tau^*)^{-1}$ and $(\sigma \circ \tau)^* = \sigma^* \circ \tau^*$ whenever $\sigma \circ \tau$ is defined.

(6) $M(I)$ is of cardinality $\mathrm{Max}(\alpha, \beta, \gamma)$ where α = cardinality of M, β = number of relations of M and γ = cardinality of I.

6. Applications for models of Peano's arithmetic

By Peano's arithmetic we mean the theory whose language includes the operation symbols + and •, and whose axioms are the usual Peano axioms, induction being interpreted as the axiom schema: $\varphi(\mathbf{0}) \wedge \forall v[\varphi(v) \to \varphi(v+\mathbf{1})] \to \forall v \varphi(v)$, where φ ranges over all formulas. We will also allow any additional predicates or function symbols, provided that in the induction schema φ ranges over all the formulas and that the total number of predicates and function symbols is countable. We will denote any such theory by **P**.

Every model of **P** has a natural ordering (defined by the formula $x \leq y$ which stands for $\exists v[x+v \approx y]$), for which we use $\leq$ (or $<$, if the inreflexive ordering is meant).

By "model" we mean in this section a model of **P**, unless otherwise stated.

DEFINITION. A proper elementary extension of M is an *end extension* if every new element is bigger, in the natural ordering, than every element of M.

A proper elementary extension, N, of M is a *minimal extension* if there is no proper elementary submodel of N which properly includes M.

A *minimal end extension* is an end extension which is also minimal.

Remember that, in case $\approx$ is not interpreted as real identity, a proper submodel of M is a submodel M' for which there exists $a \in |M|$ such that $a \not\approx b$ for all $b \in |M'|$. A submodel which is not proper in this sense will be considered the same as M.

Two models M_1 and M_2 are *isomorphic over* M if M is a submodel of both and there is an isomorphism of M_1 onto M_2 which leaves every point of M fixed. Such an isomorphism is called an *isomorphism over* M. (If $\approx$ is not interpreted as the real identity of the model we also allow as isomorphisms multivalued functions, provided that if b, c are both values of a then $M_2 \models b \approx c$.)

It was shown by MacDowell and Specker [5] that every model of **P** has an end extension. The author has proved that every model has a minimal end extension, cf. [3]. Analysing the proof one finds that the minimal end extension is constructed by means of a local extension operator. Moreover the following is true.

THEOREM 6[1]. There exist $\aleph_0$ l.e.o.'s, O_n, $n=1,2,\ldots$, each based on countably many finitary function symbols, such that $O_n(M)$ is a minimal end extension of M for all $M \in D(O_n)$ and all n, and, for all $i \neq j$, if $M \in D(O_i) \cap D(O_j)$ then $O_i(M)$ and $O_j(M)$ are not isomorphic over M. For every n $D(O_n)$ consists of all models of **P** whose underlying sets of elements are separated from the function symbols on which O_n is based.

We shall rely on this theorem in the sequel. Its proof is outside the scope of this paper, it is presented in [5]. Another theorem which we use without proof is the following (for proof see the preceding reference).

THEOREM 7. If N is a minimal end extension of M then N has no automorphisms over M except the identity. (It is to be understood that, in case $\approx$ is not interpreted as the real identity, we mean by the identity automorphism any automorphism τ such that $\tau(a) \approx a$ for all a.)

If $\varphi(v)$ is any formula of **P** then there is a corresponding $\psi(v)$ which asserts: *v is the first element such that $\varphi(v)$, and if there are no elements for which φ holds then v equals* 0. Thus, all the Skolem functions can be defined within **P**. Whenever we mention the Skolem functions of some model of **P** we shall mean those Skolem functions which are defined within **P**.

If M is any model of P and $A \subseteq |M|$ then every elementary submodel of M which contains all the members of A must also contain all the values of the Skolem functions of these members. Conversely, A together with all the values of the Skolem functions constitutes an elementary submodel. Consequently the smallest elementary submodel containing A is obtained by adding to it the values of all Skolem functions as their arguments range over A. If N is a minimal extension of M, then, by adding to $|M|$ any $a \in |N|$ which is not equal to any member of M, and closing $M \cup \{a\}$ under Skolem functions we must get the whole of N. This is indeed a characterisation of minimal extensions for models of **P**.

DEFINITION. A u.e.o., O, is an *end-extension operator* if $O(M)$ is an

---

[1]) After typing the manuscript, it was found by the author that theorem 6 can be sharpened through replacing "$\aleph_0$" by "$2^{\aleph_0}$". That is, there are $2^{\aleph_0}$ l.e.o.'s O_x, $x \in (0, 1)$, satisfying the claims of the theorem. Consequently, theorems 12 and 11* can be sharpened in a similar way through replacing partitions into countably many disjoint subsets by partitions into continuum many disjoint subsets.

end extension of M for all $M \in D(O)$. It is a *minimal-end-extension operator* if $O(M)$ is a minimal end-extension of M for all $M \in D(O)$.

PROPOSITION 7. Let O_i be an end-extension operator, for all $i \in I$, where $I = \langle I, < \rangle$. Let $M \in D(\prod_{i \in I} O_i)$. Put, as in 4 (the definition following theorem 3), $|\prod_{i \in I} O_i(M)| = M(O) \cup \bigcup_{i \in I} M(i)$. Then $a > b$ whenever $a \in M(i)$, $b \in M(j)$ and $i > j$ (here it is understood that $i > 0$ for all $i \in I$).

PROOF. We have $a \approx a' \in |O_i \circ O_{i_{k-1}} \circ \ldots \circ O_{i_1}(M)|$ and $b \approx b' \in |O_j \circ O_{j_{m-1}} \circ \ldots \circ O_{j_1}(M)|$ where $i > i_{k-1} > \ldots > i_1$ and $j > j_{m-1} > \ldots > j_1$. Thus $b' \in |\prod_{t \in J} O_t(M)|$ where $J = \{j, \ldots j_1\} \cup \{i_{k-1}, \ldots, i_1\}$, whereas $a' \in |O_i(\prod_{t \in J} O_t(M)|$ and $a' \not\approx c$ for all $c \in |\prod_{t \in J} O_t(M)|$. Consequently, since O_i always yields end extensions, we have $a' > b'$. Q.E.D.

The ordering of $\prod_{i \in I} O_i(M)$ is therefore obtained by taking M with its given ordering and placing after it ordered blocks of elements, $M(i)$, $i \in I$, where the ordering of the blocks is according to that of I (that is, each element from a block precedes all the elements from any succeeding block). If we use for the O_i's, l.e.o.'s based on countably many function symbols then it is easily seen that the cardinality of each $M(i)$ is at most $\text{Max}(\alpha, \beta)$ where α is the cardinality of M and β that of I.

Applying theorem 5 we now get the following result.

THEOREM 8. For every model, M, of **P** and any ordered set, $I = \langle I, < \rangle$, there exists an end extension $M(I)$ of M such that $|M(I)| = |M| \cup \bigcup_{i \in I} M(i)$ and the following properties hold:

(1) $\{M(i)\}_{i \in I}$ is a collection of mutually disjoint, non-empty intervals (in the ordering of $M(I)$) which are ordered by the ordering of I and all come after $|M|$.

(2) If I_1 is an initial segment of I then the submodel $M(I_1)$ consists of $|M| \cup \bigcup_{i \in I_1} M(i)$ and is an elementary submodel of $M(I)$.

(3) If I_1 and I_2 are both initial segments of I and τ is an isomorphism of I_1 onto I_2, then there is an isomorphism τ^* of $M(I_1)$ onto $M(I_2)$ such that $\tau^*(M(i)) = M(\tau(i))$.

(4) Each $M(i)$ is of cardinality = Max (cardinality of M, cardinality of $\{j \mid j \in I \,\&\, j \leq i\}$).

COROLLARY 1. If η is the order type of a model of **P** and $I = \langle I, < \rangle$ is an ordered set, then there exists a model of **P** of order type $\eta + \sum_{i \in I} \lambda_i$, where each λ_i is of cardinality $\leq$ Max (cardinality of η, cardinality of $\{j \mid j \leq i\}$) and $\lambda_{i_1} = \lambda_{i_2}$ whenever $\{i \mid i \in I \,\&\, i \leq i_1\}$ and $\{i \mid i \in I \,\&\, i \leq i_2\}$ are isomorphic.

COROLLARY 2. Let η be an order type of a model of **P** of cardinality α. For every order type ξ, in which every two initial segments of the form $\{i \mid i \leq i_0\}$ are isomorphic, there exists an order type λ and a model of **P** of order type $\eta + \lambda \cdot \xi$. The cardinality of λ is $\leq \text{Max}(\alpha, \beta)$, where $\beta =$ cardinality of ξ.

The λ_i of corollary 1, or the λ of corollary 2, depend of course on the model M, which represents the order type η, and on the order type of I. So far little can be said about λ_i (or λ). One might ask in which cases the cardinality of λ_i (or λ) can be strictly less than that of I. In some cases a negative answer can be proved. For instance take the case where the order type of I is that of the real numbers. For this case we have:

PROPOSITION 8. No model of **P** has the order type $\eta + \sum_{x \in (0,1)} \lambda_x$, where (0, 1) is taken with the usual ordering of the reals and every λ_x is an order type of cardinality less than the continuum.

PROOF. By contradiction. If N has this order type then $|N| = K_0 \cup \bigcup_{x \in (0,1)} K_x$, where K_0 is an initial segment in the ordering of N and the K_x's are non-empty mutually disjoint segments, ordered according to x, each of cardinality $< 2^{\aleph_0}$. For any $a \in K_x$ there are $2^{\aleph_0}$ different elements of N which are smaller than it (in the ordering of N). Since $b_1 \neq b_2$ implies $a + b_1 \neq a + b_2$ it cannot be that $a + b \in K_x$ for all $b < a$. Hence for some $b < a$ we have $a + b > c$, for all $c \in K_x$. Since $2a > a + b$ we must have $2a \in K_y$ where $y > x$. (The arithmetical operations are meant to be performed within the model N. "$>$" denotes the ordering of the model as well as that of (0, 1).)

Now take $a \in K_{x_0}$ and let x_n be such that $2^n \cdot a \in K_{x_n}$, where n ranges over the standard natural numbers. $x_0, x_1, \ldots, x_n, \ldots$ is a strictly increasing sequence of real numbers. It must be bounded from above by some number of (0,1), because $2^n < a$, and hence $2^n \cdot a < a \cdot a$ for all n. Let y be its least upper bound.

If $b_1, b_2 \in K_0 \cup \bigcup_{x<y} K_x$ then, for some n_1, n_2, we have $b_1 \leq 2^{n_1} a$, $b_2 \leq 2^{n_2} a$ and hence $b_1 + b_2 \leq 2^{n_1 + n_2} a$. Therefore $b_1 + b_2 \in K_0 \cup \bigcup_{x<y} K_x$ as well. This implies that $c - b \in K_y$ whenever $c \in K_y$ and $b \in K_0 \cup \bigcup_{x<y} K_x$. Fix $c \in K_y$ and let b range over $K_0 \cup \bigcup_{x<y} K_x$. One gets $2^{\aleph_0}$ different members of K_y, which is a contradiction. Q.E.D.

The argument can be used to prove the following general statement.

PROPOSITION 8*. Let ρ be any order type and let I be any ordered set in which every bounded countable set has a least upper bound. Then there are no models of **P** of order type $\rho+\sum_{i\in I}\lambda_i$ where every λ_i is of cardinality smaller than that of ρ.

Proposition 8 follows from this by putting $\rho=\eta+\sum_{0<x\leq\frac{1}{2}}\lambda_x$.

The results obtained so far rely on the iterative process for end-extension operators. The existence of such an operator can be deduced from the proof, although not from the statement, of MacDowell and Specker's result concerning the existence of end-extensions. The way in which the end-extension is constructed is uniform and leads to the construction of the operator.

More information is obtained if minimal-end-extension operators are used. For instance, if all O_i's are minimal-end-extension operators then every elementary submodel of $\prod_{i\in I}O_i(M)$ which includes M has the form $\prod_{i\in J}O_i(M)$, where $J\subseteq I$. Every isomorphism between $\prod_{i\in I_1}O_i(M)$ and $\prod_{i\in I_2}O_i(M)$ induces an isomorphism of I_1 onto I_2, the isomorphism between the models being uniquely determined by the isomorphism between the ordered sets. In particular, if all O_i's are replicas of each other, the automorphisms over M are exactly those induced by the automorphisms of the ordered set. These and other results are proved in the sequel.

PROPOSITION 9. Assume that, for every $i\in I$, O_i is a minimal-end-extension operator, $I=\langle I, <\rangle$. Let $M\in D(\prod_{i\in I}O_i)$ and, for every $i\in I$, let a_i be a member of $O_i(M)$ satisfying: $a\not\approx b$ for all $b\in|M|$. Then the closure under Skolem functions of $|M|\cup\{a_i\}_{i\in I}$ is the whole model $\prod_{i\in I}O_i(M)$.

PROOF. Since $|\prod_{i\in I}O_i(M)|=\bigcup_{i_k>\ldots>i_1}|O_{i_k}\circ\ldots\circ O_{i_1}(M)|$ it suffices to prove the claim for finite I's. This is done by induction on the number of elements of I. Let J be any finite ordered set, $i\notin J$, and extend the ordering of J by putting $i>j$ for all $j\in J$. Assume that $|\prod_{j\in J}O_j(M)|$ is the closure under Skolem functions of $|M|\cup\{a_j\}_{j\in J}$. Consider $O_i(\prod_{j\in J}O_j(M))$. Since it is a minimal extension of $\prod_{j\in J}O_j(M)$, it is the closure under Skolem functions of $|\prod_{j\in J}O_j(M)|\cup\{c\}$, whenever c is an element of it which is different from all members of $|\prod_{j\in J}O_j(M)|$. Assuming $a_i\in|O_i(M)|$ and $a_i\not\approx b$ for all $b\in|M|$, we have also $a_i\not\approx b$ for all $b\in|\prod_{j\in J}O_j(M)|$. Consequently the closure of $|\prod_{j\in J}O_j(M)|\cup\{a_i\}$ is the whole of $|O_i(\prod_{j\in J}O_j(M))|$. This implies that the closure of $|M|\cup\{a_j\}_{j\in J}\cup\{a_i\}$ is $|O_i(\prod_{j\in J}O_j(M))|$. Q.E.D.

For the proof of the following theorem we refer to [5].

THEOREM 9. Let I be a finite ordered set and let O_i be a minimal-end-extension operator for all $i \in I$. If $M \in D(\prod_{i \in I} O_i)$, and $a \in |\prod_{i \in I} O_i(M)|$ is such that, for every proper subset, J, of I, and for all $b \in |\prod_{i \in J} O_i(M)|$, $a \not\approx b$, then the closure of $|M| \cup \{a\}$ under Skolem functions is the whole model $\prod_{i \in I} O_i(M)$.

COROLLARY. If $I = \langle I, < \rangle$ and O_i is a minimal-end-extension operator for all $i \in I$, then every elementary submodel of $\prod_{i \in I} O_i(M)$ which includes M is of the form $\prod_{j \in J} O_j(M)$ where $J \subseteq I$.

PROOF. For every $a \in |\prod_{i \in I} O_i(M)|$ there is a finite subset I_1 so that $a \approx a' \in |\prod_{i \in I_1} O_i(M)|$, and $a \not\approx b$ whenever $b \in |\prod_{i \in J} O_i(M)|$ and J is properly included in I_1 (cf. theorem 3). By theorem 9 the closure under Skolem functions of $|M| \cup \{a\}$ is $|\prod_{i \in I_1} O_i(M)|$.

In particular the closure of $|M| \cup \{a\}$ includes $\bigcup_{i \in I_1} |O_i(M)|$. On the other hand, by proposition 9, the closure of $\bigcup_{i \in I_1} |O_i(M)|$ is $|\prod_{i \in I_1} O_i(M)|$ and therefore contains a as a member. Consequently every elementary submodel which includes M consists of the closure under Skolem functions of $\bigcup_{i \in J} |O_i(M)|$, for some $J \subseteq I$, hence, by proposition 9, it is $\prod_{i \in J} O_i(M)$. Q.E.D.

The lattice of all elementary submodels of $\prod_{i \in I} O_i(M)$ which include M is thereby completely described. To every element, a, of $\prod_{i \in I} O_i(M)$ there corresponds a finite subset, I_a, of I, so that the closure under Skolem functions of $|M| \cup \{a\}$ is the elementary submodel $\prod_{i \in I_a} O_i(M)$. It can also be shown that for every finite subset $J \subseteq I$ there exists a such that $J = I_a$.

The corollary implies also that if $J = I - \{j\}$, where $i \in I$, then $\prod_{i \in I} O_i(M)$ is a minimal extension of $\prod_{i \in J} O_i(M)$. In the case that j is not the largest element of I we get a minimal extension in which for every new element there is a larger old element. Such an extension is called (in [6]) *cofinal*. It is not difficult to see that every model of **P** which is not minimal has cofinal extensions (see [6, § 2]); whether all also have minimal cofinal extensions is not known.

The elementary submodel, $\prod_{i \in J} O_i(M)$, of $\prod_{i \in I} O_i(M)$ is an initial segment if J is an initial segment of I. Consequently all elementary submodels which include M and are initial segments are of the form $\prod_{i \in J} O_i(M)$, where J is an initial segment of I. This, however, can be proved directly in the following more general form.

PROPOSITION 10. Let N be an end extension of M and let $|N| = |M| \cup$

$\bigcup_{i\in I} M(i)$, where I is an ordered set and, for all $i\in I$, the submodel consisting of $|M|\cup\bigcup_{j\leq i} M(i)$ is an elementary submodel of N and a minimal end-extension of the submodel consisting of $|M|\cup\bigcup_{j<i} M(j)$. Then every elementary submodel of N which includes M and is an initial segment of N consists of $|M|\cup\bigcup_{i\in J} M(i)$ where J is an initial segment of I.

PROOF. Let K be such a submodel. If $a\in K\cap M(i)$ then

$$|M|\cup\bigcup_{j<i} M(j)\subseteq K.$$

Every member of $M(i)$ is the value of some Skolem function for arguments taken from $|M|\cup\bigcup_{j<i} M(j)\cup\{a\}$ (necessary condition for minimal extensions). Hence $M(i)\subseteq K$. Q.E.D.

PROPOSITION 11. Let N_1, N_2 be two end extensions of M, such that $|N_j|=|M|\cup\bigcup_{i\in I_j} M(i)$, $i=1, 2$, and the assumptions of proposition 10 hold for both, respectively. For every isomorphism, τ, of N_1 onto N_2 over N there exists an isomorphism τ' of I_1 onto I_2 such that $\tau(M(i))= M(\tau'(i))$ for all $i\in I_1$.

PROOF. Every isomorphism maps elementary submodels which are initial segments onto elementary submodels having the same property. Using this for both τ and τ^{-1} and applying proposition 10, it follows that every $M(i)$, $i\in I_1$, is mapped onto a corresponding $M(i')$, $i'\in I_2$. Q.E.D.

PROPOSITION 12. For all $i\in I$ let O_i be a minimal-end-extension operator, where I is an ordered set having a biggest element i^*. Then every automorphism, τ, of $\prod_{i\in I} O_i(M)$ over M leaves every member of $|O_{i^*}(M)|$ fixed (or, more precisely, $\tau(a)\approx a$ for all $a\in|O_{i^*}(M)|$).

PROOF. Put $|\prod_{i\in I} O_i(M)|=M(0)\cup\bigcup_{i\in I} M(i)$. By proposition 11, $\tau(M(i^*))=M(i^*)$. Consequently the restriction, τ_1 of τ to

$$M(0)\cup\bigcup_{i<i^*} M(i)$$

is an automorphism of $\prod_{i<i^*} O_i(M)$. Consider τ_1^{-1}. By (II) (of the definition of a u.e.o.) τ_1^{-1} can be extended to an automorphism of $O_{i^*}(\prod_{i<i^*} O_i(M))$. This extension, say τ_2, is obtained by replacing, in every member of the form $f(a_0,\ldots,a_{n-1})$, every a_k by $\tau_1^{-1}(a_k)$ (f is a function symbol of O_{i^*} and $a_0,\ldots,a_{n-1}\in|\prod_{i\in i^*} O_i(M)|$). In the case of a member of $|O_{i^*}(M)|$ all the elements which occupy the empty places of the function symbol belong to $|M|$. Since τ_1^{-1} leaves every member of M fixed, τ_2 leaves every member of $O_{i^*}(M)$ fixed. Consider $\tau\circ\tau_2$. It leaves fixed every member of $\prod_{i<i^*} O_i(M)$. Since $O_{i^*}(\prod_{i<i^*} O_i(M))$ is a minimal

end extension of $\prod_{i<i^*} O_i(M)$, theorem 7 implies that $\tau \circ \tau_2$ is the identity automorphism. Since τ_2 leaves every member of $O_{i^*}(M)$ fixed the same is true of τ. Q.E.D.

PROPOSITION 13. Let O_i be a minimal-end-extension operator for $i \in I$, and $I = \langle I, < \rangle$. If τ is an automorphism of $\prod_{i \in I} O_i(M)$ over M, and $i \in I$ is such that $\tau(M(i)) = M(i)$, then τ leaves fixed every member of $|O_i(M)|$.

PROOF. The restriction, τ_1 of τ to $|\prod_{j \leq i} O_i(M)|$ is an automorphism of that model over M. Now apply proposition 12 to τ_1. Q.E.D.

THEOREM 10. Let I, J be two ordered sets and let O_i, O_j be minimal-end-extension operators for all $i \in I$, $j \in J$.
Assume $M \in D(\prod_{i \in I} O_i) \cap D(\prod_{j \in J} O_j)$ and put:
$|\prod_{i \in I} O_i(M)| = M(0, I) \cup \bigcup_{i \in I} M(i, I)$;
$|\prod_{j \in J} O_j(M)| = M(0, J) \cup \bigcup_{j \in J} M(j, J)$.
Then, every isomorphism, τ, over M of $\prod_{i \in I} O_i(M)$onto $\prod_{j \in J} O_j(M)$ induces an isomorphism τ' of I onto J, such that $\tau(M(i, I)) = M(\tau'(i), J)$, for all $i \in I$. For every two automorphisms τ_1, τ_2, if $\tau'_1 = \tau'_2$ then $\tau_1 = \tau_2$.

PROOF. By proposition 11, for every $i \in I$ there exists $j \in J$ such that $\tau(M(i, I)) = M(j, J)$. Putting $j = \tau'(i)$ we get a one-to-one mapping of I onto J. By virtue of proposition 7 this must be an isomorphism.

Assume now $\tau'_1 = \tau'_2$. Put $\sigma = \tau_2^{-1} \circ \tau_1$. Then σ is an automorphism of $\prod_{i \in I} O_i(M)$ over M and $\sigma(M(i, I)) = M(i, I)$ for all $i \in I$. Proposition 13 implies that every element of $|O_i(M)|$ is fixed under σ, for all $i \in I$. Since, by proposition 9, the closure of $|M| \cup \bigcup_{i \in I} |O_i(M)|$ under Skolem functions is the whole model $\prod_{i \in I} O_i(M)$, σ must be the identity automorphism. Hence $\tau_1 = \tau_2$. Q.E.D.

COROLLARY. If O_i are minimal-end-extension operators for $i \in I$, $I = \langle I, < \rangle$, and all are replicas of each other, then the isomorphisms over M between elementary submodels of $\prod_{i \in I} O_i(M)$ are exactly those which are induced by the isomorphisms between subsets of I.

In particular, if I is well-ordered $\prod_{i \in I} O_i(M)$ has no non trivial automorphism over M.

Let O be a minimal-end-extension operator whose domain consists of all models of **P** whose elements are separated from its symbols (by theorem 6 there exists one). Given any model M, and any ordered set I, let $\{O_i\}_{i \in I}$ be replicas of O whose sets of symbols are separated from each other. Fix some function symbol, f, of O and members $a_1, \ldots, a_n$ of $|M|$

so that $O(M) \models f(a_1, \ldots, a_n) \not\approx b$ for all $b \in |M|$. Let f_i be the corresponding symbol of O_i. As in 5 identify every $i \in I$ with $f_i(a_1, \ldots, a_n)$ (assuming $I \cap |M| = \emptyset$). Assume also that we have already identified every two elements a, a' so that $\prod_{i \in I} O_i(M) \models a \approx a'$. Arguing as in 5 (concerning the Ehrenfeucht-Mostowski theorem) and taking into account the corollary to theorem 9 and theorem 10 we get:

THEOREM 11[1]. With every model, M, of **P** and every ordered set I, such that $|M| \cap I = \emptyset$, one can correlate an elementary extension, $M(I)$, of M so that the following are satisfied.

(i) $M(I)$ is an end extension of M, and I is a subset of the set of new elements. The embedding of I into $M(I)$ is order preserving.

(ii) If $J \subseteq I$ and its ordering is the restriction of the ordering of I, then $M(J)$ is the elementary submodel of $M(I)$ which is generated by $|M| \cup J$. If $i \in I - J$ then $i \notin M(J)$.

(iii) Every elementary submodel of $M(I)$ which includes M is of the form $M(J)$, where $J \subseteq I$.

(iv) Every isomorphism of the ordered set I_1 onto I_2 has a unique extension which is an isomorphism over M of $M(I_1)$ onto $M(I_2)$.

(v) Every isomorphism over M of $M(I_1)$ onto $M(I_2)$ is the unique extension of an isomorphism of I_1 onto I_2.

(vi) The cardinality of $M(I)$ is the maximum of the cardinalities of M and I.

(vii) If $I_1 \cap I_2 = \emptyset$ then $M(I_1)(I_2) = M(I_1 + I_2)$ where $I_1 + I_2$ consists of $I_1 \cup I_2$ ordered by placing I_2 after I_1.

Given a model M of **P**, the set of all elements which are definable within it forms an elementary submodel. This submodel is the same (except for isomorphisms) for all models which are elementarily equi-

---

1) As we remarked in the introduction a weaker result in this direction was proved by Ehrenfeucht. He has shown that if M is a minimal model and I an ordered set, then there exists an extension, N, of M (which, of course. must be an end extension) embedding I among the added elements, such that every automorphism of I has a unique extension to an automorphism of N and all automorphisms of N map I onto itself. His proof yields also (iv) and (v) for $I_1, I_2 \subseteq I$, but not (iii). It can, probably, be generalized to any countable M although not to uncountable ones. His method is completely different, uses Ramsey's theorem and is of interest in itself. A forthcoming paper by Ehrenfeucht entitled "Rigid embeddings of order types in models of arithmetic" is due: unfortunately, unless its author can be prevailed upon, there is little chance of its appearing in the forseeable future.

valent to M. Thus every completion of **P** has a unique minimal model which is an elementary submodel of every other model of this theory. The standard model of the natural numbers is such an example. If M_0 is the minimal model which is included in both M_i, $i=1, 2$, then every isomorphism between the M_i's leaves fixed every member of M_0. Consequently if we take M to be a minimal model we can replace in theorem 11 "elementary submodel including M" and "isomorphism over M" by "elementary submodel" and "isomorphism". In particular, if I is also well-ordered we get rigid models (i.e. models with no non-trivial automorphisms) of any cardinality.

Let O be a minimal-end-extension operator such that M_0, $M \in D(O)$ where M_0 is the minimal model included in M. Fix a function symbol, f, of O and formulas, $\psi_1, \ldots, \psi_k$, which define members $a_1, \ldots, a_k$ of M_0 so that $O(M_0) \models f(a_1, \ldots, a_k) \not\approx b$ for all $b \in |M_0|$. Then also $O(M) \models f(a_1, \ldots, a_k) \not\approx b$ for all $b \in |M|$. Since $O(M)$ is a minimal extension of M it consists of all the values of Skolem functions for arguments taken from $|M| \cup \{f(a_1, \ldots, a_k)\}$. (i) Replace $f(a_1, \ldots, a_k)$ by a new constant c, (ii) for every formula $\varphi(x_1, \ldots, x_n, y)$, which defines a Skolem function, let f_φ be a new function symbol of $n-1$ places, and (iii) for every $b_1, \ldots, b_{n-1} \in |M|$ replace the unique y such that $O(M) \models \varphi(f(a_1, \ldots, a_k), b_1, \ldots, b_{n-1}, y)$ by $f_\varphi(b_1, \ldots, b_{n-1})$. In this way one gets a model isomorphic to $O(M)$ over M, which consists of $\Omega(|M|)$, where $\Omega = \{c, f_\varphi\}_\varphi$. The same process can be applied to every model in $D(O)$ which is elementary equivalent to M provided that its elements are separated from the symbols of Ω. If $D(O)$ includes as members models from different elementary classes then, for every elementary class, one has to fix a function symbol, f, and formulas $\psi_1, \ldots, \psi_m$ which define elements $a_1, \ldots, a_m$ of the minimal model, M_0, of this class, so that $O(M_0) \models f(a_1, \ldots, a_m) \not\approx b$ for all $b \in |M_0|$. c is to be interpreted as $f(a_1, \ldots, a_m)$ and the f_φ's are interpreted as before. (We assume, of course, that $M_0 \in D(O)$.) In this way we get a minimal-end-extension operator O^*, based on Ω which is defined for all models in $D(O)$ whose elements are separated from the symbols in Ω. If $D(O)$ contains with every model also all models isomorphic to it whose elements are separated from the symbols of O, one can extend the definition of O^*, in a natural way, so as to include in its domain every model M which is isomorphic to some model in $D(O)$, provided that $|M|$ and Ω are separated. These considerations show that, without loss of generality,

we can assume, for minimal-end-extension operators whose existence is claimed in theorem 6, that they are all of the following form:
O is based on $\{c, f_\varphi\}_\varphi$ where c is a 0-place function symbol and, for every formula $\varphi(x_1, \ldots, x_n, y)$ which defines a Skolem function of $x_1, \ldots, x_n$, f_φ is an $n-1$-place function symbol. If $M \in D(O)$ then $O(M) \models c \not\approx b$ for all $b \in |M|$ and, for $b_1, \ldots, b_{n-1} \in |M|$, $f_\varphi(b_1, \ldots, b_{n-1})$ is the unique y such that $O(M) \models \varphi(c, b_1, \ldots, b_{n-1}, y)$.

Given replicas of O, say O_i, $i \in I$, we can put $i = c_i$. Thus one can add the following claim to theorem 11.

(viii) For a fixed ordered set I one can add function symbols to I and define an end-extension operator O_I, based on them, so that $M(I)$ is the model obtained from $O_I(M)$ by identifying equal elements. $D(O_I)$ consists of all M's whose elements are separated from its function symbols.

Let us now turn to the case of minimal-end-extension operators which yield non isomorphic models.

DEFINITIONS. Let O be a u.e.o. based on Ω. We shall say that $D(O)$ is *closed under isomorphisms* if, for every $M \in D(O)$, $D(O)$ also includes every model isomorphic to M, provided that its set of elements is separated from Ω. Two u.e.o.'s, O_1 and O_2, are said to be *nowhere isomorphic* if $O_1(M)$ and $O_2(M)$ are not isomorphic over M, for all $M \in D(O_1) \cap D(O_2)$.

PROPOSITION 14. Let O_1, O_2 be u.e.o.'s which are nowhere isomorphic and whose domains are closed under isomorphisms. If $M_i \in D(O_i)$, $i = 1,2$ and τ is an isomorphism of M_1 onto M_2 then τ cannot be extended to an isomorphism of $O_1(M)$ onto $O_2(M)$.

PROOF. Choose a model M which is isomorphic to M_1 so that its elements are separated from the symbols of O_1 and O_2. By our assumptions $M \in D(O_1) \cap D(O_2)$. Let σ_1 be an isomorphism of M onto M_1 and let $\sigma_2 = \tau \circ \sigma_1$. Then σ_1 has an extension ρ_1 which maps $O_1(M)$ onto $O_1(M_1)$ and similarly σ_2 has an extension ρ_2 from $O_2(M)$ onto $O_2(M_2)$. If τ had an extension, say τ^*, which maps $O_1(M_1)$ onto $O_2(M_2)$ then $\rho_2^{-1} \circ \tau^* \circ \rho_1^{-1}$ would be an isomorphism over M of $O_1(M)$ onto $O_2(M)$, contradicting our assumptions. Q.E.D.

PROPOSITION 15. Let O_i be end-extension operators, $i \in I_1 \cup I_2$, $I_1 = \langle I_1, < \rangle$, $I_2 = \langle I_2, < \rangle$. Assume that, for all $i \in I_1 \cup I_2$, $D(O_i)$ is closed under isomorphisms. Then an isomorphism, τ, of I_1 onto I_2 induces an isomorphism of $\prod_{i\in I_1} O_i(M)$ onto $\prod_{i\in I_2} O_i(M)$ only if, for all $i\in I_1$, O_i and $O_{\tau(i)}$ are not nowhere isomorphic.

PROOF. The isomorphism induced by τ maps $\prod_{j<i} O_j(M)$ onto $\prod_{j<\tau(i)} O_j(M)$, and $O_i(\prod_{j<i} O_j(M))$ onto $O_{\tau(i)}(\prod_{j<\tau(i)} O_j(M))$. Our claim follows from proposition 14. Q.E.D.

If in addition the O_i's are minimal-end-extension operators and, for every $i_1\in I_1$, $i_2\in I_2$, either O_{i_1} and O_{i_2} are replicas of each other or nowhere isomorphic, then the isomorphisms over M of $\prod_{i\in I_1} O_i(M)$ onto $\prod_{i\in I_2} O_i(M)$ are exactly those induced by the isomorphisms, τ, of I_1 onto I_2 for which O_i and $O_{\tau(i)}$ are replicas of each other, for all $i\in I_1$.

Theorem 6 yields now the following result.

THEOREM 12[1]). Let I and J be ordered sets and let $\{I_n\}_n$ and $\{J_n\}_n$ be partitions of I and J, respectively, into countably many disjoint subsets. Then there are minimal-end-extension operators O_i, $i\in I\cup J$, with separated sets of symbols, so that the isomorphisms over M of $\prod_{i\in I} O_i(M)$ onto $\prod_{j\in J} O_j(M)$ are exactly those induced by those isomorphisms, τ of I onto J, which satisfy $\tau(I_n)=J_n$ for all n. The same is true for all submodels $\prod_{i\in I'} O_i(M)$, $\prod_{j\in J'} O_j(M)$ (where $I'\subseteq I$, $J'\subseteq J$) with respect to the partitions $\{I_n\cap I'\}_n$, $\{J_n\cap J'\}_n$. For each $i\in I$, $D(O_i)$ consists of all models of **P** whose elements are separated from the symbols of O_i.

PROOF: Consider the operators $O_1,\ldots, O_n,\ldots$ whose existence is claimed in theorem 6. For every n let all the O_i's where $i\in I_n\cup J_n$ be replicas of O_n, with separated sets of symbols. Q.E.D.

If, in particular, we take $I=J$ and the ordering to be a well-ordering, then every partition of I into two will yield a model with no non-trivial automorphisms over M, so that different partitions will yield models which are non-isomorphic over M. Thus, every model M, of **P** has 2^α end extensions which are non-isomorphic over it, and each of these has no automorphisms over M, is of cardinality = Max (cardinality of M, cardinality of α), and the segment which is added at the end embeds a well ordered subset of order type α. For limit numbers, α, the embedded subset is cofinal in it.

Inferences concerning other order types can be drawn as well and are left to the reader.

---

1) See footnote p. 140.

Note that in this way we get a model whose group of automorphisms over a given model is isomorphic to the subgroup of the automorphisms of a given ordered set I which map every I_n onto itself, where $\{I_n\}_n$ is a partition of I. We conclude by stating a generalization of theorem 11 whose proof should now be obvious.

By a partitioned ordered set we mean a system $\Lambda = \langle I, \{I_n\}_n \rangle$ where I is an ordered set and $\{I_n\}_n$ is a partition of I into disjoint subsets, n ranges over the natural numbers. We put $\langle J, \{J_n\}_n \rangle \subseteq \langle I, \{I_n\}_n \rangle$ if $J \subseteq I$, the ordering of J is the restricted ordering of I and $J_n = I_n \cap J$ for all n.

THEOREM 11*. Let M be a model of **P**. With every partitioned set, $\Lambda = \langle I, \{I_n\}_n \rangle$, such that $|M| \cap I = \emptyset$, one can correlate an elementary extension of M, $M(\Lambda)$ so that the following are satisfied.

(i) $M(\Lambda)$ is an end extension of M, and if $\Lambda = \langle I, \{I_n\}_n \rangle$ than I is a subset of the set of the new elements which are added to M. The embedding of I into $M(\Lambda)$ is order preserving.

(ii) If $\Lambda^i = \langle I_i, \{I_n^i\}_n \rangle$, $i = 1, 2$, and $\Lambda^1 \subseteq \Lambda^2$ then $M(\Lambda^1)$ is the elementary submodel of $M(\Lambda^2)$ which is generated by $|M| \cup I^1$. If $j \in I^2 - I^1$ then $j \notin M(\Lambda^2)$.

(iii) Every elementary submodel of $M(\Lambda)$ which includes M is of the form $M(\Lambda')$ where $\Lambda' \subseteq \Lambda$.

(iv) If $\Lambda^i = \langle I^i, \{I_n^i\}_n \rangle$, $i = 1, 2$, then every isomorphism of I^1 onto I^2 which maps I_n^1 onto I_n^2, for every n, has a unique extension to an isomorphism over M of $M(\Lambda^1)$ onto $M(\Lambda^2)$.

(v) Every isomorphism over M of $M(\Lambda^1)$ onto $M(\Lambda^2)$ maps I^1 onto I^2 and every I_n^1 onto every I_n^2 $(\Lambda_i = \langle I^i, \{I_n^1\} \rangle)$.

(vi) The cardinality of $M(\Lambda)$ is the maximum of the cardinalities of M and I.

(vii) If $\Lambda^i = \langle I^i, \{I_n^i\}_n \rangle$, $i = 1, 2$, then $M(\Lambda_1)(\Lambda_2) = M(\Lambda_3)$, where $\Lambda_3 = \langle I^3, \{I_n^3\}_n \rangle$; I^3 is obtained by placing I^2 after I^1 and $I_n^3 = I_n^1 \cup I_n^2$.

(viii) For a fixed partitioned ordered set, $\Lambda = \langle I, \{I_n\}_n \rangle$, one can add function symbols to I and define an end-extension operator O_Λ, which is based on them, so that $M(\Lambda)$ is $O_\Lambda(M)$ (except for identifying elements which are equal in $O_\Lambda(M)$). $D(O_\Lambda)$ consists of all models of **P** whose elements are separated from the symbols of O_Λ.

Postscript

The following is general way to define uniform and local extension operators; it generalizes the definitions as given before and offers, it will be seen, a general setting within which the work can be carried out. According to this approach, an u.e.o. is an operator which yields, for any given model in its domain, another model together with a proper elementary embedding of the first into the second; moreover, elementary embeddings between models in the domain of the operators are carried over to elementary embeddings between their respective images.

Using O for the operator, $O(M)$ is the value of M under O, O_M the embedding of M into $O(M)$, and, if τ is an elementary embedding, $O\tau$ is the one into which it is carried by O.

The requirements are:

(a) If $M \in D(O)$ then $O_M : M \to O(M)$ is a proper elementary embedding.

(b) If $\tau : M \to N$ is an elementary embedding and M, N, $\tau(M) \in D(O)$, then $O\tau : O(M) \to O(N)$ is an elementary embedding which makes the following diagram commutative.

$$\begin{array}{ccc} O(M) & \xrightarrow{O\tau} & O(N) \\ {\scriptstyle O_M}\uparrow & & \uparrow{\scriptstyle O_N} \\ M & \xrightarrow{\tau} & N \end{array}$$

(c) $O(\tau_1 \circ \tau_2) = O\tau_1 \circ O\tau_2$ and $O(1_M) = 1_{O(M)}$ where both sides of the equalities are defined and, for every model K, 1_K is its identity mapping onto itself.

(d) If $\tau : M \to N$ is an elementary embedding, where M, N, $\tau(M) \in D(O)$, then $a \in |O(M)| - O_M(|M|)$ implies $(O\tau)(a) \in |O(N)| - O_N(|N|)$. (The equality of the model is now interpreted as the real identity!).

(d) corresponds to (IV) of the definition in the article, and means that the property of being a "new element" is preserved when passing from M to N.

U.e.o.'s, as defined in the body of the article, satisfy (a)-(d), O_M being the identity mapping of M into $O(M)$ and $O\tau$, the mapping given by: $(O\tau)(a) = \tau(a)$ and $(O\tau)(f(a_1, \ldots)) = f(\tau(a_1), \ldots)$.

It is natural to stipulate that in case $L \xrightarrow{\sigma} M \xrightarrow{\tau} N$ are elementary embeddings such that L, M, N, as well as $\sigma(L)$ and $\tau(M)$, are in $D(O)$, then $\tau \circ \sigma(L)$ is also in $D(O)$. (In fact all the cases discussed in the article, and any others one can think of, which are not constructed through artificial restrictions of the domain of some "natural" operator, satisfy this.)

Having made this stipulation, one can regard the operator O in terms of category theory. It is a functor combined with a proper elementary embedding, O_M, of every M in its domain into $O(M)$, such that the diagram in (b) is commutative. The objects of the category in question are all the models in $D(O)$, the morphisms being the elementary embedding $\tau: M \to N$, where $M, N, \tau(M) \in D(O)$. If, moreover, for every $M \in D(O)$, we have also $O(M)$, $O_M(M) \in D(O)$, then O_M itself is a morphism of the category. In this case, the commutativity of the diagram in (b) is nothing else than the condition that O_M is a natural transformation between O, as a functor, and the identity functor. Consequently, O can be described then as consisting of a functor and a natural transformation between this functor and the identity functor. Such entities are old acquaintances; consider, for example, the assignment of V^{**}, the dual of the dual of the vector space V, to V, together with the natural embedding of V into V^{**}. In our case two additional requirements are to be met: that O_M is properly into, and (d). If $D(O)$ includes, with every model, all infinite models which are elementarily equivalent to it, then, to say that O_M is not onto is the same as to say that it is not an epimorphism of the category. It is conceivable that, in this case, an equivalent, or weaker but sufficient, formulation of (d) in purely category-theoretic terms is possible.

In any case (a)-(d), if not purely category-theoretic, are at least of general algebraic character, and can be applied to other classes consisting of systems and mappings between them. This goes also for the additional requirement which is used below to define local extension operators. Simple examples are not lacking; consider for instance the extension of any field by adjoining a new transcendental element, or the natural embedding of any group into its direct product with a fixed non-trivial group.

The straightforward way to define local operators would be to use either (V) or (V*) as a defining condition. Thus an operator O, satisfying (a)-(d) is said to be local provided that the following holds:

(e) Assume $M = \bigcup_{i \in I} M_i$ is a model in $D(O)$ such that $M_i \prec M$ and $M_i \in D(O)$, for all $i \in I$, and the M_i's are directed under elementary inclusion. Then, letting τ_i be the identity embedding of M_i into M, $O(M) = \bigcup_{i \in I} (O\tau_i)(M_i)$.

Or else, if one prefers (V*), then (e) is to be replaced by the stronger condition (e*), in which the assumption that the M_i's are directed is changed to the assumption that every finite subset of M is included in some M_i. Note that, in either (e) or (e*), the more general case, in which the τ_i's are any elementary embedding satisfying $\tau_i(M_i) \in D(O)$, is implied, by virtue of (a)-(c).

The whole work can be carried through, adopting these as the definitions of uniform and local extension operators. One has, of course, to reform the constructions and the assertions, but they are essentially the same. For instance, let us indicate here how $\prod_{i \in I} O_i$ is to be defined, where I is an ordered set, and O_i operators satisfying (a)-(d).

First let I_2 be a finite ordered set and let $I_1 \subseteq I_2$. Define the mapping $f_{I_1, I_2}: \prod_{i \in I} O_i(M) \to \prod_{i \in I_2} O_i(M)$ by induction on the number of elements of I_2. If $I_2 = \emptyset$ then $I_1 = I_2$, $\prod_{i \in I_2} O_i(M) = M$ and, f_{I_1, I_2} is the identity mapping of M onto M. If $I_2 \neq \emptyset$, let j be its greatest element with respect to the ordering. Put $J_1 = I_1 - \{j\}$, $J_2 = I_2 - \{j\}$, and $N = \prod_{i \in J_2} O_i(M)$. Then $\prod_{i \in I_2} O_i(M) = O_j(N)$, and $\prod_{i \in I_1} O_i(M)$ is either $O_j(\prod_{i \in J_1} O_i(M))$ or $\prod_{i \in J_1} O_i(M)$ according as $j \in I_1$ or $j \notin I_1$. In case $j \in I_1$ we define $f_{I_1, I_2} = O_j f_{J_1, J_2}$, and in case $j \notin I_1$ we define $f_{I_1, I_2} = O_{j_N} \circ f_{J_1, J_2}$.

$$
\begin{array}{ccc}
O_j(\prod_{i \in J_1} O_i(M)) & \xrightarrow[f_{I_1, I_2}]{} & O_j(\prod_{i \in J_1} O_i(M)) \\
\uparrow & & \uparrow \\
\prod_{i \in J_1} O_i(M) & \xrightarrow[f_{J_1, J_2}]{} & \prod_{i \in J_2} O_i(M)
\end{array}
\qquad
\begin{array}{ccc}
 & & O_j(\prod_{i \in J_2} O_i(M)) \\
 & {\nearrow}^{f_{I_1, I_2}} & \uparrow \\
\prod_{i \in J_1} O_i(M) & \xrightarrow[f_{J_1, J_2}]{} & \prod_{i \in J_2} O_i(M)
\end{array}
$$

First case Second case

One can show, using (d), that $I_1' \neq I_1$ always implies $f_{I_1', I_2} \neq f_{I_1, I_2}$ (even if all O_i's are equal).

Now let I be any ordered set. For any finite subset $J \subseteq I$, let M_J be a distinct replica of $\prod_{i \in J} O_i(M)$, obtained, say, by taking as its elements the pairs $\langle a, J \rangle$, where $a \in |\prod_{i \in J} O_i(M)|$, and making the mapping $a \to \langle a, J \rangle$ an isomorphism. If $J_1 \subseteq J_2$ and both are finite subsets of I, then define $f^*_{J_1, J_2}: M_{J_1} \to M_{J_2}$ as: $f^*_{J_1, J_2}(\langle a, J_1 \rangle) = \langle f_{J_1 J_2}(a), J_2 \rangle$. This yields a directed system of elementary embeddings between the models M_J. $\prod_{i \in J} O_i(M)$ is defined as the direct limit of the M_J's with respect to these mappings.

The disadvantages of this general approach, compared with that used in the body of the article, are that, in most places, an embedding is substituted for a simple inclusion, and a direct limit for a simple union. This tends to encumber constructions and arguments: whereas, previously, some simple claim needed no argument, now one visualizes a commutative diagram to convince himself of the analogous claim which, basically, is as simple.

On the other hand, the advantages are obvious. One gets rid of the function symbols on which the operator is based, and one does not worry about identifying elements which should not be identified. Indeed, with no loss of generality, it can be assumed that the elements of $O(M)$ are always distinct from those of M: because if not, one can redefine them to be so, by making them of the form $\langle a, M\rangle$ and defining the embeddings accordingly. Consequently, there is no need to consider different replicas of the same operator and a single operator is used whenever a class of replicas was used before. Finally the equality relation of the model can be interpreted as the real identity. All these and the generality of the approach more than compensate for the inconveniences which arise.

References

[1] A. Ehrenfeucht and A. Mostowski, Models of axiomatic theories admitting automorphisms, Fund. Math. **43** (1956) 50–60.

[2] R. MacDowell and E. Specker, Modelle der Arithmetik, Infinitistic Methods, Proc. Symp. on Foundations of Mathematics, Warsaw, 1959 (Pergamon Press, 1961) pp. 257–263.

[3] H. Gaifman, Results concerning models of Peano's arithmetic, Abstract 65T–195, Am. Math. Soc. Notices, Vol. 12, No. 3 (1965) p. 377.

[4] A. Ehrenfeucht and H. Laüchli, Rigid models, Abstract, J. Symbolic Logic **27** (1962) 475–76.

[5] H. Gaifman, Structure of models of Peano's arithmetic, in preparation.

[6] M. O. Rabin, Diophantine equations and non-standard models of arithmetic, Proc. 1960 Intern. Congress for Logic, Methodology and Philosophy of Science (Stanford University Press, 1962) pp. 151–158.

REPRESENTATIONS OF PROBABILITIES DEFINED ON FIRST ORDER LANGUAGES

J. E. FENSTAD
Universitetet i Oslo, Norway

1. Introduction

Let L be a first order language, a probability c on L is a map which associates with each formula α of L a real number in the unit interval [0,1] and which satisfies the rules

(i) $c(\alpha \vee \beta) + c(\alpha \wedge \beta) = c(\alpha) + c(\beta)$;
(ii) $c(\neg \alpha) = 1 - c(\alpha)$;
(iii) $c(\alpha) = c(\beta)$, if $\underset{L}{\vdash} \alpha \leftrightarrow \beta$;
(iv) $c(\alpha) = 1$, if $\underset{L}{\vdash} \alpha$.

Carnap (in [1] and later writings) has initiated a study of logical probabilities c, in particular he has been interested in obtaining a "preferred" probability function c^* (when given a language L) on which to base the development of an inductive logic. In this paper we are going to take a somewhat different viewpoint. Instead of aiming at choosing a particular c, we shall be interested in determining the "possible forms" of any given c, i.e. we are interested in obtaining representation theorems for logical probabilities.

The first main theorem (theorem 2 of section 3) determines each probability c on the language L in terms of probabilities related to models of L. A model M of L is a set of individuals X_M together with certain relations defined over this set corresponding to the predicate symbols of L. The basic relation connecting L and M is "the sequence x of individuals from X_M satisfies the formula α of L in M". Let us denote by $\alpha[M]$ the set of sequences from X_M satisfying α in M. Further let S denote the space of models of L.

The basic representation theorem then states that with any probability

c on L there is associated a (σ-additive) probability λ on the model-space S and for each $M \in S$ a probability μ_M on the sets $\alpha[M]$, where α is a formula of L, such that

$$c(\alpha) = \int_S \mu_M(\alpha[M]) \, \mathrm{d}\lambda(M).$$

The measure λ is determined in the following way. For each sentence γ of L let S_γ be the set of models in S in which γ is true. Then λ is defined by setting $\lambda(S_\gamma) = c(\gamma)$.

Thus the theorem roughly states that any probability $c(\alpha)$ is obtained by taking a "linear combination" of probabilities in models with respect to some "weight-function" λ on the set of all models.

REMARK. Our starting point in this paper has been the work of Łoš [2]. In fact, the representation theorem is essentially due to him. However, we were not entirely satisfied with his proof, and we believe that in our exposition the proof is more complete (see in particular parts 4° and 5° of the proof as given below). Further the use of the completeness theorem of logic in part 1° of the proof seems to be a small improvement. But, the basic idea of using the Radon-Nikodym theorem to obtain the probabilities μ_M (see part 2°) is due to Łoš.

If α is a "property of individuals", i.e. α is a formula with one free variable, then $\mu_M(\alpha[M])$ ought to give some information about the number of individuals of M that have the property α. And, in fact, if we assume that individuals in models are equiprobable (i.e. they count equally in determining the number of "successes"), and if in addition we assume that no axiom of infinity receives positive probability, then $\mu_M(\alpha[M])$ is uniquely determined as the relative frequency of the property α in M, and we may restrict ourselves to the subset S_0 of finite models in the representation theorem.

If $\mathrm{fr}(\alpha, M)$ denotes the relative frequency of α in M, we may further conclude (theorem 3 of section 4) that

$$\frac{1}{n}\sum_{i=1}^{n} \mathrm{fr}(\alpha, M_i) \to c(\alpha)$$

for almost all sequences $\langle M_i \rangle$ of (finite) models. Thus in a sense the probability $c(\alpha)$ is a limit of "observed frequencies". We shall not attempt to discuss the possible foundational relevance of this result, but only remark that within the theory of logical probabilities it imposes a certain kind of consistency requirement on the choice of a confirmation function c. (In this paper we aim at presenting a few technical results on probability functions defined on first order languages. We hope in a further publication to discuss some "foundational problems" in connection with these and other similar results.)

The last main theorem included (theorem 4 of section 5) gives a simple version of de Finetti's theorem on exchangeable events as stated within the framework of logical probabilities (see de Finetti [3]). Imposing a certain symmetry condition on c we shall be able to deduce de Finetti's theorem as applied to the binomial case from the representation theorem for logical probabilities. (The proof uses only simple combinatorial arguments in addition to the representation theorem.)

De Finetti's theorem on exchangeable events roughly states that the probability of any such event is obtained by taking a "linear combination" of probabilities corresponding to cases of independent equiprobable events. The representation theorem for logical probabilities may be considered as a generalization of this result.

Remark. By the requirement (iii) above c is defined on the Boolean algebra of equivalence classes of provably equivalent formulas. Thus instead of considering L we shall work within this Boolean algebra. However, we want to carry over to this algebra the quantifier and the substitution operator. The resulting algebraic construct is called a *polyadic algebra.* So in the sequel we shall consider probabilities on polyadic algebras.

In section 2 we give a brief exposition of concepts and results from the theory of polyadic algebras needed for the subsequent development. (See Halmos [4] for a more complete exposition.)

2. Algebraic logic

In this section we shall give the necessary background from the theory of polyadic algebras. The main reference is Halmos [4].

A polyadic algebra is the algebraic counterpart of the first order predicate logic obtained by identifying equivalent formulas. More precisely, a *polyadic algebra* $\langle A, I, S, \exists\rangle$ consists of a Boolean algebra A, a non-empty set I, and two maps S and $\exists$. S is a map from transformations $\tau: I \to I$ to Boolean endomorphisms on A. The image $S(\tau)$ is called a *substitution* on A. $\exists$ is a map from subsets $J \subseteq I$ to quantifiers $\exists(J)$ on A, where by a *quantifier* we understand a map $\exists(J)$: $A \to A$ satisfying the following three conditions:

(i) $\exists(J)0 = 0$

(where $0 \in A$ denotes the zero element of the Boolean algebra);

(ii) $p \leq \exists(J)p$, for all $p \in A$;

and

(iii) $\exists(J)(p \wedge \exists(J)q) = \exists(J)p \wedge \exists(J)q$.

The reader may easily interpret the properties (i)–(iii) in terms of the existential quantifier in predicate logic.

The interplay of the maps S and $\exists$ properly defines the notion of polyadic algebra. The first two axioms assert that S is a semi-group homomorphism from transformations to substitutions, i.e.

$$S(\delta) = \text{identity}, \quad \text{where} \quad \delta i = i \quad \text{for all} \quad i \in I,$$
$$S(\sigma\tau) = S(\sigma)S(\tau).$$

The corresponding axioms for $\exists$ are:

$$\exists(\emptyset) = \text{identity},$$
$$\exists(J \cup K) = \exists(J)\exists(K).$$

For the next axiom assume that $\sigma = \tau$ on $I - J$, then

$$S(\sigma)\exists(J) = S(\tau)\exists(J).$$

And finally, if τ is injective on $\tau^{-1}J$, then

$$\exists(J)S(\tau) = S(\tau)\exists(\tau^{-1}J).$$

The polyadic algebra $\langle A, I, S, \exists\rangle$ is called *locally finite* if for all $p \in A$ there exists a finite subset $J \subseteq I$ such that $\exists(I-J)p = p$. The set J is then called a support of p. It is easily seen that the intersection of all supports of p is again a support of p which we denote by supp(p). If the set I is infinite, the polyadic algebra is said to be of *infinite degree*. In this paper all algebras are supposed to be locally finite of infinite degree.

The general algebraic theory of polyadic algebras is not very difficult being an immediate generalization of the Boolean counterpart. An exposition can be found in Halmos [4]. We recall that polyadic homomorphisms are Boolean homomorphisms commuting with $\exists$ and S, polyadic ideals are Boolean ideals closed under $\exists$ and S. A main result is that *every polyadic algebra is semi-simple.*

We shall also have occasion to refer to a "computational" result. Define the relation $\sigma J_* \tau$ to hold if $\sigma i = \tau i$ for all $i \in I - J$. Then for locally finite polyadic algebras of infinite degree

$$S(\tau)\exists(J)p = \bigvee \{S(\sigma)p : \sigma J_* \tau\}.$$

Let F be a first order language and let Γ be a set of sentences of F. Let F_Γ denote the *algebra of formulas* obtained from F by identifying two formulas α_1 and α_2 if the equivalence $\alpha_1 \leftrightarrow \alpha_2$ is deducible from Γ. It is well-known that the propositional connectives in F induce a Boolean structure on F_Γ and it is fairly straigtforward but rather laborious to verify that the quantifier and the substitution operator of the logic make F_Γ into a locally finite polyadic algebra of infinite degree (provided that there is an infinite set of variables available in the logic F).

Algebras of formulas are the first main examples of polyadic algebras. The second main examples are derived from the notion of interpretation or model of first order languages. Let $\mathbf{X}$ and I be non-empty sets and B a Boolean algebra. Define on the set of all maps $p : \mathbf{X}^I \to B$ two operations $S(\tau)$ and $\exists(J)$ in the following way.

For any transformation τ define $\tau_* x$, where $x \in \mathbf{X}^I$, by $(\tau_* x)_i = x_{\tau i}$, then $S(\tau)$ is defined by

$$S(\tau)p(x) = p(\tau_* x),$$

for all $x \in \mathbf{X}^I$ and $p : \mathbf{X}^I \to B$.

For any $J \subseteq I$ denote by $xJ_* y$ the relation that $x_i = y_i$ for all $i \in I - J$, then $\exists(J)$ is defined by

$$\exists(J)p(x) = \bigvee \{p(y) : x J_* y\}.$$

A *B-valued functional polyadic algebra A* is defined to be a Boolean subalgebra of maps from $\mathbf{X}^I$ to B closed under the operations $S(\tau)$ and $\exists(J)$. Usually B is taken to be the Boolean algebra O consisting of two elements $\{0,1\}$. A functional algebra of this kind is called a *model.* An important but easy result states that *every model is simple*. The converse statement taken in conjunction with the fact that every polyadic algebra is semi-simple, yields the following representation theorem.

THEOREM 1. Every locally finite polyadic algebra of infinite degree is isomorphic to a subdirect product of models.

A proof can be found in Halmos [4] or Fenstad [5] (among other places). A consequence of the representation theorem is that the space of models S of a polyadic algebra A is compact in the topology induced by the sets S_q, where q is a "sentence" of A (i.e. $\text{supp}(q)=\emptyset$), defined by the condition that $M\in S_q$ iff $q_M=1$. This may be seen as follows: A set of sentences $\{q_\lambda\}$ has a model iff each finite subset of $\{q_\lambda\}$ has a model. Thus $\cap S_{q_\lambda}=\emptyset$ iff some finite intersection $S_{q_1}\cap\ldots\cap S_{q_n}=\emptyset$. As every closed set in S is an intersection of sets S_q, the conclusion follows. Note that if q is a sentence, then S_q is both open and closed. Thus, in particular, if $S_q=\cup S_{q_\lambda}$, then $S_q=S_{q_1}\cup\ldots\cup S_{q_n}$ for some number n. This observation will be of use below.

REMARK. In the rest of this paper we shall assume that *all occurring algebras A are denumerable and that the index set I can be identified with the set of natural numbers.*

3. Polyadic probabilities

Let $\langle A,I,S,\exists\rangle$ be a denumerable polyadic algebra. A probability function c on A is a map $c\colon A\to[0,1]$ which satisfies the following conditions:

(i) $c(p)\geq 0$, for all $p\in A$;

(ii) $c(1)=1$, $c(0)=0$;

(iii) $c(p\vee q)+c(p\wedge q)=c(p)+c(q)$.

We do not assume that c is continuous. In this paper we do not enter into questions of elementary axiomatics investigating in more detail how c can be related to the polyadic structure of A. Rather we proceed at once to the main representation theorem.

THEOREM 2. Let $\langle A,I,S,\exists\rangle$ be a denumerable locally finite polyadic algebra of infinite degree and let c be a probability on A. Then there exists a σ-additive probability measure λ on the space S of models of A and for each model $M\in S$ a probability μ_M on the sets $p[M]=\{x\in X_M^I$:

$p_M(x)=1\}$ such that c can be given by the formula

$$c(p)=\int_S \mu_M(p[M])\,\mathrm{d}\lambda(M).$$

PROOF. The proof will be given in several steps:

1°. Let q be a sentence of A, i.e. $\operatorname{supp}(q)=\emptyset$. Define the set S_q by $M\in S_q$ iff $q_M=1$. Let $\mathfrak{A}_1$ be the collection of all sets S_q. On $\mathfrak{A}_1$ define a set function λ by

$$\lambda(A_q)=c(q).$$

$\lambda(A_q)$ is well-defined as $A_q=A_p$ implies that $q=p$ by the representation theorem of section 2. $\mathfrak{A}_1$ is an algebra and λ is an additive set function on this algebra. We shall prove that λ is continuous on $\mathfrak{A}_1$. Thus assume that $S_q=\cup S_{q_n}$. By the compactness of S this implies that $S_q=S_{q_1}\cup\ldots\cup S_{q_n}=S_{q_1\vee\ldots\vee q_n}$ for some number n. Hence $q=q_1\vee\ldots\vee q_n$. Thus $\lambda(S_q)=c(q)=c(q_1\vee\ldots\vee q_n)=\lambda(S_{q_1}\cup\ldots\cup S_{q_n})\leq\lim_n\lambda(S_{q_1}\cup\ldots\cup S_{q_n})\leq\lambda(S_q)$. This proves the continuity, therefore λ can be uniquely extended to a σ-additive probability measure on the σ-algebra $\mathfrak{A}$ generated by the algebra $\mathfrak{A}_1$. λ is a probability measure as $\lambda(S)=\lambda(S_1)=c(1)=1$.

2°. Next for each $p\in A$ define a measure λ_p on $\mathfrak{A}_1$ by

$$\lambda_p(S_q)=c(p\wedge q).$$

As above λ_p is well-defined and it is immediate that each λ_p extends to a probability measure on $\mathfrak{A}$. Further $c(p\wedge q)\leq c(q)$, thus each measure λ_p is absolutely continuous with respect to the measure λ. Hence the Radon-Nikodym theorem applies, i.e. there exist non-negative measurable functions f_p, $p\in A$, such that

$$\lambda_p(B)=\int_B f_p(M)\,\mathrm{d}\lambda(M),$$

for all sets $B\in\mathfrak{A}$. This gives

$$c(p)=c(p\wedge 1)=\lambda_p(S)=\int_S f_p(M)\,\mathrm{d}\lambda(M),$$

for each $p\in A$. It remains to convert $f_p(M)$ into a probability measure on the sets $p[M]$.

3°. As a preliminary we shall investigate the properties of the functions

f_p, $p \in A$. Each f_p can be chosen such that

(i) $0 \leq f_p \leq 1$,
(ii) $f_1 = 1$ and $f_0 = 0$,
(iii) $f_{p \vee q} + f_{p \wedge q} = f_p + f_q$.

The proof is by calculation. We indicate a few instances: Let $S_q \in \mathfrak{A}_1$, then

$$\int_{S_q} f_1(M)\,\mathrm{d}\lambda(M) = \lambda_1(S_q) = c(1 \wedge q) = c(q) = \lambda(S_q) = \int_{S_q} 1 \cdot \mathrm{d}\lambda(M),$$

thus $f_1(M)=1$, except for a subset of S of λ-measure 0. In the same way we obtain $f_0=0$ for almost all $M \in S$. Next let $p_1, p_2 \in A$ and $S_q \in \mathfrak{A}_1$:

$$\begin{aligned}\int_{S_q} (f_{p_1} + f_{p_2})(M)\,\mathrm{d}\lambda(M) &= \int_{S_q} f_{p_1}(M)\,\mathrm{d}\lambda(M) + \int_{S_q} f_{p_2}(M)\,\mathrm{d}\lambda(M) = \\ &= \lambda_{p_1}(S_q) + \lambda_{p_2}(S_q) = c(p_1 \wedge q) + c(p_2 \wedge q) = \\ &= c((p_1 \wedge q) \vee (p_2 \wedge q)) + \\ &\qquad c((p_1 \wedge q) \wedge (p_2 \wedge q)) = \\ &= c((p_1 \vee p_2) \wedge q) + c((p_1 \wedge p_2) \wedge q) = \\ &= \int_{S_q} f_{p_1 \vee p_2}(M)\,\mathrm{d}\lambda(M) + \\ &\qquad \int_{S_q} f_{p_1 \wedge p_2}(M)\,\mathrm{d}\lambda(M) = \\ &= \int_{S_q} (f_{p_1 \vee p_2} + f_{p_1 \wedge p_2})(M)\,\mathrm{d}\lambda(M),\end{aligned}$$

thus $f_{p_1 \vee p_2} + f_{p_1 \wedge p_2} = f_{p_1} + f_{p_2}$ for almost all $M \in S$. In this way we obtain a countable set $\{I_n\}$ of equalities or inequalities such that each I_n is true except for some set $B_n \subseteq S$ of measure 0. As $\lambda(\cup B_n) \leq \sum \lambda(B_n) = 0$, we obtain a set B of measure 0 such that each I_n is true except possibly on B. But then by choosing an $M_0 \in S - B$ we may redefine the functions f_p by setting $f_p(M) = f_p(M_0)$ if $M \in B$, thus obtaining the validity of (i)–(iii) for all $M \in S$ (as well as preserving the results of 2°).

4°. In order to conclude the proof we shall need the following result.

LEMMA. Let $p \in A$ and $M \in S$. If $p_M(x)=1$ for all $x \in X_M^I$, then f_p can be chosen such that $f_p(M)=1$.

PROOF. Define $B_p=\{M \in S\colon\ p_M(x)=1$ for all $x \in X_M^I\}$. Let q be the universal closure of p, i.e. $q=(\exists(I)p')'$ where p' denotes the complement of p in A. Then $q_M=1$ iff $M \in B_p$, hence $B_p = S_q$. We note that $q \leq p$, thus $q=p \wedge q$.

If $\lambda(S_q)=0$, we may modify f_p on a null-set such that $f_p(M)=1$ for $M \in B_p$. Hence we may assume that $\lambda(S_q)>0$. We have

$$\lambda_p(S_q) = \int_{Sq} f_p(M)\,\mathrm{d}\,\lambda(M).$$

But $\lambda_p(S_q)$ can also be evaluated in another way:

$$\lambda_p(S_q) = c(p \wedge q) = c(q) = \lambda(S_q) = \int_{Sq} 1\cdot \mathrm{d}\,\lambda(M).$$

Thus

$$\int_{Sq} (1-f_p)(M)\,\mathrm{d}\,\lambda(M) = 0,$$

and as $1-f_p \geq 0$ and $\lambda(S_q)>0$, we obtain that $1-f_p=0$ for almost all $M \in S_q$. Thus we may modify f_p on a set of measure zero so that $f_p(M)=1$ for all $M \in B_p$. This concludes the proof of the lemma.

5°. A natural way of converting the functions $f_p(M)$, $p \in A$, into probabilities on the models M is to interchange variable and parameter in $f_p(M)$, i.e. we may try to define

$$\mu_M(p[M]) = f_p(M),$$

where, for each $p \in A$, $p[M]$ is the subset of sequences of X_M^I which satisfy p, i.e. $p[M]=\{x \in X_M;\ p_M(x)=1\}$. The main difficulty is to verify that the definition is legitimate, i.e. that $p[M]=q[M]$ implies $f_p(M)=f_p(M)$.

Suppose there are elements $p, q \in A$ and a model $M_0 \in S$ such that $p[M_0]=q[M_0]$ but $f_p(M_0) \neq f_q(M_0)$. Consider the element $p\Delta q \in A$ defined by

$$p\,\Delta\, q = (p \vee q') \wedge (p' \vee q).$$

Using the formulas of section 3° we have

$$f_{p\Delta q} + f_1 = f_{p \vee q'} + f_{p' \vee q}.$$

From $p[M_0]=q[M_0]$ we conclude that either $p_{M_0}(x)=q_{M_0}(x)=1$ or $p_{M_0}(x)=q_{M_0}(x)=0$ for $x\in X_M^I$. Thus

$$(p\,\Delta\,q)_{M_0}(x)=1$$

for all $x\in X_M^I$. The lemma of section 4° then implies that we may take $f_{p\Delta q}(M_0)=1$. From the above identity it then follows that

$$f_{p\vee q'}(M_0)=f_{p'\vee q}(M_0)=1\,.$$

From section 3° we have the following identities

$$f_p+f_{q'}=f_{p\vee q'}+f_{p\wedge q'},$$
$$f_{p'}+f_q=f_{p'\vee q}+f_{p'\wedge q}.$$

Adding these identities and using the fact that $f_{p'}=1-f_p$ for all $p\in A$, we have

$$f_{p\vee q'}+f_{p\wedge q'}+f_{p'\vee q}+f_{p'\wedge q}=2\,.$$

Combining this result with the values of $f_{p\vee q'}(M_0)$ and $f_{p'\vee q}(M_0)$ obtained above, it follows that $f_{p\wedge q'}(M_0)=f_{p'\wedge q}(M_0)=0$. But then we have

$$f_p(M_0)+f_{q'}(M_0)=1+0=1\,,$$

i.e. $f_p(M_0)=f_q(M_0)$, contradicting our assumption above. Thus uniqueness is proved: $p[M]=q[M]$ implies $f_p(M)=f_q(M)$.

6°. Some rather trivial calculations are now all that is necessary to finish the proof.

We must show that $\mu_M(p[M])$ is a probability on the algebra $\mathfrak{A}_M=\{p[M];\ p\in A\}$. We give a sample calculation:

$$\begin{aligned}\mu_M(p[M])+\mu_M(q[M])&=f_p(M)+f_q(M)=f_{p\vee q}(M)+f_{p\wedge q}(M)=\\&=\mu_M((p\vee q)[M])+\mu_M((p\wedge q)[M])=\\&=\mu_M(p[M]\cup q[M])+\mu_M(p[M]\cap q[M]),\end{aligned}$$

using for the last equality the fact that interpretations in models are Boolean homomorphisms. Thus from 2° we obtain

$$c(p)=\int_S \mu_M(p[M])\,\mathrm{d}\lambda(M),$$

and the proof is complete.

Remark. Using the identity $\exists(J)p=\bigvee\{S(\sigma_n)p;\ \sigma_n J_* \delta\}$, where $\langle\sigma_n\rangle$ is an enumeration of all transformations being the identity outside $J \cap$ supp (p), it can be proved that if c satisfies the assumption

$$c(\exists(J)p) = \lim c(S(\sigma_1)p \vee \ldots \vee S(\sigma_n)p),$$

then each μ_M can be chosen so that

$$\mu_M(\exists(J)p[M]) = \lim \mu_M(S(\sigma_1)p[M] \cup \ldots \cup S(\sigma_n)p[M]).$$

4. A limit theorem

To state our result we shall need some further concepts from the theory of polyadic algebras. An n-place predicate of a polyadic algebra A is a map $P: I^n \to A$ such that

$$S(\tau)P(i_1, \ldots, i_n) = P(\tau i_1, \ldots, \tau i_n),$$

for all $\langle i_1, \ldots, i_n \rangle \in I^n$ and all transformations τ. An equality E for a polyadic algebra A is a binary predicate which satisfies:

(i) $E(i,i) = 1$, for all $i \in I$;

(ii) $p \wedge E(i,j) \leq S(i/j)p$,

whenever $i,j \in I$ and $p \in A$. Here $S(i/j)$ denotes the substitution which replaces the variable i by the variable j. For elementary properties of equality algebras we refer to Halmos [4].

An equality model M is a O-valued functional algebra with equality E_0 defined by:

$$E_0(i,j)(x) = \begin{cases} 1 & \text{if} \quad x_i = x_j, \\ 0 & \text{if} \quad x_i \neq x_j, \end{cases}$$

for all $x \in X_M^I$. The basic representation theorem of section 2 may be extended to assert that *every locally finite simple equality algebra of infinite degree is isomorphic to an equality model* (Halmos [4] p. 228).

Let A be an algebra with equality E. We shall assume that A contains elements $v_1, v_2, \ldots, v_n, \ldots$ which, in a sense to be made precise, denote constants. As, by assumption, I can be identified with the set of natural numbers, we shall denote variables by natural numbers. We now assume that for all n, $\text{supp}(v_n) = \{1\}$ and further that

(A) $$\exists(\{1\})[v_n \wedge \forall(\{2\})[(S(1/2)v_n)' \vee E(1,2)]] = 1$$

holds in A for all n. Next we shall let t_n express that there are exactly n

individuals, i.e. t_n is the following element of A:

(B)
$$t_n = \exists(\{1,2,\dots,n\})\left[\bigwedge_{\substack{1\le i,j\le n\\ i\ne j}} E(i,j)' \wedge \forall(\{n+1\})\left[\bigvee_{1\le i\le n} E(i,n+1)\right]\right].$$

Here $\bigwedge$ and $\bigvee$ denote repeated intersections and unions. Finally we want to express that if a model has n individuals, they are all named by some v_i, i.e. we assume that the following inequalities are satisfied in A:

(C)
$$t_n \le \bigwedge_{\substack{1\le i,j\le n\\ i\ne j}} \forall(\{1\})[v_i' \vee v_j'].$$

It is not at all difficult to verify that such algebras A exist: take any equality model over a finite domain and suitably define the functions v_n, $n=1,2,\dots$, as "characteristic functions" of individuals in the model. Thus our notational devices (A)–(C) are consistent.

We shall consider probabilities c on A satisfying:

(i) c makes individuals in models equiprobable (a "sampling-type" model), and

(ii) no extended axiom of infinity shall receive positive probability. The first requirement is made precise through the following set of identities:

(I)
$$c(S(\sigma)v_i \wedge q) = c(S(\tau)v_j \wedge q)$$

for all sentences $q \in A$, all transformations τ and σ, and all pairs of indices $i,j \in I$. Next, if B is any set of sentences of A, say $B=\{p_n\}$, we define $c(B)=\lim c(p_1 \wedge \dots \wedge p_n)$, a definition which makes $c(B)=\lambda(B^*)$, where $B^* = \cap\{S_p;\, p\in B\}$. Our second requirement is then rendered by

(II) For any set B of sentences of A, if $c(B)>0$, then there shall exist an n such that for all $q_1,\dots,q_m \in B$, $q_1 \wedge \dots \wedge q_m \wedge t_n \ne 0$.

This means, by use of the representation theorem, that if a set of sentences in A has positive probability, it is satisfied in some finite model.

One further remark, in the present context S denotes the class of *equality* models of A. But because of the representation theorem for equality algebras, the development of section 3 remains valid, so that any c on A can be represented in the form

$$c(p) = \int_S \mu_M(p[M])\,\mathrm{d}\lambda(M),$$

where each $M \in S$ is an equality model.

Let S_0 be the set of finite models in S, i.e. if $M \in S_0$, then $\text{card}(X_M)$ is finite. We shall prove that $\lambda(S_0)=1$. Obviously, $S_0 = \cap S_{t_n}$, hence

$$\lambda(S_0) = \lim \lambda(S_{t_1} \cup \ldots \cup S_{t_n}) = \lim c(t_1 \vee \ldots \vee t_n).$$

Now $\lim c(t_1 \vee \ldots \vee t_n) = 1 - \lim c(t_1' \wedge \ldots \wedge t_n') = 1 - c(\{t_n' : n > 0\})$. Suppose that $c(\{t_n' : n > 0\}) > 0$, then by (II) there is a t_n consistent with the set $\{t_n' ; n > 0\}$, which is impossible. Hence $c(\{t_n' : n > 0\}) = 0$, and the validity of $\lambda(S_0)=1$ follows. But then $\lambda(S - S_0) = 0$, and we may instead of integrating over S, restrict the domain of integration to S_0; thus for $p \in A$ we have

$$c(p) = \int_{S_0} \mu_M(p[M]) \, \mathrm{d}\lambda(M).$$

We shall next evaluate $\mu_M(v_i[M])$ for $M \in S_0$. From (I) we obtain

$$\int_{Sq} \mu_M(v_i[M]) \, \mathrm{d}\lambda(M) = c(S(\delta) v_i \wedge q) = c(S(\delta) v_j \wedge q) = \int_{Sq} \mu_M(v_j[M]) \, \mathrm{d}\lambda(M),$$

hence by modifying on null-sets we obtain the set of equalities

$$\mu_M(v_i[M]) = \mu_M(v_j[M])$$

for all i and j and all $M \in S$. Let $M \in S_0$, then $X_M = \{k_1, \ldots, k_n\}$. Define the following equivalence relation on the set X_M^I:

$$x \sim y \quad \text{iff} \quad x_1 = y_1 .$$

Then we have

$$X_M^I = \bigcup_{i=1}^{n} [k_i],$$

a disjoint union, where $x \in [k_i]$ iff $x_1 = k_i$. From definition (B) we may conclude that $(t_n)_M = 1$. Hence the inequalities (C) imply that $(v_1)_M, \ldots, (v_n)_M$ are all different functions of M, in fact, using (A) we see that there is some permutation of the set $k_1, \ldots, k_n$ such that

$$(v_j)_M(x) = 1 \quad \text{iff} \quad x_1 = k_{i_j},$$

for all $x \in X_M^I$ and $j = 1, \ldots, n$. Hence we conclude that

$$v_j[M] = [k_{i_j}],$$

$j=1,\ldots,n$. Applying this result to the decomposition of X_M^I obtained above, we get

$$1=\mu_M(X_M^I)=\mu_M\left(\bigcup_{i=1}^{n}[k_i]\right)=\sum_{i=1}^{n}\mu_M([k_i])=\sum_{i=1}^{n}\mu_M(v_i[M]).$$

From this and the equality $\mu_M(v_i[M])=\mu_M(v_j[M])$ it follows that

$$\mu_M(v_i[M])=\operatorname{card}(X_M)^{-1},\qquad i=1,\ldots,n.$$

In order not to complicate our notation unduly we shall state a special case of the limit theorem. Let $p\in A$ and suppose that $\operatorname{supp}(p)=\{1\}$. Define the function fr (p,M), $M\in S_0$, by

$$\operatorname{fr}(p,M)=\operatorname{card}(X_M)^{-1}\cdot\sum p_M(x),$$

where the sum is extended over one representative from each of the equivalence classes $[k_1],\ldots,[k_n]$, $n=\operatorname{card}(X_M)$. Thus fr (p,M) gives the observed relative frequency of the "property" p in the finite model M. We propose to show that $\mu_M(p[M])=\operatorname{fr}(p,M)$. This is seen as follows: $p[M]=\bigcup[k_i]$, where we take the union of those $[k_i]$ such that $x\in[k_i]$ implies $p_M(x)=1$; hence

$$\mu_M(p[M])=\mu_M(\bigcup[k_i])=\sum\mu_M([k_i])=\operatorname{fr}(p,M).$$

Define the following random variable X on S_0:

$$X(M)=\operatorname{fr}(p,M).$$

It is then an easy calculation to show that

$$E|X|=EX=\int_{S_0}\operatorname{fr}(p,M)\,\mathrm{d}\lambda(M)=\int_{S}\mu_M(p[M])\,\mathrm{d}\lambda(M)=c(p).$$

An application of Kolmogorov's strong law of large numbers yields the following result.

THEOREM 3. Let A be a denumerable polyadic algebra with equality and let the special elements v_n and t_n, $n=1,2,\ldots$, satisfy the requirements (A), (B) and (C). Let c be any probability on A satisfying (I) and (II). If S_0 is the set of finite models of A and p is any element of A with $\operatorname{supp}(p)=\{1\}$, then

$$\frac{1}{n}\sum_{i=1}^{n}\operatorname{fr}(p,M_i)\to c(p)$$

for almost all sequences $\langle M_i\rangle$ from S_0.

Remark. The precise content of the above convergence assertion is as follows. Let S^* be a countable power of S_0 and consider on S^* the product measure λ^* defined from the measure λ on S_0. Then for almost all sequences $\langle M_i \rangle \in S^*$, where each M_i belongs to S_0, $(1/n)\sum_{i=1}^{n} \mathrm{fr}(p, M_i)$ converges to $c(p)$ in the usual sense of numerical convergence. Thus the assertion of the theorem is true except possibly for a set $\{\langle M_i \rangle\}$ of sequences of λ^*-measure zero in the product space S^*.

5. An elementary version of de Finetti's theorem

In the previous section we imposed the symmetry condition

$$c(S(\sigma)v_i \wedge q) = c(S(\tau)v_j \wedge q),$$

and concluded that $\mu_M(v_i[M]) = 1/n$, where $n = \mathrm{card}(X_M)$. The argument only used the special case when $\sigma = \tau =$ identity. The full force of (I) implies that each μ_M, $M \in S_0$, which is a measure on a product space X_M^I, determines the normalized counting measure on each factor (i.e. if $\mathrm{card}(X_M) = n$, then each point (individual) of X_M is assigned the measure $1/n$).

We shall now impose an extended symmetry condition on c which will imply that each measure μ_M is a product of (normalized) counting measures. Hence each $M \in S_0$ corresponds to a case of independent equiprobable events, thus by using the techniques of section 4 we shall be able to derive a version of de Finetti's theorem.

The notational conventions (A)–(C) of section 4, as well as the finiteness assumption (II) will be retained. Let $v_i^m = S(1/m)v_i$, i.e. we have substituted the "variable" m for the "variable" 1 in v_i, thus $\mathrm{supp}(v_i^m) = \{m\}$. The extended symmetry condition is as follows.

(I*) $$c(v_{i_1}^1 \wedge \ldots \wedge v_{i_n}^n \wedge q) = c(v_{j_1}^1 \wedge \ldots \wedge v_{j_n}^n \wedge q)$$

for all sentences $q \in A$ and all sequences $(i_1, \ldots, i_n)$ and $(j_1, \ldots, j_n)$, $n > 0$. As in section 4 we may now calculate the value of $\mu_M((v_{i_1}^1 \wedge \ldots \wedge v_{i_n}^n)[M])$. From (I*) follows that

$$\int_{Sq} \mu_M((v_{i_1}^1 \wedge \ldots \wedge v_{i_n}^n)[M])\, \mathrm{d}\lambda(M) = \int_{Sq} \mu_M((v_{j_1}^1 \wedge \ldots \wedge v_{j_n}^n)[M])\, \mathrm{d}\lambda(M),$$

hence (by modifying on sets of measure zero, if necessary),

$$\mu_M(v^1_{i_1}[M] \cap \dots \cap v^n_{i_n}[M]) = \mu_M(v^1_{j_1}[M] \cap \dots \cap v^n_{i_n}[M]).$$

Define a partition $\{[k_{i_1} \dots k_{i_n}]\}$ of X^I_M by letting $x \in [k_{i_1} \dots k_{i_n}]$ iff $x_1 = k_{i_1}, \dots, x_n = k_{i_n}$ where $k_{i_1}, \dots, k_{i_n} \in X_M$. Then for a suitable numbering of X_M

$$v^1_{i_1}[M] \cap \dots \cap v^n_{i_n}[M] = [k_{i_1} \dots k_{i_n}],$$

hence, by the same "counting" argument as used in section 4,

$$\mu_M((v^1_{i_1} \wedge \dots \wedge v^n_{i_n})[M]) = \mu_M(v^1_{i_1}[M]) \cdot \dots \cdot \mu_M(v^n_{i_n}[M]),$$

which implies that μ_M is the product measure on X^I_M of the counting measures on the factors.

Let p be an element of A with $\operatorname{supp}(p) = \{1\}$ and let τ_i denote the transformation such that $\tau_i 1 = i$ and $\tau_i =$ identity on $I - \{1\}$. Further let $p^\varepsilon = p$, if $\varepsilon = 1$ and $p^\varepsilon = p'$, if $\varepsilon = 0$. We shall evaluate the probability of the following element p^n_r of A:

$$p^n_r = \bigvee_{(\varepsilon_1, \dots, \varepsilon_n)} S(\tau_1) p^{\varepsilon_1} \wedge \dots \wedge S(\tau_n) p^{\varepsilon_n},$$

where the supremum is taken over all sequences $(\varepsilon_1, \dots, \varepsilon_n)$ consisting of r elements equal to 1 and $n - r$ elements equal to 0. We first compute $\mu_M(p^n_r[M])$, $M \in S_0$:

$$\begin{aligned}
\mu_M(p^n_r[M]) &= \mu_M((\bigvee_{(\varepsilon_1, \dots, \varepsilon_n)} S(\tau_1) p^{\varepsilon_1} \wedge \dots \wedge S(\tau_n) p^{\varepsilon_n})[M]) \\
&= \sum_{(\varepsilon_1, \dots, \varepsilon_n)} \mu_M(\bigcap_{i=1}^n S(\tau_i) p^{\varepsilon_i}[M]) \\
&= \sum_{(\varepsilon_1, \dots, \varepsilon_n)} \prod_{i=1}^n \mu_M(S(\tau_i) p^{\varepsilon_i}[M]) \\
&= \sum_{(\varepsilon_1, \dots, \varepsilon_n)} \mu_M(p[M])^r \cdot (1 - \mu_M(p[M]))^{n-r} \\
&= \binom{n}{r} \operatorname{fr}(p, M)^r \cdot (1 - \operatorname{fr}(p, M))^{n-r}.
\end{aligned}$$

Hence by use of the representation theorem, we get:

THEOREM 4. Let A be a denumerable polyadic algebra with equality and let the special elements v_n and t_n, $n = 1, 2, \dots$, satisfy the requirement (A), (B) and (C). Let c be any probability on A satisfying (I*) and (II).

Further let p be any element of A with $\operatorname{supp}(p)=\{1\}$. If p_r^n is the following element of A (using the notation introduced above),

$$p_r^n = \bigvee_{(\varepsilon_1,\ldots,\varepsilon_n)} S(\tau_1)\, p^{\varepsilon_1} \wedge \ldots \wedge S(\tau_n)\, p^{\varepsilon_n},$$

where $(\varepsilon_1,\ldots,\varepsilon_n)$ denotes any sequence of r "successes" (ones) and $n-r$ "failures" (zeros), then

$$c(p_r^n) = \binom{n}{r} \int_{S0} \operatorname{fr}(p,M)^r \cdot (1-\operatorname{fr}(p,M))^{n-r}\, \mathrm{d}\lambda(M).$$

REMARK. By defining $\Phi(\xi)=\lambda\{M\in S_0;\ \operatorname{fr}(p,M)\leq\xi\}$, we may restate the above result as

$$c(p_r^n) = \binom{n}{r} \int_0^1 \xi^r \cdot (1-\xi)^{n-r}\, \mathrm{d}\Phi(\xi).$$

References

[1] R. Carnap, Logical foundation of probability (Chicago University Press, Chicago, 1951).

[2] J. Łoš, Remarks on foundation of probability, Proc. 1962 Intern. Congress of Mathematicians, Stockholm (1963).

[3] B. de Finetti, La prévision: ses lois logiques, ses sources subjectives, Ann. Inst. Henri Poincaré, **8** (1937). Translated in: Kyburg, Smokler, Studies in subjective probability (J. Wiley and Sons, New York, 1964).

[4] P. R. Halmos, Algebraic logic (Chelsea Publ. Comp., New York, 1962).

[5] J. E. Fenstad, On representation of polyadic algebras, Kongelige Norske Vid. Selsk. Forh. (Trondheim 1964).

ON LÖWENHEIM-SKOLEM-TYPE INSUFFICIENCIES OF SECOND ORDER LOGIC

G. HASENJAEGER
Universität Bonn, Germany

The problem. It is well known that the Löwenheim-Skolem theorem, which asserts that each formula of first order logic, satisfiable somewhere, has an at most countable model, applies similarly to second order logic – if the concept of model is understood in Henkin's sense of general models. We may ask, however, whether an analogous theorem holds for the case in which we restrict ourselves to so-called standard models.

Object language and metalanguage. The language L of the second order predicate logic, PL_2, to be discussed, can be described by introducing quantifiers on the predicate variables of first order logic. (If, for convenience, variables for mathematical functions are admitted, they must be quantifiable too.) The semantics of second order logic depends more essentially on set theoretical concepts than in the first order case. Therefore, we suppose a set theoretical metalanguage M to be at hand. In general, it will depend on our particular purpose whether it is preferable to consider the domains, on which n-place predicate variables are to range, as consisting of (1) sets of ordered n-tuples or (2) sets of functions defined on $\{x \mid x<n\}$ or (3) logical functions (attributes) of n-tuples or (4) one-place functions whose values are $(n-1)$-place logical functions.

For general purposes this latter convention often admits simpler formulations: If the basic types, o for the domain $D_o=\{\mathrm{T},\bot\}$ of truth values, ι for the domain D_ι of individuals, are given, then the general stipulation $(\alpha\beta)$ for the domain $D_{(\alpha\beta)}$ of mappings D_β into D_α, yields in particular the types ι, $o\iota=(o\iota)$, $o\iota\iota=((o\iota)\iota)$, $o\iota\iota\iota=((o\iota\iota)\iota),\ldots$ of PL_2. Let "D" indicate the family of these domains, together with the values $D(c_\alpha)\in D_\alpha$, of constants in L. (In general these may be constants of types α beyond the sequence described above; then "D_α" is used only to describe which values of c_α are admitted.)

Standard models. Within M we can formulate the (defining) condition on standard models D of L: for each of the types in question, $D_{\alpha\beta}$ is the set of *all* mappings of D_β into D_α. Note that, for standard models, all domains D_α are determined by D_ι. The Löwenheim-Skolem theorem for general models tells us that this condition cannot be insured by stipulating that some body of L-sentences be true in D. More succinctly: no adequate description of a standard D can be given in L. One may observe that, in M, conditions on D like that of satisfying sets of L-sentences are such special ones that, a posteriori, it is not astonishing that they are too weak for this purpose.

Secure knowledge from incomplete descriptions. Does this exclude the possibility of obtaining any secure knowledge about standard models? No, if we can be sure that the standard models are among the models of the axioms and rules assumed by tradition or adopted as intuitively known to be in accordance with the idea of "all mappings" in the extensionally maximal sense. If this accordance is to be checked, the explicit use of M may be of some help, even though M is subject to the same criticism. Whether the notion of "all mappings", as formulated in M, matches its intuitive meaning depends on the proper use of M. The term "proper use" cannot be explained formally without developing the semantics of M – in a meta-meta-language which in its turn demands explication. Thus there is no natural limit. One way to exclude some – more and more – improper uses is the reference to higher, even transfinite, levels of type theory, and I think it a very good reason for considering those madly strong axioms of infinity.

Satisfiability depending on the set theatre. Even if the proper use of M is established by the convention of restricting the interest to such a use of M, the possible dependence of the sense of the term "satisfiable in an arbitrary domain" on the universe of M remains, and, as we shall see, it presents a hard problem. The terms "all mappings of... into...", "extensionally maximal", "proper use", difficult as they are, concern a problem, which, in set theory, can be reduced to, or represented by, the concept of power set of a given set, which is a "local" problem compared with the "global" question: how many iterations of the power operation are to be admitted? It will turn out that the answer: "as many as possible" whenever it can be given exactly enough changes the content of "possible" in the answer. We shall refer to the world of sets (the universe S_ι, together with a structure $S(\in_{o\iota\iota})$, if a metalanguage above M were available) the set theory is about as the *set theatre* – partially in order to suggest a convention generally suitable to distinguish a theory from the world the theory is about.

A set theatre described by second order means. For the time being we shall use M to talk about that set theatre which often is taken for the world of mathematics since it yields a suitable supply of mathematical constructions in a wide sense. Starting from the empty set, the operation of forming the power set, accepted locally, is iterated in order to generate a "tower" up to each accessible level. If "accessible" is taken here as the negation of Tarski's notion of strong inaccessability, the generated tower of powers represents the world of almost modern mathematics (never being content is more modern, be it with the justification or with the supply of structures).

The pleasant fact that Zermelo-Fraenkel set theory (ZF) is a solution to the task of describing this theatre by means which are as internal as possible, is concealed by the sad fact that a purely internal description is impossible – and the mad fact that, in general, ZF is presented in a language which has been proved to be insufficient for that purpose. In fact, the adequate description of the concept of power sets within the universe S_ι of M depends on a sufficient supply of selecting properties P, in $S_{o\iota}$ hence above the universe, as needed for the axiom of subsets

$$(*) \qquad \bigwedge P \bigwedge x \bigvee y \bigwedge z (z \in y \leftrightarrow z \in x \wedge Pz)$$

and so does the concept of inaccessability, internally described by closure under all mappings P, above the universe, involved in the axiom of replacement

$$(**) \qquad \bigwedge P \bigwedge a \Big(\bigwedge_{\in a} x \bigvee y P\langle x, y\rangle \rightarrow \bigvee z \bigwedge_{\in a} x \bigvee_{\in z} y P\langle x, y\rangle\Big).$$

If the universe, as is natural at this stage, is thought of as the domain of all abstract objects, then referring to the power domain above the universe is of course a hard matter, but essential for the adequacy of this description, which will be quoted here as ZF_2.

Height of towers. Though the second order version of ZF, as suggested by (*) and (**) is a minimum condition for the described tower of powers rather than a unique one, one needs strong reasons for taking higher, and sufficiently closed, towers as universes for ZF_2, since even the minimum height, given by the first inaccessible ordinal $\mathbf{i}_1$, is too big for the average human imagination. One reason, whose origin is, at least formally, prior to set theory, is yielded by the subject of this paper.

The convention of taking the tower of the height $\mathbf{i}_1+1$ as the set theatre, which suggests a natural translation of ZF_2 into an elegant first order theory, is no way of avoiding the reference to powers outside the universe, since the first order language provides no way of describing the universe as the power domain of the sub-tower of height $\mathbf{i}_1$. If this sub-tower is denoted by "$\forall$", we need some condition like $\bigwedge P(P\subseteq\forall\rightarrow\bigvee x\, x\equiv P)$, or written in full $\bigwedge P\bigvee x\bigwedge y(y\in x\leftrightarrow y\in\forall\wedge Py)$. For the time being we drop our anticipatory *discussion* of M and return to the "minimum" *use*.

Conventions on the metalanguage. Within M we adopt the familiar convention of representing ordinals in the form: $\alpha=\{x\,|\,x<\alpha\}$, hence as transitive sets; cardinals are to be represented as initial ordinals. (Note that each cardinal m is a set of cardinality m.) Each formula A is assigned a Gödel number $\overline{\mathsf{A}}$ in such a way that each natural number n is a Gödel number of a formula A_n. Thus sets of formulas are represented by subsets of ω, but inversely, some (interesting) subsets of ω may be represented by conditions on formulas.

Truth and satisfiability. Standard methods of Tarski's yield an M-formula $\mathsf{T}(m, n)$ such that $\mathsf{T}(\aleph_\alpha, \overline{\mathsf{A}})$ expresses that the L-sentence A is true if $\aleph_\alpha$ is taken for D_ι and the domains $D_{o\iota}$, $D_{o\iota\iota}$, and so on, are determined by D_ι in the standard sense.

If A_n contains free variables, then for simplicity we take $\mathsf{T}(m, \overline{\mathsf{B}}_n)$, where B_n is the result of replacing all the free variables in A_n by $\emptyset$. (Under the previous conventions $\emptyset$ is an element of all relevant domains D_ι, $D_{o\iota}$, $D_{o\iota\iota}$, and so on.) Though the formula T is to be *used* now, we observe some properties needed for a later *discussion* of T. Since $\mathsf{T}(m, n)$ depends only on the cardinality of m, there are some advantages in restricting the definition of T on transitive m. (Otherwise the power concept $\mathsf{P}(x)$ must be replaced by the "cumulative power" $\mathsf{Q}(x)=x\cup\mathsf{P}(x)$ in some of the following applications.) We observe that all quantifiers in M can be restricted to a certain level above m. For transitive m this level can be described by a certain tower of powers $\mathsf{P}^\beta(m)$. Whereas the literal transcription of A. Church's functional semantics would yield a modestly infinite height β, for $\omega \subseteq m$ one could get a passable finite β by representing the predicates by sets of functions on finite ordinals. The related concept of satisfiability of an L-sentence B_n in an arbitrary domain can be described now by the M-formula $\bigvee \eta \mathsf{T}(\eta, n)$.

The theorem in question. There is a cardinal α confinal with $\omega = \aleph_0$ such that each L-sentence, satisfiable at all, also is true in some D where $|D_\iota| < \alpha$. Let $\aleph_*$ be the least such cardinal.

PROOF: The countable set of minimal ordinals, hence cardinals,

$$m = \{\alpha \mid \bigvee n (\bigvee \eta \mathsf{T}(\eta, n) \wedge \alpha = \mu_\xi \mathsf{T}(\xi, n))\},$$

needed to satisfy all satisfiable L-sentences contains no maximum: If $\aleph_\alpha$ is the least cardinal satisfying the sentence A, then $\aleph_{\alpha+1}$ is the least cardinal satisfying the sentence $\mathsf{A}^+ = \bigvee P(\mathsf{A}^{(P)} \wedge |P| < |\forall|)$ where $\mathsf{A}^{(P)}$ is obtained from A by relativizing the quantifiers, according to their type, to the one-place predicate P, and the inequality is short for the non-existence of a mapping from P onto the respective D_ι, denoted in L by a definable $\forall$. Hence A^+ is an L-sentence. The upper limit is the least upper bound $\aleph_* = \bigcup m$ of m. The construction shows that $\aleph_*$ is a set, by the replacement axiom, and moreover a cardinal of confinality ω.

A "universal" constant? For the subsequent discussion we describe the "universal" constant $\aleph_*$, which seems to be related to PL_2 as $\aleph_0$ is related to the first order logic, as a limit of a convergent ω-sequence f:

$$f(n) = \mu_\xi \bigwedge_{\leq n} x (\bigvee \eta \mathsf{T}(\eta, x) \rightarrow \bigvee_{\leq \xi} \eta \mathsf{T}(\eta, x)).$$

Since f describes a cumulative variant of the construction in the preceding proof, $\aleph_* = \lim f$. We shall see that $\aleph_*$ is *universal* only in the sense that it is related to the *universe* chosen for M. Though the set theatre, as described above, is too big to be accepted by some mathematicians, it is surely too tiny to yield an adequate understanding of the concept of satisfiability for L. This is shown by the instances to be discussed now. It may be observed that here the need for big cardinalities arises from problems concerning pure (second order) logic rather than from problems of set theory itself.

Looking upwards. The axioms of ZF_2, whose essential second order parts are the quoted (*) and (**), can be combined into a formula $\mathsf{S}(\in)$

of M. By a non-essential change of atomic formulas, $x \in y$ into Exy, where E is a suitable two-place predicate variable to be quantified, we obtain an L-sentence $\bigvee E\, \mathsf{S}\,(E)$. This sentence would be satisfiable only if the universe of the above described theatre could be taken for the universe of L. Since the universe of that theatre is a set in the sense of M, if a tower of powers at least up to the second inaccessible number can be, and is taken as the universe of M, the change in the universe of M produces a change in the extension of the concept of L-satisfiability, as described by $\bigvee \eta \mathsf{T}\,(\eta, n)$.

If there are inaccessible numbers within the universe of M (be it determined by external reasons or chosen arbitrarily) one can define an increasing enumeration of them, as follows:

$$\mathbf{i}_0 = \omega, \quad \mathbf{i}_\alpha = \mu_\gamma (\mathrm{In}(\gamma) \wedge \bigwedge_{<\alpha} \beta \; u_\beta < \gamma)$$

where $\mathrm{In}\,(\gamma)$ is short for the strongly inaccessible numbers. To avoid artificial conventions, let $\mu_\gamma(\ldots)$ be undefined if there are no more inaccessibles. An explicit definition of $\mathbf{i}$ (such that $\mathbf{i}_\alpha = \beta \leftrightarrow \mathsf{U}\,(\alpha, \beta))$ can then be given by

$$\mathsf{U}\,(\alpha, \beta) \leftrightarrow \{\langle \xi, \eta \rangle \mid \xi \in \eta \in \alpha\} \cong \{\langle \xi, \eta \rangle \mid \xi \in \eta \in \beta \wedge \mathrm{In}\,(\xi) \wedge \mathrm{In}\,(\eta)\} \wedge \mathrm{In}\,(\beta).$$

Now, each definable ordinal, δ, can be misused to produce an L-sentence which needs a certain degree of infinity for its universe D_ι to be true, at least, if the defining term Δ is "absolute". That is: the structure of Δ ensures that its meaning does not depend on the height of the tower above δ which might be the universe of M. For instance: The term "the first inaccessible" defines nothing if used about our first theatre, but keeps its meaning if used about any higher tower. Not so does "$\aleph_*$", at least at some levels.

If $\bigwedge \xi (\xi \in \delta \rightarrow \bigvee \eta \; \eta = \mathbf{i}_\xi)$ in M, the translation into L together with the translated axioms $\mathsf{S}\,(E)$ yields an L-sentence

$$\bigvee E (\mathsf{S}(E) \wedge \bigwedge \xi (E \xi \Delta_E \rightarrow \bigvee \eta \, \mathsf{U}_E(\xi, \eta))),$$

(Δ_E, U_E indicate the obvious translations of Δ, U into L) which requires the cardinal $\mathbf{i}_\delta$ for its least model. If $\mathbf{i}_\delta$ is undefined in M we have an additional reason for looking for a bigger universe. If even $\bigwedge\xi \bigvee\eta\ \eta=\mathbf{i}_\xi$ in M, a similar translation of this formula into L

$$\bigvee E(\mathsf{S}(E) \wedge \bigwedge \xi(\mathrm{On}_E(\xi) \to \bigvee \eta\, \mathsf{U}_E(\xi,\eta)))$$

(the relativization of ξ on ordinals and its translation, which were implicit in the earlier instance, is indicated by On_E) yields an L-sentence which is satisfiable in the sense of $\bigvee\eta \mathsf{T}(\eta, n)$ if and only if the universe of M is higher than the least tower described by $\bigwedge\xi \bigvee\eta\ \eta=\mathbf{i}_\xi$.

And these are only the first steps of a sequence of possibilities suggested by the papers of Keisler-Tarski [1], Lévy [2], Mahlo [3].

Looking down. We want a height which is sufficient to define the notion "satisfiable in an arbitrary domain" for L – but it is also natural to want an adequate description of such a height. One would like to discuss, say, the dependence of the meaning of "$\aleph_*$" on the possible universes of M by using a third language N which is like M but refers to a tower high enough not to bump our heads. (I hope this won't be taken for a technical term.) Call such a tower "safe", and note that some formulations above anticipated such a language N.

Rather than discussing in N the possible universes of M as models S – given by S_ι, $S_{o\iota}$, $S(\in_{o\iota\iota})$ – we could use M itself to refer to the safe tower, and regard the smaller possible universes of M as inner models in Shepherdson's [4] sense. If M can be used as referring to a "safe" tower, $\aleph_*$ is absolute with respect to this use, by definition, but note that most of the subsequent definitions are not restricted to that use.

In order to refer to inner models we shall denote the towers of powers, up to an ordinal level, by

$$\forall_0 = \emptyset, \quad \forall_\alpha = \bigcup_{\beta<\alpha} \{x \mid x \subseteq \forall_\beta\}, \text{ we also write } \forall(\alpha) \text{ for } \forall_\alpha \text{ (if convenient).}$$

Since exactly the sets $\forall_{\mathbf{i}_\alpha}$, $\alpha>0$, are acceptable universes of inner models, we can assign to each M-formula A a (first order-) M-formula A_α, relativizing the M-quantifiers to elements or to subsets of $\forall_{\mathbf{i}_\alpha}$ respectively, such that A is valid on $\forall_{\mathbf{i}_\alpha}$ iff A_α is valid in the sense of M. Note that the (definable) quantifications on ordinals of M are reduced by this relativization to quantifications on elements of $\mathbf{i}_\alpha$.

Relativized definitions. We denote the relativized versions of f and $\aleph_*$ by f_α and $g(\alpha)$ respectively. (We also write: $f(\alpha, n)$ for $f_\alpha(n)$.) We could obtain these by relativizing all quantifiers in the definition of f, particularly in the transcription of μ_ξ. But, by the special form of T and by the closure of $\mathbf{i}_\alpha$, i.e.

$$\bigwedge \eta (\eta < \mathbf{i}_\alpha \rightarrow \mathsf{P}^\omega(\eta) \in \forall(\mathbf{i}_\alpha)), \quad \text{for} \quad \alpha > 0,$$

one additional restriction, in the first occurrence of the quantifier $\bigvee \eta$, yields all needed relativizations in the definitions

$$f(\alpha, n) = \mu_\xi \bigwedge_{\leq n} x (\bigvee_{< \mathbf{i}_\alpha} \eta \mathsf{T}(\eta, x) \rightarrow \bigvee_{\leq \xi} \eta \mathsf{T}(\eta, x))$$
$$g(\alpha) = \lim_{n<\omega} f(\alpha, n).$$

Incidentally, in the inessential case $\alpha = 0$, the above definitions are still correct, whereas it depends on the particular form of T, whether the restriction of the quantifiers in T on $\forall_\omega$ disturbs the transcription of the natural inductive definition of T.

Relativized and "safe" concepts compared. With the intention of making the notion of safety more precise we state some obvious inequalities:

$$f(\alpha, n) \leq f(n),$$
$$\text{hence} \quad g(\alpha) \leq \aleph_*.$$

Since, in general, a greater universe presents more opportunities to satisfy an L-sentence, we have

$$\alpha < \beta \rightarrow f(\alpha, n) \leq f(\beta, n)$$

and the case of being different is explained by

$$f(\alpha, n) < f(\beta, n) \rightarrow f(\beta, n) \geq \mathbf{i}_\alpha$$

since there must have been a "jump" out of $\forall(\mathbf{i}_\alpha)$.

If, incidentally, M was used to talk about a universe even greater than the least safe one, then we should have:

$$(\dagger) \qquad \bigvee \alpha \bigwedge n f(\alpha, n) = f(n)$$

in M, but the M-validity of $(\dagger)$ is not a condition sufficient for safety. If the closure condition expressed by $\bigwedge \xi \bigvee \eta\, \xi = \mathbf{i}_\eta$ can be accepted for a safe tower, then $\mathbf{i}_{\aleph_*}$ is defined since $\aleph_*$ is an ordinal and since $\aleph_*$ is confinal with ω, $\aleph_* \in \mathbf{i}_{\aleph_*}$, hence

$$\aleph_* \in \forall(\mathbf{i}_{\aleph_*}).$$

Therefore this inner model yields all the opportunities of the universe for the satisfaction of L-formulas, and

$$f(\aleph_*, n) = f(n), \quad g(\aleph_*) = \aleph_* .$$

We know, however, that the condition $\bigwedge \xi \bigvee \eta \; \xi = \mathbf{i}_\eta$ does not suffice to describe a safe tower. See the last instance of *looking upwards*.

Towers of classes. Since our attempts to describe a safe tower failed to be successful, perhaps because of the restriction of M itself, one could try to formulate more adequate descriptions referring to a full type-theoretic hierarchy above the universe of M. Now, the easiest way to make the advantage of a type theatre above the universe available in our context, is to imbed all these structures into a second tower, say of classes, and take the union of the first tower, of sets, and the second tower, of classes, as the universe.

As for the language, M can be adapted to this purpose by introducing a constant, say **m**, to denote the class of all sets, in the former sense, and of course second order logic is still needed to describe the proper use of M for classes as well as for sets. The height of the second tower, above **m**, may be described either as sufficient to contain the translation of a type theory or as closed like the first tower, or even more strongly. In each case the supposed description of the first tower which refers to the second tower, together with a description of the second tower, can be translated into a description of the union tower as the universe of M. And a translation of that description*) into L would be another reason for looking upwards.

Sets of natural numbers. Since the formal description $\bigvee \eta \mathsf{T}(\eta, n)$ of the concept of satisfiability for L-sentences only reflects the given height of the tower of sets, one could try to force the existence of higher towers by replacing the premise in the trivial theorem

$$\bigwedge n \bigvee \xi (\bigvee \eta \mathsf{T}(\eta, n) \rightarrow \mathsf{T}(\xi, n))$$

by a condition $\mathsf{V}(n)$, to get

$$\bigwedge n \bigvee \xi (\mathsf{V}(n) \rightarrow \mathsf{T}(\xi, n)),$$

*) The case of axiom schemata in the supposed descriptions needs an additional remark: They can be handled by an **M**-definable truth definition for the first order part of **M**.

where $\mathsf{V}(n)$ is to give a syntactical description of a sequence or set of L-sentences, whose satisfiability can be ensured by intuitive considerations. For instance, the idea used above that the universe of M is as satisfactory a universe for L as a set of M, might suggest more and even iterated applications.

The comparison of the set $\{n \mid \bigvee \eta \mathsf{T}(\eta, n)\}$ with the sets of (numbers of) sentences true in given ordinals α, the family $t(\alpha) = \{n \mid \mathsf{T}(\alpha, n)\}$ may be instructive. By definition of $\aleph_*$,

$$t(\aleph_*) \subseteq \{n \mid \bigvee \eta \mathsf{T}(\eta, n)\} = \bigcup_{\alpha \in \aleph_*} t(\alpha).$$

But $t(\aleph_*) \neq t(\alpha)$ for all $\alpha \in \aleph_*$. Take the sequence of L-sentences J_i responsible for the "jumps" of f. Form the cumulative variants $J_i^* = \bigvee P J_i^{(P)}$ by relativization to a one-place predicate P bound by an existential quantifier (compare the formation of A^+ from A above). If J_i is true for α, then J_i^* is true for all $\beta \geq \alpha$. Consequently, the numbers j_i, of all J_i^* are in $t(\aleph_*)$, whereas each $t(\alpha)$, $\alpha < \aleph_*$, contains only finitely many of them. One may ask for a boundary β for the arguments of t sufficient to yield all possible values $t(\alpha)$, for $\alpha < \beta$. In fact:

$$\bigvee \beta \bigwedge \xi \bigvee_{<\beta} \eta \, t(\xi) = t(\eta).$$

Hence the boundedness of the set of values of t $(t(\alpha) \subseteq \omega)$ entails the existence of a boundary for the needed arguments. Let $\aleph^*$ be the least such β. The above observation shows that $\aleph_* < \aleph^*$. Thus $\aleph^*$ presents another problem of "safety" which, once more, relates the second order logic to higher regions of set theory.

References

[1] H. J. Keisler and A. Tarski, From accessible to inaccessible cardinals, Fundamenta Mathematicae **53** (1964) 225.

[2] A. Lévy, Axiom schemata of strong infinity in axiomatic set theory, Pacific J. Math. **10** (1960) 223.

[3] P. Mahlo, Über lineare transfinite Mengen, Ber. Kgl. Sächs. Ges. Wiss., Math.-Phys. Kl. **63** (1911) 187.

[4] J. C. Shepherdson, Inner models for set theory I-III, J. Symbolic Logic I-**16** (1951) 161; II-**17** (1952) 225; III-**18** (1953) 145.

[5] A. Tarski, Über unerreichbare Kardinalzahlen, Fundamenta Mathematicae **30** (1938) 68.

SOME PROBLEMS OF DEFINABILITY IN RECURSIVE FUNCTION THEORY

H. ROGERS Jr.*)
Massachusetts Institute of Technology, USA

In this paper, I shall be more concerned with presenting certain open problems in recursive function theory than with giving new results. These problems arose during my work on a forthcoming book on recursive function theory [1]. I do not believe that they have received much attention up to the present time. Yet they are easily stated and appear to be of central significance in the foundations of recursive function theory. Moreover, answers to some, at least, appear accessible.

The present paper is in four sections. Section 1 gives an informal review of the basic furniture, along with some of the basic facts, of elementary recursive function theory. Section 2 describes several structures that have been principal objects of study in recent development of the theory. Section 3 considers the notion of definability. Section 4 states and briefly discusses the open problems.

1. Elementary recursive function theory

Let $N=\{0, 1, 2, \ldots\}$ be the set of non-negative integers. We use $x, y, \ldots$ for members of N and $A, B, \ldots$ for subsets of N. $\emptyset$ is the empty set. Given $A \subseteq N$, $\bar{A}$ is the set $N-A$. If a relation $R \subseteq N^2$ has the property that $\langle x, y_1 \rangle, \langle x, y_2 \rangle \in R \Rightarrow y_1 = y_2$, we call R a *partial function.* If, in addition, R has the property that $(\forall x)(\exists y)\ \langle x, y \rangle \in R$, we call R a *function.* We use $\varphi, \psi, \ldots$ for partial functions, and $f, g, \ldots$ for functions. Clearly, every function gives a mapping from N into N, and every partial function gives a mapping from some subset of N (its *domain*) into N.

*) This work was supported by the National Science Foundation under grant GP-4361.

f is called a *recursive function* if an effective procedure (i.e., deterministic algorithm) exists for computing f. We can think of such a procedure as follows. We have a "black box" with an input slot and an output slot. Given any input integer x, we put (a standard notation for) x into the input slot. Eventually $f(x)$ (in some standard notation) is discharged from the output slot. For f to be recursive, we require that the internal working

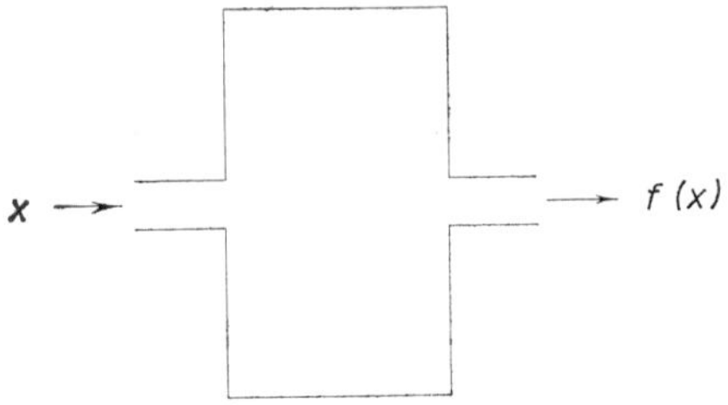

Fig. 1.

of the box be deterministic and "mechanical". An intuitively useful way to picture this is to think of the box as containing a tireless *clerk* who has unlimited supplies of pencil and paper and who follows some given finite set of instructions in carrying out his calculations. Given input x, he operates on x according to those instructions. For f to be recursive, we only require that for each input x we produce the output $f(x)$ in finite time.

Of course such a clerk might be given a set of instructions which, for some inputs, would lead to no output. (This could happen, for example, if the clerk were led into some non-terminating computation.) In such a case, our black box would be represent not a function f, but a partial function φ with domain $= \{x \mid \text{input } x \text{ leads to an output}\}$. Any partial function that is representable by a black box (i.e., deterministic algorithm) in this way is called a *partial recursive function.*

Although the notion of recursive function is the central concept in the theory, the partial recursive functions play a fundamental technical role. They do so because they can be effectively enumerated; that is to say, an effective (i.e., algorithmic) procedure exists for listing all the sets of instructions for all the partial recursive functions. To see that this is the case, consider our clerk in his box. If we understand *set of instructions* to mean finite collection of English sentences, we can effectively list all such collections by first listing all collections with a total length of 10 words or less, then all collections with 20 words or less, etc. For a given input, a set of instructions may lead to a well-defined computation and an output; or it may not (for example, the set of instructions might not make sense to our clerk). In any case, each set of instructions determines a certain partial (and hence partial recursive) function. We use the symbols $\varphi_0, \varphi_1, \varphi_2, \ldots$ to indicate the partial recursive functions corresponding to the successive sets of instructions in our fixed effective enumeration. The recursive functions by themselves cannot be enumerated in this way, as you can verify by a simple Cantor diagonalization argument.

The concepts of recursive function and partial recursive function can be rigorously defined. Descriptions of the necessary formal machinery are found in [1], [2] or [3]. The informal definitions used above will be enough for our purposes. It is hoped that they will be adequate to convince the reader of the truth of some of the proofs below, and, indeed, that they will enable him to supply several omitted proofs on his own.

We now go on to obtain a few basic theorems in the elementary theory. For any set A, let c_A be the characteristic function of A

$$(\text{i.e., } c_A = \{\langle x, 1\rangle \mid x \in A\} \cup \{\langle x, 0\rangle \mid x \notin A\}).$$

Definition. A is *recursive* if c_A is a recursive function. (Intuitive motivation: a set is recursive if there is an effective procedure such that given any integer x, we can decide whether or not x is a member of A.)

Definition. A is *recursively enumerable* if either $A=\emptyset$ or $A=\text{range}\, f$ for some recursive function f. (Intuitive motivation: a set is recursively enumerable if there is some effective procedure for listing its members. If $A=\text{range}\, f$, we have $f(0), f(1), f(2), \ldots$ as the listing (possibly with repetitions) of A.)

Our first theorem gives a fundamental relationship between these two concepts.

Theorem 1. A is recursive $\Leftrightarrow$ both A and $\bar{A}$ are recursively enumerable.

Proof. $\Rightarrow$. If A is recursive, then we can effectively list the members of A by calculating $c_A(0), c_A(1), \ldots$ and listing those x for which $c_A(x)=1$. Similarly we get $\bar{A}$ by listing those x for which $c_A(x)=0$.

⇐. If A and $\bar{A}$ can each be effectively listed, then we can effectively test for membership in A as follows. Given any x, we begin listing both A and $\bar{A}$. Eventually x must appear in one list or the other. The list in which x appears tells us whether or not x is in A. This concludes the proof.

Our second theorem gives a technically useful characterization of recursive enumerability.

THEOREM 2. A is recursively enumerable ⇔ $A = \text{domain } \varphi_x$ for some x.

PROOF. ⇒. Assume that we can effectively list A. Consider the partial recursive function ψ determined by the following set of instructions. To compute $\psi(x)$: list A and look for x in this list; if and when x appears, set $\psi(x)=1$. Evidently $A = \text{domain } \psi$.

⇐. Assume that $A = \text{domain } \varphi_z$. We obtain an effective listing of A as indicated in the following diagram.

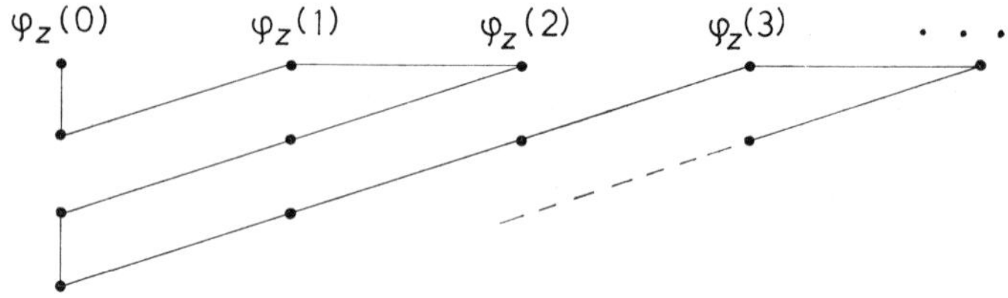

Fig. 2.

Here, the first column represents the computation of $\varphi_z(0)$, the second column the computation of $\varphi_z(1)$, etc. In the diagram, we carry out some of the computation of $\varphi_z(0)$, then some of $\varphi_z(1)$, then some of $\varphi_z(2)$, then more of $\varphi_z(1)$, then more of $\varphi_z(0)$, etc. In this way, whenever one of the column computations terminates, we find it out. Hence we can effectively list all those x for which the column of $\varphi_z(x)$ terminates. But this is just the set A. This concludes the proof.

Our third theorem answers an obvious question and foreshadows some of the concerns of later parts of the theory.

THEOREM 3. There exists a set which is recursively enumerable but not recursive.

PROOF. Define $K = \{x \mid x \in \text{domain } \varphi_x\}$.

We first show that K is recursively enumerable. By theorem 2, it will be enough to show that $K=$ domain ψ for some partial recursive ψ. Use the following instructions for ψ. To compute $\psi(x)$: find the instructions for φ_x from the fixed enumeration of all sets of instructions; then carry out the computation for $\varphi_x(x)$; if and when this computation yields an output, set $\psi(x)=1$.

It remains to show that K is not recursive. Assume K recursive. Then by theorem 1, $\bar{K}$ is recursively enumerable. Hence, by theorem 2, $\bar{K}=$ domain φ_{x_0} for some x_0. But then $x_0 \in \bar{K} \Leftrightarrow x_0 \in$ domain φ_{x_0} (by the choice of x_0), and $x_0 \in$ domain $\varphi_{x_0} \Leftrightarrow x \in K$ (by the definition of K). This is a contradiction, and hence K is not recursive. This concludes the proof. (Note that the proof is formally similar to Cantor's proof in set theory that the power set of a given set has higher cardinality than the given set.)

If we were to carry the theory further, we would begin to consider various other properties of subsets of N. We mention two such properties now. They will be useful as examples in later discussion.

DEFINITION. A is *creative* if (i) A is recursively enumerable, and (ii) there exists a partial recursive η such that for any x, if domain $\varphi_x \subseteq \bar{A}$, then $\eta(x)$ is defined and

$$\eta(x) \in (\bar{A} - \text{domain } \varphi_x).$$

(Intuitive motivation: as can be seen from a simple Venn diagram, a set A is creative if it is recursively enumerable and if there is an effective procedure for going from any set of instructions for enumerating a subset B of $\bar{A}$ to a member of $\bar{A}-B$. The set K is an example of a creative set; η may be taken as the identity function, as you can readily verify.)

DEFINITION. A is *simple* if (i) A is recursively enumerable, (ii) $\bar{A}$ is infinite, and (iii) $\bar{A}$ contains no infinite recursively enumerable subset.

You can easily show, on the basis of our informal definitions, that condition (iii) can be equivalently replaced by (iii′): for every infinite recursively enumerable set B, $A \cap B$ is infinite.

The concepts *creative* and *simple* are due to Post who introduced them in his epochal paper [4]. Post shows the existence of simple sets in [4].

What properties of subsets of N is one interested in studying in recursive function theory? Let us identify *property* with *subset of* 2^N. (2^N is the power set of N, i.e., it is the set of all subsets of N.) We use $\mathscr{P}$ to denote any given property of subsets of N.

DEFINITION. $\mathscr{P}$ is *recursively invariant* if $A \in \mathscr{P} \Rightarrow f(A) \in \mathscr{P}$ for every recursive f that maps N one-one onto N. (Any such f is called a *recursive permutation.*) This definition gives an elegant and useful characterization of the properties with which recursive function theory is concerned. It is a characterization in the spirit of Felix Klein. Just as (following Klein) Euclidean geometry studies those properties of subsets of the plane which are invariant under the group of Euclidean transformations, so recursive function theory studies those properties of subsets of N which are invariant under the group of recursive permutations. You may easily verify from our definitions that the properties of recursiveness, recursive enumerability, creativeness, and simplicity are all recursively invariant.

This concludes our brief sample of concepts and results from elementary recursive function theory.

2. Some structures in recursive function theory

(1) Let $\mathscr{E}$ be the class of recursively enumerable sets and let $\mathscr{F}$ be the class of finite sets. Evidently $\mathscr{F} \subseteq \mathscr{E}$. $\mathscr{E}$ forms a lattice under ordinary $\cup$ and $\cap$; for if we have lists for A and B, we can put the two lists together to get an effective list of $A \cup B$, and we can take the integers common to both lists to get an effective list of $A \cap B$. $\mathscr{F}$ also forms a lattice; in fact, $\mathscr{F}$ is a *lattice ideal* in $\mathscr{E}$, since (i) $\mathscr{F}$ is closed under union, and (ii) the intersection of a member of $\mathscr{F}$ with any member of $\mathscr{E}$ is also in $\mathscr{F}$. Since $\mathscr{E}$, as a lattice of sets, is a distributive lattice, we can obtain a *quotient lattice* $\mathscr{E}/\mathscr{F}$ whose elements are equivalence classes of elements of $\mathscr{E}$ under the equivalence relation: A is equivalent to B if and only if $(A-B) \cup (B-A) \in \mathscr{F}$. (The quotient lattice construction for a distributive lattice by a lattice ideal is closely parallel to the quotient ring construction for a ring by an ideal.)

(1*) The first structure which we wish to single out for special attention is the quotient lattice $\mathscr{E}/\mathscr{F}$ (along with the lattice $\mathscr{E}$).

The lattice $\mathscr{E}/\mathscr{F}$ was first considered by Myhill in [5], who pointed out that several interesting problems can be formulated in terms of the structure $\mathscr{E}/\mathscr{F}$. Myhill noted that certain properties of sets can be given an elementary definition in $\mathscr{E}/\mathscr{F}$. For example, if we let $a, b, \dots$ denote members of $\mathscr{E}/\mathscr{F}$, we have that A is recursive $\Leftrightarrow (\exists a)[A \in a$ and $(\exists b)$ $[a \cap b = 0$ and $a \cup b = 1]]$. (Here 0 and 1 are, respectively, the minimum and maximum elements of $\mathscr{E}/\mathscr{F}$; $\cap$ and $\cup$ are the *meet* and *join* operations of $\mathscr{E}/\mathscr{F}$; 0 is the equivalence class of $\emptyset$; and 1 is the equivalence class of N.) Similarly, we have that A is simple

$$\Leftrightarrow (\exists a)[A \in a \text{ and } (\forall b)[b \neq 0 \Rightarrow a \cap b \neq 0]].$$

You can readily verify these examples from our previous definitions and theorems. Can the property of creativeness be similarly defined in terms of the lattice structure of $\mathscr{E}/\mathscr{F}$? We return to this question below.

We make two further remarks in passing. First we note that the quotient lattice construction is of interest in certain other cases. For example, if we let $\mathscr{S}$ be the class of all sets that are either simple or have finite complement, then $\mathscr{S}$ forms a *dual ideal* in $\mathscr{E}$ (the intersection of any two members of $\mathscr{S}$ is in $\mathscr{S}$, and the union of a member of $\mathscr{S}$ with any member of $\mathscr{E}$ is in $\mathscr{S}$). A quotient lattice $\mathscr{E}/\mathscr{S}$ can now be formed by a construction of a kind that is dual to the previous construction (in that $\cap$ and $\cup$ play interchanged roles). In particular the members of $\mathscr{E}/\mathscr{S}$ are equivalence classes, where A is equivalent to B if and only if $(A \cap B) \cup (\bar{A} \cap \bar{B}) \in \mathscr{S}$. The quotient construction can also be used with the Boolean algebra $\mathscr{R}$ of recursive sets or the Boolean algebra $\mathscr{N}$ of all sets in place of the lattice $\mathscr{E}$. Second, we remark in passing that there is a body of recent results in recursive function theory, including some work of T. G. McLaughlin and P. R. Young, that have as a common theme that they can be reformulated in terms of $\mathscr{E}/\mathscr{F}$, $\mathscr{N}/\mathscr{F}$, and the embedding of $\mathscr{E}/\mathscr{F}$ in $\mathscr{N}/\mathscr{F}$. Apart from these results (and the solution by Friedberg of several of Myhill's problems), the lattice $\mathscr{E}/\mathscr{F}$ has not been extensively studied, and no direct algebraic study of it appears to have yet been made.

(2) Let B be a given subset of N. We define f to be *recursive in B* if there is a procedure of the following kind for computing f. We have a black box with our tireless clerk inside, and in addition we have two further slots in the box through which the clerk can communicate with a second box. This second box has the property that whenever the clerk puts a number y through one of its slots, it returns the number $c_B(y)$ through the other slot. The second box is not assumed to have any mechanical structure; it can operate by supernatural revelation if necessary, but it must always give correct answers. In the literature of recursive

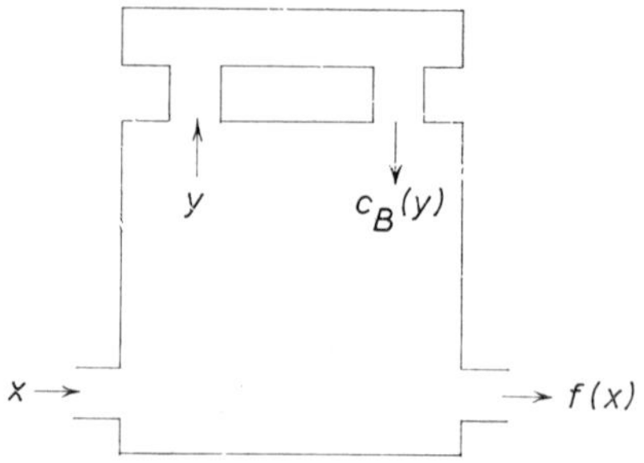

Fig. 3.

function theory, such a box is often called an *oracle.* During the course of a computation, the clerk consults his oracle if, when, and as often as, his instructions tell him to. The number y he gives to the oracle in any such consultation will be a number that has arisen in the course of his computation; it need not be the original input x. Moreover, he will, in general, use the resulting $c_B(y)$ in his subsequent computation. Note that a function can be recursive in a non-recursive set B without being a recursive function; for example, the function c_B is always recursive in B (the clerk's instructions being to consult the oracle about input x immediately).

Partial functions partial recursive in B are defined similarly. All possible sets of instructions for the clerk can be effectively enumerated in a fixed way exactly as before. We use $\varphi_0^B, \varphi_1^B, \ldots$ to indicate the partial functions partial recursive in B corresponding to the successive sets of instructions in this fixed enumeration.

Given a set B, the entire theory given in section 1 can now be "relativized" by replacing recursive functions with recursive functions in B, and partial recursive functions with partial functions partial recursive in B, in all definitions and theorems. In particular, A is defined to be *recursive in B* if c_A is recursive in B, and A is defined to be *recursively enumerable in B* if either $A=\emptyset$ or $A=\text{range } f$ for some f recursive in B. The modified versions of theorems 1, 2 and 3 are proved just as before. In particular, if K^B is defined to be $\{x \mid x \in \text{domain } \varphi_x^B\}$, we have that K^B is not recursive in B (although B is recursive in K^B).

We now make the following definition.

DEFINITION. $A \leq B$ if A is recursive in B.
$A \equiv B$ if $A \leq B$ and $B \leq A$.

As you may readily verify on the basis of our informal definitions, $\leq$ is reflexive and transitive. Hence $\equiv$ is an equivalence relation. For any A, we let $[A]$ denote the equivalence class of A. These equivalence classes are called *degrees of unsolvability*. We define a partial order on the degrees by setting $[A] \leq [B]$ if $A \leq B$. This relation on degrees is trivially seen to be well-defined. The relation $\leq$ on sets is sometimes called *Turing reducibility*, and A is said to be *reducible* to B if $A \leq B$. The degrees are sometimes called *Turing degrees*, and the relation $\leq$ on degrees is called the *reducibility ordering* of degrees. Clearly, higher and higher degrees correspond to sets which are, in some sense, less and less effective.

We note several facts about degrees.

(a) There is a minimum degree, the degree $[\emptyset]$. It consists exactly of the recursive sets.

(b) $A \equiv B \Rightarrow K^A \equiv K^B$. Hence we can define an operation $'$ on degrees (called the *jump* operation) by setting $[A]' = [K^A]$. Since $K^A \not\leq A$, the jump operation takes us from any degree to a higher degree.

(c) Define *A join B* to be

$$\{2x \mid x \in A\} \cup \{2x+1 \mid x \in B\},$$

and define $[A] \cup [B]$ (the *join* of $[A]$ and $[B]$) to be $[A \text{ join } B]$. Then $\cup$ is well defined on degrees and $[A] \cup [B]$ is the least upper bound of $[A]$ and $[B]$ in the reducibility ordering.

(d) Define $[A]$ *recursively enumerable in* $[B]$ if there exists $C \in [A]$ such that C is recursively enumerable in B. This relation is well-defined on degrees. You can readily verify the facts in (a), (b), (c) and (d) from our definitions.

(2*) The second structure which we wish to single out for special attention is the collection of degrees of unsolvability together with the relations $\leq$ and *recursively enumerable in* on degrees, and the operations $'$ and $\cup$ on degrees.

Since it was first isolated by Post in the 1940's and then studied by Post and Kleene in the early 1950's, this structure has been the object of extensive study. Sacks' monograph [6], for example, is devoted to it. The reducibility ordering proves to be highly irregular(see [6]); virtually no regularities beyond the immediately accessible ones are known to hold, and many conjectured regularities have been shown to fail. The reducibility ordering is known not to be a lattice. Various aspects of this structure, including relations to logic and to the hierarchies of set theory and number theory (see [1]) continue to be studied.

(3) Consider a black box which operates in the following way. The box

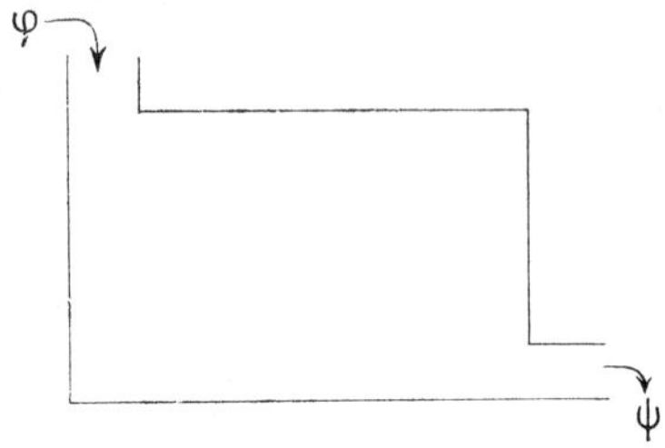

Fig. 4.

contains our tireless clerk who operates, as usual, from a finite set of instructions. Through the input slot are fed, in succession and at unit time intervals, the members (i.e., ordered pairs) of some partial function φ. As these inputs are fed in, the clerk carries out his computation and, from time to time, gives an ordered pair as output. Let us assume that for a certain input φ, the following conditions hold: (i) the set of all output ordered pairs constitutes a partial function ψ, and (ii) regardless of the serial order in which the ordered pairs of the input φ are introduced, the ordered pairs in the output constitute the same partial function ψ. (The serial order of the output ordered pairs (of ψ) is permitted to vary as the serial order of the input ordered pairs (of φ) is varied). In such a case, we say that the black box is *regular* for φ. Clearly, our black box determines a mapping F from partial functions to partial functions. The *domain* of F is the class of all φ for which the box is regular. If $\varphi\in$ domain F and ψ is the output resulting from φ, we write $\psi=F(\varphi)$. Such a mapping F, determined by a black box under some finite set of instructions for the clerk, is called a *partial recursive operator*. For example, if we instruct the clerk to give output $\langle x, 2y\rangle$ for each input $\langle x, y\rangle$, we get a partial recursive operator whose domain is the class of all partial functions. (This is the operator F such that for all φ, $F(\varphi)=2\varphi$.)

DEFINITION. $\psi\leq\varphi$ if $\psi=F(\varphi)$ for some partial recursive operator F.
$\psi\equiv\varphi$ if $\psi\leq\varphi$ and $\varphi\leq\psi$.

The relation $\leq$ on partial functions is easily seen to be reflexive and transitive. Hence $\equiv$ is an equivalence relation. We let $[\varphi]$ denote the equivalence class of φ. The equivalence classes are called *partial degrees.* We obtain a *reducibility ordering* of partial degrees by setting $[\varphi]\leq[\psi]$ if $\varphi\leq\psi$. This ordering is trivially well defined, and possesses the class of all partial recursive functions as a minimum element.

(3*) The third structure which we wish to single out for special attention is the collection of partial degrees under the relation $\leq$.

The following theorem relates the structure of degrees to the structure of partial degrees.

THEOREM 4. $[A] \leq [B] \Leftrightarrow [c_A] \leq [c_B]$.

PROOF. Left to the reader as an exercise.

This theorem gives a canonical isomorphic embedding of the ordering of degrees into the ordering of partial degrees.

The ordering of partial degrees has been much less studied than the ordering of degrees (see [1]). It is known that the embedding given by theorem 4 is proper; i.e., there is a partial degree which contains no characteristic function of a set. The ordering of partial degrees is believed, but not known, to be highly irregular.

(4) Consider subsets of N^N, i.e., classes of functions. We use $\mathscr{A}, \mathscr{B}, \ldots$ to denote such classes.

DEFINITION. $\mathscr{A}\leq\mathscr{B}$ if $F(\mathscr{B})\subseteq\mathscr{A}$ for some partial recursive operator F such that $\mathscr{B}\subseteq$ domain F.

$$\mathscr{A}\equiv\mathscr{B} \text{ if } \mathscr{A}\leq\mathscr{B} \text{ and } \mathscr{B}\leq\mathscr{A}.$$

The relation $\leq$ on classes of functions is easily seen to be reflexive and transitive. Hence $\equiv$ is an equivalence relation. We let $[\mathscr{A}]$ denote the equivalence class of $\mathscr{A}$. The equivalence classes are called *degrees of difficulty*. We obtain a *reducibility ordering* of degrees of difficulty by setting $[\mathscr{A}]\leq[\mathscr{B}]$ if $\mathscr{A}\leq\mathscr{B}$. This ordering is trivially well-defined and possesses $[N^N]$ as a minimum element and $[\emptyset]$ as a maximum element.

(4*) The last structure which we wish to single out for special attention is the collection of degrees of difficulty under the relation $\leq$.

Note that this structure is of higher (i.e., more abstract) logical type than any of the structures previously mentioned, since the elements of the structure are classes of classes of functions. This structure was first defined by Medvedev in [7]. Medvedev showed that, unlike (2*), the structure (4*) is a lattice. He also obtained certain other regularities for it (see [1]). The Medvedev lattice has been very little studied. A number of simple (and probably rather easy) questions remain unsettled. Its cardinality, for example, is not known.

The following results relate the structures of degrees and partial degrees to the Medvedev lattice. (We continue to use the word "degree" by itself to mean degree of unsolvability.) Let τ be a fixed effective one-one mapping from N^2 onto N. (For example, take $\tau(x, y) = \frac{1}{2}(x^2 + 2xy + y^2 + + 3x + y)$.) Then for any partial function φ, $\tau(\varphi)$ is an effective (and reversible) encoding of φ as a set of integers.

THEOREM 5. $[A] \leq [B] \Leftrightarrow [\{c_A\}] \leq [\{c_B\}]$.

THEOREM 6. For φ and $\psi \neq \emptyset$,

$$[\varphi] \leq [\psi] \Leftrightarrow [\{f \mid \text{range } f = \tau(\varphi)\}] \leq [\{f \mid \text{range } f = \tau(\psi)\}].$$

PROOFS. Left to the reader as an exercise.

Theorem 5 gives a canonical embedding of the degrees of unsolvability into the Medvedev lattice, and theorem 6 gives a canonical embedding of the partial degrees into the Medvedev lattice. It is easy to show that the embedding of theorem 5 factors into (i.e., is the result of composing) the embeddings given by theorems 4 and 6. The existence of $[\emptyset]$ as a maximum element in the Medvedev lattice shows that the embedding given by theorem 6 is proper. In the theory of the Medvedev lattice, degrees of difficulty of the form $[\{c_A\}]$ are known as *degrees of solvability* and degrees of difficulty of the form $[\{f \mid \text{range } f = A\}]$ are known as *degrees of enumerability*. The former are isomorphic to the structure (2*) by theorem 5; and the latter can be easily shown to coincide with the degrees of difficulty $[\{f \mid \text{range } f = \tau(\varphi)\}]$, and hence to be isomorphic to the structure (3*) by theorem 6.

This concludes our presentation of several structures that are important in the present landscape of recursive function theory. We return to these structures in section 4.

3. Definability in structures

By a *structure*, we mean an object of the form $\langle U, R_0, R_1, \ldots, F_0, F_1, \ldots \rangle$ where U is some non-empty set (not necessarily a subset of N) called the *universe* of the structure, where $R_0, R_1, \ldots$ are relations on U, and where

$F_0, F_1, \ldots$ are operations on U. (F_k is an *operation* on U if F_k is a mapping from U^{n_k} into U, for some $n_k > 0$.)

The following are examples of structures.

(1) $\langle N, +, \times \rangle$, where $+$ and $\times$ are the usual operations of addition and multiplication.

(2) $\langle N, \leq \rangle$, where $\leq$ is the usual linear ordering of N.

(3) $\langle Z, + \rangle$, where Z is the set of all integers, negative as well as non-negative, and $+$ is the usual operation of addition.

(4) $\langle Z, \leq \rangle$, where $\leq$ is the usual linear ordering of Z.

Given a structure with universe U, we wish to consider the notion of a subset of U being "definable in the structure". Logicians usually consider definability in terms of a formal system. For instance, in example (1), if a first-order logic with symbols for $+$ and $\times$ is used, the subsets of N explicitly definable prove to be just the sets studied as the *arithmetical sets* in recursive function theory. If a second-order logic is used in example (1), the *analytical sets* are obtained. If a first-order logic is used in example (2), a very limited class of subsets of N is obtained. Similarly, in example (3), a very limited class of subsets of Z is obtained. If a first- or even a second-order logic is used in example (4), only the two sets Z and $\emptyset$ are definable.

Is there an *absolute* notion of definability? Although logicians, in their concern with particular formal systems, have largely ignored it, a natural notion for absolute definability has been current in mathematics for some time. This is the notion of invariance under automorphisms. More specifically, we say that f is an *automorphism* of the structure $\langle U, R_0, \ldots, F_0, \ldots \rangle$ if f is a one-one mapping of U onto U such that $R_0, R_1, \ldots, \bar{R}_0, \bar{R}_1, \ldots$, and $F_0, F_1, \ldots$ are preserved under f. (Here $\bar{R}_0, \bar{R}_1, \ldots$ are the relations complementary to $R_0, R_1, \ldots$, i.e., $\bar{R}_i$ holds exactly when R_i fails.) For example, the mapping $f(n) = n+1$ is an automorphism of (4) but not of (3). We say that $V \subseteq U$ is *invariant under all automorphisms* if $f(V) = V$ for every automorphism f. It is clear that if V is to be "definable" (in some sense) in a given structure, it must be invariant under all automorphisms of the structure; for $f(V)$ must satisfy any "definition" that V satisfies. Conversely, it can be argued that the invariant subsets of U are just the sets which are determined (in some sense) by the structure, and hence that they should be called "definable". We amplify this latter argument in theorem 7 below.

We therefore propose the following.

DEFINITION AND THESIS. Given a structure $\langle U, \ldots \rangle$ and $V \subseteq U$, V is said to be *absolutely definable* in the structure if V is invariant under all automorphisms of the structure*.

What sets are absolutely definable in examples (1), (2), (3) and (4)? In (1), and similarly in (2), the only automorphism is the trivial (identity) automorphism. (Structures with only one automorphism are said to be *rigid*.) Hence, in both (1) and (2), all subsets of N are absolutely definable. In (3), the set $\{1\}$ is not absolutely definable, since it is not preserved under the automorphism $f(n) = -n$. The set $\{-1, 1\}$ on the other hand is invariant under all automorphisms and hence is absolutely definable. (We can define $\{-1, 1\}$, in second-order logic, as the set of those elements which generate the infinite cyclic group $\langle Z, + \rangle$. Indeed, $f(n) = -n$ is the only non-trivial automorphism of (3), and hence a set is absolutely definable in (3) if and only if it is closed under the mapping $f(n) = -n$. In (4), $f(n) = n + k$ is an automorphism for every $k \in Z$. In particular, given any two elements, one can be mapped to the other by an automorphism; hence the only absolutely definable sets are the sets Z and $\emptyset$.

The fact that, in (2), every subset of N is definable, appears to run counter to the logician's intuition of definability as expressibility in some formal language. We answer such objections in theorem 7 below. In theorem 7, we shall use a first-order infinitary logic $L_{\alpha\beta}$ of the kind recently studied by Karp and others (see [8]). The formulas of $L_{\alpha\beta}$ may be of infinite length. Quantifiers of the form $(\exists x_0, x_1, x_2, \ldots, x_\lambda)$ for $\lambda < \beta$, disjunctions of the form $(\varphi_0 \vee \varphi_1 \vee \ldots \vee \varphi_\mu)$ for $\mu < \alpha$, and conjunctions of the form $(\varphi_0 \wedge \varphi_1 \wedge \ldots \wedge \varphi_\mu)$ for $\mu < \alpha$ are allowed. If α and β are greater than ω, these quantifiers and disjunctions can be of infinite length. ($L_{\omega\omega}$ gives the ordinary (finite) first-order predicate logic.) Meaning is attributed to formulas in $L_{\alpha\beta}$ in the obvious way. For simplicity, we limit ourselves in theorem 7 to structures of the form $\langle U, R \rangle$ where R is a binary relation on U, and to infinitary languages $L_{\alpha\beta}$ with a single binary predicate symbol P. (In $L_{\alpha\beta}$ we also have the usual logical symbols of first-order predicate calculus with identity.)

*) The word "absolute" is sometimes used in a *minimum* sense: in such cases, we say that something is "absolutely $\mathscr{P}$" if it has property $\mathscr{P}$ under all circumstances. Note that we are here using "absolute" in a different *maximum* or *limiting* sense.

THEOREM 7. Given a structure $\langle U, R\rangle$, and $V \subseteq U$, V is absolutely definable in $\langle U, R\rangle$ if and only if for some α, β, there is a formula of $L_{\alpha\beta}$ (with the predicate symbol P) which defines V, provided that P is interpreted as R and quantifiers are interpreted as ranging over U.

PROOF. $\Leftarrow$. Assume V is definable in $L_{\alpha\beta}$ by some formula $\varphi(x)$. Thus $u \in V \Leftrightarrow \varphi(u)$ is true in $\langle U, R\rangle$. (We use "$\varphi(u)$" to indicate the formula $\varphi(x)$ with the variable x interpreted as the object $u \in U$.) Let f be an automorphism of $\langle U, R\rangle$. By the definition of automorphism, $\langle u_1, u_2\rangle \in R \Leftrightarrow \langle f(u_1), f(u_2)\rangle \in R$. Hence (following through the definition of truth for $\varphi(x)$ in the usual inductive way familiar to logicians), we have that $\varphi(u)$ is true $\Leftrightarrow \varphi(f(u))$ is true. Hence $u \in V \Leftrightarrow f(u) \in V$, and we have that V is absolutely definable.

$\Rightarrow$. Assume that V is absolutely definable in $\langle U, R\rangle$. We also assume that U is infinite. (The case for U finite is obtained by an obvious modification of the construction below.) Let γ be an ordinal of the same cardinality as U. Take α and β to be ordinals of higher cardinality than γ. Let $\{e_\lambda\}_{\lambda<\gamma}$ be an enumeration of U without repetitions. Let $J = \{\lambda \mid e_\lambda \in V\}$. For every pair λ, $\mu < \gamma$, let $\psi_{\lambda\mu}$ be the formula $Px_\lambda x_\mu$ if $\langle e_\lambda, e_\mu\rangle \in R$, and let $\psi_{\lambda\mu}$ be the formula $\neg Px_\lambda x_\mu$ if $\langle e_\lambda, e_\mu\rangle \notin R$. ($x_0, x_1, \ldots, x_\lambda, \ldots$ are individual-variables in $L_{\alpha\beta}$.) The formula $\varphi(x)$ is now taken to be

$$(\exists x_0, x_1, \ldots, x_\lambda, \ldots)_{\lambda<\gamma} \Big[\Big(\bigwedge_{\substack{\lambda,\mu<\gamma \\ \lambda\neq\mu}} x_\lambda \neq x_\mu\Big) \wedge \Big(\bigwedge_{\lambda,\mu<\gamma} \psi_{\lambda\mu}\Big) \wedge (\forall y)\Big[\bigvee_{\mu<\gamma} y = x_\mu\Big] \wedge \Big(\bigvee_{\lambda\in J} x = x_\lambda\Big)\Big].$$

It remains to show that $u \in V \Leftrightarrow \varphi(u)$ is true.

If $u \in V$, then $u = e_{\lambda_0}$ for some $\lambda_0 \in J$. Interpreting $x_0, x_1, \ldots, x_\lambda, \ldots$ as $e_0, e_1, \ldots, e_\lambda, \ldots$, we immediately have that $\varphi(u)$ is true.

Conversely, assume that $\varphi(u)$ is true. Let $d_0, d_1, \ldots, d_\lambda, \ldots$ be an interpretation for $x_0, x_1, \ldots, x_\lambda, \ldots$ which makes $\varphi(u)$ true. By the first and third parts of the formula, $\{d_\lambda\}_{\lambda<\gamma}$ is an enumeration of U without repetitions. Define f to be the mapping from U onto U which carries e_λ to d_λ, for all $\lambda < \gamma$. By the second part of the formula, f is an automorphism. By the fourth part of the formula, $u = d_{\lambda_0}$ for some $\lambda_0 \in J$. By the assumed invariance of V under automorphisms, $\{d_\lambda\}_{\lambda\in J} = V$ (since $\{e_\lambda\}_{\lambda\in J} = V$). Hence $u \in V$. This concludes the proof of the theorem*.

---

*) In an infinitary logic, α and β are usually taken to be cardinals (i.e., minimum ordinals of a given cardinality). Given a structure, obvious questions arise as to the

4. Problems of definability

We now indicate several groups of open questions that concern the structures described in section 2. We give a sample of such questions here. Others will occur to the reader.

The first group of questions concern the structures (2*) (the degrees), (3*) (the partial degrees) and (4*) (the Medvedev lattice), and possible automorphisms of these structures.

(a) Consider each of the structures (2*), (3*) and (4*) as a partial ordering. Are the degrees absolutely definable in the partial degrees (under the embedding of theorem 4)? Are the degrees absolutely definable in the Medvedev lattice (under the embedding of theorem 5)? Are the partial degrees absolutely definable in the Medvedev lattice (under the embedding of theorem 6)?

(b) Consider each of the structures (2*), (3*) and (4*) as a partial ordering. Does each or any of these structures possess a non-trivial automorphism (i.e., is none or any of these structures rigid)?

(c) Consider (2*) as a partial ordering. Are the jump operation and the relation *recursively enumerable in* (as a relation on degrees) invariant under all automorphisms of this partial ordering?

(d) By the embedding of theorem 5, a jump operation is defined on the degrees of solvability of (4*). Is this operation invariant under all automorphisms of (4*) which map the collection of degrees of solvability onto itself? (Evidently, an affirmative answer to (c) implies an affirmative answer to (d).)

The notion of absolute definability can be extended, in the obvious way, to relations and operations. Thus question (c) asks whether or not the jump operation is absolutely definable in the reducibility ordering of degrees. Moreover, given a structure $\langle U, \ldots \rangle$, and given $V \subseteq U$ and $W \subseteq U$, we can define *V is absolutely definable in $\langle U, \ldots \rangle$ with respect to W* to mean that for every automorphism f of $\langle U, \ldots \rangle$, if $f(W) = W$ then $f(V) = V$. (This is the absolute or limiting version of the notion of V being

minimum choice possible for the infinite cardinals α and β. It follows as a corollary to a theorem of Scott (see the paper of Scott in [9]), that if U is denumerable, then a defining formula $\varphi(x)$ can always be found (for any absolutely definable $V \subseteq U$) in $L_{\omega_1 \omega}$.

definable in a formal system which has symbols for the relations and operations of $\langle U, \ldots \rangle$ together with a special symbol for membership in W.) Thus question (d) can be restated: is the jump operation on degrees of solvability absolutely definable in (4*) with respect to the collection of degrees of solvability?

(e) Given any fixed set $A \subseteq N$, is there a one-one mapping from the family of all degrees onto $\{[B] \mid [A] \leq [B]\}$ which is an isomorphism with respect to the reducibility ordering $\leq$ (and hence with respect to the operation $\cup$?)

(e′) Given any fixed set $A \subseteq N$, is there a one-one mapping from the family of all degrees onto $\{[B] \mid [A] \leq [B]\}$ which is an isomorphism with respect to the operation ′, the relation *recursively enumerable in*, and the reducibility ordering $\leq$?

Virtually all structural results which are known to hold for the ordering of all degrees are also known to hold for the ordering of $\{[B] \mid [A] \leq [B]\}$ (see [6]). This fact has been established in the case of each particular result on degrees by supplying a separate, more general, and usually more complex, "relativized" proof. An affirmative answer to (e′) would provide all such generalizations at one stroke. Answers to (e′) (and to the weaker (e)) have been tantalizingly elusive. It seems likely that a successful answer to (e) or (e′) will provide valuable new insights into the notions of computability and relative computability.

The second group of questions concerns definability and automorphisms in the structures $\mathscr{E}$ and $\mathscr{E}/\mathscr{F}$. Let $\mathscr{P}$ be a property of sets (i.e., $\mathscr{P} \subseteq 2^N$). We say that $\mathscr{P}$ is *well-defined on* $\mathscr{E}/\mathscr{F}$, if $\mathscr{P}$ is the union of some set of elements of $\mathscr{E}/\mathscr{F}$. We say that $\mathscr{P}$ is *invariant under the automorphisms of* $\mathscr{E}/\mathscr{F}$, if $\mathscr{P}$ is the union of some set Φ of elements of $\mathscr{E}/\mathscr{F}$, where Φ is invariant under all automorphisms of $\mathscr{E}/\mathscr{F}$. If $\mathscr{P}$ is invariant under the automorphisms of $\mathscr{E}/\mathscr{F}$, we say, more briefly, that $\mathscr{P}$ is *lattice-theoretic in* $\mathscr{E}/\mathscr{F}$. If $\mathscr{P}$ is invariant under the automorphisms of $\mathscr{E}$, we say that $\mathscr{P}$ is *lattice-theoretic in* $\mathscr{E}$. Evidently, to say that a property is lattice-theoretic is the same as to say that it is absolutely definable.

We note several facts about $\mathscr{E}$. (1) If $\mathscr{P}$ is lattice-theoretic in $\mathscr{E}$, then $\mathscr{P}$ is recursively invariant. (This follows from the fact that every recursive permutation induces an automorphism of $\mathscr{E}$.) (2) The converse to (1) fails. If $\mathscr{P}$ is recursively invariant, then $\mathscr{P}$ need not be lattice-theoretic in $\mathscr{E}$. This follows by applying a technique of C. F. Kent; see theorem 12-IX and exercise 12-32 in [1].) (3) We next note that the counterpart to (1) holds for $\mathscr{E}/\mathscr{F}$. If $\mathscr{P}$ is lattice-theoretic in $\mathscr{E}/\mathscr{F}$, then $\mathscr{P}$ is well-defined on $\mathscr{E}/\mathscr{F}$ and recursively invariant. (This follows from the fact that every recursive permutation induces an automorphism of $\mathscr{E}/\mathscr{F}$.) The converse to (3) is an open question:

(f) If $\mathscr{P}$ is recursively invariant and well-defined on $\mathscr{E}/\mathscr{F}$, must it follow that $\mathscr{P}$ is lattice-theoretic in $\mathscr{E}/\mathscr{F}$?

I suspect that question (f) is the most accessible of the questions listed in the present paper, and I conjecture that the answer is negative. It seems unlikely, for example, that the property of creativeness would be lattice-theoretic.

Fact (3) can be broken into two parts. (4) If $\mathscr{P}$ is lattice-theoretic in $\mathscr{E}/\mathscr{F}$, then $\mathscr{P}$ is lattice-theoretic in $\mathscr{E}$ and well-defined on $\mathscr{E}/\mathscr{F}$ (since every automorphism of $\mathscr{E}$ induces an automorphism of $\mathscr{E}/\mathscr{F}$). (5) If $\mathscr{P}$ is lattice-theoretic in $\mathscr{E}$ and well-defined on $\mathscr{E}/\mathscr{F}$, then $\mathscr{P}$ is recursively invariant and well-defined on $\mathscr{E}/\mathscr{F}$ (since every recursive permutation induces an automorphism of $\mathscr{E}$).

(f′) The converse to (4) is an open question.

(f″) The converse to (5) is an open question.

Questions (f), (f′) and (f″) are evidently closely related to the following open questions.

(g) Is every automorphism of $\mathscr{E}/\mathscr{F}$ induced by some recursive permutation?

(g′) Is every automorphism of $\mathscr{E}/\mathscr{F}$ induced by some automorphism of $\mathscr{E}$?

(By the proof of (2) above, it is not the case that every automorphism of $\mathscr{E}$ is induced by some recursive permutation.)

An affirmative answer to (g′) evidently implies an affirmative answer to (f′), and an affirmative answer to (g) evidently implies affirmative answers to all of (f), (f′), (f″) and (g′).

References

[1] H. Rogers Jr., Theory of recursive functions and effective computability (McGraw-Hill, New York, 1966).

[2] S. C. Kleene, Introduction to metamathematics (North-Holland Publ. Co., Amsterdam and Van Nostrand, Princeton, 1952).

[3] M. Davis, Computability and unsolvability (McGraw-Hill, New York, 1958).

[4] E. L. Post, Recursively enumerable sets of integers and their decision problems, Bull. Amer. Math. Soc. **50** (1944) 284.

[5] J. Myhill, The lattice of recursively enumerable sets, J. Symbolic Logic **21** (1956) 220 (Abstract).

[6] G. E. Sacks, Degrees of unsolvability, Ann. Math. Studies **55** (Princeton, 1963).

[7] Yu. T. Medvedev, Degrees of difficulty of the mass problem, Dokl. Acad. Nauk SSSR (n.s.) **104** (1955) 501.

[8] C. R. Karp, Languages with expressions of infinite length (North-Holland Publ. Co., Amsterdam, 1964).

[9] Theory of models, Proceedings of the 1963 International Symposium at Berkeley, eds. J. W. Addison, L. Henkin and A. Tarski (North-Holland Publ. Co., Amsterdam, 1965).

COMPUTABLE FUNCTIONALS OF FINITE TYPE I

R. O. GANDY
Manchester University, England

Ordinary recursion theory ('ORT') has proved important both for its applications and for its intrinsic interest. It is natural, therefore, to try to extend it in various ways. In particular, one may seek to set up a recursion theory for objects of higher type. Such a theory has been defined and developed by Kleene in a series of papers [1–6]. The theory has two salient features: (a) although *partial* recursive functionals are constructed, the arguments of these functionals are required to be *totally* defined; (b) the arguments are considered solely as extensions, i.e., as given only by their graphs. Kleene has shown that his theory can be regarded as extending several different approaches to ORT: via computability, via λ-definability and via reckonability in an equational calculus. He based his theory on a new approach – also possible for ORT – involving numerically indexed schemata and a reflection principle.

The present paper (part I) is intended as an elementary introduction to the theory[1]). In section 1, after some notational preliminaries, we describe various classes of functionals which must certainly be counted as computable. In particular, we single out the elementary functionals as constituting a simple class of total functionals which can readily be used for the arithmetisation of the description of higher type computing processes. This arithmetisation will be treated in part II.

The aim of section 2 is to make Kleene's notion of a *recursive functional of finite type* as intuitive as possible. The method used is to extend to

---

1) The lectures from which this paper arose were based wholly on the approach described in section 2; this made the going sometimes rather heavy. At the Summer School Y. N. Moschovakis told me of a simple characterisation (using indexing) of the hyperarithmetic sets, which he had discovered. This suggested to me the schemata of section 3.

The lectures also dealt with normal forms, selection operators and applications to hierarchy theory (which will be described in part II), and with continuity properties (which will be treated in a forthcoming paper).

higher types a particularly perspicuous definition of computability. I think this approach is not only of pedagogic value, but is also important for the foundations of the subject. Each of the definitions given by Kleene contains, so it seems to me, some arbitrary elements: one asks oneself whether alternative choices would not have led to different, but equally interesting classes of objects. I believe that the intuitions which dictated the actual choices are best understood through the approach adopted here. It is shown that if one tries to extend the notion of computability to higher types while preserving the features (a) and (b) above, then one is led ineluctably to a definition which is equivalent to Kleene's [2]).

Of course there are other characterisations of the class of recursive functions which may be used as launching platforms in the search for extensions of the notion *recursive*. Platek [7] develops a recursion theory based on the first recursion theorem; however this necessitates abandoning the feature (a). The characterisation which promises the widest scope for generalisation is that of invariant definability (by means of languages adequate for arithmetic in models which at least satisfy Peano's first four postulates). Particular extensions of this characterisation have already proved illuminating (cf. [8–10]). But although a general method for extending the characterisation to arbitrary structures has been described (cf. [10, 11]), and although an attempt has been made to apply it to the universe of the simple theory of types (in [9]) [3]), it is not yet clear what its correct application to that universe will yield. I see little reason to suppose that the correct application, when discovered, will result in a notion which will coincide with Kleene's [4]). And this is another reason for our preoccupation in this paper with the notion of computability.

Both the programmes and the computations described in section 2 con-

---

[2]) Any reader who becomes conversant with the definitions given here (2.4.2 and 3.1.10) and with those given by Kleene will see that they are all equivalent. Formal equivalence proofs will be given in part II.

[3]) Kreisel (in [9]) defines, model-theoretically, a notion *extensionally definite* which is applicable to functions of higher type. He conjectures that it is co-extensive with *general recursive*. But attempts to prove the conjecture have not been successful, and, for reasons given in the next footnote, I think it may well be false.

[4]) The fact that sets which are invariantly definable on the natural numbers are computable is a consequence of the existence of a recursive enumeration of formal proofs which allows a search to be made. It is not clear that this process has an analogue at higher types.

tain a lot of detail, belonging to ORT, which is irrelevant to the specific problems raised by the use of higher type arguments. In section 3 we develop a description of computable functionals which, like Kleene's first approach (in [1]), is based on indexed schemata. But by suppressing, as far as possible, the irrelevant detail, we have been able to get by with only two schemata. And this also allows us greatly to simplify the manipulations which are required to prove that various processes are computable. If the reader will compare the treatment given here of the substitution process (in 3.3.4 and 3.3.5) with Kleene's (theorem XXII of [1]), he will, I think, agree that the simplification is worth achieving. I have thought it my duty as an expositor to try out notations and definitions alternative to those used by Kleene. But I should like to emphasize that the proposed alternatives are relatively superficial; the underlying ideas are all his.

After the lectures on which this paper is based had been given, and a first draft of it written, Platek's dissertation [7] became available. This contains one radical innovation germane to our exposition: the introduction of the class of *hereditarily consistent* functionals as a substratum for higher-type recursion theory. A definitive exposition of the subject would certainly be largely concerned with those functionals; all we have been able to do is to indicate the way in which our definitions should be modified to suit them.

It is assumed that the reader is familiar with the fundamentals of ORT, as expounded, for example, in [12]. A slight acquaintance with the simple theory of types is also presupposed.

1. Preliminaries

1.1. *Notations of ORT*

We use lower case italic letters for numerical variables, and bold face lower case italic letters for finite sequences of such variables. We use $\mathscr{E}^1$ and $\mathscr{P}^1$ ($\mathscr{E}^1_n$ and $\mathscr{P}^1_n$) to denote, respectively, the classes of elementary and primitive recursive functions and predicates (of n variables). Our interest in $\mathscr{E}^1$ arises from the fact that it is adequate for the arithmetisation of all the usual notions of elementary syntax. Similarly, we write $\mathscr{R}^1$ ($\mathscr{R}^1_n$) for the class of partial recursive functions and (total) recursive predicates (of n variables).

1.1.2. We assume a system of Gödel-numbering for descriptions of members of $\mathscr{R}_n^1$; we write $e \in \mathscr{R}_n^1$ to mean that e is such a GN and $[e]_n$ (or just $[e]$) for the partial function it specifies. Also $e \in \mathscr{R}_0^1$ means that e is the GN of a single computation which, if it is defined, has the numerical value $[e]$. The expression $[e](\boldsymbol{x})$ denotes both the computation and its value (if defined); $\mathscr{D}$ is the class of computations whose value is defined. By convention, if $e \in \mathscr{R}_n^1$ and $m \neq n$, then $[e](x_1, \dots, x_m) \notin \mathscr{D}$. The relation between two computations of giving the same value or being both undefined is denoted by '$\simeq$'. There exist $U, T_n \in \mathscr{E}^1$ such that $[e]_n(\boldsymbol{x}) \simeq \simeq U((\mu y)\, T_n(e, \boldsymbol{x}, y))$[5]).

We write $[e; \boldsymbol{x}]$ in place of Kleene's $S_n^m(e, \boldsymbol{x})$. Thus

$$[e; \boldsymbol{x}]\,(\boldsymbol{y}) \simeq [e]\,(\boldsymbol{x}, \boldsymbol{y}).$$

There is a function $(e \circ f)$ such that

$$[e \circ f]\,(x) \simeq [e]\,([f]\,(x)).$$

The functions $\lambda e\boldsymbol{x} \cdot [e; \boldsymbol{x}]$ and $\lambda ef \cdot (e \circ f)$ are all elementary.

1.1.3. There is a 1:1 mapping $\phi: (a_0, \dots, a_{n-1}) \to \langle a_1, \dots, a_{n-1} \rangle$, of the set of all finite sequences of numbers into N such that:

(i) for each n, $\phi(a_0, \dots, a_{n-1})$ is elementary;

(ii) $\phi(\langle\rangle) = 1$, where $\langle\rangle$ is the empty sequence;

(iii) the predicate '$x \in$range of ϕ' (denoted by Seq(x)) is elementary;

(iv) the length $\mathrm{lh}(x)$ $(=n)$ of $x = \langle a_0, \dots, a_{n-1} \rangle$ is an elementary function;

(v) the inverses a_i, denoted by $(x)_i$ or simply x_i, of $x = \langle a_0, \dots, a_{n-1} \rangle$ are elementary functions of x, i; conventionally, $x_i = 0$ if $i \geqslant \mathrm{lh}(x)$.

Further notations for handling sequence numbers:

$$\begin{aligned}
\bar{x} &=_{\mathrm{Df}} \mathrm{lh}(x) \dot{-} 1;\\
\langle x \restriction m \rangle &=_{\mathrm{Df}} \langle x_0, \dots, x_{m-1} \rangle;\\
\langle x^{-} \rangle &=_{\mathrm{Df}} x \restriction \bar{x};\\
x \subseteq y &\equiv_{\mathrm{Df}} (\exists\, m \leq \mathrm{lh}(y))\, (x = \langle y \restriction m \rangle);\\
\langle x * y \rangle &=_{\mathrm{Df}} \langle x_0, \dots, x_{\bar{x}}, y \rangle;\\
\langle x^\frown y \rangle &=_{\mathrm{Df}} \langle x_0, \dots, x_{\bar{x}}, y_0, \dots, y_{\bar{y}} \rangle.
\end{aligned}$$

All these are elementary.

---

[5]) We use $\boldsymbol{x}$ to denote a list $x_1, \dots, x_n$ of numerical variables.

1.2. *Notations of type theory*

1.2.1. Types and the symbols for them are defined as follows.

(i) $N(=\{0, 1, 2, \ldots\})$ and $D(=\{0, 1\})$ are *pure* types of *level* 0.

(ii) If σ, τ are types of levels s, t, and $\sigma \neq D$, then $(\sigma \to \tau)$ is a type of level $\max(s+1, t)$; it is the type of functions from σ into τ. If τ is N or D, and σ is a pure type, then $(\sigma \to \tau)$ is a pure type [6].

(iii) If D does not occur in σ, then σ is *wholly number-theoretic*. If σ contains no part of the form $(\tau \to N)$, then σ is *wholly set-theoretic*.

(iv) A pure wholly number-theoretic type is called *numerical* and is often denoted by its level; thus type 0 is N, type 1 is $(N \to N)$, type 2 is $((N \to N) \to N)$.

(v) We omit brackets with association to the right. Hence any type σ can be written $\sigma_1 \to \sigma_2 \to \cdots \sigma_r \to X$, where X is N or D. The σ_i are the *argument* types of σ.

(vi) A type is said to be *restricted* if all its argument types are numerical. Notice that if $\sigma_1, \ldots, \sigma_r$ are numerical and τ is restricted, then $\sigma_1 \to \cdots \sigma_r \to \tau$ is also restricted.

1.2.2. *Terms and formulae of type theory.* We do not set up a complete formalism, but merely give a guide to our usage [7].

1. For variables of type σ we use $\alpha^\sigma, \beta^\sigma, \gamma^\sigma, \delta^\sigma, \varepsilon^\sigma, \eta^\sigma, \alpha'^\sigma, \ldots$. A wide variety of expressions will be used for constants; in particular 0^0 for zero, and S^1 for successor.

2. If A, B are terms of types $(\sigma \to \tau)$, σ, respectively, then (AB) is a term of type τ; it denotes the result of applying the functional A to the argument B. And $(\lambda\alpha^\tau \cdot B)$ is a term of type $(\tau \to \sigma)$ which denotes the functional whose value for argument α^τ is B. If B is a formula, then $(\lambda\alpha^\tau \cdot B)$ (of type $(\tau \to D)$ or $(\tau \to N)$) shall denote the corresponding characteristic function. Thus

$$(\lambda\alpha^\tau \cdot \mathrm{B})\,\beta^\tau = {0 \atop 1} \quad \text{as} \quad \beta^\tau {\in \atop \notin} \{\alpha^\tau | \mathrm{B}\}.$$

3. We use the logical symbols $\neg$, &, $\mathbf{v}$, $\to$, $\leftrightarrow$, $(\forall\alpha^\sigma)$, $(\exists\alpha^\sigma)$, with their

---

[6]) Notice that, technically speaking, all types have a single argument. However, we identify, in the natural way, a function of type $(\sigma_1 \to (\sigma_2 \to \ldots (\sigma_r \to \tau)\ldots))$ with a function from $\sigma_1 \times \sigma_2 \ldots \times \sigma_r$ into τ, and in this way are free to speak of functionals with several arguments.

[7]) The basic notations are due to Church [13].

usual meanings. Also we use (μx) for the *effective* least number operator; i.e., $(\mu x)\, A$ is undefined if $\neg(\exists x)\, A$.

4. We omit brackets freely, sometimes replacing them by dots. E.g., 'FAB' for '$((FA)\, B)$', '$A \,\&\, B. \rightarrow .C \vee D$' for '$(A \,\&\, B) \rightarrow (C \vee D)$'. We also omit repeated occurrences of 'λ': '$\lambda\alpha^\sigma\beta^\tau \cdot A$' for '$(\lambda\alpha^\sigma \cdot (\lambda\beta^\tau \cdot A))$', etc.

5. We often drop the type superscript of a variable from occurrences subsequent to the one by which it was introduced. E.g., '$\{\alpha^{n+1} | (\forall \beta^n)(\alpha(\beta)=0)\}$', 'let α^τ lie in the range of $\beta^{(\sigma\rightarrow\tau)}$, then $(\exists \gamma^\sigma)(\beta(\gamma)=\alpha)$'. This convention serves to show that the variable is either bound or restricted by hypothesis, and that it cannot be freely substituted for. Similarly, we often omit the type superscript from constants.

6. We use $\mathfrak{a}$, $\mathfrak{b}$, $\mathfrak{c}$, for strings or lists of variables of mixed types. If $\mathfrak{a}$ is $\alpha_1^{\sigma_1}, \ldots, \alpha_r^{\sigma_r}$, then $\lambda\mathfrak{a}$ stands for $\lambda\alpha_1^{\sigma_1}, \ldots, \alpha_r^{\sigma_r}$, $(\forall \mathfrak{a})$ stands for $(\forall \alpha_1^{\sigma_1}) \cdots (\forall \alpha_r^{\sigma_r})$, etc. We shall mostly be concerned with strings of variables of numerical type; in that case we use the associated italic letter to encode the type composition of the string. So if $\mathfrak{a}$ has exactly a_i variables of type i for $0 \leqslant i \leqslant r$, where r is the highest type occurring in $\mathfrak{a}$, then $a = \langle a_0, \ldots, a_r \rangle$; note that $\bar{a}$ is the highest type in $\mathfrak{a}$.

1.2.3. *Hereditarily consistent partial functionals.* We do not develop a recursion theory for partial functionals with partial arguments, but the class of hereditarily consistent (HC) functionals (introduced by Platek [7]) will be relevant to our discussions. The class HC(σ) of HC functionals of type σ is defined as follows.

(i) $\mathrm{HC}(N) = N$, $\mathrm{HC}(D) = D$.

(ii) $\mathrm{HC}(\sigma \rightarrow \tau)$ consists of all those partial functions from HC(σ) to HC(τ) which, if defined for some g, take the same value for all extensions of g.

1.3. *Elementary functionals*

Let $\mathscr{C}^1$ be a class of total number-theoretic functions (of level 1) which contains the zero functions $\lambda \boldsymbol{x} \cdot 0$ and the successor function S. There is a natural way of extending $\mathscr{C}^1$ to a class $\mathscr{C}^T$ of functionals of all types. Namely, $\mathscr{C}^T$ shall consist of all those functionals which can be defined from variables of all types, and constants for the functions of $\mathscr{C}^1$ by functional application and abstraction. We call $\mathscr{C}^T$ the class of $\mathscr{C}^1$-*composed* functionals. It is well-known (see, e.g., [14]) that functional abstraction can be replaced by the introduction of constants for the combinators

$\lambda\alpha^\sigma\beta^\tau\cdot\alpha$ and $\lambda\alpha^{(\sigma\to\tau\to\rho)}\,\beta^{(\sigma\to\tau)}\,\gamma^\sigma\cdot\alpha\gamma(\beta\gamma)$. Yet another method of obtaining $\mathscr{C}^T$ is by giving schemata for introducing functionals; since this method foreshadows several points which will be important in later sections, we give one version of it. However, in future applications we shall require only functionals which are of restricted type. So we confine ourselves to defining $\mathscr{C}$, the subclass of $\mathscr{C}^T$ which is determined by this condition.

1.3.1. *Inductive definition of* $\mathscr{C}$.

C1 (*Schema of trivial abstraction*): If $\phi\in\mathscr{C}^1$, $\phi\boldsymbol{x}\in N$, and $\mathfrak{a}$ is a list of variables of numerical types which contains all the variables $\boldsymbol{x}$, then $\lambda\mathfrak{a}\cdot\phi\boldsymbol{x}\in\mathscr{C}$.

C2 (*Numerical substitution*): If $\phi^{(N\to\sigma)}, \psi^\sigma\in\mathscr{C}$, then $\lambda\mathfrak{a}\cdot\phi(\psi\mathfrak{a})\mathfrak{a}\in\mathscr{C}$.

C3 (*Application schemata*):

C3^0 If $x\in\mathfrak{a}$, then $\lambda\mathfrak{a}\cdot x\in\mathscr{C}$.

C3^1 If $\alpha^1\in\mathfrak{a}$, $\phi\in\mathscr{C}$, then $\lambda\mathfrak{a}\cdot\alpha(\phi\mathfrak{a})\in\mathscr{C}$.

C3^{n+2} If $\alpha^{n+2}\in\mathfrak{a}$, $\phi\in\mathscr{C}$, then $\lambda\mathfrak{a}\cdot\alpha(\lambda\delta^n\cdot\phi\mathfrak{a}\delta)\in\mathscr{C}$.

NOTES. (a) The various expressions must be well-formed; hence $\psi\mathfrak{a}$, $\phi(\psi\mathfrak{a})\,\mathfrak{a}$ in C2, $\phi\mathfrak{a}$ in C3^1 and $\phi\mathfrak{a}\delta$ in C3^{n+2} must all be of type N.

(b) If $\lambda x\cdot x\in\mathscr{C}^1$ then C3^0 is redundant.

(c) Case C3^1 can be subsumed under C3^{n+2} by applying the following convention: '$\lambda\delta^{-1}\cdot A$' stands for the expression obtained by omitting all occurrences of δ from A. We shall use this convention to shorten both definitions and proofs.

(d) C2 is Kleene's schema S4 ([1] p. 3). C3^0, C3^1, C3^{n+2} correspond respectively to his S3, S7, S8 taken in conjunction with S6 (permutation of arguments).

(e) If $\phi\in\mathscr{C}$ there is a proof (in the form of a construction-tree) that this is so; each step of the proof corresponds to one of the schemata. Hence we establish properties of $\phi\in\mathscr{C}$ by 'induction on ϕ'.

THEOREM 1.3.2. (1) $\lambda\mathfrak{a}\cdot S...SO\in\mathscr{C}$.

(2) *If* $\alpha^n\in\mathfrak{a}$ *then* $\lambda\mathfrak{a}\cdot\alpha\in\mathscr{C}$.

(3) $\mathscr{C}$ *is closed under permutation of arguments.*

(4) *If* $\phi\in\mathscr{C}$ *and* $\mathfrak{a}$ *is any list then* $\lambda\mathfrak{a}\cdot\phi\in\mathscr{C}$.

(5) $\mathscr{C}$ *is closed under functional substitution.*

PROOFS. (1) By C1 and conditions on $\mathscr{C}^1$.

(2) By induction on n; for $n=0$ use C3^0. For $0<n$, $\lambda\mathfrak{a}\cdot\alpha=\lambda\mathfrak{a}\beta^{n-1}\cdot\alpha(\beta)=$ $=\lambda\mathfrak{a}\beta^{n-1}\cdot\alpha(\lambda\delta^{n-2}\cdot\phi\mathfrak{a}\beta\delta)$, where $\phi(=\lambda\mathfrak{a}\beta^{n-1}\cdot\beta)\in\mathscr{C}$ by induction hypothesis ('IH'). Therefore $\lambda\mathfrak{a}\cdot\alpha\in\mathscr{C}$, by C3^n.

(3) By induction on ϕ. Cases C1 and C3 are immediate. For C2, let $\mathfrak{a}^{\pi}$ be a permutation of $\mathfrak{a}$, and let $\psi^{\pi}\mathfrak{a}^{\pi}=\psi\mathfrak{a}$, $\phi^{\pi}x\mathfrak{a}^{\pi}=\phi x\mathfrak{a}$; so ψ^{π}, $\phi^{\pi}\in\mathscr{C}$ by IH. Hence $\lambda\mathfrak{a}^{\pi}\cdot\phi(\psi\mathfrak{a})\mathfrak{a}=\lambda\mathfrak{a}^{\pi}\cdot\phi^{\pi}(\psi^{\pi}\mathfrak{a}^{\pi})\mathfrak{a}^{\pi}\in\mathscr{C}$.
(4) By straightforward induction on ϕ. (4) allows one to pad out any two lists of arguments to a common list.
(5). By (3) and (4), it will suffice to prove:

$$(6) \qquad \lambda\mathfrak{a}\cdot\psi(\lambda\gamma^{n-1}\cdot\chi\gamma\mathfrak{a})\mathfrak{a}\in\mathscr{C} \quad \text{when} \quad \psi,\chi\in\mathscr{C}.$$

Use induction on n with a subsidiary induction on ψ. The case $n=0$ is just C2. For $0<n$ the induction on ψ is immediate except when ψ arises by C3^n and

$$\psi = \lambda\alpha^n\mathfrak{a}\cdot\alpha(\lambda\delta^{n-2}\cdot\phi\alpha\mathfrak{a}\delta).$$

Let θ be the functional occurring in (6). Then

$$\begin{aligned}\theta &= \lambda\mathfrak{a}\cdot(\lambda\gamma^{n-1}\cdot\chi\gamma\mathfrak{a})\,(\lambda\delta^{n-2}\cdot\phi\,(\lambda\gamma^{n-1}\cdot\chi\gamma\mathfrak{a})\,\mathfrak{a}\delta)\\ &= \lambda\mathfrak{a}\cdot\chi(\lambda\delta^{n-2}\cdot\phi\,(\lambda\gamma^{n-1}\cdot\chi\gamma\mathfrak{a})\,\mathfrak{a}\delta)\,\mathfrak{a}\\ &= \lambda\mathfrak{a}\cdot\chi(\lambda\delta^{n-2}\cdot\eta\delta\mathfrak{a})\,\mathfrak{a},\end{aligned}$$

where $\eta=\lambda\delta^{n-2}\mathfrak{a}\cdot\phi(\lambda\gamma^{n-1}\cdot\chi\gamma\mathfrak{a})\,\mathfrak{a}\delta$. But $\eta\in\mathscr{C}$ by (3) and IH on ψ; therefore $\theta\in\mathscr{C}$ by IH on n.

COROLLARY. *$\mathscr{C}$ is the class of $\mathscr{C}^1$-composed functionals of restricted type.*

For, it is obvious that the functionals of $\mathscr{C}$ are $\mathscr{C}^1$-composed. The converse follows readily from 1.3.2 by an induction on the explicit definition of any member of $\mathscr{C}^T$ of restricted type.
1.3.3. *If $\phi\in\mathscr{C}$ and $\phi\mathfrak{a}$ is of type N, then there is a construction-tree for ϕ in which all the variables are of type $\leqslant\bar{a}$.*

This is immediately apparent from C1-3.
1.3.4. A functional is called *elementary* if it is $\mathscr{E}^1$-composed.

It will turn out that $\mathscr{E}^T$ – or more precisely $\mathscr{E}$ – is just the class which is needed for arithmetising computations of functionals and for normal forms of type-theoretic predicates[8]). As usual, we count a predicate as

[8]) In ORT it is known that smaller classes of *predicates* are adequate for the arithmetisation of syntax; e.g., the rudimentary predicates of Smullyan. It may be that such classes could be extended to higher types. But these classes do not give rise to classes of *functions* with satisfactory closure properties; for this reason, and also to avoid wasting effort on technical ingenuities, we rest content with the elementary functionals.

belonging to $\mathscr{E}$ if its characteristic function does. Evidently $x=y$ is elementary, but note that $\alpha^{n+1}=\beta^{n+1}$ is not.

1.3.5. *$\mathscr{E}$ is closed with respect to* (1) *operations of the propositional calculus,* (2) *bounded quantification,* (3) *application of a bounded μ-operator,* (4) *definition by cases.*

This follows from the fact that $\mathscr{E}^1$ is closed with respect to these operations.

1.3.6. There are elementary functionals with elementary inverses which encode finite sequences of objects of type n in type n.

Namely, take

$$\langle \alpha_0^n, \ldots, \alpha_{r-1}^n \rangle = \lambda \beta^{n-1} \cdot \langle \alpha_0^n(\beta), \ldots, \alpha_{r-1}^n(\beta) \rangle;$$
$$\alpha_i = \lambda \beta^{n-1} \cdot (\langle \alpha_0^n, \ldots, \alpha_{r-1}^n \rangle (\beta))_i .$$

But note that the range of these encoding functions (which may be written $\{\alpha^n | (\forall \beta^{n-1}) (\mathrm{Seq}(\alpha\beta) \,\&\, \mathrm{lh}(\alpha\beta) = \mathrm{lh}(\alpha(\lambda\gamma^{n-2}\cdot 0)))\}$) is not elementary.

1.3.7. THEOREM. *For all n, j, there are elementary functionals* $\mathrm{Map}_{n,j}$ *and* $\mathrm{Map}_{n,j}^{-1}$ *of types $(n \to n+j)$ and $(n+j \to n)$ such that*

(i) $$\mathrm{Map}_{n,j}^{-1}(\mathrm{Map}_{n,j}(\alpha^n)) = \alpha^n ,$$

(ii) $$\mathrm{Map}_{n+1,j}(\alpha^{n+1})\,\mathrm{Map}_{n,j}(\beta^n) = \alpha^{n+1}\,\beta^n .$$

PROOF. For brevity we write $\{\alpha^n\}^{+j}$, $\{\alpha^{n+j}\}^{-j}$ in place of $\mathrm{Map}_{n,j}(\alpha^n)$, $\mathrm{Map}_{n,j}^{-1}(\alpha^{n+j})$. Also we set $\mathbf{0}^m = \lambda\gamma^{m-1}\cdot 0$, with the convention that $\mathbf{0}^{-1}$ is omitted. The functionals are defined by recursion:

(1) $$\{a^0\}^{+j} = \lambda\gamma^{j-1}\cdot a^0;$$

(2) $$\{\alpha^j\}^{-j} = \alpha^j(\mathbf{0}^{j-1});$$

(3) $$\{\alpha^{n+1}\}^{+j} = \lambda\gamma^{n+j}\cdot \alpha^{n+1}(\{\gamma\}^{-j});$$

(4) $$\{\alpha^{n+j+1}\}^{-j} = \lambda\delta^n\cdot \alpha^{n+j+1}(\{\delta\}^{+j}).$$

Evidently these functionals are elementary. We prove (i) by induction on n; the case $n=0$ is trivial.

$$\begin{aligned}\{\{\alpha^{n+1}\}^{+j}\}^{-j} &= \lambda\delta^n\cdot(\lambda\gamma^{n+j}\cdot\alpha^{n+1}(\{\gamma\}^{-j}))(\{\delta\}^{+j})\\ &= \lambda\delta^n\cdot\alpha^{n+1}(\{\{\delta\}^{+j}\}^{-j})\\ &= \lambda\delta^n\cdot\alpha^{n+1}(\delta) \qquad \text{(by IH)}\\ &= \alpha^{n+1} .\end{aligned}$$

To prove (ii):

$$\{\alpha^{n+1}\}^{+j}(\{\beta^n\}^{+j}) = \alpha^{n+1}(\{\{\beta^n\}^{+j}\}^{-j})$$
$$= \alpha^{n+1}(\beta^n), \qquad \text{by (i)}.$$

Thus we can encode the objects of a given numerical type in any higher type. Combining this with 1.3.6 we get:

1.3.8. *There is an elementary encoding* $\langle \mathfrak{a} \rangle$ *in type* $\bar{a}$ *of any list* $\mathfrak{a} = \alpha_0^{n_0}, \ldots, \alpha_s^{n_s}$ *of objects of numerical types. The inverses,* $\{(\langle \mathfrak{a} \rangle)_i\}^{-(\bar{a}-n_i)}$, *are also elementary.*

Suppose we have mapped each of the argument types of σ into the numerical type of its level; then by using 1.3.8 we can do the same for σ itself. Hence, by recursion on the level we can prove:

1.3.9. *For each type* σ *(of level s) there are elementary functionals* Tr_σ^s, Tr_s^σ *of types* $(\sigma \to s)$, $(s \to \sigma)$, *such that*

(i) $$\mathrm{Tr}_s^\sigma(\mathrm{Tr}_\sigma^s(\alpha^\sigma)) = \alpha^\sigma;$$

(ii) $$\mathrm{Tr}_{(\sigma\to\tau)}^u(\alpha^{(\sigma\to\tau)})(\mathrm{Tr}_\sigma^s(\beta^\sigma)) = \mathrm{Tr}_\tau^t(\alpha^{(\sigma\to\tau)}\beta^\sigma);$$

(iii) *the range of* Tr_σ^s *can be expressed by a formula whose quantified variables are all of numerical types* $< s$.

1.3.10. THEOREM. *Let A be a formula of type theory whose free variables* $\mathfrak{a}$ *are all of numerical type. Besides logical symbols (including* $=$, λ, μ*) A may contain constants for functionals of* $\mathscr{E}$. *Suppose*

(a) *all the free variables are of type* $\leqslant n+1$,

(b) *all the quantified variables are of level* $\leqslant n$,

(c) '$=$' *stands only between terms of level* $\leqslant n+1$.

Then either

(i) $$A \leftrightarrow (\forall\, \beta_1^n)(\exists\, \beta_2^n)\ldots(\mathbf{Q}\beta_m^n)(\mathbf{Q}'\gamma^{n-1})\,P(\mathfrak{a}, \boldsymbol{\beta}, \gamma)$$

or

(ii) $$A \leftrightarrow (\exists\, \beta_1^n)(\forall\, \beta_2^n)\ldots(\mathbf{Q}\beta_m^n)(\mathbf{Q}'\beta^{n-1})\,P(\mathfrak{a}, \boldsymbol{\beta}, \gamma),$$

where $\boldsymbol{\beta}$ *stands for* $\beta_1^n, \ldots, \beta_m^n$, $\mathbf{Q}'$ *is a quantifier of the opposite kind to* $\mathbf{Q}$, *and P is elementary* (i.e. $\lambda\mathfrak{a}\boldsymbol{\beta}\gamma \cdot P(\mathfrak{a}, \boldsymbol{\beta}, \gamma) \in \mathscr{E}$). *Also, if* $m > 1$ *then* $(\mathbf{Q}'\gamma^{n-1})$ *can be omitted.*

REMARKS.

(1) Considerable interest attaches to minimising m; hence the alternatives, and the $(\mathbf{Q}'\gamma^{n-1})$ when $m=1$.

(2) In case (i) A is said to be a Π^n_m *predicate with elementary scope*. We write '$A \in \Pi^n_m(\mathfrak{a})$' or '$A \in \Pi^n_m(p)$' (where p is the highest type in $\mathfrak{a}$) or simply '$A \in \Pi^n_m$'. Similarly, in case (ii) A is said to be a Π^n_m predicate, etc. And if both cases hold, A is said to be a Δ^n_m predicate, etc.

PROOF. We deal only with the case that the bound (quantified and abstracted) variables of A are all of numerical type. The general case is handled similarly, but 1.3.9 has to be applied at appropriate points. We reduce A to one of the given forms in a number of steps; after the ith step the resulting formula A_i will satisfy (a)–(c). Note that all prime formulae are equations.

Step 1. Replace all constants of $\mathscr{E}$ of level >1 by the corresponding λ-terms (cf. 1.3.2 corollary).

Step 2. Reduce to λ-normal form. Thus A_2 contains no parts of the form $(\lambda\beta^p \cdot B)C$. Therefore a term of highest level in A_2 must either be a variable or a λ-term which stands on one side of '='. So, by (c),

(d) every term has level $\leqslant n+1$.

Step 3. By using universal quantification, eliminate all occurrences of '=' between terms of level >0, and reduce to normal form. Note that (b) is still satisfied, and that all the λ-terms in A_3 have level $\leqslant n$.

Step 4. By using quantification and 1.3.9, eliminate all occurrences of 'λ' and 'μ'. E.g., a part

$$\alpha^{n+1}(\lambda\gamma^{n-1} \cdot S(\beta^n(\lambda\delta^{n-2} \cdot (\mu x)(\gamma\delta = x)))) = 0$$

becomes

$$(\exists\,\varepsilon^n)\,\{\alpha^{n+1}\varepsilon = 0\,\&\,(\forall\,\gamma^{n-1})\,(\exists\,\eta^{n-1})\,[\varepsilon\gamma = S(\beta^n\eta)$$
$$\&\,(\forall\,\delta^{n-2})\,(\exists\,x)\,(\eta\delta = x\,\&\,\gamma\delta = x\,\&\,(\forall\,y < x)\,(\gamma\delta \neq y))]\}\,.$$

Step 5. Reduce to prenex normal form. The scope of the quantifier prefix of A_5 is evidently an elementary predicate of all the variables occurring in it. The quantified variables are all of numerical types $\leqslant n$.

Step 6. We manipulate the quantifiers, using the following equivalences. ($\mathbf{Q}$ stands for the same quantifier – $\forall$ or $\exists$ – throughout a formula, $\mathbf{Q}'$ for the opposite one; a Q-*variable* is one which is bound by $\mathbf{Q}$.)

(A) Type raising:

$$(\mathbf{Q}\beta^p)\,B(\beta) \leftrightarrow (\mathbf{Q}\beta^{p+j})\,B(\{\beta^{p+j}\}^{-j})\,.$$

(B) Amalgamation:

$$(\mathbf{Q}\beta^p_0)\dots(\mathbf{Q}\beta^p_r)\,B(\beta^p_0,\dots,\beta^p_r) \leftrightarrow (\mathbf{Q}\beta^p)\,B((\beta)_0,\dots,(\beta)_r)\,.$$

(C) Commutation:

$$(\mathbf{Q}\beta^p)\,(\mathbf{Q}'\gamma^{p+1})\,B(\beta,\gamma)\leftrightarrow(\mathbf{Q}'\gamma^{p+1})\,(\mathbf{Q}\beta^p)\,B(\beta,\gamma_{(\beta)}),$$

where $\gamma_{(\beta)}=\lambda\delta^p\cdot\gamma(\langle\beta,\delta\rangle)$.

To prove (C) let $\mathbf{Q}$ be $\forall$ and $\mathbf{Q}'$ be $\exists$, and use the axiom of choice – indeed the equivalence can be thought of as a formulation of a particular case of that axiom; by duality the other case follows.

Each of the above manipulations, when applied to A_5, preserves the elementarity of the scope. Also observe that (A) and (B) can be used to amalgamate any string of like quantifiers, and (A) and (C) can be used to commute unlike quantifiers of different types.

Suppose now that A_5 contains at least one quantifier of type n; then we divide all the quantifiers of type $<n$ into two sorts as follows: $(\mathbf{Q}\beta^p)$ is of the first sort if either there is a type n quantifier to its right and the nearest such is of the same kind as $\mathbf{Q}$, or if there is no type n quantifier to its right and the nearest type n quantifier (to its left) is of the same kind; otherwise $(\mathbf{Q}\beta^p)$ is of the second sort. Now we raise all the quantifiers of the first sort to type n and all those of the second sort to type $n-1$. Then ws pass each quantifier of the second sort to the right (using (C)) until either it meets a type n quantifier of the same kind, with which it is then amalgamated, or until there are no type n quantifiers to its right. Finally we amalgamate all strings of consecutive quantifiers of the same kind. The result of this process is that the quantifier prefix now has one of the forms (i), (ii), except that the rightermost (type $n-1$) quantifier may be absent; it can be inserted by vacuous quantification. We give an example of the above process, using subscripts in place of letters for variables.

$$\forall_1^1\,\exists_2^1\,\forall_3^3\,\exists_4^2\,\forall_5^3\,\exists_6^0\,\forall_7^0\,\exists_8^3\,\forall_9^0\,\exists_{10}^2$$

becomes

$$\forall_1^3\,\exists_2^2\,\forall_3^3\,\exists_4^2\,\forall_5^3\,\exists_6^3\,\forall_7^2\,\exists_8^3\,\forall_9^2\,\exists_{10}^3$$

and then

$$\forall_1^3\,\forall_3^3\,\forall_5^3\,\exists_2^2\,\exists_4^2\,\exists_6^3\,\exists_8^3\,\exists_{10}^3\,\forall_7^2\,\forall_9^2$$

and finally

$$\forall_5^3\,\exists_8^3\,\forall_9^2.$$

Evidently if there is more than one quantifier in the final form, then the innermost, type $n-1$, quantifier can be commuted with last type n quantifier and amalgamated with the penultimate one. Notice that the reduction process does not increase the number of alternations in kind of the type n quantifiers.

If A_5 contains no type n quantifier, we can vacuously introduce one of either kind; so that in this case $A \in \Delta_1^n$. This completes the proof of the theorem.

1.4. *Extensions of the class* $\mathscr{E}$

1.4.1. *Relativisation*: let $\mathfrak{b}$ be a list of objects of arbitrary types, and let $\mathfrak{b}^*$ be the list of objects of numerical type obtained by applying the appropriate Tr functional to each member of $\mathfrak{b}$. A functional ϕ of restricted type is said to be *elementary in* $\mathfrak{b}$ (written '$\phi \in \mathscr{E}(\mathfrak{b})$') iff there is a $\psi \in \mathscr{E}$ such that $\phi = \psi \mathfrak{b}^*$. Evidently the notion is reflexive and transitive. Observe that although this definition calls for uniformity in $\mathfrak{b}^*$, it is possible to define functionals from $\mathfrak{b}$ which will only be elementary in $\mathfrak{b}$ for certain $\mathfrak{b}$. E.g., let

$$\Phi = \lambda \beta^1 x \cdot (\beta(0) = 0 \vee . \beta(0) \neq 0 \,\&\, (\exists y)\, T^\beta(x, x, y)).$$

Then $\Phi\beta \in \mathscr{E}(\beta)$ iff $\beta(0) = 0$.

The notion of relativisation is extended to type-theoretic predicates in the obvious way. We separate the constants (sometimes also called parameters) from the arguments of the predicate by a ';'. Thus, writing 'A' for '$\lambda \mathfrak{a} \cdot A(\mathfrak{a})$', '$A \in \Pi_m^n(\mathfrak{b})$' '$A \in \Pi_m^n(\mathfrak{b};\, \bar{a})$', and '$A(\mathfrak{a}) \in \Pi_m^n(\mathfrak{b};\, \mathfrak{a})$' all mean that there is a $C(\mathfrak{a}, \mathfrak{b})$ such that

(i) $C(\mathfrak{a}, \mathfrak{b}) \in \Pi_m^n(\mathfrak{a}, \mathfrak{b})$,

(ii) for the given $\mathfrak{b}$, $(\forall \mathfrak{a})\,(A(\mathfrak{a}) \leftrightarrow C(\mathfrak{a}, \mathfrak{b}))$.

1.4.2. *Classes of primitive recursive functionals.* Let It_p, the *iteration operator for type* $p \to p$, be the unique functional of type $((p \to p) \to p \to 0 \to p)$ $(= \sigma$, say) which satisfies

$$\mathrm{It}_p \alpha^{p \to p}\, \beta^p y = \alpha^{p \to p}(\ldots \alpha^{p \to p}(\beta^p) \ldots),$$

where there are y occurrences of α. Set

$$\mathscr{G}_p = \mathscr{E}(\mathrm{Tr}_\sigma^{p+2}(\mathrm{It}_p)).$$

Then we define the following classes.

(1) $\mathscr{P}$ is the class of $\mathscr{P}^1$-composed functionals of restricted type.

(2) $\mathscr{K} = \mathscr{G}_0$ is the class of primitive recursive functionals in the sense of Kleene (c.f. [1]).

(3) $\mathscr{G} = \bigcup_p \mathscr{G}_p$ is the class of primitive recursive functionals of restricted type in the sense of Gödel (cf. [15])[9].

The functional ϕ is *defined by primitive recursion at type p from ψ and χ with parameters* $\mathfrak{a}$, if $\phi\mathfrak{a}$ is of type $(0\to p)$, $\psi\mathfrak{a}$ is of type p, $\chi\mathfrak{a}$ is of type $(0\to p\to p)$, and

$$\left.\begin{aligned} \phi\mathfrak{a}0 &= \psi\mathfrak{a}\,, \\ \phi\mathfrak{a}(x+1) &= \chi\mathfrak{a}x(\phi\mathfrak{a}x)\,. \end{aligned}\right\} \quad (\mathrm{PR}_p)$$

1.4.3. *$\mathscr{G}_p$ is closed under* (PR_p). For, let ϕ be as above and let

$$\theta = \lambda\mathfrak{a}\alpha^p \cdot \langle (\{\alpha_0\}^{-p} + 1), (\chi\mathfrak{a}(\{\alpha_0\}^{-p})\,\alpha_1)\rangle\,.$$

Evidently $\theta \in \mathscr{E}(\chi)$. Also, recalling that, by 1.3.8, $\langle x, \alpha^p\rangle = \langle \{x\}^{+p}, \alpha^p\rangle$, we see that

$$\theta\mathfrak{a}\,\langle x, \alpha^p\rangle = \langle x+1, \chi\mathfrak{a}x\alpha^p\rangle\,.$$

Therefore

$$\phi\mathfrak{a}x = (\mathrm{It}_p(\theta\mathfrak{a})\,(\langle 0, \psi\mathfrak{a}\rangle)\,x)_1\,;$$

this suffices to prove 1.4.3.

Evidently $\mathscr{P} \subseteq \mathscr{K} \subseteq \mathscr{G}$. Now it is easy to show that any doubly recursive function belongs to $\mathscr{G}$ (and indeed to $\mathscr{G}_1$). Thus $\mathscr{K}^1 \subset \mathscr{G}^1$, where '$\subset$' denotes strict inclusion, and the superscripts 1 indicate that the classes are restricted to functions of level 1. On the other hand, $\mathscr{P}^1 = \mathscr{K}^1$ (cf. [1]). Other obvious questions are answered by means of

1.4.4. *Let ψ^1 grow faster than any primitive recursive function, and let it satisfy $x < \psi(x)$. Then for any $\phi \in \mathscr{P}^1(\psi)$ there is a q such that for all* $\boldsymbol{x}$

$$\phi(\boldsymbol{x}) < \mathrm{It}_0\psi(\mathrm{Max}(\boldsymbol{x}))\,q\,.$$

For if $\phi \in \mathscr{P}^1(\psi)$, then it can be constructed from ψ and functions of $\mathscr{P}^1$ by means of the schemata C2 and C3^1 (cf. 1.3.1). The required result is now easily proved by induction on the construction of ϕ.

COROLLARY 1. $\mathscr{P}^1(\psi) \subset \mathscr{K}^1(\psi)$.

For $\lambda x \cdot \mathrm{It}_0\psi xx$ cannot belong to $\mathscr{P}^1(\psi)$.

COROLLARY 2. $\mathscr{P} \subset \mathscr{K}$.

For, by corollary 1, $\mathrm{It}_0 \notin \mathscr{P}$.

---

[9]) The classes $\mathscr{K}$ and $\mathscr{G}$ are sometimes referred to respectively as the *predicative* and the *impredicative* primitive recursive functionals. The names refer to the fact that 1.3.3 holds in $\mathscr{K}$ but not in $\mathscr{G}$.

2. Computable functionals

The purpose of this section is to make as intuitive as possible Kleene's concept of a recursive functional of finite type. I think this is most easily done by extending the idea of computation. Kleene himself has described (in [4] and [5]) such an extension for Turing machines. However, although Turing machines are very suitable for describing computations on strings of symbols, they are not particularly well adapted to numerical computations. The register machines of Shepherdson and Sturgis [16] are much better for numerical work: their action is perspicuous, their basic operations are simple, and they differ from real computers only in allowing an arbitrarily large number to be stored in a given register.

2.1. *Register machines*

A register machine consists of a finite number, $R+1$ say, of registers and a table, or programme, of numbered instructions ('NIs'). Each register i contains a number $r_i \geqslant 0$. When an instruction is obeyed, the contents of some indicated register, i say, is altered from r_i to r_i', other registers are left unaltered, and the number of the next instruction to be obeyed – depending, perhaps, on r_i – is selected. Instruction number 0 is, by convention, a halting instruction; when the machine halts the *value* of the computation is r_0. The other types of instruction are as follows:

Name	Symbol	Action	Next NI
Add	$i+/j$	$r_i' = r_i + 1$	j
Subtract	$i-/j$	$r_i' = r_i \dot{-} 1$	j
Jump	$i \rightarrow/k, j$	none	$\begin{cases} k \text{ if } r_i \neq 0 \\ j \text{ if } r_i = 0 \end{cases}$

It is possible to roll 'Subtract' and 'Jump' into a single instruction. It is also possible to insist that j in the above table is always one greater than the number of the instruction which is being obeyed.

2.1.1. We give the complete programme for a multiplication machine. If this be started with x, y, z in the registers 0, 1, 2, then it will come to a halt with the value $r_0 = x + yz$. To make the action easy to grasp we divide the table up into sub-routines; double primes are used to denote the contents of a register at the end of a complete sub-routine. (S stands for 'sub-routine', I for 'instruction'.)

S No.	I No.	I	S Action	Next S
1	1 2	3 →/2,3 3 −/1	$r_3'' = 0$	**2**
2	3	1 →/4,0		**3, 0**
3	4 5 6 7 8	1 −/5 2 →/6,9 2 −/7 0 +/8 3 +/5	$r_0'' = r_0 + r_2$ $r_1'' = r_1 \dot{-} 1$ $r_2'' = 0$ $r_3'' = r_3 + r_2$	**4**
4	9 10 11	3 →/10,3 3 −/11 2 +/9	$r_2'' = r_3 + r_2$ $r_3'' = 0$	**2**

2.1.2. In general, we say that a partial function $\phi(x_1, \ldots, x_n)$ is *computable* if there is a machine such that if it is started at the beginning of its programme, with $r_0 = 0$, $r_1 = x_1, \ldots, r_n = x_n$, $r_{n+1} = 0, \ldots$, then it will come to a halt (with the correct value) if and only if $\phi(x_1, \ldots, x_n)$ is defined.

2.1.3. *Every primitive recursive function is computable.* A formal proof is unnecessary for him who has understood the action of the multiplication machine.

Next we give a programme schema for the μ-operator.

I No.	I	Next I
1	$r_1'' = \phi(r_0)$	2
2	1→	3,0
3	0+	1

Here the first 'instruction' stands for a sub-routine for computing ϕ. If initially $r_0 = x$, then the machine computes $(\mu y \geqslant x)(\phi(y) = 0)$, provided

$$(\exists\, y \geq x)\,(\phi(y) = 0 \,\&\, (\forall\, z)\,(x \leq z \leq y \rightarrow \phi(z)) \text{ is defined;}$$

if not, then the machine does not halt.

2.1.4. *Every partial recursive function is computable.* This follows from Kleene's normal form (cf. 1.1.2).

2.2. *Computations from arguments of higher type*

As in section 1 we shall restrict ourselves to considering arguments of numerical type. Since we shall ensure that all the functionals of $\mathscr{E}$ are computable, this restriction will not entail any real loss in generality.

An object of type greater than zero cannot be stored in a finite register. It would be possible to consider machines with infinite registers, but we shall not do so. Instead we shall consider the arguments for a computation (hereinafter 'c.as') as existing outside the machine. We then introduce 'call' instructions; these place the value of a specified c.a (of type $m+1$, say) for a specified argument (of type m) in a specified register. Turing [17] described this process as consulting an oracle. More prosaically, for $m=0$, it can be compared to reading a data tape. It is the mechanical analogue of the schema C3 of 1.3.1. Consider the case $m=1$; we call for the value $\alpha^2(\beta^1)$, where α^2 is one of the c.as and β^1 is a 'specified' function. The crucial question is: what forms of specification shall we allow?

In the first place we insist that β^1 shall itself be computable from the same c.as ($\mathfrak{a}$ say) as the computation in which the call instruction considered occurs; this includes the case that $\beta^1 \in \mathfrak{a}$. Otherwise the 'computation' would include a step which was not 'computable'. Secondly, we insist that β^1 be total; in other words, we regard the c.a α^2 as undefined for non-total arguments. Thus there must be a machine M which, for every x, computes the value $\beta^1(x)$ from the c.as $\mathfrak{a}$, x. So we must answer the question: what specifications of machines M shall be allowed?

It might be thought that it would be sufficient to write out a programme for M, and insert this as a seperate sub-routine under the call instruction as the specification of β^1. Such a procedure would suffice for computing the functionals of $\mathscr{K}$, but not those of $\mathscr{G}$. For example, let $\eta^{1\to 1} = \lambda y^1 x \cdot \alpha^2(\langle x, y \rangle)$, let $\xi^1 = \lambda y \cdot \mathrm{It}_1 \eta \delta^1 y 0$, and consider the computation of $\varepsilon^2 \xi$; this must have a subroutine which can compute $\xi(y)$ for each y. But the computation of $\xi(y)$ involves computing successively the functions $\beta_0 = \delta$, $\beta_1 = \eta\delta$, $\beta_{y-1} = \eta(\ldots\eta\delta)$. A value $\beta_i(z)$ will be got by calling for the value of α for the argument $\langle z, \beta_{i-1} \rangle$, and this argument will be provided by a sub-routine M. (A detailed programme for computing ξ will be given in 2.3.1.) Thus it must be possible for M to make use of the *same* call instruction which gave rise to it: in other words, it must be possible for M to form part of the same loop as the call instruction. Just as in ordinary computations, this circularity may give rise to an infinite regress, but need not do so. A possible way of achieving the aim is to introduce an indexing of all machines, and allow M to be specified by its index (cf. the second recursion theorem). This method is the one adopted by Kleene. However it seems more intuitive, and somewhat simpler, to specify M by jumping to another instruction on the same programme. Account must be taken, however, of the fact that the subroutine M which performs the subordinate computation of β^1, has one more numerical argument than the principal computation. And, as the iterative computation considered above shows, no bound can be set on the number of additional arguments which may be introduced in this way. But observe that if n be the highest type of argument, then additional arguments for subordinate computations arise only at types $<n-1$.

These facts guide us to the following modifications:

(a) A machine for computing from arguments of type $\leqslant n$ is equipped with n *type registers*; the ith such register contains the number a_i of arguments of type i. When a subordinate computation (like that of $\beta_i^1(x)$ above) is entered, the content of the appropriate type register is increased by one.

(b) Numerical arguments also are thought of as being outside the machine; when one is required, it must be called for.

(c) A call instruction for the ith argument of type m does not specify i (which may be arbitrarily large) directly; rather, it specifies a register in which i is to be found.

2.2.1. Before giving the details of the call instructions, it is convenient to introduce a notation for describing computations. Let t stand for (or be a Gödel number of) a programme for a machine with $\bar{r}+1$ ordinary registers and n type registers; let $r=\langle r_0, \ldots, r_{\bar{r}}\rangle$, $a=\langle a_0, \ldots, a_{\bar{a}}\rangle$. Then $\{t:k:r, a\}$ $(\mathfrak{b})$ shall stand for the value, if defined, of the computation which results when the programme t is started at instruction k, with r, a as the contents of its registers and with arguments $\mathfrak{b}(=\beta_1^0, \ldots, \beta_{b_0}^0, \beta_1^1, \ldots, \beta_1^n, \ldots, \beta_{b_n}^n$, where $n=\bar{b}$, cf. 1.2.2(vi)). The exact conditions under which a computation is counted as defined are given below. $\{t:k:r, a\}$ $(\mathfrak{b})$ will be counted as undefined if the programme t does not contain an instruction with number k, or if $a\neq b$. We normally assume $a=b$, and omit the

'a'; if 'k' is omitted it is assumed that $k=1$, and then r is omitted if it is clear what the initial contents of the registers should be. Note that $\{t:0:r\}(\mathfrak{b})$ always has the value r_0.

2.2.2. The following table specifies the call instructions for each type.

Case	Symbol	Action
$m=0$	p^0 in q	$r'_q = \alpha^0_{r_p+1}$ if $r_p < a_m$, 0 otherwise
$m=1$	$p^1(s)$ in q	$r'_q = \alpha^1_{r_p+1}(r_s)$ if $r_p < a_m$, 0 otherwise
$m>1$	$p^m\{k\}$ in q	$r'_q = \alpha^m_{r_p+1}(\gamma^{m-1})$ if $r_p < a_m$, 0 otherwise

where α_i^m is the ith type m argument of the computation in progress when the instruction is obeyed (provided $i \leqslant a_m$). To define γ^{m-1}, let t be the programme in which the instruction appears, and let the list $\mathfrak{a}'$, with type number a', be obtained by adding δ^{m-2} as an $(a_{m-2}+1)$-th type $m-2$ argument to $\mathfrak{a}$. Then

$$\gamma^{m-1}(\delta^{m-2}) \simeq \{t:k:r, a'\}(\mathfrak{a}'),$$

where r is the contents of the registers just before the call instruction is obeyed.

NOTES.

(1) Each call instruction also names the next instruction to be obeyed (not shown in table).

(2) It is apparent that an interchange of two adjacent arguments of different types in the list $\mathfrak{a}$ will have no effect on the course of the computation. Hence we equate two lists which, for each type, have the same arguments arranged in the same way. In particular, therefore, we can write the definition of γ^{m-1} as

$$\gamma^{m-1}(\delta^{m-2}) \simeq \{t:k:r\}(\mathfrak{a}, \delta^{m-2}).$$

(3) We defer an investigation of what it means for a computation to be undefined until we have considered some examples. Suppose however that for a given computation, the values $\alpha^m(\gamma^{m-1})$ $(m>1)$ which are called for are all defined. The course of the computation proceeds as in ORT, except that at the call instructions the content of some register is altered as if by magic. This computation is defined iff the halting instruction is

reached; and if that happens, then the complete course C say, of the computation is a finite object. We call C the *principal* computation. But if we wish to understand what is going on during the magical alterations, then we must consider the computations $\{t{:}k{:}r\}(\mathfrak{a}, \delta^{m-2})$ $(=C_\delta$, say) by which γ is defined. We say that the (infinitely many) computations C_δ are *directly subordinate* to C. The C_δ may themselves have subordinates, and so on.

(4) If there are no arguments of type greater than 1, then the notion considered here is identical with the notions 'recursive in' and 'computable from' of ORT.

2.3. *Examples of computable functionals*

In the following tables we abbreviate heavily, combining several instructions into one, and using symbols for functions which are known to be computable. When an instruction, or part of one, consists of one of the basic operations, we use the symbolic form, e.g., $p+$ for $r'_p = r_p + 1$. Otherwise we give it in full, e.g., $r'_p = 0$. Where an instruction calls for a fixed argument we use the letter for that argument instead of the number of the register containing its subscript. As a consequence of these abbreviations the actual machines described may have more registers than appears from our description of them.

2.3.1. *An iteration machine.* This machine has four arguments which we denote by x, y, α^1, β^2.

I No.	Action	Next I
1	x in 1	2
2	6^0 in 4, 7^0 in 5	3
3	if $r_1 \neq 0$, $r'_1 = r_1 \dot{-} 1$	4
	if $r_1 = 0$, $r'_1 = r_1$	6
4	$\beta^2\{5\}$ in 3	7
5	$r'_2 = 1$, $6+$, $7+$	2
6	$\alpha^1(5)$ in 3	7
7	$2\rightarrow$	8,9
8	$r'_0 = \langle r_4, r_3\rangle$	0
9	$r'_0 = r_3$	0

Initially all the registers are to contain 0 except r_7 which contains 1. We denote the value of the computation by $\phi_x(y)$. It is easily verified that

$\phi_0(y)=\alpha^1(y)$; thus $\phi_0=\alpha^1$. For $x>0$, the sequence of steps in the principal computation is as follows:

I No.	Registers								Arguments
1	r_0	r_1	0	r_3	r_4	r_5	0	1	x, y, α, β
2	r_0	x	0	r_3	r_4	r_5	0	1	
3	r_0	x	0	r_3	r'_4	y	0	1	
4	r_0	$x-1$	0	r_3	r'_4	y	0	1	
7, 9	r_0	$x-1$	0	$\beta(\gamma^1)$	r'_4	y	0	1	
0	$\beta(\gamma^1)$								

Here we have written r_i instead of the actual content of a register whenever that content is wholly irrelevant to the subsequent computation. (N.B. 'y' in r_5 would be relevant for the case $x=0$.)

A subordinate computation for a value of γ runs as follows:

I No.	Registers								Arguments
5	r_0	$x-1$	0	r_3	r'_4	r_5	0	1	x, y, z, α, β
2	r_0	$x-1$	1	r_3	r'_4	r_5	1	2	
3	r_0	$x-1$	1	r_3	y	z	1	2	
4	r_0	$x-2$	1	r_3	y	z	1	2	
7, 8	r_0	$x-2$	1	v	y	z	1	2	
0	$\langle y, v\rangle$								

Here $v=\alpha(z)$ in case $x=1$, and $v=\beta(\delta)$ for appropriate δ if $x>1$. But, by comparing the two computations, we see that

$$v \simeq \{t:3:r_0, x-1, 0, r_3, r_4, z, 1, 2\}\,(x_1, y, z, \alpha, \beta),$$

where r_0, r_3, r_4, x_1 can take any values. And then examination of the instructions 2 and 5 shows that

$$v \simeq \{t:3:r_0, x-1, 0, r_3, r_4, z, 0, 1\}\,(y, z, \alpha, \beta).$$

Hence $v=\phi_{x-1}(z)$, and $\gamma=\lambda z\cdot\langle y, \phi_{x-1}(z)\rangle=\langle y,\phi_{x-1}\rangle$.

Thus ϕ is defined by the recursion:

$$\phi_0 = \alpha,$$
$$\phi_{x+1}(y) = \beta(\langle y, \phi_x\rangle).$$

Hence

$$\phi_x = \mathrm{It}_1 \left(\lambda\delta^1 y \cdot \beta^2 (\langle y, \delta\rangle)\right) \alpha^1 x .$$

In similar fashion it is possible to show that the functionals of restricted type which correspond to It_2, $\mathrm{It}_3, \ldots$, are all computable.

2.3.2. *A modulus of continuity machine.* We consider the space S of infinite dyadic sequences with the usual order topology (Cantor's discontinuum). Let $\beta_{(p)} (= \lambda x \cdot \beta^1 (\langle p, x\rangle))$ be a monotonic sequence of points of S whose limit is α^1; thus α, β, take only 0,1 as values. Let γ^2 be continuous on the sequence: i.e. $\mathrm{Lt}_{p\to\infty}\gamma(\beta_{(p)}) = \gamma(\alpha)$. Let $\delta^1 =_z \varepsilon^1$ stand for $(\forall x<z)(\delta^1(x) = \varepsilon^1(x))$. We exhibit machines which compute $p_0 = (\mu p)(\forall q \geqslant p)(\gamma(\beta_{(q)}) = \gamma(\alpha))$ and $m = (\mu z)(\forall q)(\beta_{(q)} =_z \alpha \to \gamma(\beta_{(q)}) = \gamma(\alpha))$; ($2^{-m}$ is the modulus of continuity of γ on the given sequence).

First we observe that $\delta^1 =_z \varepsilon^1$ can be decided by a computation from δ^1, ε^1, z. The table for the machine which computes p_0 is:

1	$\gamma\{4\} = \gamma\{3\}$	2,0
2	$0+$	1
3	$\alpha(x)$ in 0	0
4	$r_1' = (\mu p \geq r_0)(\gamma(\beta_{(p)}) \neq \gamma\{3\} \vee \alpha =_{x+1} \beta_{(p)})$	5
5	$\alpha =_{x+1} \beta_{(r_1)}$	6,3
6	$\beta(\langle r_1, x\rangle)$ in 0	0

The first instruction means that the next instruction is 0 if the equality holds, 2 otherwise; similarly for 5. Also x stands for the argument of the subordinate computations. Initially we set $r_0 = 0$.

Observe first that $\{t{:}3{:}r\}(x) = \alpha(x)$. Let $\delta_s(x) \simeq \{t{:}4{:}s, r_1\}(x)$. Now, by the postulated convergence, $(\forall s)(\forall x)(\exists p \geqslant s)(\beta_{(p)} =_x \alpha)$; thus instruction 4 always leads to a value for r^0, and therefore $\delta_s(x)$ is defined for all s, x.

The effect of instructions 1–3 is to compute

$$(\mu s)(\gamma(\delta_s) = \gamma(\alpha)) \; (= s_0, \text{ say}).$$

Thus to prove that the machine computes p_0, it suffices to prove

(1) $$(\exists\, p \geq s)(\gamma(\beta_{(p)}) \neq \gamma(\alpha)) \leftrightarrow \gamma(\delta_s) \neq \gamma(\alpha) .$$

If the left hand side is false, then instructions 4, 5, 3 ensure that $\delta_s = \alpha$, and so the right hand side of (1) is also false. If the left hand side holds, take the least $p \geqslant s$ which satisfies the scope of the quantifier, and take the greatest y which satisfies $\beta_{(p)} =_y \alpha$. For $x < y$, instruction 4 (with $r_0 = s$) sets $r_1 \leqslant p$, and so $\beta_{(r_1)} =_{x+1} \alpha$, and $\delta_s(x) = \alpha(x)$ $(= \beta_{(p)}(x))$. If $x \geqslant y$, then instruction 4 sets $r_1 = p$, for we postulated that the sequence $\beta_{(p)}$ is monotonic; hence, via instruction 6, $\delta_s(x) = \beta_{(p)}(x)$. Thus $\delta_s = \beta_{(p)}$, and the right hand side of (1) holds. This completes the proof of (1).

If $p_0 = 0$, take $m = 0$; otherwise $m = (\mu z)\,(\beta_{(p_0-1)} \neq_z \alpha)$.

REMARK. The only values of γ which the computation uses are $\gamma(\alpha)$ $(= a$, say) and $\gamma(\beta_{(p)})$ $(= \delta^1(p)$, say). The interesting thing is that although p_0 is defined from a, δ, it is obviously not computable from them.

It will be shown elsewhere that a modulus of continuity for a continuous function defined on an interval of S cannot be computed.

PROBLEM. Can a modulus (i.e. some $n \geqslant m$) be computed when the sequence is required only to be convergent, but need not be monotonic?

2.3.3. The following machine, which computes from the arguments α^1, β^2, is of interest not for the value computed, but for the circumstances in which the computation is defined (i.e. leads to a value). For the notations used see 1.1.3.

1	$\beta^2\{2\}$ in 0	0
2	$\alpha^1(r_1) = 0$	3,0
3	2^0 in 3	4
4	$2+, r_1' = \langle r_1 * r_3 \rangle$	1

Initially we set $r_1 = 1$, $r_0 = r_2 = r_3 = 0$.

Let $x_0, x_1, \ldots,$ be the numerical arguments for the subordinate computations. We say that such a sequence (or a finite sequence $x_0, \ldots, x_r$) is *secured* if, for some $s (\leqslant r)$, $\alpha(\langle x_0, \ldots, x_s \rangle) = 0$, or if $\alpha(1) = 0$ (recall that $1 = \langle\rangle$).

Let $\phi(\alpha, \beta)$ be the partial functional which the machine computes. Then $\phi(\alpha, \beta) \simeq \beta(\dot{\gamma}^1_{\langle\rangle})$,[10] where

$$\dot{\gamma}_{\langle\rangle}(x_0) \simeq 0 \quad \text{if } \langle\rangle \text{ is secured,}$$
$$\simeq \beta(\dot{\gamma}_{\langle x_0 \rangle}) \quad \text{if not.}$$

[10]) We use $\dot{\gamma}$ rather than γ as a variable here to emphasise that it ranges over *partial* functions.

Here

$$\dot{\gamma}_{\langle x_0 \rangle}(x_1) \simeq 0 \quad \text{if } \langle x_0 \rangle \text{ is secured,}$$
$$\simeq \beta(\dot{\gamma}_{\langle x_0, x_1 \rangle}) \quad \text{if not.}$$

In general, if $\langle x^- \rangle$ is not secured, the computation will call for $\beta(\dot{\gamma}_x)$, where

(a) $$\dot{\gamma}_x(y) \simeq 0 \quad \text{if } x \text{ is secured,}$$

(b) $$\simeq \beta(\dot{\gamma}_{\langle x*y \rangle}) \quad \text{if not.}$$

For the computation as a whole, two cases arise.

CASE A. There is an infinite sequence $x_0, x_1, \ldots$ which is not secured. Then for each r, putting $x = \langle x_0, \ldots, x_{r-1} \rangle$, $\beta(\dot{\gamma}_x)$ is called for; and $\dot{\gamma}_x(x_r) \simeq \simeq \beta(\dot{\gamma}_{\langle x*x_r \rangle})$. Thus we are involved in an infinite regress, and none of the $\dot{\gamma}_x$ can ever get completely defined. So $\phi(\alpha, \beta)$ is undefined.

CASE B. Every infinite sequence is secured. Then $\phi(\alpha, \beta)$ is defined. For if not, $\dot{\gamma}_{\langle\rangle}(x_0)$ must be undefined for some x_0, $\dot{\gamma}_{\langle x_0 \rangle}(x_1)$ undefined for some x_1, and so on. But we must reach an r such that x $(= \langle x_0, \ldots, x_{r-1} \rangle)$ is secured, and then, by (a), $\dot{\gamma}_x(y)$ is defined for all y; contradiction.

Thus we have proved

2.3.4. $\phi(\alpha, \beta) \in \mathscr{D} \leftrightarrow (\forall \delta^1)(\exists x)(\alpha(\bar{\delta}(x)) = 0)$.

NOTES.

1. The characteristic functional of the right hand side of 2.3.4 as a predicate of α (i.e. $\lambda\alpha \cdot \text{RHS}$) was introduced by Tugué in [18]; he called it $\boldsymbol{E}_1$. We study it further in part II.

2. Evidently the right hand side $\in \Pi_1^1(\alpha)$. Conversely, for every $A \in \Pi_1^1$, one can find a ϕ such that

$$A(\alpha) \leftrightarrow \phi(\alpha, \beta) \in \mathscr{D}.$$

3. The right hand side holds if the set of non-secured sequences is well-ordered by the lexicographic ordering $\preccurlyeq$:

$$x \preccurlyeq y \equiv_{\text{Df}} (\exists r \le \text{lh}(x))(\forall i < r)(x_i = y_i \,\&\, (x_r < y_r \vee r = \text{lh}(y))).$$

4. The right hand side does not depend on β. So we can get a particularly simple equivalent for the right hand side by substituting $\mathbf{0}^2 (= \lambda\gamma^1 \cdot 0)$ for β. One might then be tempted to replace the first instruction in the table

for computing ϕ by a subroutine (e.g., $r_0'=0$, halt) for computing $\mathbf{0}^2\{2\}$. But evidently the new table will yield the value 0 for *all* α, and so represents a functional which is quite distinct from ϕ. The discrepancy arises because we treated β^2 as defined only for total arguments, while the subroutine for $\mathbf{0}^2$ never calls for its argument, and so represents a functional which is defined for *all* partial functions. This matter will be discussed further in section 3.3.

2.4. *Computation trees*

Example 2.3.3 suggests describing the whole of a computation by an infinite tree. A *complete configuration* (c.c) for a given programme t consists of the current instruction i, the contents r, a of all the registers, and the list $\mathfrak{a}$ of arguments. At the vertex of the tree we place the initial c.c. If $(i, r, a, \mathfrak{a})$ stands at a point P of the tree, and if $i\neq 0$, then P is joined to the *next* point P', which is placed to the right of P. At P' stands the next c.c – i.e. the result of performing i. If i is '$p^m\{k\}$ in q', with $m>1$ and $r_p<a_m$, then P is also joined to points P_δ, one for each object δ in type $m-2$; these are placed vertically below P'. The c.c at P_δ is, of course, $(k, r, a', \mathfrak{a}, \delta)$. If the computations which are initiated at the points P_δ do not all give rise to definite values, then there is no next c.c to place at P', and there will be no points beyond P'. In this case we say that P is a *half stump*. If the current instruction at a point P is 0, then P is a *tip*, and there are no points to the right of it. A *branch* is a sequence of points, starting with the vertex, such that each point is joined to its successor, and which is either infinite or terminates in a tip.

A detailed analysis of the recursions by which the points of a tree, the c.cs at them, and the values to which the c.cs give rise, will be given in part II. But an inductive definition of 'is defined' is given in section 3. Meanwhile, consideration of example 2.3.3 and of fig. 1, which shows part of the relevant tree, should make the following statement plausible.
2.4.1. *The computation which is initiated by the c.c standing at a point P of a computation tree has a defined value if and only if every branch through P terminates. The value is then the value of* r_0 *at the tip which is on the same horizontal level as P.*

In particular, the original computation has a defined value iff every branch terminates. Note that if P is a half stump, then there must be an infinite branch through it.

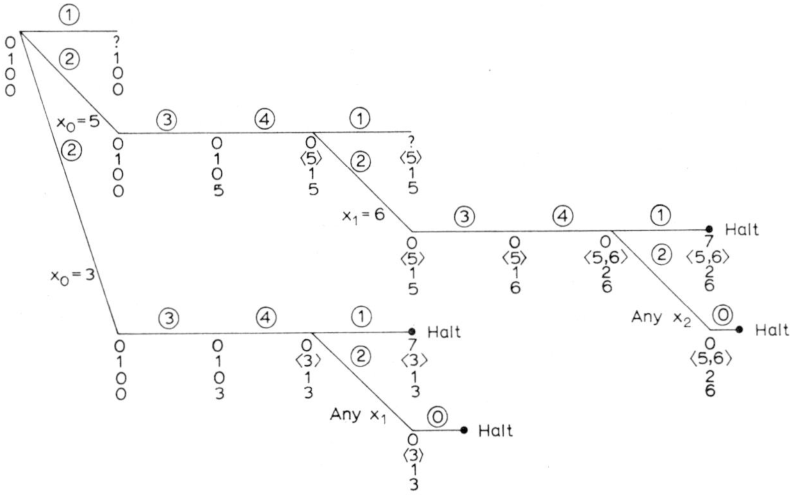

Fig. 1. Part of the computation tree for a computation by the machine of 2.3.3. It is assumed that $\beta(0) = 7$, $\alpha(\langle 3\rangle) = \alpha(\langle 5, 6\rangle) = 0$, $\alpha(\langle\rangle) \neq 0$, $\alpha(\langle 5\rangle) \neq 0$. The vertical columns of figures give the contents of the registers $r_0 - r_3$; each encircled figure is the IN which is being obeyed.

2.4.2. A partial functional ϕ of a list $\mathfrak{a}$ of (total) arguments of numerical type is *computable* if there is a programme t for a machine and an initial assignment r of the contents of its registers such that

$$\phi\mathfrak{a} \simeq \{t:1:r, a\}(\mathfrak{a}).$$

The class of partial computable functionals of restricted type is denoted by $\mathscr{R}$. The functional ϕ is *computable from* $\mathfrak{b}$, in symbols $\phi \in \mathscr{R}(\mathfrak{b})$, if there is a $\psi \in \mathscr{R}$ such that $\phi\mathfrak{a} \simeq \psi\mathfrak{a}\mathfrak{b}$ for all $\mathfrak{a}$.

2.4.3. $\mathscr{E} \subseteq \mathscr{R}$.

It suffices to prove that $\mathscr{R}$ is closed under C1-3. This is immediate for C1, C3. For C2, let t be a programme which computes $\phi x\mathfrak{a}$ for all x, $\mathfrak{a}$. Let t' be the programme obtained by replacing each instruction of the form 'p^0 in q/j' in t by the subroutine:

1	$p \rightarrow$	2,3
2	p^0 in q	j
3	$r'_q = \psi\mathfrak{a}$	j

where instruction 3 stands for a programme which computes ψ (with appropriate terminal instructions), and all instructions are suitably re-numbered when inserted in t. Then t' evidently computes $\phi(\psi\mathfrak{a})\,\mathfrak{a}$ for all $\mathfrak{a}$.

2.4.4. $\mathscr{G} \subseteq \mathscr{R}$.

Cf. example 2.3.1.

2.4.5. There is no difficulty in modifying the action taken at call instructions so as to make them apply when the arguments are hereditarily consistent functionals. In section 3 we shall indicate the obvious requisite modification in the definition of 'is defined'. It will then be obvious that a computable functional of HC arguments is itself HC.

3. Computation indices and their manipulation

The description of computable functionals given in section 2 was chosen for the insight it gives into their nature. But the specification of a programme and of a computation tree contains a lot of detail which, though it may be relevant for ORT, is not relevant to the specific problems raised by the introduction of arguments of higher type. So we shall now use the resources of ORT to suppress the irrelevant detail.

A c.c consists of a list of arguments and a purely numerical part $(t{:}i{:}r, a)$ which we call the *index* z; formally $z = \langle t, i, r, a \rangle$. Now we observe:

(a) if i is a call instruction, then the next index is determined recursively from z and the value called for; also the index of the subordinate computations is determined recursively from z.

(b) If the c.c Z leads to the c.c Z' through a sequence of instructions none of which is a call instruction, then the index z' is determined recursively from z; further, if Z' is a halt, then the value of the c.c Z is determined recursively from its index z.

So it is possible to introduce a new system of indexing in which every index corresponds either to a call instruction or to an outright determination of value, and in which the recursive determinations mentioned in (a) and (b) can be read off from the index.

3.1. *Definition of indices and their schemata*

3.1.1. The number z is an *index from a list of arguments with type-composition a* (written '$z \in I(a)$') iff $z = \langle m, e, u, j, a \rangle$ where:

(i) $$m = u = j = 0 \quad \text{and} \quad e \in \mathscr{R}_0^1,$$

or

(ii) $$m = u = 0, 1 \leq j \leq a_0 \quad \text{and} \quad e \in \mathscr{R}_1^1,$$

or

(iii) $$1 \leq m \leq \bar{a}, 1 \leq j \leq a_m, e \in \mathscr{R}_1^1 \quad \text{and} \quad u \in I(a'),$$

where

$$a' = \langle a_0, \ldots, a_m + 1, \ldots, a_{\bar{a}} \rangle .$$

Since $u < z$, and u, a' are determined elementarily from z, a, the above definition and the predicate $z \in I(a)$ are primitive recursive. (Indeed, the predicate is actually elementary.)

3.1.2. Unless otherwise stated, we assume that

$$\mathfrak{a} = \alpha_1^0, \ldots, \alpha_{a_0}^0, \alpha_1^1, \ldots, \alpha_{a_1}^1, \ldots, \alpha_1^n, \ldots, \alpha_{a_n}^n,$$

where $n = \bar{a}$. Two lists of variables are regarded as the same if the order of the variables of each type is the same (cf. 2.2.2(2)). And we write $\mathfrak{a} \in z$ in place of $z \in I(a)$; $\mathfrak{a} \in z$ implies that z_4 gives the type composition of $\mathfrak{a}$.

3.1.3. A *computation* consists of a number z and a list of arguments $\mathfrak{a}$; it is denoted by $\{z\}(\mathfrak{a})$. The computation (or more precisely, its value) may be undefined ('$\{z\}(\mathfrak{a}) \notin \mathscr{D}$') or defined ('$\in \mathscr{D}$') with a value which is again denoted by $\{z\}(\mathfrak{a})$. The value, defined or undefined, is determined by the following schemata:

R0 If $z \notin I(a)$, then $\{z\}(\mathfrak{a}) \notin \mathscr{D}$.

R1 $\{\langle 0, e, 0, 0, a \rangle\}(\mathfrak{a}) \simeq [e]_0$.

R2^0 $\{\langle 0, e, 0, j, a \rangle\}(\mathfrak{a}) \simeq \{[e]_1(\alpha_j^0)\}(\mathfrak{a})$.

R2^1 $\{\langle 1, e, u, j, a \rangle\}(\mathfrak{a}) \simeq \{[e]_1(\alpha_j^1(\{u\}(\mathfrak{a})))\}(\mathfrak{a})$.

R2^m $\{\langle m, e, u, j, a \rangle\}(\mathfrak{a}) \simeq \{[e]_1(\alpha_j^m(\lambda\delta^{m-2} \cdot \{u\}(\mathfrak{a}, \delta)))\}(\mathfrak{a})$.

NOTES.

(1) In future we adopt the convention of 1.3.1 (c) for interpreting metamathematical expressions of the form $\lambda\delta^{-1} \cdot A$, and the further convention that $(\lambda\delta^{-2} \cdot A)$ is to be interpreted as the empty expression. Then the schemata R2^0 and R2^1 are both subsumed under R2^m.

(2) Schema R2^m is to be read as follows:

$\{\langle m, e, u, j, \mathfrak{a}\rangle\}$ $(\mathfrak{a})$ is defined and has the value y iff: (a) for all δ^{m-2}, $\{u\}$ $(\mathfrak{a}, \delta)\in\mathscr{D}$ and $=\beta(\delta)$, say, and (b) $[e]_1(\alpha_j^m(\beta))\in\mathscr{D}$, and $=w$, say, and (c) $\{w\}$ $(\mathfrak{a})\in\mathscr{D}$ and has the value y.
(3) The schemata can be taken over as they stand to the theory of HC functionals. All variables stand for HC functionals, and the λ-term in R2 defines a partial functional. Condition (a) in note (2) is replaced by the condition that the HC β lies in the domain of the HC α_j^m.
3.1.4. The schemata constitute, in effect, an inductive definition of the value of a computation; there is a tacit assumption that a computation only gets a value if it does so as a consequence of them. (For the intuitive justification of this assumption, see 2.3.3.) We analyse the form of this inductive definition in greater detail.

We must distinguish between the computation and its value. We simply use the encoding $\langle z, \mathfrak{a}\rangle$ for the computation, where it is understood that the list $\mathfrak{a}$ is, if necessary, rearranged in ascending type order before being encoded.

We fix on a given highest type n for the arguments. Observe that in applying the schemata no new variable of types $n, n-1$ are introduced. So we set $\mathfrak{a}=\mathfrak{b}, \mathfrak{c}$, where $\bar{b}\leqslant n-2$, $\bar{c}=n$, and $c_i=0$ for $i<n-1$; and then we treat the $\mathfrak{c}$ as parameters in the inductive definition.
3.1.5. The *valuation functional* $V_\mathfrak{c}$ is the partial functional with smallest domain ('Dom $V_\mathfrak{c}$') such that:

(i) $\quad$ Dom $V \subseteq \{\langle z, \mathfrak{b}\rangle | \bar{b} \leq n-2 \;\&\; z\in I(\mathfrak{b}, \mathfrak{c})\}$;

(ii) $\quad$ if $e\in\mathscr{R}_0^1\cap\mathscr{D}$, then $V(\langle\langle 0, e, 0, 0, a\rangle, \mathfrak{b}\rangle) = [e]$;

(iii) $\quad$ if (a) $\;(\forall\,\delta^{z_0-2})\,(\langle z_2, \mathfrak{b}, \delta\rangle \in \text{Dom } V)$, and

$$\text{(b)}\quad (\exists\, w)\,(w = [z_1]_1\,(\alpha_{z_3}^{z_0}(\lambda\delta^{z_0-2}\cdot V(\langle z_2, \mathfrak{b}, \delta\rangle))) \;\&\; V(\langle w, \mathfrak{b}\rangle) = y),$$

then $V(\langle z, \mathfrak{b}\rangle) = y$.

NOTES.

(1) By an obvious extension of the conventions 3.1.3 (1), the quantifier and 'δ' are omitted from (a) if $z_0=1$, and the whole of (a) is omitted if $z_0=0$.
(2) We observe that the inductive step is monotonic in V; i.e. if (a) and (b) are satisfied by some V, then they are also satisfied by any extension of V.

(3) The graph of $V_{\mathfrak{c}}$ can be encoded by a functional of type $n-1$ (η, say), or by a subset of type $n-2$. If this be done, and the free variables (e, y and $\langle \mathfrak{b} \rangle$) in (i)–(iii) be universally quantified, then it is not hard to see that conditions (i)–(iii) are represented by a predicate of $\Delta_1^{n-1}(\eta, \mathfrak{c})$; (the type $n-1$ quantifier is needed for the elimination of the λ-term). And the minimality condition on η is expressed by a universal type $n-1$ quantifier. Hence both the graph and the domain of $V_{\mathfrak{c}}$ belong to $\Pi_1^{n-1}(\mathfrak{c})$.

3.1.6. *Definition of $V_{\mathfrak{c}}$ by transfinite recursion.* We can think of the graph of $V_{\mathfrak{c}}$ as being the limit of a transfinite sequence of 'approximations' V^{λ}. V^0 is the graph determined by (i) and (ii) of 3.1.5.

$$V^{\lambda} = \bigcup_{\mu<\lambda} V^{\mu} \cup \{\langle y, \langle z, \mathfrak{b} \rangle \rangle \mid \text{(i)} \,\&\, \text{(iii)}\,\text{(a)}* \,\&\, \text{(iii)}\,\text{(b)}*\}$$

where the '*' means that V is to be replaced by $\bigcup_{\mu<\lambda} V^{\mu}$. Thus the V^{λ} form an increasing sequence of subsets of the set of objects of type $n-2$. Hence there is a (least) closure ordinal $\nu(=\nu(\mathfrak{c}))$ for which $V^{\nu}=V^{\nu+1}$. The cardinal of ν is not greater than the cardinal of type $n-2$; in particular, ν is countable if $n=2$. The above construction leads to the following definition.

3.1.7. The *ordinal*, $|\{z\}(\mathfrak{a})|$, of any defined computation is

$$(\mu\lambda)\,(\exists\, y)\,(\langle y, \langle z, \mathfrak{b} \rangle \rangle \in V^{\lambda}),$$

where $\mathfrak{a}$ is to be separated into $\mathfrak{b}$, $\mathfrak{c}$, as above. Note that

$$\begin{aligned} \nu(\mathfrak{c}) &= \operatorname{Sup}\{|\{z\}\,(\mathfrak{a})| : \{z\}\,(\mathfrak{a}) \in \mathscr{D}\} \\ &= \operatorname{Sup}\{|\{z\}\,(\mathfrak{c})| : \{z\}\,(\mathfrak{c}) \in \mathscr{D}\}. \end{aligned}$$

3.1.8. It is useful to have a terminology for the computations which appear on the right hand side of the schemata R1-2. Let $z=\langle m, e, u, j, a \rangle \in \in I(a)$. Then if $m>0$, $\{z\}\,(\mathfrak{a})$ has as its *direct subordinates* all the computations $\{u\}\,(\mathfrak{a}, \delta^{m-2})$, where δ is omitted if $m=1$. If $j>0$ and the index $[e]_1(\ldots)$ of the right hand side of $R2^m$ is defined, then $\{z\}\,(\mathfrak{a})$ has as its *next* computation the RHS of $R2^m$. The *direct inferiors* of $\{z\}(\mathfrak{a})$ are its next computation and its direct subordinates. The *inferiors* of $\{z\}(\mathfrak{a})$ are its direct inferiors, their direct inferiors, and so on. Note the following:

(a) If $m=j=0$, then $\{z\}\,(\mathfrak{a})$ has no inferiors.

(b) If $\{z\}\,(\mathfrak{a})$ is defined, but not by R1, then there is a next computation, and its value is the same as that of $\{z\}\,(\mathfrak{a})$.

(c) If there is a computation next to $\{z\}(\mathfrak{a})$, then the direct subordinates of $\{z\}(\mathfrak{a})$ are all defined; the converse of this statement may be false.

(d) The ordinal of a computation is the least ordinal greater than the ordinals of its inferiors.

3.1.9. *The principle of induction for computations.* If a defined computation has the property P whenever all its direct inferiors have property P, then every defined computation has property P.

Observe that the hypothesis implies, by (a) above, that a computation which is defined by R1 has property P. Kleene calls the corresponding principle for his schemata 'induction on $\{z\}(-)$'. We shall also define functions of defined computations by recursion; e.g., by (d) above the ordinal of a defined computation can be defined by recursion.

3.1.10. DEFINITION. A partial function $\phi(\mathfrak{a})$ of restricted type is *recursive* (or *recursive in the parameters* $\mathfrak{L}$) iff there is a number z such that

$$\left.\begin{array}{r} \phi(\mathfrak{a}) \simeq \{z\}(\mathfrak{a}) \\ \text{or} \quad \phi(\mathfrak{a}) \simeq \{z\}(\mathfrak{a}, \mathfrak{b}) \end{array}\right\} \quad \text{for all } \mathfrak{a} \in z\,.$$

In anticipation of a proof of equivalence between 'recursive' and 'computable' we use the notations of 2.4: $\phi \in \mathscr{R}$, $\phi \in \mathscr{R}(\mathfrak{b})$. We take it as obvious that if the arguments are of types 0 and 1, then the above definition is co-extensive with the definition given in ORT; hence no confusion with the notations of 1.1 arises if we write $\mathscr{R}^n(\mathfrak{b})$ for the subclass of $\mathscr{R}(\mathfrak{b})$ whose elements all belong to types of level n. Using the functionals of 1.3.9, one can extend the definition to allow ϕ, $\mathfrak{b}$, to belong to arbitrary types.

It will often be necessary to consider functionals ϕ which are total in some of their arguments; but in our experience if a recursive functional which occurs naturally is total in all its arguments, then it also belongs to $\mathscr{G}$. Hence we do not bother to extend the notion of 'general recursive' to arguments of higher types.

We observe that the class $\mathscr{R}(\mathfrak{b})$ does not depend on the numerical arguments in $\mathfrak{b}$: $\mathscr{R}(\mathfrak{b}) = \mathscr{R}(x, \mathfrak{b})$.

3.2. *Simple closure properties of* $\mathscr{R}$

For each of the operations under which we prove closure, we construct an appropriate function of indices. These indicial functions are easily seen to be primitive recursive; in fact they are all elementary.

In order to avoid a plethora of subscripts, throughout this section we assume

(a) $$z \in I(a),$$

(b) $$z = \langle m, e, u, j, a \rangle;$$

thus $\mathfrak{a} \in z$, and m, e, u, j, a can all be determined from z in an elementary way.

3.2.1. *Closure under functional application.* If $\phi \in \mathscr{R}$ and $\beta^n \in \mathfrak{b}$, then $\lambda \mathfrak{b} \cdot \beta^n(\lambda \delta^{n-2} \cdot \phi(\mathfrak{b}, \delta)) \in \mathscr{R}$.

Let $\mathfrak{a} = \mathfrak{b}, \delta^{n-2}$ (δ omitted if $n < 2$), and let z be an index for ϕ.

Let i be a GN of the identity function in type 1, and let $\theta (\in \mathscr{E}^1)$ be defined so as to satisfy

$$[\theta(n, z)]_1(x) = \langle 0, i; x, 0, 0, b \rangle \quad \text{for all } x.$$

Then

$$\{\langle n, \theta(n, z), z, k, b \rangle\}(\mathfrak{b}) \simeq \{\langle 0, i; x, 0, 0, b \rangle\}(\mathfrak{b}) \simeq [i]_1(x) \simeq x,$$

where

$$x \simeq \beta_k^n(\lambda \delta^{n-2} \cdot \{z\}(\mathfrak{a})).$$

3.2.2. *Closure under permuation of arguments.* Suppose

(1) $$q = \langle q_0, \ldots, q_{\bar{a}} \rangle,$$

where each q_m encodes a permutation $j \to q_m(j)$ of $\{1, \ldots, a_m\}$. Let $\mathfrak{a}^{(q)}$ be the list which has $\alpha^m_{q_m(j)}$ as its j-th member of type m. Then there is a function $\pi \in \mathscr{P}^2$ such that

(2) $$\{\pi(q, z)\}(\mathfrak{a}) \simeq \{z\}(\mathfrak{a}^{(q)}).$$

PROOF. The function π with GN p is defined by the following recursion:

$$\pi(q, z) \simeq 0 \quad \text{if } z \notin I(a), \text{ or if } q \text{ does not satisfy (1);}$$

otherwise

$$\pi(q, z) \simeq z \quad \text{if } j = 0,$$
$$\simeq \langle m, (p; q) \circ e, \pi(q, u), q_m(j), a \rangle \quad \text{if } j > 0.$$

Once p has been found (by the second recursion theorem), the above becomes a primitive recursion for π. Actually it can be shown that π is elementary.

We prove that π satisfies (2) by induction on the computation. The proof is trivial if $z \in \mathrm{R1}$ (i.e., if $\{z\}(\mathfrak{a})$ is defined by R1). For $z \in \mathrm{R2}^m$ we have

$$\begin{aligned}\{\pi(q, z)\}(\mathfrak{a}) &\simeq \{[(p; q) \circ e]_1 (x)\}(\mathfrak{a}) \\ &\simeq \{\pi(q, [e]_1 (x))\}(\mathfrak{a}) \\ &\simeq \{[e]_1 (x)\}(\mathfrak{a}^{(q)}) \quad \text{by IH},\end{aligned}$$

where

$$x \simeq \alpha^m_{q_m(j)}(\lambda \delta^{m-2} \cdot \{\pi(q, u)\}(\mathfrak{a}, \delta)).$$

But if q satisfies (1) with respect to the list $\mathfrak{a}$, it also satisfies (1) with respect to the list $\mathfrak{a}, \delta^{m-2}$, and $(\mathfrak{a}, \delta^{m-2})^{(q)} = \mathfrak{a}^{(q)}, \delta^{m-2}$. Hence, by IH,

$$x \simeq \alpha^m_{q_m(j)}(\lambda \delta^{m-2} \cdot \{u\}(\mathfrak{a}^{(q)}, \delta)).$$

Thus (2) holds. For $z \in \mathrm{R2}^0$ we must also verify that $\pi(q, z) \in I(a)$; but in this case $u=0$, so u is not an index, and therefore $\pi(q, u)=0$, and $\pi(q, z) \in I(a)$.

3.2.3. *Addition of irrelevant arguments.* There is a function $\kappa \in \mathscr{P}^1_2$ such that, for all $\mathfrak{a}, \mathfrak{b}$,

(1) $$\{\kappa(b, z)\}(\mathfrak{b}, \mathfrak{a}) \simeq \{z\}(\mathfrak{a}).$$

By using this in conjunction with 3.2.2, we can disperse irrelevant arguments among the relevant ones.

PROOF. Set $\mathfrak{c} = \mathfrak{b}, \mathfrak{a}$. Define κ, with GN k, by:

$$\begin{aligned}\kappa(b, z) &= 0 && \text{unless } z \in I(a), \\ &= \langle 0, e, 0, 0, c \rangle && \text{if } j = 0, \\ &= \langle m, (k; b) \circ e, \kappa(b, u), j + b_m, c \rangle && \text{if } j > 0.\end{aligned}$$

The verification that κ satisfies (1) is straightforward and is left to the reader. It can be shown that κ is elementary.

Kleene incorporates the addition of irrelevant arguments in one of his primitive schemata (S9). However, for his system also, it is possible to derive the stronger schema S9 from one – S9′, say – which does not have irrelevant arguments, together with the other schemata S1–8. The schema S9′ is in fact the subject of our next proposition.

3.2.4. *The reflection principle* (A). For each type-composition a there is a $\phi \in \mathscr{R}$ such that

S9′ $$\phi(z, \mathfrak{a}) \simeq \{z\}(\mathfrak{a}).$$

For, letting $\mathfrak{b} = z, \mathfrak{a}$, it is easily verified that

$$\{\langle 0, k; \langle 1\rangle, 0, 1, b\rangle\}(z, \mathfrak{a}) \simeq \{z\}(\mathfrak{a}),$$

where k is the GN introduced in 3.2.3.

3.2.4 allows one to use an argument as an index; more often one wishes to use the value of a previous computation as an index. Kleene achieves this by using S9 in conjunction with his S4 (substitution for a numerical variable), but we need it to derive that schema.

3.2.5. *The reflection principle* (B). There is a $\rho \in \mathscr{E}_1^1$ such that

$$\{\rho(z)\}(\mathfrak{a}) \simeq \{\{z\}(\mathfrak{a})\}(\mathfrak{a}).$$

Set $\rho(z) = 0$ if $z \notin I(a)$. If $a \neq 1$, then $\alpha_1^{\bar{a}} \in \mathfrak{a}$; set $\rho(z) = \langle \bar{a}, z^*, v, 1, a\rangle$, where z^* is a GN of $\lambda x \cdot z$, and v is chosen so that $\{v\}(\mathfrak{a}, \delta^{\bar{a}}) = 0$ for all $\mathfrak{a}, \delta^{\bar{a}}$. If $a = 1$, then $\mathfrak{a}$ is empty, and if $z \in I(a)$ then $z = \langle 0, e, 0, 0, 1\rangle$; set $\rho(z) = \langle 0, f, 0, 0, 1\rangle$, where f is a GN of $(\mu x)([e]_0 = \langle 0, x, 0, 0, 1\rangle)$. Evidently z^*, v, f can all be determined elementarily from z. Hence $\rho \in \mathscr{E}_1^1$.

3.2.6. *Substitution functions.* There are primitive recursive functions σ_1, σ_2, σ_3, such that

(1) $$\{\sigma_1(f, z)\}(\mathfrak{a}) \simeq [f]_1(\{z\}(\mathfrak{a}));$$

(2) $$\{\sigma_2(f, z)\}(\mathfrak{a}) \simeq \{[f]_1(\{z\}(\mathfrak{a}))\}(\mathfrak{a});$$

(3) $$\{\sigma_3(y, z)\}(\mathfrak{b}) \simeq \{z\}(y, \mathfrak{b}).$$

Proof. Define σ_1 with GN s_1 by:

$$\begin{aligned} \sigma_1(f, z) &= 0 && \text{unless } z \in I(a), \\ &= \langle 0, f \circ e, 0, 0, a\rangle && \text{if } j = 0, \\ &= \langle m, (s_1; f) \circ e, u, j, a\rangle && \text{if } j \neq 0. \end{aligned}$$

Define

$$\sigma_2(f, z) = \rho(\sigma_1(f, z)).$$

Evidently σ_1 and σ_2 are elementary.

For (3), let $\mathfrak{a}=\alpha_1^0, \mathfrak{b}$; define σ_3 with GN s_3 by:

$$\begin{aligned}\sigma_3(y, z) &= 0 && \text{unless } z \in I(a),\\ &\simeq \langle 0, e, 0, 0, b\rangle && \text{if } j=0,\\ &\simeq \rho(\langle 0, (((s_3; y)\circ e); y), 0, 0, b\rangle) && \text{if } m=0, \quad j=1,\\ &\simeq \langle 0, (s_3; y)\circ e, 0, j-1, b\rangle && \text{if } m=0, \quad j>1,\\ &\simeq \langle m, (s_3; y)\circ e, \sigma_3(y, u), j, b\rangle && \text{if } m>0.\end{aligned}$$

We verify the case $m=0, j=1$. Then

$$\begin{aligned}\{\sigma_3(y, z)\}(\mathfrak{b}) &\simeq \{\{\langle 0, g, 0, 0, b\rangle\}(\mathfrak{b})\}(\mathfrak{b}), \quad \text{say, by 3.2.4},\\ &\simeq \{[g]_0\}(\mathfrak{b}),\end{aligned}$$

where

$$[g]_0 \simeq [((s_3; y)\circ e); y]_0 \simeq [(s_3; y)\circ e]_1(y) \simeq \sigma_3(y, [e]_1(y)).$$

But, in the given case,

$$\begin{aligned}\{z\}(y, \mathfrak{b}) &\simeq \{[e]_1(y)\}(y, \mathfrak{b}),\\ &\simeq \{\sigma_3(y, [e]_1(y))\}(\mathfrak{b}) && \text{by IH}\\ &\simeq \{\sigma_3(y, z)\}(\mathfrak{b}) && \text{by the above.}\end{aligned}$$

The function σ_3 does just the same job for indices as does the semicolon function for GNs. So let us write '$z{:}y$' for $\sigma_3(y, z)$, '$z{:}y, w$' for $(z{:}y){:}w$, etc. Occasionally, as in the next proposition, we wish to indicate the effect of a substitution for some numerical argument other than the first; we use commas to show the arguments which are not substituted for. Thus $[e;, y](x) \simeq [e](x, y)$.

3.2.7. *Closure under substitution for numerical arguments.* In view of 3.2.2, 3.2.3, it is sufficient to prove that if $\phi, \psi \in \mathscr{R}$, then so does $\lambda\mathfrak{b}\cdot\phi(\psi\,\mathfrak{b}, \mathfrak{b})$; (cf. C2 of 1.3.1).

Let $\sigma_0(v, z)=\sigma_2((s_3;, z), v)$. Then

$$\begin{aligned}\{\sigma_0(v, z)\}(\mathfrak{b}) &\simeq \{[s_3;, z]_1(\{v\}(\mathfrak{b}))\}(\mathfrak{b}),\\ &\simeq \{\sigma_3(\{v\}(\mathfrak{b}), z)\}(\mathfrak{b}),\\ &\simeq \{z\}(\{v\}(\mathfrak{b}), \mathfrak{b}),\end{aligned}$$

which proves the required closure property.

3.2.8. *Translation from Gödel numbers to indices.* There is a primitive recursive τ such that

$$\{\tau(f)\}\,(\mathbf{x}) \simeq [f]\,(\mathbf{x}).$$

PROOF. We define functions τ_n with GNs t_n as follows:

$$(1)\qquad \begin{cases} \tau_0(f) = \langle 0, f, 0, 0, 1\rangle \\ \tau_{n+1}(f) = \langle 0, g, 0, 1, \langle n+1\rangle\rangle, \end{cases}$$

where g is a GN for $\lambda x\cdot\kappa(\langle 1\rangle, \tau_n(f;x))$. Then

$$\begin{aligned} \{\tau_{n+1}(f)\}\,(x_1, \ldots, x_{n+1}) &\simeq \{[g]\,(x_1)\}\,(x_1, \ldots, x_{n+1}), \\ &\simeq \{\tau_n(f;\, x_1)\}\,(x_2, \ldots, x_{n+1}) \\ &\simeq \{\tau_0(f;\, x_1, \ldots, x_{n+1})\}\,() \\ &\simeq [f]\,(x_1, \ldots, x_{n+1}). \end{aligned}$$

By (1), $\tau_n(f)$ can be determined elementarily from f, n, t_n; therefore t_n is a primitive recursive function of n, and $\tau(n, f)\,(=\tau_n(f))$ is primitive recursive. But, if f is a GN, one can find the number n of its arguments elementarily from f. So $\tau(f)=\tau(n,f)$ is the required function.
3.2.9. *The fixed point theorem.* Given y one can find an index z such that

$$(1)\qquad \{z\}\,(\mathfrak{a}) \simeq \{y\}\,(z, \mathfrak{a}).$$

This is also referred to as *the second recursion theorem*. In most applications the right hand side of (1) depends only on the extension – the graph – of the partial functional $\{z\}$, not on the particular index z. For this case in ORT, one can arrange that $\{z\}$ is minimal; i.e., that no proper restriction of $\{z\}$ satisfies (1). This is not in general possible in our theory; a counter-example will be given in 3.3.
PROOF. By 3.2.7, 3.2.8, we can determine (primitive recursively from y) an index v such that

$$\{v\}\,(x, \mathfrak{a}) \simeq \{y\}\,(x\!:\!x, \mathfrak{a}).$$

Set $z=v\!:\!v$. Then

$$\{z\}\,(\mathfrak{a}) \simeq \{v\}\,(v, \mathfrak{a}) \simeq \{y\}\,(v\!:\!v, \mathfrak{a}) \simeq \{y\}\,(z, \mathfrak{a}).$$

The theorem provides an analogue to the facility which machines have for iterating a process by jumping back to a previous instruction. For example, we use it to show that the μ-operator is recursive.

3.2.10. *There is a* $\mu \in \mathscr{P}_1^1$ *such that*

$$(1)\quad (\exists x)(\{z\}(x, \mathfrak{a}) = 0 \,\&\, (\forall y < x)(\{z\}(y, \mathfrak{a}) \in \mathscr{D})) \rightarrow \{\mu(z)\}(\mathfrak{a}) = (\mu x)(\{z\}(x, \mathfrak{a}) = 0).$$

PROOF. Let v be determined by 3.2.9 to satisfy

$$(2)\qquad \{v\}(x, \mathfrak{a}) \simeq (1 \dot{-} (1 \dot{-} \{z\}(x, \mathfrak{a})))\cdot(\{v\}(x+1, \mathfrak{a}) + 1).$$

Then $\mu(z) = v{:}0$ (which is evidently primitive recursive). We assume that $x \cdot y$ is defined in such a way that if $x=0$ and y is undefined, then $x \cdot y = 0$. Hence if x satisfies the scope of '$(\exists x)$' in (1), then $\{v\}(x, \mathfrak{a}) = 0$,
$\{v\}(x-1, \mathfrak{a}) = 1, \ldots, \{v\}(0, \mathfrak{a}) = x$.

3.3. *Substitution of higher type arguments*

3.3.1. Let $\dot{\alpha}^n$ be a partial function of total arguments; i.e., $\dot{\alpha}^n(\gamma^{n-1})$ need not be defined for all γ^{n-1}, but shall be undefined unless γ^{n-1} is a total functional. The definition of the value of a computation $\{z\}(\dot{\alpha}^n, \mathfrak{b})$ is obtained by interpreting schema R2^n in the obvious way – namely, $\{\langle n, e, u, 1, a\rangle\}(\dot{\alpha}^n, \mathfrak{b})$ shall be undefined if $\dot{\alpha}^n(\lambda\delta^{n-2}\cdot\{u\}(\dot{\alpha}^n, \mathfrak{b}, \delta))$ is undefined. Suppose now that $\dot{\alpha}^n$ is presented as the result of a computation: $\dot{\alpha}^n = \lambda\gamma^{n-1}\cdot\{v\}(\mathfrak{c}, \gamma)$.
There is a natural method by which we should attempt to compute $\{z\}(\dot{\alpha}^n, \mathfrak{b})$ from $\mathfrak{b}$, $\mathfrak{c}$. On account of 3.2.2, 3.2.3, we may, without loss of generality, suppose $\mathfrak{b} = \mathfrak{c}$. The method will then provide us with an index, $\theta_n(v, z)$ say, for which, hopefully,

$$(\mathrm{A})\qquad \{\theta_n(v, z)\}(\mathfrak{b}) \simeq \{z\}(\dot{\alpha}^n, \mathfrak{b}).$$

Consider, however, the case where $\{z\}(\dot{\alpha}^n, \mathfrak{b})$ calls for the application of $\dot{\alpha}^n$ to a computed functional γ^{n-1}. By definition, the right hand side of (A) will be defined only if γ^{n-1} is total. But the corresponding computation for the left hand side will be a subroutine for computing $\{v\}(\mathfrak{b}, \gamma^{n-1})$ which may call for only certain values of γ^{n-1}. Thus the left hand side of (A) may be defined while the right hand side is undefined. (For a simple example, see note 4 of 2.3.4.) It might be thought that this difficulty could be avoided by using an artificial method for computing the result of the substitution[11]). But the following example, due to Kleene,

[11]) Platek [7] and Hinman [19] have both used such artificial methods to widen the range of conditions under which (A) shall hold.

shows that the partial functional on the right hand side of (A) may be non-computable.

3.3.2. Let $\{w\}(y, x) \simeq 0$ if $\neg T(x, x, y)$, and be undefined otherwise. Thus $\lambda y \cdot \{w\}(y, x)$ ($= \gamma_x$, say) is total if and only if $(\forall y) \neg T(x, x, y)$. Let $z = \langle 2, i, w, 1, \langle 1, 0, 1 \rangle \rangle$, so that

$$\{z\}(\alpha^2, x) \simeq \alpha^2(\gamma_x);$$

hence $\{z\}(\alpha^2, x) \in \mathscr{D}$ if and only if $(\forall y) \neg T(x, x, y)$.

Now let α^2 be any recursive functional; e.g.:

$$\alpha^2(\gamma^1) = \gamma^1(0) \ (= \{v\}(x, \gamma^1), \text{ say}).$$

Then the domain of the function $\lambda x \cdot \{z\}(\alpha^2, x)$ is not recursively enumerable, and so the function cannot be recursive. I.e., there can be no number t such that, for all x,

$$\{t\}(x) \simeq \{z\}(\lambda \gamma^1 \cdot \{v\}(x, \gamma), x).$$

Notice that the natural definition of $\theta_2(v, z)$ in this case will evidently satisfy $\{\theta_2(v, z)\}(x) \simeq \gamma_x(0)$; thus $\{\theta_2(v, z)\}(x) \simeq 0$ if $\neg T(x, x, 0)$, and is undefined otherwise.

This example proves:

3.3.3. *The class $\mathscr{R}$ of partial computable functionals is not closed under functional substitution.*

Platek [7] has shown how the same example can be used to prove that the first recursion theorem does not hold in $\mathscr{R}$. Consider the following recursion:

$$\begin{aligned} \zeta^2(\alpha^1, x) &\simeq 0 && \text{if } x = 0, \\ &\simeq \zeta^2(\gamma_x, 0) && \text{otherwise}. \end{aligned}$$

Evidently the *minimal* partial functional of total arguments which satisfies this recursion is ξ^2, where $\xi^2(\alpha^1, x) = 0$ if $x = 0$ or $(\forall y) \neg T(x, x, y)$, and is undefined otherwise. But ξ^2 is certainly not a computable functional of ORT, and hence $\xi^2 \notin \mathscr{R}$.

The fact that $\mathscr{R}$ is not closed under the two operations considered is a consequence of the requirement that the arguments of a functional which is called for in a computation be total. If one considers computations from functionals of HC, then these anomalies disappear; this was discovered by Platek, and is expounded in his dissertation.

We now define the natural index of a substitution.

3.3.4. The function $\theta(n, v, z)\,(=\theta_n(v, z))$ with GN h is defined by the following recursion.

(a)
$$\theta(0, v, z) = \sigma_0(v, z).$$

It follows from 3.2.7 that

$$\{\theta_0(v, z)\}(\mathfrak{b}) \simeq \{z\}(\{v\}(\mathfrak{b}), \mathfrak{b}).$$

(b) For $n>0$, let $\mathfrak{a}=\alpha^n, \mathfrak{b}$, and let $\pi(v)$ be calculated from v according to 3.2.2, so that

$$\{v\}(\mathfrak{b}, \gamma^{n-1}) \simeq \{\pi(v)\}(\gamma^{n-1}, \mathfrak{b}).$$

(bi) If $z \notin I(a)$, then

$$\theta_n(v, z) = 0.$$

(bii) If $z=\langle 0, e, 0, 0, a\rangle$, then

$$\theta_n(v, z) = \langle 0, e, 0, 0, b\rangle;$$

hence

$$\{\theta_n(v, z)\}(\mathfrak{b}) \simeq \{z\}(\dot{\alpha}^n, \mathfrak{b}).$$

(biii) If $z=\langle m, e, u, j, a\rangle$ and $m \neq n$, or $m=n$ and $j \neq 1$, then

$$\theta_n(v, z) = \langle m, (h; n, v)\circ e, \theta_n(v, u), j, b\rangle;$$

hence

$$\{\theta_n(v, z)\}(\mathfrak{b}) \simeq \{\theta_n(v, w)\}(\mathfrak{b}),$$

where

$$w \simeq [e]\,(\beta_j^m(\lambda\delta^{m-2}\cdot\{\theta_n(v, u)\}(\mathfrak{b}, \delta))).$$

(biv) If $z=\langle n, e, u, 1, a\rangle$, then

$$\theta_n(v, z) = \sigma_2((h; n, v)\circ e, \theta_{n-1}(\theta_n(v, u), \pi(v)));$$

hence

$$\{\theta_n(v, z)\}(\mathfrak{b}) \simeq \{\theta_n(v, w)\}(\mathfrak{b}),$$

where

$$w \simeq [e]\,(\{\theta_{n-1}(u', \pi(v))\}(\mathfrak{b}))$$

and

$$u' = \theta_n(v, u).$$

3.3.5. THEOREM. *If* $\dot{\alpha}^n = \lambda\gamma^{n-1}\cdot\{v\}(\mathfrak{b}, \gamma)$ *is a partial functional of total arguments, and* $\{z\}(\dot{\alpha}^n, \mathfrak{b}) \in \mathscr{D}$, *then*

$$\{\theta_n(v, z)\}(\mathfrak{b}) = \{z\}(\dot{\alpha}^n, \mathfrak{b}).$$

PROOF. The theorem is true for $n=0$, by 3.2.7. Assume it is true for $n-1$, and that $\{z\}(\dot{\alpha}^n, \mathfrak{b}) \in \mathscr{D}$. We argue by induction on the computation; we consider only the case that z falls under (biv) above. Then

$$\{z\}(\dot{\alpha}^n, \mathfrak{b}) = \{[e](t)\}(\dot{\alpha}^n, \mathfrak{b}),$$

where

$$t = \dot{\alpha}^n(\lambda\delta^{n-2}\cdot\{u\}(\dot{\alpha}^n, \mathfrak{b}. \delta)).$$

But, by IH,

$$\lambda\delta^{n-2}\cdot\{u\}(\dot{\alpha}^n, \mathfrak{b}, \delta) = \lambda\delta^{n-2}\cdot\{u'\}(\mathfrak{b}, \delta)$$
$$= \gamma, \quad \text{say}.$$

So

$$t = \dot{\alpha}^n(\gamma) = \{v\}(\mathfrak{b}, \gamma) = \theta_{n-1}(u', \pi(v)),$$

by the assumption about $n-1$. Thus $[e](t) = w$, and so, by IH and the equalities stated under (biv),

$$\{\theta_n(v, z)\}(\mathfrak{b}) = \{z\}(\dot{\alpha}^n, \mathfrak{b}).$$

This theorem shows that (A) holds, with the natural θ, whenever the left hand side is defined. In part II we shall prove that (A) also holds for the natural θ under somewhat weaker conditions. But 3.3.5 is already strong enough to show that 'recursive in' is a transitive relation between *total* functionals. More precisely:

3.3.6. *If* $\gamma^m \in \mathscr{R}(\mathfrak{a})$ *and* $\delta^n \in \mathscr{R}(\gamma, \mathfrak{b})$, *then* $\delta^n \in \mathscr{R}(\mathfrak{a}, \mathfrak{b})$.

For, since γ and δ are total, for all ε^{n-1}

$$\delta(\varepsilon) = \{z\}(\gamma, \mathfrak{b}, \varepsilon), \quad \text{say},$$
$$= \{z'\}(\gamma, \mathfrak{a}, \mathfrak{b}, \varepsilon), \quad \text{say, by 3.2.3};$$

and similarly, for all η^{m-1}

$$\gamma(\eta) = \{v'\}(\mathfrak{a}, \mathfrak{b}, \varepsilon, \eta), \quad \text{say}.$$

Hence, by 3.3.5, for all ε^{n-1}

$$\delta(\varepsilon) = \{\theta_m(z', v')\}(\mathfrak{a}, \mathfrak{b}, \varepsilon).$$

References

[1] S. C. Kleene, Recursive functionals and quantifiers of finite types I, Trans. Amer. Math. Soc. **91** (1959) 1.

[2] S. C. Kleene, Recursive functionals and quantifiers of finite types II, Trans. Amer. Math. Soc. **108** (1963) 106.

[3] S. C. Kleene, Herbrand-Gödel-style recursive functionals of finite types, Proc. Symp. Pure Math. (Amer. Math. Soc.) **5** (1961) 49.

[4] S. C. Kleene, Turing-machine computable functionals of finite types I, Logic, methodology and philosophy of science, Proc. 1960 Intern. Congr., Stanford, Calif. (1962) 38.

[5] S. C. Kleene, Turing-machine computable functionals of finite types II, Proc. London Math. Soc. **12** (1962) 245.

[6] S. C. Kleene, Lambda-definable functionals of finite types, Fundamenta Mathematica **50** (1962) 281.

[7] R. Platek, Foundations of recursion theory, Doctoral Dissertation, Stanford University, Calif., 1965.

[8] A. Grzegorczyk, A. Mostowski and C. Ryll-Nardzewski, The classical and the ω-complete arithmetic, J. Symbolic Logic **23** (1958) 188.

[9] G. Kreisel, Set-theoretic problems suggested by the notion of potential totality, Infinitistic Methods, Proc. Symp. Foundations of Math., Warsaw 1959 (Pergamon, Oxford and Warsaw, 1961) 103.

[10] G. Kreisel, Model-theoretic invariants, in: Theory of models, Proc. 1963 Intern. Symp., Berkeley, eds. J. W. Addison, L. Henkin and A. Tarski (North-Holland Publ. Co., Amsterdam, 1965) 190.

[11] R. Fraïssé, Une notion de recursivité relative, Infinitistic Methods, Proc. Symp. Foundations of Math., Warsaw 1959 (Pergamon, Oxford and Warsaw, 1961) 323.

[12] S. C. Kleene, Introduction to metamathematics (North-Holland Publ. Co., Amsterdam, 1952).

[13] A. Church, A formulation of the simple theory of types, J. Symbolic Logic **5** (1940) 56.

[14] A. Grzegorczyk, Recursive objects in all finite types, Fundamenta Mathematica **54** (1964) 73.

[15] K. Gödel, Über ein bisher noch nicht benützte Erweiterung des finiten Standpunktes, Dialectica **12** (1958) 280.

[16] J. C. Shepherdson and H. E. Sturgis, Computability of recursive functions, J. Assoc. Comput. Mach. **10** (1963) 217.

[17] A. M. Turing, Systems of logic based on ordinals, Proc. London Math. Soc. **45** (1939) 161.

[18] T. Tugué, Predicates recursive in a type-2-object and Kleene hierarchies, Comment. Math. Univ. St. Paul **8** (1960) 97.

[19] P. G. Hinman, Ad astra per aspera: hierarchy schemata in recursive function theory, Doctoral Dissertation, Univ. Calif., Berkeley, 1966.

METARECURSION THEORY

G. E. SACKS*)
Massachusetts Institute of Technology, USA

1. Introduction

Metarecursion theory is a stepping stone towards abstract recursion theory, first put down by Kreisel and Sacks [1]. In a sense to be made precise later [2], it is the minimal generalization of recursion theory. The natural numbers are replaced by the recursive ordinals [3], the recursive sets of natural numbers are replaced by the metarecursive sets of recursive ordinals, and most important of all, the finite sets of natural numbers are replaced by the metafinite sets of recursive ordinals, some of which are infinite. Many other generalizations of recursion theory exist [4–7], but all of them fail to stress the following essential point: when recursion theory is generalized, it is necessary to simultaneously enlarge the notions of recursiveness and finiteness. After all, the more interesting arguments of recursion theory depend on simple combinatorial properties of finite sets; for example: the union of finitely many finite sets is finite. In metarecursion theory, the corresponding principle is: the union of metafinitely many metafinite sets is metafinite. Metarecursion theory, if nothing else, clarifies the role of finite sets in ordinary recursion theory.

In this paper we again define the basic notions of metarecursion theory [1], and we state the principal results of the subject with intuitive outlines of proof. In addition, we prove some new results. Finally, we end with a discussion of some conjectures.

---

*) The preparation of this paper was supported by U.S. Army Contract ARO-D-373. Once again the author wishes to thank Professor G. Kreisel for guiding him through the wilderness of ordinary recursion theory towards the promised land of milk, honey, and abstract recursion theory.

2. The notion of metarecursiveness

Let Q be a non-hyperarithmetic, Π_1^1 set of natural numbers well-ordered by the restriction of some recursive relation R to the members of Q such that Q is an initial segment of the field of R. It follows that the order-type of Q is the same as that of the recursive ordinals. For each recursive ordinal α, let $|\alpha|$ be the unique $n \in Q$ such that the ordinals less than α are order-isomorphic to the members of Q less than (in the sense of R) n; we call Q a set of unique notations for the recursive ordinals [8]. What follows is independent of the choice of Q.

A set A of recursive ordinals is said to be *metarecursively enumerable* if the set $\{|\alpha| \mid \alpha \in A\}$ is Π_1^1. A set A of recursive ordinals is said to be *metarecursive* if the sets $\{|\alpha| \mid \alpha \in A\}$ and $Q - \{|\alpha| \mid \alpha \in A\}$ are Π_1^1. A set K of recursive ordinals is said to be *metafinite* if the set $\{|\alpha| \mid \alpha \in K\}$ is hyperarithmetic. Finally, a partial function f from a subset of the recursive ordinals into the recursive ordinals is said to be *partial metarecursive* if the set $\{\langle |\alpha|, |\beta| \rangle \mid f(\alpha) = \beta\}$ is Π_1^1.

One readily sees: (1) a set is metarecursive if and only if it and its complement (with respect to the recursive ordinals) are metarecursively enumerable; (2) a set is metafinite if and only if it is metarecursive and bounded (by some recursive ordinal); (3) the range of a metarecursive function (total and partial metarecursive) restricted to a metafinite set is metafinite. The intimate connection between Π_1^1 sets of natural numbers and metarecursively enumerable sets of recursive ordinals is not startling, since the analogy between Π_1^1 sets and recursively enumerable sets is well-known; however, we connect hyperarithmetic sets with metafinite sets rather than with metarecursive sets. Point (2) suggests that "finite" in ordinary recursion theory means "recursive and bounded". It is not difficult to verify that every occurrence of "finite" in every proof of ordinary recursion theory can be replaced by "recursive and bounded"; of course, some proofs have to be rewritten, since some authors use the fact that a finite set has a greatest member.

Our initial definition of metarecursiveness has at least two defects: it makes use of notations; it obscures the intuitive notion of metarecursive computability. Kripke [4] has devised an equation calculus which eliminates both defects. His calculus can be thought of as Kleene's calculus [9] with an ω-rule added. For each recursive ordinal α, let $\boldsymbol{\alpha}$ be a numeral for α. The primitive symbols are: function letters $f, g, h, \ldots$; numerals, $'$ (successor), $=$, variables $x, y, z, \ldots$, and $(Ex <)$ (bounded existential quantifier). The terms are: variables; $f(t_1, \ldots, t_n)$, where $t_1, \ldots, t_n$ are terms; and $(Ex<t_1)(t_2(x))$, where t_1 and $t_2(x)$ are terms. An equation is two terms separated by $=$. The intended interpretation of $(Ex<t_1)(t_2(x))=\boldsymbol{O}$ is: it is true that there exists an x less than t_1 such that $t_2(x)=\boldsymbol{O}$. Kripke needs three deduction rules. The first two are the familiar substitution rules of Kleene [9]. The third (R3) is: (a) $(Ex<\boldsymbol{\beta})(t_2(x))=\boldsymbol{O}$ is an immediate consequence of $t_2(\boldsymbol{\alpha})=\boldsymbol{O}$, where α and β are recursive ordinals such that $\alpha<\beta$; (b) $(Ex<\boldsymbol{\beta})(t_2(x))=\boldsymbol{l}$ is an immediate consequence of the set of premises $\{t_2(\boldsymbol{\alpha})=\boldsymbol{l} \mid \alpha<\beta\}$. The first two rules and (R3) (a) are finitary; (R3) (b) is a special kind of ω-rule: if one knows that $t_2(\boldsymbol{\alpha})=\boldsymbol{l}$ for all α less than some recursive ordinal β, then one can deduce (putting it in more familiar notation) $(x)_{x<\beta}(t_2(x)=\boldsymbol{l})$. It is (R3) (b) that makes infinite computations possible.

Kripke defines the set of all equations deducible from E, a finite set of equations, by transfinite induction. Let $S_0^E=E$. If $\alpha>0$, then S_α^E equals the set of all immediate consequences (by rules (R1)–(R3)) of members of $\cup\{S_\gamma^E \mid \gamma<\alpha\}$; note: if rule (R3) (b) is applied to a subset of $\cup\{S_\gamma^E \mid \gamma<\alpha\}$, then the β bounding the existential quantifier must be less than α. Kripke shows:

$$S_{\omega_1}^E = \cup\{S_\gamma^E \mid \gamma < \omega_1\}$$

for every finite E, where ω_1 is the least non-recursive ordinal; in other words, any equation deducible from E at some ordinal is already deducible from E at some recursive ordinal. If the "shortest" deduction of an equation from E is given the standard tree-form, then the height of the deduction must be a recursive ordinal.

Let ϕ be a partial function from the recursive ordinals into the recursive ordinals. We say ϕ is partial metarecursive if for some finite E with principal letter f,

$$\phi(\alpha) = \beta \leftrightarrow f(\boldsymbol{\alpha}) = \boldsymbol{\beta} \in S_{\omega_1}^E .$$

It is easy to show this definition equivalent to the previous one, if one observes that Kripke's calculus is ideal for enumerating Π_1^1 sets of natural numbers: it suffices to see this for O, the set of all recursive notations. In addition, it is necessary to introduce a Gödel numbering of equations and check that the set of Gödel numbers of members of $S_{\omega_1}^E$ is Π_1^1. If the height of a deduction in tree form is a recursive ordinal, then it is not difficult to view the deduction as a metafinite object. Then we can think of the finite computations of ordinary recursion theory as having been replaced by the metafinite computations of metarecursion theory. If we permit metafinite E to be used as defining sets of equations, then the class of partial metarecursive functions is not enlarged. The enumeration theorem for Π_1^1 predicates leads immediately to an enumeration theorem for the partial metarecursive functions.

THEOREM 1 ([1]). For each $n>0$: there exists a partial metarecursive function $\phi_n(z, x_1, \ldots, x_n)$ such that for each partial metarecursive function $\psi(x_1, \ldots, x_n)$ there exists a natural number e such that

$$(x_1) \ldots (x_n) [\psi(x_1, \ldots, x_n) \simeq \phi_n(e, x_1, \ldots, x_n)].$$

In theorem 1, the x_i's range over the recursive ordinals, and $\simeq$, the symbol for strong equality, has the same meaning as it has in Kleene [9].

Next we wish to lift the notion of relative recursiveness up into metarecursion theory. Unfortunately, if one lifts up equivalent definitions of relative recursiveness, one does not necessarily obtain equivalent notions of reducibility for metarecursion theory. It is not yet absolutely clear what the correct notion of reducibility (corresponding to relative recursiveness) is for metarecursion theory. Kreisel [10] discusses various possibilities. We favor $\leq_M$, defined below. First we consider the notion of A being weakly metarecursive in $B(A \leq_w B)$, where A and B are sets of recursive ordinals. We need a metarecursive indexing of the metafinite sets. Let j and k be metarecursive functions such that for each metafinite set K there exists a unique α such that

$$(x)[x \in K \leftrightarrow (x < j(\alpha) \,\&\, k(\alpha, x) = 0)].$$

For each α, let $K_\alpha = \{x \mid x < j(\alpha) \,\&\, k(\alpha, x) = 0\}$. The existence of j and k follows from consideration of the standard indexing of hyperarithmetic sets. With the help of j and k, we can introduce partial metarecursive functions taking metafinite sets as arguments. We say A is *weakly metarecursive in B* if there exist partial metarecursive functions ψ and ϕ such that for all α,

$$\alpha \in A \leftrightarrow (EK)(EL)(\psi(K, L, \alpha) = 0 \,\&\, K \subseteq B \,\&\, L \subseteq cB)$$
$$\alpha \notin A \leftrightarrow (EK)(EL)(\phi(K, L, \alpha) = 0 \,\&\, K \subseteq B \,\&\, L \subseteq cB),$$

where K and L range over the metafinite sets. The definition of $\leq_w$ is a straightforward lifting up of a much-used form of the definition of relative recursiveness; the finite neighborhood condition for B has been replaced by a metafinite neighborhood condition. Driscoll [11] obtained a very surprising result which implies the next theorem.

THEOREM 2. $\leq_w$ is not transitive.

On the other hand, $\leq_w$ has a simple characterization in terms of the equation calculus. Let B be an arbitrary set of recursive ordinals. We consider now how to make deductions from B and some finite set E. Let $S_0^{E,g} = E \cup \{g(\alpha) = \boldsymbol{l} \mid \alpha \notin B\} \cup \{g(\alpha) = \boldsymbol{O} \mid \alpha \in B\}$; for each $\alpha > 0$, let $S_\alpha^{E,g}$ equal the set of all immediate consequences of $\cup\{S_\gamma^{E,g} \mid \gamma < \alpha\}$. (Do not forget the condition made in the definition of S_α^E concerning the use of (R3) (b).) It is not true that

$$S_{\omega_1}^{E,g} = \cup\{S_\gamma^{E,g} \mid \gamma < \omega_1\}$$

for all B and E. Thus it is possible to make deductions whose heights are not recursive ordinals. To make matters worse, for some B, we will obtain deductions which are of recursive ordinal height but which are not metafinite; i.e., $S_\alpha^{E,g}$ for some B and recursive α may contain an equation deducible from B whose deduction-tree is not metafinite. Let $S^{E,g} = \cup\{S_\alpha^{E,g} \mid \alpha < \aleph_1\}$.

We define $A \leq_{mc} B$ (A is metafinitely computable from B) to mean that for some finite E containing the principal function letter f and the given function letter g,

$$\alpha \in A \leftrightarrow f(\boldsymbol{\alpha}) = \boldsymbol{O} \in S^{E,g,m}$$
$$\alpha \notin A \leftrightarrow f(\boldsymbol{\alpha}) = \boldsymbol{l} \in S^{E,g,m},$$

where $S^{E,g,m}$ is the set of all members of $S^{E,g}$ whose deduction-trees are metafinite. Clearly, the height of each member of $S^{E,g,m}$ is a recursive ordinal. $A \leq_{mc} B$ means the membership of A is computable from B using the equation calculus and metafinite deductions only.

THEOREM 3 ([12]). $A \leq_w B \leftrightarrow A \leq_{mc} B$.

We say $A \leq_c B$ (A is computable from B), if

$$\alpha \in A \leftrightarrow f(\boldsymbol{\alpha}) = \boldsymbol{O} \in S^{E,g}$$
$$\alpha \notin A \leftrightarrow f(\boldsymbol{\alpha}) = \boldsymbol{l} \in S^{E,g}.$$

$A \leq_c B$ means A is computable from B using the equation calculus without restrictions. Suppose we identify the natural numbers with the finite recursive ordinals. Then if A and B are sets of natural numbers and A is hyperarithmetic in B, it follows $A \leq_c B$. It is readily seen that $\leq_c$ is transitive. It follows from theorems 2 and 3 that $\leq_{mc}$ is not transitive. We say $A \leq_{\omega_1} B$ (A is ω_1-computable from B) if

$$\alpha \in A \leftrightarrow f(\alpha) = \boldsymbol{O} \in \cup \{S_\gamma^{E,g} \mid \gamma < \omega_1\}$$
$$\alpha \notin A \leftrightarrow f(\alpha) = \boldsymbol{l} \in \cup \{S_\gamma^{E,g} \mid \gamma < \omega_1\}.$$

Clearly, $A \leq_{mc} B \rightarrow A \leq_{\omega_1} B \rightarrow A \leq_c B$; it is possible to show that these three relations are distinct.

One of our major hopes for metarecursion theory is the lifting up of various theorems about relative recursiveness. Such theorems are proved by manipulating finite computations and using combinatorial properties of finite sets. It seems to us the correct notion of computation for metarecursion theory must be such that each computation is a metafinite object. To our mind, the notion of computation is absolute; by that, we mean the computations can be given in advance; they do not depend on the set we are computing from. Although $\leq_{\omega_1}$ and $\leq_c$ are worthy of study to see how strong we can make our incomparability results, we reject them as candidates for the generalization of relative recursiveness, since they permit non-metafinite computations whose acceptability depends on the set being computed from. We would accept $A \leq_{mc} B$ if it were transitive. The lack of transitiveness is easily remedied. We say $A \leq_M B$ (A is metarecursive in B) if there exist partial metarecursive functions ψ and ϕ such that for all metafinite H,

$$H \subseteq A \leftrightarrow (EK)(EL)(\psi(K, L, H) = 0 \;\&\; K \subseteq B \;\&\; L \subseteq cB)$$
$$H \subseteq cA \leftrightarrow (EK)(EL)(\phi(K, L, H) = 0 \;\&\; K \subseteq B \;\&\; L \subseteq cB).$$

The transitiveness of $\leq_M$ follows from the symmetry of its definition.

Kreisel considers two notions of A invariantly definable from B in [10] and several others in private communications. In a future publication he will present the most desirable of these notions; for now, let us denote it by $\leq_I$ and list some of Kreisel's observations concerning it: $\leq_I$ is transitive; if A and B are sets of recursive ordinals and $A \leq_I B$, then $A \leq_c B$; if A and B are sets of natural numbers, then $A \leq_I B \leftrightarrow A \leq_c B \leftrightarrow A$ is hyperarithmetic in B.

All the notions of reducibility mentioned in this section coincide on a large class of sets, and it is possible to obtain incomparability results within this class, as we shall see in sections 5 and 6.

3. Regularity

A set of recursive ordinals is called *regular* if its intersection with every metafinite set is metafinite. Our interest in regular sets stems from the fact that regular, metarecursively enumerable sets behave in large measure like recursively enumerable sets. If we enumerate a regular, metarecursively enumerable set, then for each α, we eventually finish enumerating all the members of the set less than α. Let Q be a non-hyperarithmetic, Π_1^1 set. If we identify the natural numbers with the finite recursive ordinals, then Q is an example of a non-regular, metarecursively enumerable set. In this section we will see that all non-regularity for metarecursively enumerable sets has its origin in sets like Q.

If one attempts to lift a theorem about recursively enumerable sets up into metarecursion theory, one usually finds the lack of regularity a primary source of difficulty. A good example is a well-known theorem of Dekker [13]: each non-recursive, recursively enumerable set has the same Turing-degree as some simple set. The obvious generalization is: each non-metarecursive, metarecursively enumerable set has the same metadegree as some simple set. (Two sets have the same metadegree if each is metarecursive in the other; a set S is simple if it is metarecursively enumerable, if its complement is unbounded, and if every non-metafinite, metarecursively enumerable set touches S.) Dekker's argument lifts up beautifully if the given set is regular; otherwise, it collapses. We regard the lack of regularity not as an unfortunate anomaly, but as a source of interesting arguments. It appears that most, if not all, arguments of ordinary recursion theory can be lifted up if one is sufficiently immune to the pain of lengthy combinatorial arguments. The next theorem helps.

THEOREM 4 ([12]). Each metarecursively enumerable set has the same metadegree as some regular, metarecursively enumerable set.

PROOF. We are inspired by Dekker's notion of deficiency set [13]. Let $\{K_\alpha \mid \alpha<\omega_1\}$ be the standard metarecursive indexing for the metafinite sets. Let Q be a Π_1^1 set of unique notations such that Q is a linearly ordered subset of Kleene's O, the set of all notations for recursive ordinals. We write $A \leq_m B$ (A is many-one reducible to B) to indicate that for some metarecursive f, we have $\alpha\in A \leftrightarrow f(\alpha)\in B$. Let $\{F_\alpha\}$ be a standard, metarecursive enumeration of all the finite sets of recursive ordinals. We write $A \leq_f B$ (A is finitely reducible to B) to indicate $A \leq_w B$ and there is a metarecursive (in B) g such that for each α, the metafinite computation of the truth-value of $\alpha \in A$ uses only the information about B expressed by $F_{g(\alpha)} \subseteq B$ and $F_{g(\alpha)} \subseteq cB$. If $A \leq_f B$ and $B \leq_w C$, then $A \leq_w C$. Let A be a metarecursively enumerable set, and let $A^* = \{\alpha \mid A \cap K_\alpha \neq \phi\}$. A^* is metarecursively enumerable and has the same metadegree as A, since

$$K_\alpha \subseteq cA^* \leftrightarrow K_{h(\alpha)} \subseteq cA \leftrightarrow h(\alpha) \in cA^*$$

for some metarecursive h. Let f be a one-one, metarecursive function whose range is A^*. We define:

$$D_f^2 = \{\alpha \mid (E\beta)(f(\beta) < f(\alpha) \; \& \; |f(\beta)| < |f(\alpha)| \; \& \; \beta > \alpha)\}.$$

D_f^2 is metarecursively enumerable and regular! In addition, D_f^2 is metarecursive in A^*. We define

$$\rho(\alpha) = \mu\beta(f(\beta) > \alpha \; \& \; |f(\beta)| > |\alpha| \; \& \; \beta \notin D_f^2).$$

If ρ is total, then ρ is weakly metarecursive in D_f^2, and consequently, A^* is metarecursive in D_f^2.

Suppose ρ is not total. Let γ be the least ordinal such that

$$(\beta)(f(\beta) \leq \gamma \vee |f(\beta)| \leq |\gamma| \vee \beta \in D_f^2).$$

Let $A_\gamma^* = \{\beta \mid \beta \in A^* \; \& \; \beta < \gamma\}$. Then A_γ^* and A^* have the same metadegree. Let $B = \{|\alpha| \mid \alpha \in A_\gamma^*\}$. Then $B \leq_m A_\gamma^*$ and $A_\gamma^* \leq_m B$, since A_γ^* is bounded. Let g be a one-one metarecursive function whose range is B. Let σ be such that $(\beta)_{\beta \geq \sigma}(f(\beta) \leq \gamma \vee \beta \in D_f^2)$. Let

$$D_g = \{\alpha \mid (E\beta)(g(\beta) < g(\alpha) \; \& \; \beta > \alpha)\}.$$

D_g is regular. We claim D_g and A_γ^* have the same metadegree. D_g is metarecursive in B, and hence in A_γ^*. Let

$$A^1 = A^* - \{\alpha \mid \alpha \leq \gamma \vee (E\delta)_{\delta \leq \sigma}(\alpha = f(\delta))\}.$$

Then $K_\alpha \subseteq cA_\gamma^* \leftrightarrow m(\alpha) \in cA^1$ for some metarecursive m. Now $A_\gamma^* \leq_w D_g$, since $A_\gamma^* \leq_m B$ and $B \leq_w D_g$. Then $A^1 \leq_w D_g$, since $A^1 \leq_f A_\gamma^*$. Finally, $A_\gamma^* \leq_M D_g$, because of the above property of m.

THEOREM 5. Each non-regular, metarecursively enumerable set has the same metadegree as some Π_1^1 set of natural numbers.

PROOF. Let A be a non-regular, metarecursively enumerable set. By theorem 4, there is a regular, metarecursively enumerable set B of the same metadegree as A. Let f be a one-one metarecursive function whose range is B. Let

$$D_f = \{\alpha \mid (E\beta)(\beta > \alpha \,\&\, f(\beta) < f(\alpha))\}.$$

A straightforward lifting up of the arguments of Dekker [13] shows that D_f is simple and has the same metadegree as B. Let K be a metafinite set such that $K \cap A$ is not metafinite. Let $C = \{|\alpha| \mid \alpha \in K \cap A\}$. Then C is a non-hyperarithmetic, Π_1^1 set which is metarecursive in A. Let g be a one-one, metarecursive function whose range is C. Let $D_f^* = \{g(\alpha) \mid \alpha \in D_f\}$. Then D_f^* is Π_1^1, and D_f is metarecursive in D_f^*. We need only show D_f^* is metarecursive in D_f.

Let K be a metafinite subset of ω such that $K \subseteq cD_f^*$. Then

$$K = [K \cap (C - D_f^*)] \cup K - C.$$

We claim both components of K are metafinite. Let

$$R = \{\beta \mid g(\beta) \in K \cap (C - D_f^*)\}.$$

Since $K \subseteq cD_f^*$, we have that R is metarecursively enumerable and that $R \subseteq cD_f$. But then R is metafinite, since D_f is simple; consequently, $g(R) = K \cap (C - D_f^*)$ is metafinite. In short,

$$K \subseteq cD_f^* \leftrightarrow g^{-1}[K \cap (C - D_f^*)] \subseteq cD_f \,\&\, K - C \subseteq cC, R \subseteq cD_f^* \rightarrow K - C$$

is metafinite, and $C \leq_M D_f$. It follows $D_f^* \leq_M D_f$.

Theorem 5 should be of some help in the study of metadegrees of Π_1^1 sets. Corollary 1 below is a typical example of an application of theorem 5.

THEOREM 6 (Driscoll [11]). If $\boldsymbol{a}$ and $\boldsymbol{b}$ are metadegrees of metarecursively enumerable sets such that $\boldsymbol{a} < \boldsymbol{b}$, then there exists a metadegree $\boldsymbol{c}$ of a metarecursively enumerable set such that $\boldsymbol{a} < \boldsymbol{c} < \boldsymbol{b}$.

COROLLARY 1. If $\boldsymbol{a}$ and $\boldsymbol{b}$ are metadegrees of Π_1^1 sets such that $\boldsymbol{a} < \boldsymbol{b}$, then there exists a metadegree $\boldsymbol{c}$ of a Π_1^1 set such that $\boldsymbol{a} < \boldsymbol{c} < \boldsymbol{b}$.

Driscoll's proof of theorem 6 is far from a mere translation of the principal argument of [14] into the language of metarecursion theory. He is forced to deal with the phenomenon of non-regularity in a surprisingly non-constructive fashion; of course he makes use of theorem 4. In section 5, we note the existence of *completely regular*, non-metarecursive, metarecursively enumerable sets; a set is completely regular if every set weakly metarecursive in it is regular.

4. Post's problem and admissible ordinals

Kripke [4] introduced the notion of admissible ordinal in order to study a wide range of extensions of recursion theory; if α is an admissible ordinal, then the ordinals less than α, viewed through the spectacles of a recursion-theorist, resemble the natural numbers*. Now let α be an arbitrary ordinal. We enlarge the equation calculus outlined in section 2 in order to give the condition for admissibility of α. For each ordinal $\beta<\alpha$, we have a formal numeral $\boldsymbol{\beta}$ at our disposal. The class of terms and equations are enlarged to accomodate the additional numerals, but the rules of deduction are the same. For each finite system E of equations and ordinal $\gamma>0$, we define S^E_γ, as before, to be the set of all equations immediately deducible from $\cup\{S^E_\delta \mid \delta<\gamma\}$. We say α is *admissible* if

$$S^E_\alpha = \cup\{S^E_\gamma \mid \gamma<\alpha\}.$$

Intuitively, α is admissible if every deduction, containing only numerals less than α from every finite system of equations has height less than α. It is not hard to show that Kleene's ω_1 is the first admissible ordinal after ω, and that every cardinal is admissible.

Now suppose α is admissible. A partial function ϕ is partial α-recursive if for some finite E with principal function letter f, we have

$$\phi(\alpha)=\delta \leftrightarrow f(\boldsymbol{\gamma})=\boldsymbol{\delta}\in S^E_\alpha$$

for all γ, $\delta<\alpha$. The *α-finite* sets are those α-recursive sets bounded by an ordinal less than α. The α-recursively enumerable sets are the ranges of the partial α-recursive functions. The definitions of "α-recursive in" and "weakly α-recursive in" are made in strict analogy with the definitions of "metarecursive in" and "weakly metarecursive in" given in section 2. Kripke [4] succeeded in generalizing the usual solution of Post's problem

* Platek [23], independently of Kripke, introduced the notion of recursivery regular ordinal, a notion equivalent to that of admissible ordinal.

to a proper subclass of the admissible ordinals which properly includes the cardinals. In [12] we gave a solution to Post's problem which works for every admissible ordinal, the argument is outlined below. On the other hand, there are many theorems about degrees of recursive enumerable sets that we do not know how to lift up to every admissible ordinal. For example, we do not know if the α-degrees of α-recursively enumerable sets are dense for every admissible α. (Two subsets of the ordinals less than α have the same α-degree if each is α-recursive in the other.)

THEOREM 7 ([12]). For each admissible ordinal α, there exist α-recursively enumerable sets A and B such that A is not weakly α-recursive in B and B is not α-recursive.

PROOF. The trick is not to insist that B be not weakly α-recursive in A; then the conflict between requirements is helpfully minimized. Let α^*, the *projectum* of α [4], be the least ordinal that bounds the range of a one-one, α-recursive function; thus $\omega_1^* = \omega$. The ordinals less than α^* serve in a standard fashion as indices of the partial α-recursive functions. Let $\{\{\varepsilon\}^\beta \mid \varepsilon < \alpha^*\}$ be a standard enumeration of all the partial functions weakly α-recursive in B. Our first set of requirements is: $A \neq \{\varepsilon\}^B$ for any $\varepsilon < \alpha^*$. Our second set is: if R_ε, the ε-th α-recursively enumerable set in some standard enumeration is unbounded, then $B \cap R_\varepsilon$ is non-empty. For the sake of the second requirement, we arrange the construction so that cB is unbounded; such an arrangement is trivial. The purpose of the second set of requirements is to make B non-α-recursive by making it "simple". At stage σ of the construction, we consider putting γ in A for the sake of the first set of requirements or in B for the sake of the second set. Observe that if γ is put in A, no injury to the second set can occur! Thus we make at most one attempt to meet each requirement of the second set. On the other hand if we put γ in B, we may injure some requirement of the first set. Our system of priorities is: do not put γ in B for the sake of R_ε if for some $\delta < \varepsilon$, an injury to the requirement $A \neq \{\delta\}^B$ would result.

It follows that the requirement $A \neq \{\varepsilon\}^B$ is injured at most once for each $\gamma \leq \varepsilon$. But then the set of stages σ such that $A \neq \{\varepsilon\}^B$ is injured at stage σ is an α-recursively enumerable set in α-recursive one-to-one correspondence with an α-recursively enumerable subset of the ordinals less than or equal to $\varepsilon < \alpha^*$, and consequently, is α-finite. This means eventually we stop injuring the requirement $A \neq \{\varepsilon\}^B$, and consequently, we have plenty of time to meet it. A similar argument shows we eventually stop trying to meet $A \neq \{\delta\}^B$ for all $\delta < \varepsilon$, and consequently, we are eventually free to make $B \cap R_\varepsilon$ non-empty if R_ε is unbounded.

The proof of theorem 7 is typical among priority constructions for arbitrary ordinals. One always deals with α^*, the projectum of α, because any α-recursively enumerable set bounded by an ordinal less than α^* is α-finite. This corresponds to the fact that finite sets are metafinite in metarecursion theory. Sad to say, we avoided a hard convergence problem in the proof of theorem 7 by not letting any attempt to meet a requirement in the first set injure any requirement in the second set.

All the ideas and results of sections 2 and 3 save theorem 6 generalize to arbitrary admissible ordinals without much difficulty if one fixes one's mental eye on the notion of projectum. It turns out that our use of "finite" in metarecursion theory is equivalent to "in one-to-one metarecursive correspondence with a metarecursively enumerable set bounded by an ordinal less than the projectum of ω_1". The last equivalence helps enormously in lifting proofs from metarecursion theory up to arbitrary admissible ordinals.

5. Subgeneric sets

The notion of subgeneric set is an invention of Kreisel and was studied in [12]. Let α be an admissible ordinal, and let A be a set of ordinals less than α. Intuitively, A is subgeneric if every possible deduction from A by means of the enlarged equation calculus described in section 4 has height less than α. (It does not follow that every deduction from A is an α-finite object.) The admissibility of α implies that every α-recursive set is subgeneric. Kreisel observed that a routine forcing argument sufficed to prove the existence of non-α-recursive, subgeneric sets. He asked the author: is there a non-α-recursive, α-recursively enumerable, subgeneric set? In [12] the answer was found to be yes by means of a non-forcing, priority argument.

Let $S_0^{E,g} = E \cup \{g(\gamma) = \boldsymbol{1} \mid \gamma \notin A\} \cup \{g(\gamma) = \boldsymbol{0} \mid \gamma \in A\}$, and let $S_\gamma^{E,g}$ be defined as in section 2 for each $\gamma < 0$ (of course, we are using the equation calculus associated with α, and g is a given function letter). We say A is *subgeneric* if for all E,

$$S_\alpha^{E,A} = \cup \{S_\gamma^{E,A} \mid \gamma < \alpha\}.$$

Our interest in subgeneric sets stems from the fact that various notions of reducibility coincide for the subgeneric sets. If B is computable from A ($\leq_c$) using the equation calculus and permitting deductions of arbitrary height, then B is computable from A using the equation calculus and deductions of height less than α. In this section, we also consider a notion related to subgenericity, namely, hyper-regularity. It turns out that if B is computable from A and A is both regular and hyper-regular, then B is α-recursive in A. Intuitively, a regular set is hyper-regular if every deduction from A is an α-finite object. The most desireable incomparability results, consequently, mention only hyper-regular sets; moreover, familiar arguments concerning recursively enumerable sets are more readily generalized if one assumes hyper-regularity.

We say A is hyper-regular if the range of each function weakly α-recursive in A, when restricted to a set bounded by an ordinal less than α, is bounded by an ordinal less than α.

THEOREM 8 ([12]). The following three properties of a regular set A are equivalent to hyper-regularity:

(a) every deduction from A is an α-finite object;

(b) the range of each function weakly α-recursive in A, when restricted to an α-finite set, is α-finite;

(c) the restriction of each function weakly α-recursive in A to an α-finite set is an α-finite, partial function.

PROOF. We show only that hyper-regularity implies (a). Let E be a finite system of equations. Suppose each member of $\{f(\gamma)=\boldsymbol{O} \mid \gamma<\beta\}$ is deducible from E and A by means of an α-finite deduction. Then there exist functions $s(\gamma)$ and $t(\gamma)$ weakly α-recursive in A such that some deduction of $f(\gamma)=\boldsymbol{O}$ from E and A uses only the membership information about A expressed by $K_{s(\gamma)}\subseteq A$ and $K_{t(\gamma)}\subseteq cA$. ($\{K_\gamma \mid \gamma<\alpha\}$ is a standard enumeration of the α-finite sets.) Since A is hyper-regular, it follows that $\{s(\gamma) \mid \gamma<\beta\}$ and $\{t(\gamma) \mid \gamma<\beta\}$ are bounded. But then there is an α-finite K such that all members of $\{f(\gamma)=\boldsymbol{O} \mid \gamma<\beta\}$ are deducible from E and $A \cap K$. Finally, $A \cap K$ is α-finite, since A is regular.

COROLLARY 2. Each regular, hyper-regular set is subgeneric.

THEOREM 9 ([12]). A regular set of recursive ordinals is hyper-regular if and only if it is subgeneric.

PROOF. Suppose A is subgeneric. First we show A is completely regular. Let B be bounded and weakly metarecursive in A. Let γ be the least upper bound of B. There exist functions $m(\delta)$ and $n(\delta)$ weakly metarecursive in A such the truth-value of $\delta \in B$ is deducible from A (and some E independent of δ) using only membership information about A expressed by $K_{m(\delta)} \subseteq A$ and $K_{n(\delta)} \subseteq cA$. Suppose $P = \{m(\delta) + n(\delta) \mid \delta < \gamma\}$ is unbounded. Then $Q \leq_c \{|\tau| \mid \tau \in P\}$. But then $Q \leq_c A$, and consequently, Q is subgeneric. No non-metarecursive Π_1^1 set is subgeneric, so P is bounded. It follows from the regularity of A that B is metafinite.

Now let f be weakly metarecursive in A, and let K be a metafinite set. Then $\{\langle |\alpha|, |f(\alpha)| \rangle \mid \alpha \in K\}$ is bounded and weakly metarecursive in A; by the previous paragraph, it is metafinite.

COROLLARY 3 [12]. A metarecursively enumerable set is subgeneric if and only if it is hyper-regular.

PROOF. Any subgeneric, metarecursively enumerable set is regular.

It follows from theorem 8 that all notions of reducibility mentioned by us coincide for regular, hyper-regular sets. To our mind, corollary 3 tells us that all notions of subgenericity coincide for metarecursively enumerable sets. The weakest notion we can think of says that all deductions have height equal to a recursive ordinal. The strongest notion we can possibly have says that all deductions are metafinite objects.

Theorem 8 is of immense importance in [2]. In that paper a system of axioms for recursion theory will be given that makes no mention of all well-ordering of the individuals. Any model of the axioms is called a recursion theory. It will be shown that each recursion theory is isomorphic to a collection of subsets of α (definable with the help of the notion of hyper-regularity) for some admissible α, and that two recursion theories on α may or may not use the same notion of "finite"; in fact, there is a recursion theory on the recursive ordinals non-isomorphic to metarecursion theory where the "finite" sets are the metafinite sets. This means that if two recursion systems have the same "recursive" sets, then they have the same "finite" sets, but not conversely. In ordinary recursion theory, one has the belief that the finite sets determine the recursive sets, but the belief is false in the sense that the axiomatic properties of recursion theory do not suffice to prove it.

THEOREM 10 ([12]). For each admissible α, there exists a regular, non-α-recursive, α-recursively enumerable, hyper-regular set.

PROOF. We consider only the metarecursive case. As in the proof of theorem 7, we have two sets of requirements, although we are only enumerating one set B. The e-th member of the first set is: if $\{e\}^B$, the e-th partial function weakly metarecursive in B according to some standard enumeration, is defined for all finite n, then the restriction of $\{e\}^B$ to the natural numbers is a metafinite, partial function. The e-th member of the second set is: if R_e, the e-th metarecursively enumerable set is unbounded, then $B \cap R_e$ is non-empty. Harmless steps are taken to insure that the complement of B is unbounded; consequently, the second set guarantees that B is not metarecursive.

At stage σ, we consider putting γ into B for the sake of the e-th requirement of the second set. First we approximate $\{c\}^B(n)$ for all $c<e$ and all finite n. Our approximation of $\{c\}^B(n)$ at stage σ is obtained by taking for B that subset of B enumerated prior to stage σ and by allowing only those metafinite deductions whose indices are less than σ. We do not put γ into B at stage σ for the sake of the e-th requirement of the second set if for some $c<e$ and $n<w$, the addition of γ to B would alter the current approximate value of $\{c\}^B(n)$. It follows that the approximate value of $\{c\}^B(n)$ is altered at stage σ for only finitely many σ. But then there is a σ^* independent of n, such that the final value of $\{e\}^B(n)$, if it exists, is equal to the σ-th approximation for all $\sigma \geq \sigma^*$. It follows that if $\{e\}^B$ is defined for all finite n, then the restriction of $\{e\}^B$ to ω is a metafinite, partial function. It also follows that for each e and all sufficiently large σ, there is no obstacle to adding γ to B for the sake of the e-th requirement of the second set.

THEOREM 11 ([12]). There exist two metarecursively enumerable sets such that neither is computable from the other.

PROOF. Let B be a hyper-regular, non-metarecursive, metarecursively enumerable set. Imitate the proof of corollary 2 of theorem 1 of [15] p. 67 to split B into two metarecursively enumerable sets such that neither is weakly metarecursive in the other. It follows that both of the sets are hyper-regular and hence incomparable in the sense of the equation calculus.

We regard theorem 11 as the correct generalization of Post's problem to metarecursion theory, since it is free of the controversy concerning reducibility that infects theorem 7. Although we have theorem 10 available for all admissible α, we are very much in the dark concerning convergence questions connected with the priority method that arise for arbitrary admissible α. On the other hand, the most intricate priority arguments of ordinary recursion theory have counterparts in metarecursion theory, and we include those priority arguments in which the conflict between requirements compels us to injure some requirements infinitely often as in [14].

6. Applications to Π_1^1 sets and maximality

The initial ideas of section 2 make clear that if we identify the natural numbers with the finite ordinals, then the Π_1^1 sets of natural numbers coincide with the metarecursively enumerable sets of natural numbers. But then it is possible to apply priority arguments to Π_1^1 sets. In this manner the familiar but vague analogy between Π_1^1 sets and recursively enumerable sets suddenly becomes as sharp as the edge of a pastrami slicer in a New York delicatessen. Let us call a Π_1^1 set M *maximal* if each Π_1^1 set $R \supset M$ is such that $R-M$ is finite or cR is finite, and if cM is infinite.

THEOREM 12 ([12]). There exists a maximal Π_1^1 set.

The proofs of theorems 12 and 13 are modifications of the proof of theorem 2 of [16], with the help of Yates [17]. Call a metarecursively enumerable set M maximal if each metarecursively enumerable set $R \supset M$ is such that $R-M$ is finite or cR is finite and if cM is unbounded.

THEOREM 13 ([12]). There exists a maximal, metarecursively enumerable set.

Let α be an admissible ordinal. Call an α-recursively enumerable set M maximal if each α-recursively enumerable set R is such that $R-M$ or cR is bounded by an ordinal less than α and if cM is unbounded.

THEOREM 14 ([12]). There exists a countable, admissible ordinal such that no α-recursively enumerable set is maximal.

PROOF. Use the countability and denseness of the rationals together with the axiom of constructibility ($V=L$) to show that there is no $\aleph_1$-recursively enumerable, maximal set. Then observe that this argument holds in some countable initial segment I of the constructible sets which is a model I of finitely many axioms of set theory. Finally, the $\aleph_1$ of I is the desired α, since steps can be taken to insure admissibility has the same meaning inside and outside I.

After hearing about theorem 12, Hartley Rogers Jr. conjectured that the lattice under inclusion of recursively enumerable sets modulo finite sets is order-isomorphic to the lattice under inclusion of Π_1^1 sets modulo finite sets. Owings [18] has observed that this conjecture is false in the following precise sense. Let us say an element p in a partial ordering P has rank n if every maximal, linear ordering of elements of P greater than p has cardinality n. Then every rank 2 element of the lattice arising from the recursively enumerable sets is the greatest lower bound of two rank 1 elements, but there is a rank 2 element in the lattice arising from the Π_1^1 sets which does not have this property. Owings makes use of a priority argument concerning Π_1^1 sets.

Spector [19] proved that any two non-hyperarithmetic Π_1^1 sets have the same hyperdegree. It follows that if A and B are Π_1^1 and B is not hyperarithmetic, then A is computable from $B(A \leq_c B)$ by means of the equation calculus with deductions of arbitrary height permitted; in fact, A is computable from B if only deductions of height at most ω_1 are permitted. Thus the strongest incomparability one can hope to obtain for a pair of Π_1^1 sets, from the viewpoint of the equation calculus, is that neither be computable from the other $(\leq_{\omega_1})$ by means of deductions (possibly not metafinite) whose heights are less than ω_1. The first step in this direction was theorem 15.

THEOREM 15 ([12]). There exist two Π_1^1 sets such that neither is weakly metarecursive in the other.

The trick needed to prove theorem 15 consists of considering only a proper subset of the reducibility procedures associated with "weakly metarecursive in" in the course of the construction. Suppose A and B are the Π_1^1 sets to be constructed. We have to show $A \neq \{e\}^B$ and $B \neq \{e\}^A$ for all e, where $\{\{e\}^B | e < \omega\}$ is a standard enumeration of all the partial functions weakly metarecursive in B. We define $[e]$ as follows: $[e]^B(\alpha)$ is defined and is equal to β if $\{e\}^B(\alpha)$ is defined and equal to β and if the deduction of the value of $\{e\}^B$ makes use of membership information about B expressed by $K \subseteq B$ and $L \subseteq cB$, where $\omega - (K \cup L)$ is infinite. Clearly, if B is a non-hyperarithmetic Π_1^1 set, $\{e\}^B \simeq [e]^B$. The construction of A and B contains primary steps designed to insure $B \neq [e]^A$ and $A \neq [e]^B$ and secondary steps designed to insure A and B are not hyperarithmetic. The primary steps and secondary steps conflict with each other, but the secondary steps are of such a nature that it is possible to show that A and B are not hyperarithmetic without fully considering the effect of the primary steps. The reason we use $[e]^B$ instead of $\{e\}^B$ is that $[e]^B$ depends only on deductions which fail to mention infinitely many natural numbers. The fact that our deductions are "bounded" in a special sense gives us room to maneuver. An analogous situation occurs when we study $\{e\}^B$ for B an arbitrary set of recursive ordinals. Each deduction associated with $\{e\}^B$ fails to mention unboundedly many recursive ordinals; the existence of this last bound is what enables us to construct unbounded metarecursively enumerable sets A and B such that $A \neq \{e\}^B$ and $B \neq \{e\}^A$. After all, in Friedberg's solution to Post's problem [20], the most important combinatorial fact used is that the deductions are finite, hence bounded.

In order to obtain two Π_1^1 sets such that neither is ω_1-computable ($\leq_{\omega_1}$) from the other, we introduce the notion of ω_1-subgenericity. Intuitively, a set of recursive ordinals A is ω_1-subgeneric if there exists a uniform method for replacing each deduction from A which has recursive height by an equivalent deduction which is metafinite. Formally, we say A is ω_1-subgeneric if there exists a metarecursive function t such that for all equations d and finite systems of equations E,

$$d \in \cup \{S_\alpha^{E,g} \mid \alpha < \omega_1\} \leftrightarrow d \in \cup \{S_\alpha^{t(E),g,m} \mid \alpha < \omega_1\},$$

where

$$S_0^{E,g} = E \cup \{g(\gamma) = 1 \mid \gamma \notin A\} \cup \{g(\gamma) = 0 \mid \gamma \in A\},$$

and where $S_\alpha^{E,g,m}$ consists of all members of $S_\alpha^{E,g}$ where deduction-trees are metafinite.

It follows from theorem 3 that if A is ω_1-subgeneric and B is ω_1-computable from $A (\leq_{\omega_1})$, then B is weakly metarecursive in A. The proofs of theorems 16 and 17 will appear in [21]. The main idea is to combine the proof of the existence of subgeneric sets (theorem 10), the use of "bounded" metafinite deductions (theorem 15), and a forcing argument. Each statement of the form "$d \in \cup \{S_\alpha^{E,g} | \alpha < \omega_1\}$" is forced or its negation is forced by metafinitely much information P about the membership of B. Each P is "bounded" in the sense that it fails to mention infinitely many natural numbers. The priority aspect of the argument manifests itself in that more than one attempt has to be made to force each statement; this phenomenon is typical of combinations of priority and forcing. In order that B be Π_1^1, it is necessary that the forcing relation be metarecursively enumerable. The metarecursiveness of t follows from the fact that the forcing relation is metarecursively enumerable uniformly in E. Thus an equation d is deducible from E and A by means of a deduction of recursive height if and only if it is forced to be by some metafinite neighborhood condition P on A. But such a P exists if and only if it can be shown to exist by means of some metafinite computation involving A, E and the forcing relation in a uniform fashion. In this manner a non-hyperarithmetic, ω_1-subgeneric Π^1_1 set can be obtained. Theorem 17 is proved by splitting such a set into two ω_1-subgeneric Π^1_1 sets such that neither is weakly metarecursive in the other.

THEOREM 16. There exists a non-hyperarithmetic, ω_1-subgeneric Π^1_1 set.

THEOREM 17. There exist two Π^1_1 sets such that neither is ω_1-computable from the other.

As we remarked above, the incomparability attained in theorem 17 is the strongest possible for Π^1_1 sets from the point of view of the equation calculus. We regard theorem 15, and possibly theorem 17, as the correct solution of Post's problem for Π^1_1 sets. Spector [19] felt that his proof that all non-hyperarithmetic, Π^1_1 sets occupy the same hyperdegree constituted a solution to Post's problem for Π^1_1 sets. We disagree on the grounds that Spector wrongly permitted non-metafinite computations to be used on sets that were metarecursively enumerable. It seems to us that in any formulation of Post's problem, the set of all computations permitted must be enumerable by the same methods used to enumerate the sets being examined for incomparability. It follows that the individuals must be on a par with the computations; both must be absolute in that they are independent of the set being reduced.

7. Questions and conjectures

In this section we single out some of the question and conjectures listed in the final section of [12]. There is one fundamental question: which true statements of ordinary recursion theory remain true when appropriately generalized to metarecursion theory? In particular, how does one define the jump operator for metarecursion theory. (In ordinary recursion theory, the jump of a set A is the recursive union of all sets recursively enumerable in A.)

Q1. If α is admissible, is α^*, the projectum of α, admissible?* This question was suggested by Kripke who has shown that α^* must be the

* *Note added in proof*: Kripke has recently answered Q1 in the affirmative.

limit of admissible ordinals. An affirmative answer to this question would make it possible to apply a wide range of priority arguments to arbitrary admissible ordinals.

Q2. Is there a maximal, α-recursively enumerable set for some uncountable, admissible α? We think not.

Q3. Does there exist a metarecursive function f such that for all e $R_{f(e)}$ is regular and has the same metadegree as R_e? (R_e is the e-th metarecursively enumerable set in some standard enumeration.) The proof of theorem 4 does not provide such an f.

If A is weakly metarecursive in B, then $A=\{e\}^B$ for some e as described in [1]. The computations used to compute A from B are members of the metarecursively enumerable set $\{t(e,\sigma)|\sigma<\omega_1\}$. A typical value of the metarecursive function $t(e,\sigma)$ is $\langle e, M, N, \alpha, \gamma\rangle$; if $M\subseteq B$ and $N\subseteq cB$, then $\{e\}^B(\alpha)=\gamma$, where M and N are metafinite sets. We say e is *intrinsically consistent* if for all α, σ_1 and σ_2, if $t(e,\sigma_1)=\langle e, M_1, N_1, \alpha, \gamma_1\rangle$, $t(e,\sigma_2)=\langle e, M_2, N_2, \alpha, \gamma_2\rangle$, and $(M_1\cup M_2)\cap(N_1\cup N_2)=\phi$, then $\gamma_1=\gamma_2$.

Q4. For each e, does there exist an intrinsically consistent e^* such that $\{e\}^A\simeq\{e^*\}^A$ for all A? We think not. In ordinary recursion theory the answer is yes, since we can require that M and N define a finite, initial segment of a characteristic function rather than an arbitrary, basic neighborhood.

So far the only differences we know between recursion theory and metarecursion theory appear to stem from inescapable cardinality considerations. For example, Kripke has shown that Myhill's theorem that all creative sets are recursively isomorphic [22] fails in metarecursion theory. But his argument consists of exhibiting a bounded and an unbounded creative set. We do not know if there is an elementary, true statement of recursion theory, free of cardinality considerations, which is false in metarecursion theory.

References

[1] G. Kreisel and G. E. Sacks, Metarecursive sets, J. Symbolic Logic **30** (1965) 318.
[2] G. Kreisel and G. E. Sacks, Axiomatic recursion theory, in preparation.
[3] S. C. Kleene, On the forms of the predicates in the theory of constructive ordinals, Amer. J. Math. **77** (1955) 405.
[4] S. Kripke, Transfinite recursions on admissible ordinals, I and II (Abstracts), J. Symbolic Logic **29** (1964) 161.

[5] A. Levy and M. Machover, Recursive functions of ordinal numbers (North-Holland Publ. Co., Amsterdam) in preparation.

[6] M. Machover, The theory of transfinite recursion (Hebrew), Ph. D. Thesis, Hebrew University, Jerusalem, 1962.

[7] G. Takeuti, On the recursive functions of ordinal numbers, J. Math. Soc. Japan **12** (1960) 119.

[8] R. O. Gandy, Proof of Mostowski's conjecture, Bull. Acad. Polonaise des Sciences **8** (1960) 571.

[9] S. C. Kleene, Introduction to metamathematics (New York, Toronto, Amsterdam and Groningen, 1952).

[10] G. Kreisel, Model-theoretic invariants: applications to recursive and hyper-arithmetic operations, in: Theory of models, Proc. 1963 Intern. Symp., Berkeley, eds. J. W. Addison, L. Henkin and A. Tarski (North-Holland Publ. Co., Amsterdam, 1965) 190.

[11] G. Driscoll, Contributions to metarecursion theory, Ph. D. Thesis, Cornell University, 1965.

[12] G. E. Sacks, Post's problem, admissible ordinals, and regularity, Trans. Amer. Math. Soc. **124** (1966) 1.

[13] J. C. E. Dekker, A theorem on hypersimple sets, Proc. Amer. Math. Soc. **5** (1954) 791.

[14] G. E. Sacks, The recursively enumerable degrees are dense, Ann. of Math. **80** (1964) 300.

[15] G. E. Sacks, Degrees of unsolvability, Ann. of Math. Study No. 55 (Princeton, 1963).

[16] R. M. Friedberg, Three theorems on recursive enumeration, J. Symbolic Logic **23** (1958) 309.

[17] C. E. M. Yates, Three theorems on the degrees of recursively enumerable sets, Duke Math. J. **32** (1965) 461.

[18] J. C. Owings, Ph. D. Thesis, Cornell University, 1966.

[19] C. Spector, Recursive well-orderings, J. Symbolic Logic **20** (1955) 151.

[20] R. M. Friedberg, Two recursively enumerable sets of incomparable degrees of unsolvability, Proc. Nat. Acad. Sci. USA **43** (1957) 236.

[21[G. E. Sacks, On the reduction of Π_1^1 sets, in preparation.

[22] J. Myhill, Creative sets, Zeitschr. f. Math. Logik and Grundl. d. Math. **1** (1955) 310.

[23] R. A. Platek, Ph. D. Thesis, Stanford University, 1965.

RECURSIVELY ENUMERABLE DEGREES AND THE DEGREES LESS THAN $\mathbf{0}^{(1)}$

C. E. M. YATES[1]
Manchester University, UK

It was proved by Shoenfield [1] that there is a degree between $\mathbf{0}$ and $\mathbf{0}^{(1)}$ which is not recursively enumerable (r.e.) – in other words is not the degree of a r.e. set. This also follows from the more recent proof by Sacks ([2] and § 9 of [3]) that there is a minimal degree between $\mathbf{0}$ and $\mathbf{0}^{(1)}$, since there are no minimal r.e. degrees. Our purpose in the present note is to directly strengthen Shoenfield's result by proving that there is a degree $\mathbf{a}$ between $\mathbf{0}$ and $\mathbf{0}^{(1)}$ which is incomparable with every r.e. degree between $\mathbf{0}$ and $\mathbf{0}^{(1)}$.

We recall that Sacks has proved ([2] and § 5 of [3]) that if $\mathbf{a}<\mathbf{0}^{(1)}$ then there is a degree $\mathbf{c}$ such that $\mathbf{a}<\mathbf{c}<\mathbf{0}^{(1)}$, and also that if $\mathbf{a}$ is r.e. and $\mathbf{a}<\mathbf{0}^{(1)}$ then there is a r.e. degree $\mathbf{c}$ such that $\mathbf{a}<\mathbf{c}<\mathbf{0}^{(1)}$ [4]. In fact, both of these results are proved with $\mathbf{0}^{(1)}$ replaced by an arbitrary nonzero r.e. degree. A natural question to ask is whether if $\mathbf{a}<\mathbf{0}^{(1)}$ then there is a r.e. degree $\mathbf{c}$ such that $\mathbf{a}<\mathbf{c}<\mathbf{0}^{(1)}$, since this would imply both the above results. Our theorem gives a negative answer to this question. Here $\mathbf{0}^{(1)}$ can again be replaced by an arbitrary nonzero r.e. degree, but the proof of this is tedious and so we shall not describe it.

Before we turn to the proof of the theorem, it is necessary to make some preliminary definitions. In this we have been influenced by a recent paper of Shoenfield [5] in which much of the heavy symbolism of recursion theory is elegantly avoided, although we do not succeed to quite the same extent. We shall let a *string* be a finite (possibly empty) sequence of ones and twos; we use lower case Greek letters for strings. The number of elements of a string σ will be denoted by length(σ), the n-th element by

[1]) This work was done during the academic year 1964–1965 while the author held a grant from the Institute for Advanced Study in Princeton.

$\sigma(n)$ and the initial segment of σ which has length n by $\sigma[n]$. We shall write $\sigma \subset \tau$ to mean that τ is a proper extension of σ, in other words to mean that τ is obtained from σ by adding ones and twos to the right hand end of σ. Since we identify a set T with its representing function and this in turn can be considered as an infinite sequence of ones and twos, we also write $\sigma \subset T$ to mean that σ represents T on the segment of the integers which has length equal to length(σ). There exist a number of obvious recursive enumerations of the set of all strings and we can do recursion theory with strings just as easily as with integers. This is usually done indirectly by explicitly representing strings by integers. In what follows, whenever we talk about a recursive enumeration of objects involving strings, it may be associated with a recursive enumeration of integers which explicitly represent these objects, but we regard the manner in which this may be done as obvious and so we shall not go into details.

We shall depart from the standard notation for dealing with partial recursive functionals. We define an enumeration $\mathbf{F}_1, \mathbf{F}_2, \ldots$ of all partial recursive functionals in the following manner. We start by assuming the existence of a recursive enumeration of ordered quadruples $Q(1), Q(2), \ldots$ where $Q(s) = \{e\langle s\rangle, \sigma\langle s\rangle, x\langle s\rangle, y\langle s\rangle\}$, and for each s:

(i) there is a computation from the equations with Godel number $e\langle s\rangle$ and the finite number of equations $\mathbf{g}(\mathbf{n}) = \mathbf{m}$ corresponding to the equations $\sigma\langle s\rangle(n) = m$ which yields $\mathbf{f}(\mathbf{x}\langle\mathbf{s}\rangle) = \mathbf{y}\langle\mathbf{s}\rangle$. Here, $\mathbf{f}$ and $\mathbf{g}$ are just function letters occurring in the equations with Godel number $e\langle s\rangle$;

(ii) if $e\langle s\rangle = e\langle s'\rangle, \sigma\langle s\rangle \subset \sigma\langle s'\rangle$ and $x\langle s\rangle = x\langle s'\rangle$ then $y\langle s\rangle = y\langle s'\rangle$;

(iii) if $\sigma\langle s\rangle \subset \sigma'$ then there is a number s' such that

$$\sigma' = \sigma\langle s'\rangle, \quad e\langle s'\rangle = e\langle s\rangle \quad \text{and} \quad x\langle s\rangle = x\langle s'\rangle.$$

We do not go any further into the particulars of the enumeration $Q(1), Q(2), \ldots$ since these can easily be obtained by adapting the standard enumeration theorems, which can be found for example in Kleene [6]. Next, for each number a and set T, we define a partial function:

$$\mathbf{G}_a^T(x) = \min s(e\langle s\rangle = a \,\&\, \sigma\langle s\rangle \subset T \,\&\, x\langle s\rangle = x),$$

and follow this up with

$$\mathbf{F}_a^T(x) = y\langle \mathbf{G}_a^T(x)\rangle.$$

Clearly, $\mathbf{F}_1, \mathbf{F}_2, \ldots$, is an enumeration of all partial recursive functionals. It can be seen that $\mathbf{F}_a^T(x)$ is defined whenever $\mathbf{G}_a^T(x)$ is defined: we then say that $\mathbf{F}_a^T(x)$ is computed at stage $\mathbf{G}_a^T(x)$.

For any set C, we write $C(n)=1$ or $C(n)=2$ depending on whether $n \in C$ or $n \notin C$ respectively. We also write $C[n]$ for the string $C(1)\ C(2) \ldots \ldots C(n)$. We say that a sequence of sets $C_1, C_2, \ldots$ is *uniformly of degree* $\leq \mathbf{b}$ if there is a two-place function c of degree $\leq \mathbf{b}$ such that $c(m,n) = C_m(n)$ for all m and n. The r.e. sets in their standard enumeration are uniformly of degree $\leq \mathbf{0}^{(1)}$ and it is this property that Shoenfield exploited in [1] to obtain a non-r.e. degree between $\mathbf{0}$ and $\mathbf{0}^{(1)}$. We further this exploitation in the following theorem.

THEOREM. Let $C_1, C_2, \ldots$, be a sequence of sets which is uniformly of degree $\leq \mathbf{0}^{(1)}$, and for each e let $\mathbf{c}_e$ be the degree of C_e. Then there is a degree $\mathbf{a}$ such that $\mathbf{0} < \mathbf{a} < \mathbf{0}^{(1)}$ and $\mathbf{a} \mid \mathbf{c}_e$ for every e such that $\mathbf{0} < \mathbf{c}_e < \mathbf{0}^{(1)}$.

PROOF. We shall assume that there is a number e such that $\mathbf{0} < \mathbf{c}_e < \mathbf{0}^{(1)}$ since otherwise the theorem holds trivially. Our task is essentially threefold. We wish to construct a set A of degree $\mathbf{a}$ satisfying the theorem, and this will be clearly achieved if

(I) A is of degree $\leq \mathbf{0}^{(1)}$,

(II) $\mathbf{F}_{(k)_1}^{C_{(k)_2}} \neq A$ for each k such that $C_{(k)_2}$ is of degree $< \mathbf{0}^{(1)}$,

(III) $\mathbf{F}_{(k)_1}^{A} \neq C_{(k)_2}$ for each k such that $C_{(k)_2}$ is not recursive. (As k ranges over the integers, $\{(k)_1, (k)_2\}$ ranges recursively over all ordered pairs of integers.)

The usual conflict between requirements such as (II) and (III) is easily resolved in the present case by the standard diagonal method of Kleene-Post [7] as developed by Spector [8] and Shoenfield [1]. The only real conflict between these three requirements occurs between (I) and (II). This is because the double sequence $\{\mathbf{F}_j^{C_i}\}$ is uniformly of degree $\leq \mathbf{0}^{(2)}$ but need not be uniformly of degree $\leq \mathbf{0}^{(1)}$. (Since the sequence $\{\mathbf{F}_j^A\}$ is to some extent under our control and is implicitly arranged to be uniformly of degree $\leq \mathbf{0}^{(1)}$ the same problem does not arise with (III).) Although a conflict of this type can be the source of some difficulty when the requirement corresponding to (I) is that A be r.e. (see [4] and [9]), in situations such as the present one a relatively simple technique does the trick: we use a fixed function of degree $\mathbf{0}^{(1)}$ to majorise our efforts to satisfy (II). (A similar and simpler method will be found in a recent paper by Shoenfield [5] but it does not seem strong enough for the present theorem. The reason for this is that we have to deal with C_e for all e even though we can only hope to satisfy (II) for C_e of degree $<\mathbf{0}^{(1)}$.)

Let B be a fixed set of degree $\mathbf{0}^{(1)}$. This means that there is (by Theorem 2 of [1]) a recursive function b such that for all n: $\lim_s b(s, n)$ exists and is equal to $B(n)$. Hence, we may also define:

$$d(n)=\min s(\forall r)_{r>s}(b(s, n)=b(r, n)).$$

Clearly, d is of degree $\leq\mathbf{0}^{(1)}$ and, in fact, since $B(n)=b(d(n), n)$ it follows that B is recursive in d so that d is of degree $\mathbf{0}^{(1)}$. It is d that we use to majorise our attempts to satisfy (II).

We may now describe the construction of A. We shall define a sequence of strings $\alpha_1, \alpha_2, \ldots$, such that $\alpha_k \subset \alpha_{k+1}$ for all k. A will then be the unique set that extends α_k for all k. We commence by letting α_1 be the null string, and then define α_k inductively as follows. For each $k>1$ let n_k be the least $n>\text{length}(\alpha_{k-1})$ such that $n_k \neq n_h$ for all $h<k$ such that n_h exists and such that $\mathbf{F}_{(k)_1}^{C_{(k)2}}(n)$ has been computed at some stage $s\leq d(n)$. Clearly, n_k may not always exist, but as we shall now show it does exist whenever we want it to do so.

LEMMA 1. For each k, if $C_{(k)_2}$ is of degree $<\mathbf{0}^{(1)}$ and $\mathbf{F}_{(k)_1}^{C_{(k)2}}(n)$ is defined for all n then n_k exists.

PROOF. Suppose that n_k does not exist. Let n^* exceed length (α_{k-1}) and also exceed n_h for all $h<k$ such that n_h exists. Since $\mathbf{F}_{(k)_1}^{C_{(k)2}}(n)$ is defined for all n, it follows that $\mathbf{F}_{(k)_1}^{C_{(k)2}}(n)$ is computed at a stage $s>d(n)$ for all $n\geq n^*$. In other words, $\mathbf{G}_{(k)_1}^{C_{(k)2}}(n)>d(n)$ for all $n\geq n^*$, which implies that $B(n)= =b(\mathbf{G}_{(k)_1}^{C_{(k)2}}(n), n)$ for all $n\geq n^*$. Since $\mathbf{G}_{(k)_1}^{C_{(k)2}}(n)$ is defined for all n and since b is recursive, it follows that B is recursive in $C_{(k)2}$ and so $C_{(k)2}$ is of degree $\mathbf{0}^{(1)}$. This completes the proof of Lemma 1.

Next, for each $k>1$ we define:

$$\Gamma(k,\tau)\leftrightarrow\alpha_{k-1}\subset\tau\,\&\,(\forall h)_{h<k}\,(\text{if } n_h \text{ exists and } n_h<\text{length}(\tau) \text{ then } \tau(n_h)\neq\mathbf{F}_{(h)_1}^{C_{(h)2}}(n_h)).$$

Then we set:

$$\Delta(k,p,q)\leftrightarrow e\langle p\rangle = e\langle q\rangle = (k)_1\,\&\,x\langle p\rangle = x\langle q\rangle\,\& \; y\langle p\rangle \neq y\langle q\rangle\,\&\,\Gamma(k,\sigma\langle p\rangle)\,\&\,\Gamma(k,\sigma\langle q\rangle).$$

Finally, we define:

$$\alpha_k = \begin{cases} \sigma\langle \min p\,[(\exists\, q)\,\Delta\,(k,p,q)\;\&\; y\langle p\rangle \neq C_{(k)_2}(x\langle p\rangle)]\rangle \\ \qquad\qquad\qquad\qquad\qquad \text{if} \quad (\exists\, p)(\exists\, q)\,\Delta\,(k,p,q), \\ \text{the least proper extension of } \alpha_{k-1}, \text{ otherwise.} \end{cases}$$

Notice that

$$(\exists\, p)(\exists\, q)\,\Delta\,(k,p,q) \leftrightarrow (\exists\, p)(\exists\, q)(\Delta\,(k,p,q)\;\&\; y\langle p\rangle \neq C_{(k)_2}(x\langle p\rangle)),$$

since Δ is symmetric in p and q, so α_k is well defined. This completes the definition of A, which we recall is the unique extension of α_k for all k. Now we shall prove that A satisfies (I), (II) and (III).

(I) *A is of degree $\leq \mathbf{0}^{(1)}$*. This follows essentially from the fact that Γ is uniformly recursive in α_{k-1} and $\mathbf{0}^{(1)}$. We do, however, need the slightly stronger proposition that $(\exists p)(\exists q)\Delta(k, p, q)$ is uniformly recursive in α_{k-1} and $\mathbf{0}^{(1)}$. This all follows from the next lemma.

LEMMA 2. For each $k>1$, there is a sequence of predicates $\Delta_k^1, \Delta_k^2, \ldots$ uniformly recursive in α_{k-1}, such that for some number s_k, if $s \geq s_k$ then

$$\Delta_k^s(p,q) \leftrightarrow \Delta\,(k,p,q)$$

for all p and q.

PROOF. First, we define:

$$g\,(j,i,n) = \begin{cases} \mathbf{G}_j^{C_i}(n) & \text{if} \quad \mathbf{G}_j^{C_i}(n) \leq d\,(n), \\ 0 & \text{otherwise.} \end{cases}$$

Since we can write

$$\mathbf{G}_j^{C_i}(n) \leq d\,(n) \leftrightarrow (\exists\, s)_{s \leq d(n)}(e\langle s\rangle \leq j \;\&\; \sigma\langle s\rangle \subset C_i \;\&\; x\langle s\rangle = n),$$

and since the sequence $C_1, C_2, \ldots$ is uniformly of degree $\leq \mathbf{0}^{(1)}$, it easily follows that g is of degree $\leq \mathbf{0}^{(1)}$. Next, we observe that

$$n = n_h \leftrightarrow g\,((h)_1,(h)_2,n) > 0 \;\&\; (\forall\, m)_{m<n}(g\,((h)_1,(h)_2,m) = 0),$$

so that the predicate $\Phi(h, n) \leftrightarrow n = n_h$ is of degree $\leq \mathbf{0}^{(1)}$. Hence there is a uniformly recursive sequence of functions $f^1, f^2, \ldots$, such that $\Phi(h, n) \leftrightarrow \leftrightarrow \lim_s f^s(h, n) = 1$ for all h, n. Similarly there is a uniformly recursive sequence of functions $g^1, g^2, \ldots$, such that $g(j, i, n) = \lim_s g^s(j, i, n)$ for all j, i, n. Now we define:

$$\Gamma_k^s(\tau) \leftrightarrow \alpha_{k-1} \subset \tau \;\&\; (\forall n)_{n<\text{length}(\tau)} (\forall h)_{h<k} (f^s(h,n) = 1 \rightarrow \tau(n) \neq y\langle g^s((h)_1,(h)_2,n)\rangle),$$

$$\Delta_k^s(p,q) \leftrightarrow e\langle p\rangle = e\langle q\rangle = (k)_1 \;\&\; x\langle p\rangle = x\langle q\rangle \;\&\; y\langle p\rangle \neq y\langle q\rangle \;\&\; \Gamma_k^s(\sigma\langle p\rangle) \;\&\; \Gamma_k^s(\sigma\langle q\rangle).$$

Clearly, $\Gamma_k^1, \Gamma_k^2, \ldots$, and $\Delta_k^1, \Delta_k^2, \ldots$, are both uniformly recursive in α_{k-1}. Now we observe that, for each $k>1$, there is a number s_k such that if $s \geq s_k$ then $\Phi(n,h) \leftrightarrow f^s(n,h)=1$ and $g((h)_1,(h)_2,n_h) = g^s((h)_1,(h)_2,n_h)$ for all $h<k$. Hence, if $s \geq s_k$, then

$$\Gamma_k^s(\tau) \leftrightarrow \alpha_{k-1} \subset \tau \;\&\; (\forall n)_{n<\text{length}(\tau)} (\forall h)_{h<k}$$

$$(\text{if } n_h \text{ exists and } n_h < \text{length}(\tau) \text{ then } \tau(n_h) \neq y\langle g((h)_1,(h)_2,n_h)\rangle) \leftrightarrow \Gamma(k,\tau),$$

since $\mathbf{F}_{(h)_1}^{C_{(h)2}}(x_h) = y\langle g((h)_1,(h)_2,n_h)\rangle$. It easily follows that if $s \geq s_k$ then

$$\Delta_k^s(p,q) \leftrightarrow \Delta(k,p,q),$$

and this completes the proof of Lemma 2.

It follows immediately from Lemma 2 that

$$(\exists p)(\exists q)\Delta(k,p,q) \leftrightarrow (\exists s)(\exists p)(\exists q)(r)_{r>s}\Delta_k^r(p,q)$$

and

$$(p)(q)\bar{\Delta}(k,p,q) \leftrightarrow (\exists s)(p)(q)(r)_{r>s}\bar{\Delta}_k^r(p,q),$$

so the predicate $(\exists p)(\exists q)\Delta(k,p,q)$ is uniformly recursive in α_{k-1} and $\mathbf{0}^{(1)}$. It easily follows by examining the definition of α_k that $\{\alpha_k\}$ is uniformly of degree $\leq \mathbf{0}^{(1)}$, and so A is of degree $\leq \mathbf{0}^{(1)}$.

(II) *$\mathbf{F}_{(k)_1}^{C_{(k)2}} \neq A$ for each k such that $C_{(k)_2}$ is of degree $<\mathbf{0}^{(1)}$.* If $C_{(k)_2}$ is of degree $<\mathbf{0}^{(1)}$ then n_k exists by Lemma 1. Let m^* be the least m such that length $(\alpha_m) > n_k$. Then the definition of α_{m^*} ensures that $\alpha_{m^*}(n_k) \neq \mathbf{F}_{(k)_1}^{C_{(k)2}}(n_k)$, so that as $\alpha_{m^*} \subset A$ we have $A(n_k) \neq \mathbf{F}_{(k)_1}^{C_{(k)2}}(n_k)$.

(III) *If $\mathbf{F}_{(k)_1}^A(n)$ is defined for all n and $C_{(k)_2}$ is not recursive then $\mathbf{F}_{(k)_1}^A \neq C_{(k)_2}$.* We prove this by showing that if $\mathbf{F}_{(k)_1}^A(n)$ is defined and equal to $C_{(k)_2}(n)$ for all n, then $C_{(k)_2}$ is recursive. We recall that:

$$(\exists p)(\exists q)\Delta(k,p,q)\leftrightarrow(\exists p)((\exists q)\Delta(k,p,q)\,\&\,y\langle p\rangle\neq C_{(k)_2}(x\langle p\rangle)).$$

Therefore let $p^*=\min p((\exists q)\Delta(k,p,q)\&\,y\langle p\rangle\neq C_{(k)_2}(x\langle p\rangle))$. Then $\alpha_k=\sigma\langle p^*\rangle$ so $C_{(k)_2}(x\langle p^*\rangle)=\mathbf{F}^A_{(k)_1}(x\langle p^*\rangle)=\mathbf{F}^{\alpha_k}_{(k)_1}(x\langle p^*\rangle)\neq C^{(x\langle p^*\rangle)}_{(k)_2}$ which is impossible, therefore p^* does not exist. We deduce that $(\forall p)(\forall q)$ $\bar{\Delta}(k,p,q)$ and so for each n:

$$C_{(k)_2}(n)=\mathbf{F}^A_{(k)_1}(n)=y\langle\min p(e\langle p\rangle=(k)_1\,\&\,x\langle p\rangle=n)\rangle.$$

This means that $C_{(k)_2}$ is recursive, and so we have proved (III) and hence the theorem.

It is possible to relativise the proof of this theorem in the usual way to an arbitrary degree $\mathbf{d}$ so as to read: if $\mathbf{d}$ is any degree and $C_0, C_1, \ldots$ is a sequence of sets which is uniformly of degree $\leq\mathbf{d}^{(1)}$ then there is a degree $\mathbf{a}$ such that $\mathbf{d}<\mathbf{a}<\mathbf{d}^{(1)}$ and $\mathbf{a}|\mathbf{c}_e$ for each e such that $\mathbf{d}<\mathbf{c}_e<\mathbf{d}^{(1)}$ (where $\mathbf{c}_e$ is the degree of C_e for each e). In particular this generalisation holds for the following corollary.

COROLLARY. There is a degree $\mathbf{a}$ such that $\mathbf{0}<\mathbf{a}<\mathbf{0}^{(1)}$ and $\mathbf{a}|\mathbf{c}$ for each r.e. degree $\mathbf{c}$ such that $\mathbf{0}<\mathbf{c}<\mathbf{0}^{(1)}$.

PROOF. Let $R_e=\{n|(\exists y)T(e,n,y)\}$; then $R_e(n)=1\leftrightarrow(\exists y)T(e,n,y)$ and $R_e(n)=2\leftrightarrow(\forall y)\bar{T}(e,n,y)$, whence it is easy to see that the sequence of r.e. sets $R_1, R_2, \ldots$ is uniformly of degree $\leq\mathbf{0}^{(1)}$. The rest follows from the theorem.

As we mentioned in the introduction, it is possible to replace $\mathbf{0}^{(1)}$ by an arbitrary nonzero r.e. degree both in the theorem and in the corollary. The proofs are rather different from and more detailed than the proofs above, especially for the corollary. The reason for the extra difficulties with the corollary is that it cannot be assumed for an arbitrary r.e. degree $\mathbf{b}$ that the r.e. sets of degree $\leq\mathbf{b}$ are uniformly of degree $\leq\mathbf{b}$; for example, even the recursive sets are not uniformly recursive.

References

[1] J. R. Shoenfield, On degrees of unsolvability, Ann. of Math. **69** (1959) 644–653.
[2] G. E. Sacks, On the degrees less than $\mathbf{0}^{(1)}$, Ann. of Math. **77** (1963) 211–231.
[3] G. E. Sacks, Degrees of unsolvability, Ann. of Math. Study number 55, Princeton (1963).

[4] G. E. Sacks, The recursively enumerable degrees are dense, Ann. of Math. **80** (1964). 300–312.

[5] J. R. Shoenfield, A theorem on minimal degrees, J. Symbolic Logic **31** (1966) 539–544.

[6] S. C. Kleene, Introduction to metamathematics (Van Nostrand, New York, 1952).

[7] S. C. Kleene and E. L. Post, The upper semi lattice of degrees of recursive unsolvability, Ann. of Math. **59** (1954) 379–407.

[8] C. Spector, On degrees of recursive unsolvability, Ann. of Math. **64** (1956) 581–592.

[9] C. E. M. Yates, On the degrees of index sets, Trans. Amer. Math. Soc. **121** (1966) 309–328.

REGRESSIVE ISOLS

J. C. E. DEKKER
Rutgers, The State University, New Brunswick, N. J., USA

This is an expository paper which deals with the following four questions:

I. What are isols?

II. What are combinatorial functions?

III. What are regressive isols?

IV. What do we know about regressive isols?

The first three questions will be discussed in sections 1, 2, 3 respectively; the last question is considered in sections 4 to 10. One of the reasons why isols are of interest is the following fact: *there exists an intimate connection between isols and certain non-standard models of arithmetic.* This was recently discovered by Nerode [1].

1. What are isols?

We shall consider non-negative integers (*numbers*), collections of numbers (*sets*) and collections of sets (*classes*). We write ε for the set of all numbers, card (Γ) for the cardinality of the collection Γ and c for the cardinality of the continuum. A mapping from a subcollection of ε^n into ε is called a *function*; if f is such a mapping, its domain and its range will be denoted by δf and ρf respectively. We write $\subset$ for inclusion (proper or not) and $\subset_+$ for proper inclusion. The set α is *recursively equivalent* to the set β [written: $\alpha \simeq \beta$], if there is a partial recursive one-to-one function $f(x)$ such that $\alpha \subset \delta f$ and $f(\alpha) = \beta$. The $\simeq$ relation between sets is clearly reflexive, symmetric and transitive. A set α is *isolated*, if it has no infinite r.e. [i.e., recursively enumerable] subset; α is *immune*, if α is infinite and isolated. The sets α and β are *separable* [written: $\alpha \mid \beta$], if there exist disjoint r.e. sets γ and δ such that $\alpha \subset \gamma$ and $\beta \subset \delta$. We also use the following notations:

$$\nu_n = \{x \in \varepsilon \mid x < n\}, \quad \text{for} \quad n \in \varepsilon,$$

$$j(x, y) = x + \tfrac{1}{2}(x + y)(x + y + 1),$$
$$j_3(x, y, z) = j(j(x, y), z),$$
$$Q = \text{the class of all finite sets},$$
$$I = \text{the class of all isolated sets},$$
$$V = \text{the class of all sets}.$$

We recall that j is a primitive recursive function which maps ε^2 one-to-one onto ε. This implies that j_3 is a primitive recursive function which maps ε^3 one-to-one onto ε. The following four propositions are basic.

P1. $Q \subset_+ I \subset_+ V$, where $I - Q$, I, $V - I$ and V all have cardinality c.

P2. A set is isolated if and only if it is not recursively equivalent to a proper subset.

P3. For any two finite sets α and β,
(i) $\alpha \simeq \beta \Leftrightarrow \text{card}(\alpha) = \text{card}(\beta)$,
(ii) $\alpha | \beta \Leftrightarrow \alpha$ and β are disjoint.

P4. Let α and β be recursively equivalent. Then $\alpha \in I \Leftrightarrow \beta \in I$.

We proceed to introduce the notions of a recursive equivalence type [abbreviated: RET] and of an isol.

NOTATION. For $\alpha \in V$,
$$\text{Req}(\alpha) = \{\sigma \in V \mid \sigma \simeq \alpha\}.$$

DEFINITIONS. Req (α) is called the RET of α. An RET is called an *isol*, if it contains at least one isolated set, or equivalently (cf. P4), if it consists entirely of isolated sets. An RET is called *finite* if it consists of finite sets, *infinite* if it consists of infinite sets.

NOTATIONS. $\Omega = \{\text{Req}(\alpha) \mid \alpha \in V\}$,
$\Lambda = \{\text{Req}(\alpha) \mid \alpha \in I\}$.

Ω is therefore the collection of all RETs and Λ the collection of all isols. For every number n, we identify Req (v_n) with the number n. This is justified by P3 (i).

DEFINITIONS. Let $\alpha, \beta \in V$. Then
(i) $\text{Req}(\alpha) + \text{Req}(\beta) = \text{Req}(\alpha \cup \beta)$, provided $\alpha | \beta$,
(ii) $\text{Req}(\alpha) \cdot \text{Req}(\beta) = \text{Req}\, j(\alpha \times \beta)$.

It can be shown that

P5. Every two RETs have separable representatives.

P6. The operations $+$ and $\cdot$ are well-defined, i.e., independent of the choice of the representatives.

P7. Λ is closed under $+$ and $\cdot$.

In view of P3(ii) we see that in the special case that α and β are finite, addition and multiplication are defined in the usual manner. Thus

P8. $[\varepsilon, +, \cdot] \subset_+ [\Lambda, +, \cdot] \subset_+ [\Omega, +, \cdot]$.

Addition and multiplication in Ω are associative and commutative; moreover, multiplication is distributive over addition. We also have for $X, Y \in \Omega$,

$$X + 0 = X, \quad X \cdot 1 = X, \quad X \cdot Y = 0 \Leftrightarrow [X = 0 \text{ or } Y = 0].$$

The following proposition is essential.

P9. For $X \in \Omega$, $\quad X \in \Lambda \Leftrightarrow X \neq X + 1$.

An isol could therefore also be defined as an RET which does not additively absorb the number 1. There is one member of $\Omega - \Lambda$ which is important for our present purposes, namely the RET $R = \text{Req}(\varepsilon)$, i.e., the class of all infinite r.e. sets. With the exception of R we shall in general restrict our attention to the system $[\Lambda, +, \cdot]$.

P10. For $A, B, C, X \in \Lambda$,

(i) $\quad X \neq X + 1,$

(ii) $\quad A + C = B + C \Rightarrow A = B,$

(iii) $\quad X \neq 0 \Rightarrow X \neq 2X,$

(iv) $\quad [AC = BC \,\&\, C \neq 0] \Rightarrow A = B.$

We note that (ii) implies (i), and (iv) implies (iii), but we have retained (i) and (iii) in order to stress the fact that there is no additive or multiplicative absorption in Λ.

Let us write ε^* for the collection of all integers. The properties of Λ mentioned so far are strong enough to imbed Λ in a ring using the same procedure by which ε can be imbedded in the ring ε^* of all integers.

NOTATION. Λ^* is the smallest ring into which Λ can be imbedded.

DEFINITION. Λ^* is called the ring of all *isolic integers*.

DEFINITION. An isol is called *cosimple*, if it is finite or contains at least one immune set with a r.e. complement.

The collection of all cosimple isols forms a denumerable subsystem of $[\Lambda, +, \cdot]$ which is closed under addition and multiplication. The reader is referred to [2] and [25] for a detailed discussion of this subsystem.

A partial ordering relation can be defined in Λ in the following manner.

NOTATIONS. Let $A, B, C, D \in \Lambda$. Then

$$\begin{aligned} A \leq B &\text{ means } && (\exists X)[A + X = B], \\ A < B &\text{ means } && (\exists X)[A + X = B \ \& \ X \neq 0], \\ C \geq D &\text{ means } && D \leq C, \\ C > D &\text{ means } && D < C. \end{aligned}$$

NOTATION. If $A, B \in \Lambda$ and $A \leq B$, then $B - A$ is the unique solution of the equation $A + X = B$.

P11. Let $A, B, C \in \Lambda$. Then

(i) The $\leq$ relation is a partial ordering, but not a total ordering relation.

(ii) $[A \text{ finite} \ \& \ B \text{ infinite}] \Rightarrow A < B$.

(iii) $A < B \Leftrightarrow A + C < B + C$.

(iv) Let $C > 0$. Then $A < B \Rightarrow AC < BC$, but not conversely.

In connection with the first part of P11 we mention the stronger result: *an isol is finite if and only if it is comparable with every isol.* This means that for $X \in \Lambda$,

$$X \in \varepsilon \Leftrightarrow (\forall Y)[X \leq Y \quad \text{or} \quad Y \leq X].$$

Every infinite isol is therefore incomparable with at least one other infinite isol.

For proofs of the propositions P1–P11 we refer the reader to [3].

2. What are combinatorial functions?

We have seen that the operations of addition and multiplication can be extended in a natural manner from ε to Λ. There are, however, many other recursive functions which can be extended from ε to Λ so that many of their basic algebraic properties are preserved, e.g., x^y, $x!$ and $\binom{x}{y}$.

P12. For $X, Y, Z \in \Lambda$,

$$\begin{aligned} &\text{(i)} && X^Y \cdot X^Z = X^{Y+Z}, \ (XY)^Z = X^Z Y^Z, \ (X^Y)^Z = X^{YZ}, \\ &\text{(ii)} && [X^Y = X^Z \ \& \ X \geq 2] \Rightarrow Y = Z, \\ &\text{(iii)} && [Y^X = Z^X \ \& \ X \geq 1] \Rightarrow Y = Z. \end{aligned}$$

P13. For $X \in \Lambda$, $(X+1)! = (X+1) \cdot X!$.

P14. For X, $Y \in \Lambda$ and $Y+1 \leq X$,

$$\binom{X+1}{Y+1} = \binom{X}{Y} + \binom{X}{Y+1}.$$

Combinatorial functions were introduced by Myhill in 1958 in order to describe a uniform procedure for extending certain recursive functions from ε to Λ (cf. [4] and [5]). His procedure was generalized by Nerode in 1961 (cf. [6] and [7]) in order to extend all recursive functions from ε^* to Λ^*.

P15. For every function $f(m)$ from ε into ε (or into ε^*) there exists a unique function c_i from ε into ε^* such that for $m \in \varepsilon$,

$$(\alpha) \qquad f(m) = \sum_{i=0}^{m} c_i \binom{m}{i}.$$

Remark. We have for $i \in \varepsilon$,

$$(\beta) \qquad c_i = [\Delta^i f(m)]_{m=0}, \quad \text{where} \quad \Delta f(m) = f(m+1) - f(m).$$

Definition. A function $f(m)$ from ε into ε is *combinatorial*, if the function c_i from ε into ε^* related to $f(m)$ by (α) [or defined by (β)] assumes no negative values.

P16. For every function $g(m, n)$ from ε^2 into ε (or into ε^*) there exists a unique function c_{ik} from ε^2 into ε^* such that for $m, n \in \varepsilon$,

$$(\gamma) \qquad g(m,n) = \sum_{i=0}^{m} \sum_{k=0}^{n} c_{ik} \binom{m}{i} \binom{n}{k}.$$

Remark. We have for $i, k \in \varepsilon$,

$$(\delta) \qquad \begin{aligned} c_{ik} &= [\Delta_m^i \Delta_n^k g(m,n)]_{m=0,n=0}, \quad \text{where} \\ \Delta_m g(m,n) &= g(m+1,n) - g(m,n), \\ \Delta_n g(m,n) &= g(m,n+1) - g(m,n). \end{aligned}$$

Definition. A function $g(m, n)$ from ε^2 into ε is *combinatorial*, if the function c_{ik} from ε^2 into ε^* related to $g(m, n)$ by (γ) [or defined by (δ)] assumes no negative values.

Propositions P15 and P16 are special cases of a proposition concerning functions $f(X_n)$ from ε^n into ε (or into ε^*). Such a function $f(X_n)$ from ε^n into ε is called *combinatorial*, if the associated function $c_{i(1),\cdots,i(n)}$ from ε^n

into ε^* assumes no negative values. However, for our present purposes the one- and two-variable cases are the most important. Since

$$m+n=\binom{m}{1}+\binom{n}{1}, \quad m\cdot n=\binom{m}{1}\cdot\binom{n}{1},$$

we see that

$$f(m,n)=m+n \Rightarrow c_{10}=c_{01}=1, \quad c_{ik}=0, \quad \text{otherwise},$$
$$f(m,n)=m\cdot n \Rightarrow c_{11}=1, \quad c_{ik}=0, \quad \text{otherwise}.$$

Thus $m+n$ and $m\cdot n$ are combinatorial functions.

We need an effective enumeration of the class Q of all finite sets.

NOTATIONS.

$$\rho_0 \;=\text{the empty set},$$
$$\rho_{x+1}=\begin{cases}(a_1,\ldots,a_k), \text{ where } a_1,\ldots,a_k \text{ are the distinct}\\ \text{numbers such that } x+1=2^{a_1}+\cdots+2^{a_k},\end{cases}$$
$$r(x)\;=\text{card}\,(\rho_x).$$

It is readily seen that $\{\rho_n\}$ is an enumeration without repetitions of Q and that $r(x)$ is a recursive function.

NOTATION. Let $f(m)$ be a recursive, combinatorial function and let c_i be the function associated with $f(m)$ by (α). Then for $\alpha\in V$,

$$(\varepsilon) \qquad \Theta_f(\alpha)=\{j(x,y)\mid \rho_x\subset\alpha \;\&\; y<c_{r(x)}\}.$$

P17. The mapping Θ_f from V into V has the following properties:

(i) $\alpha\in Q$ & card $(\alpha)=m \Rightarrow \Theta_f(\alpha)\in Q$ & card $\Theta_f(\alpha)=f(m)$,

(ii) $\alpha_1\simeq\alpha_2 \Rightarrow \Theta_f(\alpha_1)\simeq\Theta_f(\alpha_2)$,

(iii) $\alpha\in I \Rightarrow \Theta_f(\alpha)\in I$.

We can now define *Myhill's canonical extension* of a recursive combinatorial function $f(m)$ from ε into ε to a function $C_f(X)$ from Ω into Ω.

DEFINITION. Let $f(m)$ be a recursive, combinatorial function and let Θ_f be defined in terms of $f(m)$ by (ε). Then for $X\in\Omega$,

$$C_f(X)=\text{Req}\,\Theta_f(\xi), \quad \text{for} \quad \xi\in X.$$

Note that C_f is a well-defined extension of f which maps Λ into Λ by P17. The two-variable case can be treated in a similar manner.

NOTATION. Let $g(m, n)$ be a recursive, combinatorial function and let c_{ik} be the function associated with $g(m, n)$ by (γ). Then for $\alpha, \beta \in V$,

$$(\zeta) \qquad \Theta_g(\alpha, \beta) = \{j_3(x, y, z) \mid \rho_x \subset \alpha \ \& \ \rho_y \subset \beta \ \& \ z < c_{r(x),r(y)}\}.$$

P18. The mapping $\Theta_g(\alpha, \beta)$ from V^2 into V has the following properties

$$\text{(i)} \qquad \alpha, \beta \in Q \ \& \ \text{card}(\alpha) = m \ \& \ \text{card}(\beta) = n \Rightarrow \Theta_g(\alpha, \beta) \in Q \ \& \ \text{card}\, \Theta_g(\alpha, \beta) = g(m, n),$$

$$\text{(ii)} \qquad [\alpha_1 \simeq \alpha_2 \& \beta_1 \simeq \beta_2] \Rightarrow \Theta_g(\alpha_1, \beta_1) \simeq \Theta_g(\alpha_2, \beta_2),$$

$$\text{(iii)} \qquad \alpha, \beta \in I \Rightarrow \Theta_g(\alpha, \beta) \in I.$$

DEFINITION. Let $g(m, n)$ be a recursive, combinatorial function and let Θ_g be defined in terms of $g(m, n)$ by (ζ). Then for $X, Y \in \Omega$,

$$C_g(X, Y) = \text{Req}\, \Theta_g(\xi, \eta), \quad \text{for} \quad \xi \in X, \eta \in Y.$$

Note again that C_g is a well-defined extension of g which maps Λ^2 into Λ by P18. We shall now define *Nerode's canonical extension* of a recursive function $f(m)$ from ε into ε to a function $D_f(X)$ from Λ into Λ^*. Let $f(m)$ be a recursive function and

$$f(m) = \sum_{i=0}^{m} c_i \binom{m}{i}, \quad \text{for} \quad m \in \varepsilon.$$

Since we are no longer assuming that f be combinatorial, the function c_i may assume negative values. Put

$$(\eta) \qquad f^+(m) = \sum_{c_i \geq 0} c_i \binom{m}{i}, \quad f^-(m) = \sum_{c_i \leq 0} -c_i \binom{m}{i},$$

then

$$f(m) = f^+(m) - f^-(m), \quad \text{for} \quad m \in \varepsilon,$$

where f^+ and f^- are recursive, combinatorial functions.

DEFINITION. Let $f(m)$ be a recursive function and let $f^+(m)$ and $f^-(m)$ be defined by (η). Then for $X \in \Lambda$,

$$D_f(X) = C_{f^+}(X) - C_{f^-}(X).$$

The function $D_f(X)$ need not map Λ into Λ. However,

$$X \in \Lambda \Rightarrow C_{f^+}(X) \in \Lambda \ \& \ C_{f^-}(X) \in \Lambda \Rightarrow D_f(X) \in \Lambda^*.$$

The two-variable case [and in fact the n-variable case] can be handled similarly. While many properties of recursive functions are preserved if we replace these functions by their canonical extensions, this is not true for all their properties. The reader is referred to [4–7] for a detailed discussion of these questions.

3. What are regressive isols?

DEFINITION. A function t_n from ε into ε is *regressive*, if
(i) t_n is one-to-one,
(ii) there exists a partial recursive function $p(x)$ such that

$$\rho t \subset \delta p, \quad p(t_0) = t_0, \quad p(t_{n+1}) = t_n, \quad \text{for} \quad n \in \varepsilon.$$

It is readily seen that every one-to-one recursive function is regressive. The converse is false. For let q_r denote the $(r+1)$st odd prime and let for every function $f(n)$ from ε into ε,

$$f^{\#}(n) = 2^{n+1} \prod_{r=0}^{n} q_r^{f(r)}.$$

Then $f^{\#}(n)$ is a regressive function and the mapping $f \to f^{\#}$, for $f \in \varepsilon^{\varepsilon}$, is one-to-one. Since f can be chosen in c distinct ways there are at least c and hence exactly c regressive functions [in fact, even c strictly increasing regressive functions]. We have therefore proved:

P19. Every one-to-one recursive function is regressive, but there are c regressive functions which are not recursive.

DEFINITION. Let t_n and t_n^* be functions from ε into ε. Then t_n and t_n^* are *recursively equivalent* [written: $t_n \simeq t_n^*$], if they are one-to-one and there exists a partial recursive one-to-one function $p(x)$ such that $\rho t \subset \delta p$ and $p(t_n) = t_n^*$, for $n \in \varepsilon$.

DEFINITION. A set is *regressive* if it is finite on the range of a regressive function.

Regressive functions of n variables and their ranges (regressive sets of order n) have been discussed [8, 9], but only the one-variable case is relevant for what follows. It is readily seen that the $\simeq$ relation between one-to-one functions from ε into ε is reflexive, symmetric and transitive. Every r.e. set is regressive and every regressive set is r.e. or immune. Note that the simplest regressive function is the identity function $i(n)$ and the simplest infinite regressive set the range of $i(n)$, i.e., ε.

P20 [10, p. 83]. Let $\alpha \simeq \beta$. Then the set α is regressive if and only if the set β is regressive.

P21 [10, p. 82]. Let t_n and t_n^* be regressive functions ranging over τ and τ^* respectively. Then

$$\tau \simeq \tau^* \Leftrightarrow t_n \simeq t_n^* .$$

DEFINITION. An isol is *regressive*, if it contains at least one regressive set or equivalently (cf. P20), if it consists entirely of regressive sets.

NOTATION. Λ_R = the collection of all regressive isols.

It can be shown that Λ_R has cardinality c. Regressive isols were introduced in 1962 [cf. 10] in connection with the definition of infinite series of finite isols (i.e., of ordinary numbers). Let a_n be a recursive function and suppose we wish to define

$$(\vartheta) \qquad a_0 + a_1 + a_2 + \dots .$$

It is clear that we can represent each term by a set, for writing $a(n)$ for a_n we have Req $\nu_{a(n)} = a_n$. However, if $a_n > 0$ for at least two values of n, these representatives of (ϑ) are not disjoint. We can obtain disjoint representatives as follows. Let τ be any immune set and t_n any one-to-one function from ε onto τ. We then define

$$\underbrace{a_0 + a_1 + a_2 + \dots}_{t_n} = \text{Req} \sum_{n=0}^{\infty} j(t_n, \nu_{a(n)}) .$$

This infinite sum depends, however, on the function t_n and not only on the isol $T = \text{Req}\, \tau$; this is quite unsatisfactory. If we take for T a regressive isol and for t_n a regressive function, we can eliminate this difficulty.

P22 [10, p. 85]. Let a_n be any function from ε into ε. Let t_n and t_n^* be any two regressive functions which range over sets which belong to some $T \in \Lambda_R - \varepsilon$ [or to the RET R]. Then

$$\sum_{n=0}^{\infty} j(t_n, \nu_{a(n)}) \simeq \sum_{n=0}^{\infty} j(t_n^*, \nu_{a(n)}) .$$

This proposition enables us to give the following

DEFINITION. Let a_n be any function from ε into ε. Let T be any infinite regressive isol or $T=R$. Then

$$(\iota) \qquad \underbrace{a_0 + a_1 + a_2 + \dots}_{T} = \mathrm{Req} \sum_{n=0}^{\infty} j\left(t_n, v_{a(n)}\right),$$

where t_n is any regressive function such that $\rho t \in T$.

NOTATION. The infinite sum defined above will also be denoted by $\sum_T a_n$.

For every infinite sequence $\{a_n\}$ of numbers $\sum_T a_n$ is a function from $\Lambda_R - \varepsilon$ into Λ. Moreover, if a_n is a recursive function $\sum_T a_n$ maps $\Lambda_R - \varepsilon$ into Λ_R [Barback and independently Sansone]. Identities like the following can be proved for $T \in \Lambda_R - \varepsilon$:

$$\underbrace{a + a + a + \dots}_{T} = aT, \quad \text{for} \quad a \in \varepsilon,$$

$$\underbrace{1 + 2 + 3 + \dots}_{T} = \tfrac{1}{2} T(T + 1),$$

$$\underbrace{1^2 + 2^2 + 3^2 + \dots}_{T} = \tfrac{1}{6} T(T + 1)(2T + 1),$$

$$\underbrace{1 + 3 + 5 + \dots}_{T} = T^2,$$

$$\underbrace{1 + r + r^2 + \dots}_{T} = \frac{r^T - 1}{r - 1}, \quad \text{for} \quad r > 1.$$

4. Algebraic properties of Λ_R

P23 [10, p. 92]. $B \leq A \,\&\, A \in \Lambda_R \Rightarrow B \in \Lambda_R$.

P24 [10, p. 94]. If $f(x)$ is a recursive, combinatorial function, then Λ_R is closed under $C_f(X)$.

P25 [11, p. 360]. Λ_R is not closed under addition or multiplication. In fact, there exist two infinite, regressive isols A and B such that neither $A+B$ nor AB belongs to Λ_R.

While Λ_R is not closed under addition or multiplication, one can extend the ordinary min (x, y) function from ε^2 into ε to a function min (X, Y) from Λ_R^2 into Λ_R.

DEFINITION. Let $A, B \in \Lambda_R$. If A and B are finite, min (A, B) has the ordinary meaning. If A is finite and B infinite, min $(A, B)=A$. If A is infinite and B finite, min $(A, B)=B$. If both A and B are infinite,

$$\min(A, B) = \text{Req}\, \rho j\,(a_n, b_n),$$

where a_n and b_n are any two regressive functions such that $\rho a \in A$ and $\rho b \in B$.

The function min (X, Y) as defined above is a well-defined function from Λ_R^2 into Λ_R. We note in passing that the function min (x, y) from ε^2 into ε is not combinatorial. It was first proved by Barback (unpublished) that the function min (X, Y) from Λ_R^2 into Λ_R is identical with the restriction of the function $D_{\min}(X, Y)$ [i.e., the canonical extension of min (x, y)] to the domain Λ_R^2.

P26 [11, pp. 362–364]. The min (X, Y) function from Λ_R^2 into Λ_R is such that for $A, B, C \in \Lambda_R$,

(i) min $(A, A)=A$,
(ii) min (min $(A, B), C$)=min $(A$, min $(B, C))$,
(iii) min (A, B)=min (B, A),
(iv) $A \leq B \Rightarrow$ min $(A, B)=A$, but not conversely,
(v) there exist regressive isols A and B such that min (A, B) assumes neither of the values A and B.

Let $f(x)$ be a recursive function which is not combinatorial. Then $D_f(X)$ may or may not map Λ_R into itself, depending on the nature of the function $f(x)$. The recursive functions of one variable whose canonical extensions map Λ_R into itself can be simply characterized.

DEFINITION. A function $f(x)$ from ε into ε is said to be *increasing*, if

$$x < y \Rightarrow f(x) \leq f(y), \quad \text{for} \quad x, y \in \varepsilon.$$

It is called *eventually increasing*, if for some number n, the function $g(x)$ defined by: $g(x)=f(x+n)$, is an increasing function of x.

P27 (Barback [12, pp. 37, 38]). Let $f(x)$ be a recursive function. Then $D_f(X)$ maps Λ_R into itself if and only if $f(x)$ is eventually increasing.

Since Λ_R is closed under $D_{\min}(X, Y)$, but not under addition or multiplication, the question arises how one can characterize the recursive functions of two variables whose canonical extensions map Λ_R^2 into Λ_R.

DEFINITION. A recursive function $f(x, y)$ is *flat*, if there exists a recursive function $g(x, y)$ such that

(i) $$f(x,y)=\sum_{i=0}^{x}\sum_{k=0}^{y} g(i,k), \quad \text{for} \quad x, y \in \varepsilon,$$

(ii) there exist numbers p and q such that $g(x, y)=0$, whenever $x>p$ or $y>q$.

DEFINITION. A recursive function $f(x, y)$ is *reducible to the one-variable case*, if

(i): there exist eventually increasing recursive functions $f_0(y), \ldots, f_m(y)$ such that

$$f(x,y)=\begin{cases} f_x(y), & \text{for} \quad x \leq m, \\ f_m(y), & \text{for} \quad x \geq m, \end{cases}$$

or (ii): condition (i) holds with the roles of x and y interchanged.

P28 (Hassett [13]). Let $f(x, y)$ be a recursive function. Then $D_f(X, Y)$ maps Λ_R^2 into Λ_R if and only if there is a number n such that

(1) for $i \leq n$, $f(i, y)$ is an eventually increasing function of y and $f(x, i)$ is an eventually increasing function of x, and

(2) $f(x+n, y+n)=m(x, y)+c_1(x, y)-c_2(x, y)$, where c_1 and c_2 are flat recursive functions and $m(x, y)$ is either reducible to the one-variable case or of the form min $(g(x), h(y))$, where $g(x)$ and $h(y)$ are eventually increasing recursive functions.

COROLLARY. The function $D_{\max}(X, Y)$ from Λ^2 into Λ^* does not map Λ_R^2 into Λ_R.

5. The mapping Φ_f

The fact that Λ_R is not closed under addition or multiplication suggests that one should study subcollections of Λ_R which are closed under these operations, for example, the collection $\Lambda_R(T)$ defined in [11, p. 360].

We now discuss a family of mappings from $\Lambda_R - \varepsilon$, into itself which have very natural properties.

DEFINITION. Let $f(n)$ be any strictly increasing, recursive function. Then for $T \in \Lambda_R - \varepsilon$,

$$\Phi_f(T) = \operatorname{Req} \rho t_{f(n)},$$

where t_n is any regressive function such that $\rho t \in T$.

P29. For every strictly increasing, recursive function $f(n)$, Φ_f is a well-defined mapping from $\Lambda_R - \varepsilon$ into itself.

Let $f(x)$ and $g(x)$ be strictly increasing, recursive functions such that ρf and ρg are complementary. Then it is readily seen that

$$\Phi_f(T) + \Phi_g(T) = T, \quad \text{for} \quad T \in \Lambda_R - \varepsilon.$$

This implies that $\Phi_f(T) \leq T$ in case $T - \Phi_f(T)$ is infinite. If $f(x)$ is a strictly increasing, recursive function such that ρf has a finite complement, $\Phi_f(T) \leq T$ is immediate, for in this case $\Phi_f(T) = T - k$ for some number k. We have therefore: *if $f(x)$ is a strictly increasing, recursive function, then*

$$\Phi_f(T) \leq T, \quad \text{for} \quad T \in \Lambda_R - \varepsilon.$$

Sansone [14, p. 64] raised the question whether for $T \in \Lambda_R - \varepsilon$, $U \leq T$ and U infinite, it is true that $U = \Phi_f(T)$, for some strictly increasing, recursive function $f(n)$. This question was answered in the negative.

P30 (Hassett [15]). There exist two infinite regressive isols U and T such that $U \leq T$, while $U \neq \Phi_f(T)$, for every strictly increasing, recursive function f.

Φ_f acts as the left inverse of the mapping C_f, in case $f(n)$ is a strictly increasing, recursive combinatorial function.

P31 (Sansone [16, p. 706]). Let $f(n)$ be any strictly increasing, recursive combinatorial function. Then

$$\Phi_f(C_f(T)) = T, \quad \text{for} \quad T \in \Lambda_R - \varepsilon.$$

The last proposition can be generalized in different ways [17]. We mention one of these generalizations.

NOTATION. Let $f(n)$ be any strictly increasing function from ε into ε. Then

$$\bar{f}(n) = (\mu y)[f(y) \geq n].$$

We note that if $f(n)$ is recursive and strictly increasing, then $\bar{f}(n)$ is recursive and increasing, but not necessarily strictly increasing.

P32 (Sansone [17]). For every strictly increasing, recursive function $f(n)$,

$$\Phi_f(T) = D_{\bar{f}}(T), \quad \text{for} \quad T \in \Lambda_R - \varepsilon.$$

DEFINITION. An isol X is *even*, if $X = 2Y$, for some isol Y. An isol X is *odd*, if $X = 2Z + 1$, for some isol Z.

It is known [3, p. 156] that an isol cannot be both even and odd, though there exist c isols which are neither even nor odd. It immediately follows from [3, p. 148, Lemma B] that there exists an infinite *regressive* isol T which is neither even nor odd; thus for every positive number n, $T+n$ and $T-n$ are also infinite regressive isols which are neither even nor odd.

P33 (Ferguson [18, p. 96]). Let $T \in \Lambda_{\mathrm{R}} - \varepsilon$. Then

$$T \text{ is even } \Leftrightarrow \Phi_{2n}(T) = \Phi_{2n+1}(T),$$
$$T \text{ is odd } \Leftrightarrow \Phi_{2n}(T) = \Phi_{2n+1}(T) + 1.$$

6. Infinite series

The evaluations of infinite series mentioned at the end of section 3 are special cases of a proposition which we now state.

DEFINITION. Let a_n be any function from ε into ε. Then the function $s(n)$ such that

$$s(0) = 0, \quad s(n+1) = \sum_{i=0}^{n} a_i,$$

is the *partial sum* function of a_n.

P34 [10, p. 86]. If the function a_n is recursive and combinatorial, so is its partial sum function $s(n)$.

P35 [10, p. 86]. Let a_n be a recursive combinatorial function and let $s(n)$ be its partial sum function. Then

$$\sum_T a_n = C_s(T), \quad \text{for} \quad T \in \Lambda_{\mathrm{R}} - \varepsilon.$$

This proposition can be generalized.

P36 (Barback). Let a_n be a recursive function and let $s(n)$ be its partial sum function. Then

$$\sum_T a_n = D_s(T), \quad \text{for} \quad T \in \Lambda_{\mathrm{R}} - \varepsilon.$$

Barback and Sansone proved independently that under the hypothesis of P36, $\sum_T a_n$ maps $\Lambda_{\mathrm{R}} - \varepsilon$ into Λ_{R}. In the next proposition we shall abbreviate max (i, k) as $\mathrm{m}(i, k)$.

P37 (Sansone [17]). Let a_n and b_n be recursive functions, k any number and $T \in \Lambda_R - \varepsilon$. Then

(i) $$\sum_T k \cdot a_n = k \cdot \sum_T a_n,$$

(ii) $$\sum_T a_n + \sum_T b_n = \sum_T (a_n + b_n),$$

(iii) $$\sum_T a_n \cdot \sum_T b_n = \sum_T h_n, \quad \text{where}$$

$$h_n = \sum_{\mathrm{m}(i,k)=n} a_i b_k$$
$$= a_0 b_n + \cdots + a_n b_n + a_n b_{n-1} + \cdots + a_n b_0 .$$

It is clear that (i) and (ii) are straight generalizations of the case where T is finite. This is also true for (iii), since, for example

$$\underbrace{(a_0 + \cdots + a_9)}_{10} \cdot \underbrace{(b_0 + \cdots + b_9)}_{10} = \underbrace{h_0 + \cdots + h_9}_{10},$$

where $h_0 = a_0 b_0$,

$$h_1 = a_0 b_1 + a_1 b_1 + a_1 b_0,$$
$$\vdots$$
$$h_9 = a_0 b_9 + \cdots + a_9 b_9 + a_9 b_8 + \cdots + a_9 b_0 .$$

P38. Let a_n be any function from ε into ε and let $f(n)$ and $g(n)$ be any two strictly increasing, recursive functions such that ρf and ρg are complementary. Then we have for $T \in \Lambda_R - \varepsilon$,

$$\sum_T a_n = \sum_{T_1} a_{f(n)} + \sum_{T_2} a_{g(n)},$$

where $T_1 = \Phi_f(T)$ and $T_2 = \Phi_g(T)$.

Definition. A function a_n from ε into ε^* is *recursive*, if there exist recursive functions b_n and c_n from ε into ε such that $a_n = b_n - c_n$, for $n \in \varepsilon$.

P39. Let a_n be a recursive function from ε into ε^* and let b_n, c_n, $\bar{b}_n$, $\bar{c}_n$ be recursive functions from ε into ε such that $a_n = b_n - c_n$ and $a_n = \bar{b}_n - \bar{c}_n$, for $n \in \varepsilon$. Then for $T \in \Lambda_R - \varepsilon$,

$$\sum_T b_n - \sum_T c_n = \sum_T \bar{b}_n - \sum_T \bar{c}_n .$$

The last proposition follows immediately from P37(ii). Note that its conclusion has the form of an equality between two members of Λ^* [which need not belong to Λ]. P39 enables us to give the following

DEFINITION (Sansone). Let a_n be any recursive function from ε into ε^* and let $T \in \Lambda_R - \varepsilon$. Then

$$\sum_T^* a_n = \sum_T b_n - \sum_T c_n,$$

where b_n and c_n are any two recursive functions from ε into ε such that $a_n = b_n - c_n$, for $n \in \varepsilon$.

DEFINITION. $\sum_T^* a_n$ is called the *star sum with respect to T* of the infinite series $a_0 + a_1 + \dots$.

Note that if the function a_n is always ≥ 0, we can take $b_n = a_n$ and $c_n = 0$, for $n \in \varepsilon$; in this case the star sum is identical with the ordinary sum.

P40 (Sansone [17]). Let a_n and b_n be recursive functions from ε into ε^*, k any number and $T \in \Lambda_R - \varepsilon$. Then

$$\text{(i)} \qquad \sum_T^* k \cdot a_n = k \cdot \sum_T^* a_n,$$

$$\text{(ii)} \qquad \sum_T^* a_n + \sum_T^* b_n = \sum_T^* (a_n + b_n),$$

$$\text{(iii)} \qquad \sum_T^* a_n \cdot \sum_T^* b_n = \sum_T^* h_n, \quad \text{where} \quad h_n = \sum_{\mathrm{m}(i,k)=n} a_i b_k .$$

7. An application

The ring Λ^* has zero-divisors. This was first proved by Myhill [3, p. 148]. The second proof is due to Nerode. He showed [6, p. 403] that every polynomial $P(X)$ with coefficients in ε^* which has at least two zeros in ε^* has new zeros in Λ^*. Thus $X^2 - X$ has zeros in Λ^* other than 0 and 1. If X_0 is such a zero, we have $X_0(X_0 - 1) = 0$, while both X_0 and $X_0 - 1$ are different from zero. See also [7, p. 427]. We here present a third proof, because it is shorter than the first two and because it uses the mapping $\Phi_f(T)$ discussed in section 5 and the star sum introduced in section 6. It is due to Sansone [17].

P41. The ring Λ^* has zero-divisors.

PROOF. Let $c_n = (-1)^n$. With every infinite regressive isol T we associate the isolic integer E_T such that

$$E_T = \sum_T^* c_n, \quad \text{i.e.,} \quad E_T = \underbrace{1 - 1 + 1 - 1 + \cdots}_{T}.$$

Using P40 and P38 we see that

$$\begin{aligned} E_T &= \underbrace{1 + 0 + 1 + 0 + \cdots}_{T} + \underbrace{0 + (-1) + 0 + (-1) + \cdots}_{T} \\ &= \underbrace{1 + 1 + 1 + \cdots}_{\Phi_{2n}(T)} - \underbrace{1 + 1 + 1 + \cdots}_{\Phi_{2n+1}(T)} \\ &= \Phi_{2n}(T) - \Phi_{2n+1}(T). \end{aligned}$$

It now follows by P33 that $E_T = 0$ if and only if T is even, while $E_T = 1$ if and only if T is odd. Thus, if T is neither even nor odd, $E_T \neq 0$ and $E_T \neq 1$. Using P40 (iii) we see that

$$E_T^2 = \sum_T^* c_n \cdot \sum_T^* c_n = \sum_T^* h_n, \quad \text{where}$$

$$h_n = \sum_{\mathrm{m}(i,k) = n} c_i c_k = c_n.$$

Thus $E_T^2 = E_T$ for $T \in \Lambda_R - \varepsilon$, and if T is neither even nor odd we have $E_T^2 = E_T$, i.e., $E_T(E_T - 1) = 0$, while both E_T and $E_T - 1$ are different from zero. Hence the ring Λ^* has zero-divisors.

8. Double series

These series were introduced by Barback [19]. Here the summation is performed with respect to an ordered pair of infinite regressive isols. In the following we often write $j_3[x, y, z]$ instead of $j_3(x, y, z)$ and $v(n)$ instead of v_n in order to make some formulas easier to read.

DEFINITION. Let a_{ij} be any function from ε^2 into ε and let $S, T \in \Lambda_R - \varepsilon$. Then

$$\sum_{(S,T)} a_{ij} = \mathrm{Req} \sum_{k=0}^{\infty} \sum_{l=0}^{\infty} j_3[s_k, t_l, v(a_{kl})],$$

where s_k and t_l are any two regressive functions ranging over sets in S and T respectively.

If a_{ij} is a fixed function from ε^2 into ε, $\sum_{(S,T)} a_{ij}$ is a well-defined function from $(\Lambda_R - \varepsilon)^2$ into Λ. We shall, however, restrict our attention to the case where a_{ij} is a recursive function.

NOTATIONS.

$$e_{ij} = 1, \quad \text{for} \quad i,j \in \varepsilon,$$

$$d_{ij} = \begin{cases} 1, & \text{for} \quad i,j \in \varepsilon \quad \text{and} \quad i = j, \\ 0, & \text{for} \quad i,j \in \varepsilon \quad \text{and} \quad i \neq j. \end{cases}$$

P42 (Barback [19, pp. 41, 42]). For $S, T \in \Lambda_R - \varepsilon$,

(i) $$\sum_{(S,T)} e_{ij} = ST,$$

(ii) $$\sum_{(S,T)} d_{ij} = \min(S, T).$$

Combining the first part of P42 with the fact that Λ_R is not closed under multiplication, we see that $\sum_{(S,T)} a_{ij}$ need not belong to Λ_R for a recursive function a_{ij} and $S, T \in \Lambda_R - \varepsilon$.

P43 (Barback [19, pp. 48, 52]). Let a_{ij} and b_{ij} be any two recursive functions, k any number and $S, T \in \Lambda_R - \varepsilon$. Then

(i) $$\sum_{(S,T)} k \cdot a_{ij} = k \cdot \sum_{(S,T)} a_{ij},$$

(ii) $$\sum_{(S,T)} a_{ij} + \sum_{(S,T)} b_{ij} = \sum_{(S,T)} (a_{ij} + b_{ij}),$$

(iii) $$\sum_{(S,T)} a_{ij} \cdot \sum_{(S,T)} b_{ij} = \sum_{(S,T)} h_{uv},$$

where $h_{uv} = \sum a_{kl} b_{pq}$, the summation being performed over all ordered quadruples (k, l, p, q) for which $\mathrm{m}(k, p) = u$ and $\mathrm{m}(l, q) = v$.

P44 (Barback [19, p. 45]). Let a_i and b_j be two recursive functions and let $S, T \in \Lambda_R - \varepsilon$. Then

$$\sum_S a_i \cdot \sum_T b_j = \sum_{(S,T)} a_i b_j.$$

Double series were extensively used by Hassett [13] in his proof of P28.

9. Series with terms of the form $T - k$

These series were introduced by Sansone [14, 20]. If T is a natural number we obviously have

$$\underbrace{1+2+3+\cdots}_{T} = \underbrace{T+(T-1)+(T-2)+\cdots}_{T}, \quad \text{i.e.,}$$

$$(\kappa) \qquad \sum_{T}(n+1) = \sum_{T}(T-n).$$

If T is an infinite regressive isol, we can still define the right side of (κ) in a natural manner so that (κ) holds.

NOTATION. Let t_n be a regressive function and let $a(n)$ be any function from ε into ε. Then

$$\begin{aligned}
\rho t_{n+a(0)} &= (t_{0+a(0)}, t_{1+a(0)}, \ldots),\\
\rho t_{n+a(1)} &= (t_{0+a(1)}, t_{1+a(1)}, \ldots),\\
&\vdots\\
\rho t_{n+a(k)} &= (t_{0+a(k)}, t_{1+a(k)}, \ldots),\\
&\vdots
\end{aligned}$$

Note that if the regressive function t_n ranges over a set in T, then

$$\rho t_{n+a(k)} \in T - a(k), \quad \text{for} \quad k \in \varepsilon.$$

DEFINITION. Let T and U be infinite regressive isols and let a_n be any recursive function. Then

$$\sum_{U}(T-a_n) = \operatorname{Req} \sum_{k=0}^{\infty} j(u_k, \rho t_{n+a(k)}),$$

where u_k and t_n are any two regressive functions ranging over sets in U and T respectively.

It can be shown that for any fixed recursive function a_n, $\sum_U(T-a_n)$ is a well-defined function from $(\Lambda_R-\varepsilon)^2$ into Λ. Observe that the isol T and the recursive function a_n are only determined by the terms of the infinite series $\sum_U(T-a_n)$ up to a finite constant. This does not lead to any ambiguity in the definition of $\sum_U(T-a_n)$. For let $U, T \in \Lambda_R - \varepsilon$ and let a_n be a recursive function. Then it can be shown that

$$\text{(a)} \qquad \sum_{U}[(T+k)-(a_n+k)] = \sum_{U}(T-a_n), \quad \text{for} \quad k \in \varepsilon,$$

$$\text{(b)} \qquad \sum_{U}[(T-k)-(a_n-k)] = \sum_{U}(T-a_n),$$

for every $k \in \varepsilon$ such that $k \leq a_n$, for $n \in \varepsilon$.

The reader will find in [20] several theorems concerning the evaluation of $\sum_U(T-a_n)$, but we shall here restrict our attention to the special case $U=T$.

P45 (Sansone [20]). Let a_n be a recursive function such that $a_n \leq n+1$, for $n\in\varepsilon$. Then for $T\in \Lambda_{\mathrm{R}}-\varepsilon$,

$$\sum_T (T-a_n) = T^2 - \sum_T a_n .$$

NOTATION. Let a_n be an increasing, unbounded function from ε into ε. Then $\tilde{a}_n=(\mu y)\,[a_y>n]$, for $n\in\varepsilon$.

It is clear that if the function a_n is increasing, unbounded and recursive, then $\tilde{a}_n$ is a recursive function.

P46 (Sansone [20]). Let a_n be an increasing, recursive function such that $a_n \geq n$ for $n\in\varepsilon$. Then for $T\in \Lambda_{\mathrm{R}}-\varepsilon$,

$$\sum_T (T-a_n) = \sum_T \tilde{a}_n .$$

We observe that the equality (κ) stated at the beginning of this section can be obtained as a corollary of either P45 or P46. For according to P45,

$$\sum_T (T-n) = T^2 - \sum_T n = T^2 - \tfrac{1}{2}T(T-1)$$
$$= \tfrac{1}{2}T(T+1) = \sum_T (n+1).$$

On the other hand, if $a_n=n$, then $\tilde{a}_n=n+1$, hence we have according to P46,

$$\sum_T (T-n) = \sum_T (n+1).$$

10. Infinite products

These products were introduced independently by Ellentuck [21] and Ferguson [18]. The definition is suggested by the definition of exponentiation for RETs given in [3, Ch. XIV].

DEFINITION. A function $f(x)$ from ε into ε is *finite*, if it is almost identically zero, i.e., if $\{x\in\varepsilon \mid f(x)\neq 0\}$ is a finite set.

NOTATIONS. Let $f(x)$ be a finite function. Then

$$\delta_e f = \{x\in\varepsilon \mid f(x)\neq 0\},$$
$$\rho_e f = \{f(x)\in\varepsilon \mid f(x)\neq 0\}.$$

P47 [3, p. 181]. There exists a recursive function $r_n(x)$ of two variables such that

(i) every function occurring in the sequence $r_0(x), r_1(x), \dots$ is finite and every finite function occurs exactly once in this sequence,

(ii) given any number n, we can effectively find $r_n(x)$, i.e., we can find both the members and the cardinality of $\delta_e r_n$ and for every $x \in \delta_e r_n$ we can compute $r_n(x)$,

(iii) given any finite function $f(x)$ ["given" in the sense described under (ii)] we can effectively find the unique number n such that $f(x) = r_n(x)$,

(iv) $r_0(x)$ is identically zero.

DEFINITION. A finite function *from* α *into* β is a finite function $f(x)$ such that $\delta_e f \subset \alpha$ and $\rho_e f \subset \beta$.

NOTATION. Let $\alpha, \beta \in V$. Then

$$\alpha^\beta = \{n \mid r_n(x) \text{ is a finite function from } \beta \text{ into } \alpha\}.$$

DEFINITION. Let $A, B \in \Lambda$. Then

$$0^B = \begin{cases} 1, & \text{for } B = 0, \\ 0, & \text{for } B > 0. \end{cases}$$

If $A \neq 0$, $A^B = \text{Req } \alpha^\beta$, where $0 \in \alpha \in A$, $\beta \in B$.

It can be shown that the function A^B from Λ^2 into Λ is a well-defined extension of the function a^b from ε^2 into ε and that it has the properties listed in P12 (proofs can be found in [3, Ch. XIV]). Let us now consider the case where a is a positive number and T an infinite regressive isol. Any natural definition of an infinite product of positive numbers with respect to T should be such that

$$\underbrace{a \cdot a \cdot a \cdots}_{T} = a^T, \quad \text{for} \quad a \geq 2.$$

The definition we shall discuss satisfies this requirement.

NOTATION. Let t_n be any regressive function and let $\{a_n\}$ be any infinite sequence of positive numbers. Then

$$\pi(t_n; a_n) = \{n \mid \delta_e r_n \subset \rho t \;\&\; (\forall x)[r_n(t_x) < a_x]\}.$$

DEFINITION. Let $\{a_n\}$ be any sequence of positive numbers and let

$T \in \Lambda_{\mathrm{R}} - \varepsilon$. Then

$$(\lambda) \qquad \prod_T a_n = \mathrm{Req}\, \pi(t_n; a_n),$$

where t_n is any regressive function such that $\rho t \in T$.

It can be shown that for every fixed sequence of positive numbers $\{a_n\}$, $\Pi_T a_n$ is a well-defined function from $\Lambda_{\mathrm{R}} - \varepsilon$ into Λ. We shall sometimes denote the leftside of (λ) by

$$\underbrace{a_0 \cdot a_1 \cdot a_2 \cdot \cdots}_{T} .$$

P48 (Ferguson [18, p. 57]). If a is a number ≥ 2 and $T \in \Lambda_{\mathrm{R}} - \varepsilon$, then

$$\underbrace{a \cdot a \cdot a \cdot \cdots}_{T} = a^T .$$

P49 (Ferguson [18, p. 59]). Let a_n and b_n be recursive functions which assume only positive values. Then for $T \in \Lambda_{\mathrm{R}} - \varepsilon$,

$$\prod_T a_n \cdot \prod_T b_n = \prod_T \; a_n \cdot b_n .$$

Corollary 1. Let a_n be a recursive function which assumes only positive values and let k be a positive number. Then for $T \in \Lambda_{\mathrm{R}} - \varepsilon$,

$$\prod_T a_n^k = \left(\prod_T a_n\right)^k .$$

Corollary 2. Let a_n be a recursive function which assumes only positive values and let c be a positive number. Then for $T \in \Lambda_{\mathrm{R}} - \varepsilon$,

$$\prod_T c \cdot a_n = c^T \cdot \prod_T a_n .$$

P50 (Ferguson [18, p. 65]). Let a_n be a recursive function which assumes only positive values. Let $f(x)$ and $g(x)$ be strictly increasing recursive functions such that ρf and ρg are complementary sets. Then for $T \in \Lambda_{\mathrm{R}} - \varepsilon$,

$$\prod_T a_n = \prod_{T_1} a_{f(n)} \cdot \prod_{T_2} a_{g(n)} ,$$

where $T_1 = \Phi_f(T)$ and $T_2 = \Phi_g(T)$.

Definition. Let a_n be any function from ε into ε. Then the function $\tilde{a}_n$ such that

$$\tilde{a}_0 = 0, \quad \tilde{a}_{n+1} = a_0 \cdot \cdots \cdot a_n, \quad \text{for} \quad n \in \varepsilon ,$$

is the *partial product* function of a_n.

P51 (Ferguson [18, p. 80]). If a_n is a strictly increasing function such that $a_0 > 0$, then its partial product function $\tilde{a}_n$ is strictly increasing and combinatorial.

P52 (Ferguson [18, p. 81]). Let a_n be a strictly increasing recursive function such that $a_0 > 0$. Then for $T \in \Lambda_R - \varepsilon$,

$$\prod_T a_n = C_{\tilde{a}}(T).$$

COROLLARY. Under the hypothesis of P52, $\Pi_T a_n$ is a regressive isol.

Ellentuck [21, p. 51] proved a weaker version of P52. He obtained the same conclusion under the hypothesis that $a_n = 1 + f(n)$, for some recursive combinatorial function $f(n)$. As a simple corollary of P52 we obtain

$$\underbrace{1 \cdot 2 \cdot 3 \cdot \ldots}_{T} = T!, \quad \text{for} \quad T \in \Lambda_R - \varepsilon.$$

We mention four more propositions concerning infinite products.

P53 (Ferguson [18, p. 72]). Let a_n be a recursive function which assumes only positive values. Let the function $\bar{a}_n$ be defined by

$$\bar{a}_0 = a_0, \quad \bar{a}_{n+1} = a_0 \cdot \dots \cdot a_n \cdot (a_{n+1} - 1), \quad \text{for} \quad n \in \varepsilon.$$

Then for $T \in \Lambda_R - \varepsilon$,

$$\prod_T a_n = \sum_T \bar{a}_n.$$

P54 (Ferguson [18, p. 84]). Let a_n be a recursive combinatorial function and let c be a number ≥ 2. Then for $T \in \Lambda_R - \varepsilon$,

$$\prod_T c^{a_n} = c^S, \quad \text{where} \quad S = \sum_T a_n.$$

P55 (Ferguson [18, pp. 90, 91]). Let $p_0, p_1, \ldots$ be the sequence of primes arranged according to size. Let a_n and b_n be two recursive functions. Then for $T \in \Lambda_R - \varepsilon$,

$$(\mu) \qquad \prod_T p_n^{a_n} = \prod_T p_n^{b_n} \Rightarrow (\forall n)[a_n = b_n].$$

REMARK. It can be shown that (μ) even holds for two arbitrary functions a_n and b_n from ε into ε. Let us now keep T fixed. Then one can use $\Pi_T p_n^{a_n}$ to characterize the infinite sequence $a_0, a_1, \ldots$. This yields a generalization of the classical procedure in which finite sequences of numbers are characterized by their Gödel numbers.

P56 (Ferguson [18, p. 92]). Let a_n be a recursive function which assumes only values ≥ 2. Then for $S, T \in \Lambda_R - \varepsilon$,

$$\prod_S a_n = \prod_T a_n \Rightarrow S = T.$$

This concludes our survey. We have not touched upon infinite series of functions of isols [19, Chapters 2, 3] or the results contained in [22], [23] and [24].

References

[1] A. Nerode, Diophantine correct non-standard models in the isols, Ann. of Math. **84** (1966) 421.

[2] L. S. Hay, Topics in recursion theory: I. The co-simple isols, II. Creative sets, Doctoral Thesis, Cornell University, 1965.

[3] J. C. E. Dekker and J. Myhill, Recursive equivalence types, Univ. California Publ. Math. (N.S.) **3** (1960) 67.

[4] J. Myhill, Recursive equivalence types and combinatorial functions (Part 1), Bull. Amer. Math. Soc. **64** (1958) 373.

[5] J. Myhill, Recursive equivalence types and combinatorial functions (Part 2), Proc. Int. Congress in Logic, Methodology and Philosophy of Science, Stanford, 1962, p. 46.

[6] A. Nerode, Extensions to isols, Ann. of Math. **73** (1961) 362.

[7] A. Nerode, Extensions to isolic integers, Ann. of Math. **75** (1962) 419.

[8] J. C. E. Dekker, Closure properties of regressive functions, Proc. London Math. Soc. (Third series) **15** (1965) 226.

[9] W. H. Richter, Regressive sets of order *n*, Math. Z. **86** (1965) 372.

[10] J. C. E. Dekker, Infinite series of isols, Proc. Symposia Pure Math. **5** (1962) 77.

[11] J. C. E. Dekker, The minimum of two regressive isols, Math. Z. **83** (1964) 345.

[12] J. Barback, Recursive functions and regressive isols, Math. Scand. **15** (1964) 29.

[13] M. J. Hassett, Some theorems on regressive isols and isolic groups, Doctoral Thesis, Rutgers, The State University, 1966.

[14] F. J. Sansone, The summation of certain infinite series of isols, Doctoral Thesis, Rutgers, The State University, 1964.

[15] M. J. Hassett, A note on regressive isols, Math. Z. **97** (1967) 425.

[16] F. J. Sansone, Combinatorial functions and regressive isols, Pacific J. Math. **13** (1963) 703.

[17] F. J. Sansone, A mapping of regressive isols, Illinois J. Math. **9** (1965) 726.

[18] D. C. Ferguson, Infinite products of non-negative integers, Doctoral Thesis, Rutgers, The State University, 1963.

[19] J. Barback, Contributions to the theory of isols, Doctoral thesis, Rutgers, The State University, 1964.

[20] F. J. Sansone, The summation of certain series of infinite regressive isols, Proc. Amer. Math. Soc. **16** (1965) 1135.
[21] E. Ellentuck, Infinite products of isols, Pacific J. Math. **14** (1964) 49.
[22] J. Barback, A note on regressive isols, Notre Dame J. Formal Logic **7** (1966) 203.
[23] J. C. E. Dekker, An infinite product of isols, Illinois J. Math. **7** (1963) 668.
[24] F. J. Sansone, On order-preserving extensions to regressive isols, Michigan J. Math. **13** (1966) 353.
[25] L. S. Hay, The co-simple isols, Ann. of Math. **83** (1966) 231.
[26] J. C. E. Dekker, Les fonctions combinatoires et les isols (Gauthier-Villars, Paris, 1966).
[27] J. Barback, Two notes on regressive isols, Pacific J. Math. **16** (1966) 407.

$\mathscr{E}^n$-ARITHMETIC

J. P. CLEAVE
Bristol University, UK

and

H. E. ROSE
Leeds University, UK

In [1] Grzegorczyk defined the class of functions $\mathscr{E}^n$ (for each $n \geq 0$) by the following procedure: The initial functions are

$$U_0(x) = x + 1, \quad U_1(x, y) = x, \quad U_2(x, y) = y \quad \text{and} \quad f_n(x, y),$$

which is given by

$$f_0(x, y) = y + 1, \quad f_1(x, y) = x + y, \quad f_2(x, y) = (x + 1) \cdot (y + 1),$$
$$f_{k+3}(0, y) = f_{k+2}(y + 1, y + 1),$$
$$f_{k+3}(x + 1, y) = f_{k+3}(x, f_{k+3}(x, y)),$$

and the class is closed under the operations of substitution (replacing a free variable by a function, another variable or a constant) and limited recursion given by

$$\phi(0, x_1, \ldots, x_m) = p(x_1, \ldots, x_m)$$
$$\phi(y + 1, x_1, \ldots, x_m) = q(y, x_1, \ldots, x_m, \phi(y, x_1, \ldots, x_m))$$
$$\phi(y, x_1, \ldots, x_m) < r(y, x_1, \ldots, x_m),$$

where the functions p, q and r have already been defined.

It is shown in [1] that $f_n(x, y)$ is monotonic increasing in x, y and n and that $\mathscr{E}^n$ contains $f_i(x, y)$ if $i < n$.

$\mathscr{E}^n$-arithmetic is the free variable system of arithmetic whose formulae are equations between $\mathscr{E}^n$ functions and whose rules of inference are the usual ones for primitive recursive arithmetic, that is substitution of a function for a variable in an equation, transitivity of equality, from the equation $A = B$ follows $F(A) = F(B)$ and the uniqueness rule, i.e. if two functions have the same defining equations then they are equal. (See [2] for further details.)

In this paper we shall discuss some metamathematical properties of $\mathscr{E}^n$-arithmetic. We begin by giving a new characterisation of $\mathscr{E}^n$ functions by showing that the function $f_n(x, y)$ may be replaced by the Ackermann function. Using some of the results of this work we show that the addition of a certain class of limited doubly recursive functions to $\mathscr{E}^n$ does not extend the system and this is sufficient to establish that the valuation function for equations of $\mathscr{E}^n$-arithmetic is an $\mathscr{E}^{n+1}$ function provided $n \geq 2$. Applying this to Rose [3] we get our second main result: If $n \geq 2$ the consistency of $\mathscr{E}^n$-arithmetic is derivable in $\mathscr{E}^{n+1}$-arithmetic. Finally, adapting Kreisel [4], we prove that, again if $n \geq 2$, $\mathscr{E}^n$-arithmetic is categorical with respect to recursive models. These results are analogous to those in Wang [5] where it is shown that the consistency of a certain partial system of elementary number theory (obtained by restricting the number of quantifiers involved) may be established in a similar but slightly more complicated system (that is, by allowing one more quantifier in the proofs); whereas extending $\mathscr{E}^n$-arithmetic to $\mathscr{E}^{n+1}$-arithmetic increases the complexity of the functions involved [1]). We note that all the results quoted or proved in this paper about $\mathscr{E}^n$ functions and $\mathscr{E}^n$-arithmetic are valid for $n \geq 2$; that is, $\mathscr{E}^2$-arithmetic (and not $\mathscr{E}^3$-arithmetic – which by analogy with the $\mathscr{E}^3$ functions, the elementary functions, would be called *Elementary Arithmetic* –) is the smallest system in the Grzegorczyk hierarchy having these properties. So $\mathscr{E}^2$-arithmetic, rather than $\mathscr{E}^3$-arithmetic, is the system which should be singled out by giving a special name to it; we suggest *Primary Arithmetic*.

1. The Ackermann function

The Ackermann function $g_n(x, y)$ is given by

$$g_0(x, y) = y + 1, \quad g_1(x, y) = x + y, \quad g_2(x, y) = x \cdot y,$$
$$g_{n+3}(0, y) = 1, \quad g_{n+3}(x + 1, y) = g_{n+2}(g_{n+3}(x, y), y).$$

(So, in particular, $g_3(x, y) = y^x$.) Let $\mathscr{F}^n$ be the class of functions obtained from $\mathscr{E}^n$ by replacing $f_n(x, y)$ with $g_n(x, y)$.

[1]) In [6] Cleave has given an ω^2 chain of classes of functions E_α computed in such a way that the length of the computation of a function $f(x)$ of $E_{\alpha+1}$ considered as a function of x must itself belong to E_α and it can be shown that $E_{\omega \cdot r} = \mathscr{E}^{r+1}$ $(r = 1, 2, \ldots)$. Hence the position of a function in the Grzegorczyk hierarchy is a measure of its complexity.

THEOREM 1. The class of functions $\mathscr{F}^n$ is identical to the class $\mathscr{E}^n$. (Problem 7 of [1].)

For $n=0$, 1 and 2 the result is obvious. To prove the result for $n>2$ we first show

LEMMA 2. There is a function $G_n(x, y)$ belonging to $\mathscr{E}^n$ with the property $G_n(x, y)>g_n(x, y)$.

Then $g_n(x, y)$ is defined in $\mathscr{E}^n$ by

$$g_n(0, y)=1, \qquad g_n(x+1, y)=g_{n-1}(g_n(x, y), y), \qquad g_n(x, y)<G_n(x, y).$$

Conversely we show

LEMMA 3. There is a function $F_n(x, y)$ belonging to $\mathscr{F}^n$ with the property $F_n(x, y)>f_n(x, y)$.

Then $f_n(x, y)$ is defined in $\mathscr{F}^n$ by the following procedure. Define first $h_n(x, y)$ by

$$h_n(0, y)=y, \quad h_n(x+1, y)=f_{n-1}(h_n(x, y), h_n(x, y)),$$
$$h_n(x, y)<F_n(x, y).$$

(This last inequality follows as $h_n(x, y)<f_n(x, y)$.) Now $f_n(x, y)$ is given by

$$f_n(0, y)=f_{n-1}(y+1, y+1), \quad f_n(x+1, y)=h_n(x+1, f_n(x, y)),$$
$$f_n(x, y)<F_n(x, y).$$

Theorem 1 follows easily from these lemmas.

To prove lemma 2 we show that

$$G_n(x, y)=f_n(x, y)>g_n(x, y).$$

By induction we get first

$$f_n(x+1, y)>f_{n-1}(f_n(x, y), f_n(x, y))$$

and so, as

$$f_n(x, y)>y, \quad f_n(x+1, y)>f_{n-1}(f_n(x, y), y).$$

Using the defining equations of $g_n(x, y)$ the result follows.

Proof of lemma 3. We need first three further lemmas.

LEMMA 4. For $n>1$, $g_n(x\cdot y, z)\geq g_n(x, g_n(y, z))$.

This is derived by induction on n. For $n=2$ both sides of the inequality are equal to $x\cdot y\cdot z$ and for $n=3$ both sides are equal to $z^{x\cdot y}$. Assuming the result for $n=k$ we get immediately, since $g_n(x, y)\geq x\cdot y$ for $n>2$,

$$g_k(g_k(x, y), z)\geq g_k(x, g_k(y, z)). \tag{1}$$

Now, as $g_n(1, y) = y$,

$$g_{k+1}(x \cdot y, z) = g_k((g_k \ldots g_k(z, z), \ldots z), z)$$

where g_k occurs $x \cdot y - 1$ times and

$$g_{k+1}(x, g_{k+1}(y, z)) =$$
$$= g_k[g_k \ldots g_k[g_k(\ldots g_k(z, z) \ldots z), g_k(\ldots g_k(z, z) \ldots z)], \ldots$$
$$g_k(\ldots g_k(z, z) \ldots z)]$$

where g_k occurs $(x-1) \cdot (y-1)$ times, and the result follows using (1).
We define now $g_n^m(x, y)$ by

$$g_n^0(x, y) = y, \quad g_n^{m+1}(x, y) = g_n(x, g_n^m(x, y))$$

and we get from lemma 4

LEMMA 5. (a) $g_n^m(x, y) \leq g_n(x^m, y)$,
(b) $g_n^m(x, y)$ belongs to $\mathscr{F}^n$, if $n > 2$.

LEMMA 6. For $n > 2$, $g_{n+1}(x \cdot (m+1), y) > g_n^m(x, y)$.

PROOF. We have

$$\begin{aligned} g_n^m(x, y) &\leq g_n(x^m, y) \quad \text{by lemma 5} \\ &\leq g_n(g_{n+1}(m, x), y) \quad \text{as } g_{n+1}(m, x) \geq x^m \\ &< g_n(g_{n+1}(m, g_{n+1}(x, y)), g_{n+1}(x, y)) \\ &= g_{n+1}(m + 1, g_{n+1}(x, y)) \\ &\leq g_{n+1}(x \cdot (m + 1), y) \quad \text{by lemma 4.} \end{aligned}$$

To prove lemma 3 we show now that

$$F_n(x, y) = g_n^{2^x}((2^{y+2} + 1)^n, y) > f_n(x, y).$$

We derive this by induction on n and x, the result holds for $n=3$ since

$$f_3(x, y) < y^{2^{2^x}} \quad \text{and} \quad g_3^{2^x}((2^{y+2} + 1)^3, y) > y^{2^{3.y.2^x}}.$$

As inductive hypothesis we assume the result for $n=k$ and for all $x \leq y+2$, then

$$\begin{aligned} g_{k+1}((2^{y+2} + 1)^{k+1}, y) &> g_k^{2y+2}((2^{y+2} + 1)^k, y) && \text{by lemma 6} \\ &> f_k(y + 2, y) && \text{by hypothesis} \\ &> f_k(y + 1, y + 1) && \text{by a simple inductive argument} \\ &= f_{k+1}(0, y). \end{aligned}$$

The lemma follows by noting that, for any t,

$$f_{k+1}(x+1, y) = f_{k+1}(x, f_{k+1}(x, y)),$$

and

$$g_{k+1}^{2x+1}(t, y) = g_{k+1}^{2x}(t, g_{k+1}^{2x}(t, y)).$$

Let $f_n^m(x, y)$ be defined by

$$f_n^0(x, y) = y, \quad f_n^{m+1}(x, y) = f_n(x, f_n^m(x, y)).$$

LEMMA 7. $f_n^m(x, y)$ is a function of $\mathscr{E}^n$.

PROOF. By lemmas 3 and 5 we have

$$f_n(x, y) < g_n((2^{y+2}+1)^{n \cdot 2^x}, y)$$

and so

$$f_n^m(x, y) < g_n^m((2^{y+2}+1)^{n \cdot 2^x}, y)$$

and lemma 7 follows.

We consider now limited double recursion; we use the schema for this as given in [7].

THEOREM 8. If $n>2$ and $p(x, y)$ and $f^m(x, y)$ [where $f^0(x, y)=y$ and $f^{m+1}(x, y)=f(x \dot{-} m, f^m(x, y))$] belong to $\mathscr{E}^n$ then so does $\phi(x, y)$ given by

$$\begin{aligned} &\phi(x, y) = p(x, y) \quad \text{if} \quad x \cdot y = 0 \\ &\phi(x+1, y+1) = \phi(x, \phi(x+1, y)) \\ &\phi(x, y) < f(x, y). \end{aligned}$$

(*Note.* In [8] it is shown that $f^m(x, y)$ may be replaced by $f(x, y)$ if $n>4$.) To calculate $\phi(x, y)$ we look at the sequence

$$\begin{aligned} &\phi(x, y), \phi(x, y \dot{-} 1), \ldots, \phi(x, 0), \\ &\phi(x \dot{-} 1, f(x, y \dot{-} 1)), \phi(x \dot{-} 1, f(x, y \dot{-} 1) \dot{-} 1), \ldots, \phi(x \dot{-} 1, 0), \\ &\phi(x \dot{-} 2, f(x \dot{-} 1, f(x, y \dot{-} 1))), \ldots, \phi(x \dot{-} 2, 0), \\ &\vdots \\ &\phi(x \dot{-} c, f^c(x, y \dot{-} 1)), \ldots, \phi(x \dot{-} c, 0), \\ &\vdots \\ &\phi(0, f^x(x, y \dot{-} 1)), \phi(0, f^x(x, y \dot{-} 1) \dot{-} 1), \ldots, \phi(0, 0). \end{aligned}$$

(We may assume that $f(x, y)$ is monotonic in both x and y, if it is not we can replace it by $\sum_{i=0}^{x} \sum_{j=0}^{y} f(i, j)$.) This sequence has the property that all the information required to calculate any one of its terms occurs in the succeeding terms and the first equation in the schema of the theorem, to calculate $\phi(t, u)$ we require $\phi(t, u \dot{-} 1)$ and $\phi(t \dot{-} 1, \phi(t, u \dot{-} 1))$ but this occurs as one of $\phi(t \dot{-} 1, 0)$, $\phi(t \dot{-} 1, 1), \ldots,$ $\phi(t \dot{-} 1, f(t, u \dot{-} 1))$. We will now give a formal expression $R(x, y, z)$ belonging to $\mathscr{E}^n$ corresponding to the relation $z = \phi(x, y)$ using this sequence.

Let p_a be the a-th prime number, $(m)_a$ the exponent of p_a in the prime factorisation of m, A_n^x and E_n^x the usual bounded universal and existential quantifiers, $g(a) = \sum_{i=0}^{a} (f^{x \dot{-} i}(x, y \dot{-} 1) + 1)$ – so $g(a)$ is the number of terms in the last $a+1$ lines of the sequence above and

$$F(x, y) = (p_{g(x)})^{f(x,y)} (g(x) + 1)$$

then

$$R(x, y, z) \equiv E_m^{F(x,y)} [A_i^{g(0)} [(m)_i = p(0, i)] \mathbin{\&} A_j^x [(m)_{g(j)+1} = p(j+1, 0) \mathbin{\&} A_k^{g(j+1) \dot{-} (g(j)+2)} [(m)_{g(j)+k+2} = (m)_{g(j) \dot{-} 1 + (m)_{g(j)+k+1} + 1}]] \mathbin{\&} z = (m)_{g(x)}].$$

In this expression $\phi(t, u)$ corresponds to $(m)_{g(t \dot{-} 1)+u+1}$. If $n > 2$, $R(x, y, z)$ is a relation of $\mathscr{E}^n$ and now $\phi(x, y)$ is defined in $\mathscr{E}^n$ by

$$\phi(x, y) = \mu_z [z \leq f(x, y) \mathbin{\&} R(x, y, z)].$$

(See [1] for a discussion of the least number operator μ in $\mathscr{E}^n$.)

2. The consistency of $\mathscr{E}^n$-arithmetic

In this section we shall show, for $n \geq 2$ and using the proof procedures of $\mathscr{E}^{n+1}$-arithmetic, that $\mathscr{E}^n$-arithmetic is consistent. (It will follow also that the proof of the consistency of $\mathscr{E}^0$- and $\mathscr{E}^1$-arithmetic can be carried out in $\mathscr{E}^3$-arithmetic.) The proof will mirror exactly that given in [3] where five conditions are laid down on systems of recursive arithmetic R_a and R_b such that the consistency of R_a is derivable in R_b. We will give these conditions now and show that they can be adapted, where necessary, to our case.

CONDITION 1. R_a contains primitive recursive arithmetic.

This condition can be weakened considerably without affecting the proof. All that is really required in this condition is that R_a contains a function $\text{th}(y)$ which is the Gödel number of the y-th theorem of R_a and it is clear from [3] that $\text{th}(y)$ is a function of $\mathscr{E}^2$ (a pairing function is an essential requirement for the definition of $\text{th}(y)$; this is contained in $\mathscr{E}^2$

and no other function used in the definition increases faster). So condition 1 may be replaced by: R_a contains $\mathscr{E}^2$-arithmetic.

CONDITION 2. R_a may be given a finite codification by introducing function variables for functions of some finite number of argument places.

CONDITION 3. The axioms of R_a are finite in number and, upon arbitrary substitution of numerals for numerical variables and functions for function variables, are verifiable.

CONDITION 4. The axiom schemata of R_a are those of primitive recursive arithmetic and rules of substitution for function variables.

Ternary recursive arithmetic [9] is a codification of primitive recursive arithmetic satisfying conditions 2, 3 and 4. In this formulation *functions* of one, two and three argument places are given by recursion and composition (i.e. functions are obtained by substitution of a particular function for a function variable in a schema of composition or recursion) and *terms* are obtained by substitution of functions, in the sense above, for numerical variables. The set of terms in this system is the set of primitive recursive functions; this is established in [9] and the proof uses only the functions and methods of $\mathscr{E}^2$-arithmetic. Hence, for $n \geq 2$, a similar codification of $\mathscr{E}^n$-arithmetic can be given. In fact a simpler formulation can be given in the following manner.

$w(a, b)$ is the pairing function given in [9] as are the functions $m_1 a$ and $m_2 a$ where $m_i w(a_1, a_2) = a_i$, $(i=1, 2)$ and $w(m_1 a, m_2 a) = a$. The functions of this codification are $w(a, b)$, min (a, b) the minimum of a and b and a finite number of one variable functions $\phi_i(a)$ $(i=0, \ldots, k)$, including $m_1 a$, $m_2 a$ and $f_n(m_1 a, m_2 a)$, and the function definition schemata will be

Composition $\mathrm{C}\, fg(a) = f(g(a))$ and

Limited recursion $\mathrm{R}\, fg(a)$ where $\mathrm{R}\, fg(0) = 0$ and

$\mathrm{R}\, fg(a+1) = \min\,(f(a+1), g(\mathrm{R}\, fg(a)))$.

(It is clear that this form of limited recursion is equivalent to the original one $\phi(0)=0$, $\phi(a+1) = g(\phi(a))$, $\phi(a) \leq f(a)$.) Further, a finite set of axioms giving the main properties of the functions $\phi_i(a)$ and the substitution rules for function variables in the schemata of composition and limited recursion above will be added to the rules of procedure. It is clear that this codification will be adequate for $\mathscr{E}^n$-arithmetic if $n \geq 2$ and that conditions 2, 3 and 4 will be satisfied.

CONDITION 5. R_b contains R_a and functions Φ_i which give an enumeration (valuation) of the i-argument place functions of R_a.

A valuation function $v_n(a, b)$ for the single variable functions of $\mathscr{E}^n$-arithmetic as codified above is given by the following definition: $v_n(a, b)$ is the value of the a-th function at argument b.

$$\begin{aligned} v_n(i, b) &= \phi_i(b) \quad \text{for} \quad i = 0, \dots, k \\ v_n(4a + k + 1, b) &= w(v_n(m_1 a, b), v_n(m_2 a, b)) \\ v_n(4a + k + 2, b) &= \min(v_n(m_1 a, b), v_n(m_2 a, b)) \\ v_n(4a + k + 3, b) &= v_n(m_1 a, v_n(m_2 a, b)) \\ v_n(4a + k + 4, 0) &= 0 \\ v_n(4a + k + 4, b + 1) &= v_n(m_2 a, v_n(4a + k + 4, b)) \end{aligned}$$

where

$$v_n(4a + k + 4, b) \le v_n(m_1 a, b).$$

LEMMA 9. If $n \ge 2$ then $v_n(a, b) \le f_{n+1}(a, b)$.

Proof by induction treating each equation above as a separate case.

Case 1. The result can easily be made to hold in this case by arranging the functions $\phi_i(b)$ in increasing order (and inserting a few zeros if necessary).

Case 2. As $w(a, b) = \frac{1}{2}(a+b)\cdot(a+b+1)+b$ we have

$$w(a, b) < (a + b + 1)^2 \le 4w(a, b) + 1. \tag{2}$$

So

$$\begin{aligned} v_n(4a + k + 1, b) &= w(v_n(m_1 a, b), v_n(m_2 a, b)) \\ &\le w(f_{n+1}(m_1 a, b), f_{n+1}(m_2 a, b)) \quad \text{by hypothesis} \\ &< (f_{n+1}(m_1 a, b) + f_{n+1}(m_2 a, b) + 1)^2 \quad \text{by (2)} \\ &\le f_{n+1}((m_1 a + m_2 a + 1)^2, b) \quad \text{using properties of } f_{n+1}(a, b) \\ &\le f_{n+1}(4a + 1, b) \quad \text{by (2)} \\ &< f_{n+1}(4a + k + 1, b). \end{aligned}$$

Case 3. This follows similarly as $\min(a, b) \le w(a, b)$.

Case 4.

$$\begin{aligned} v_n(4a + k + 3, b) &\le f_{n+1}(m_1 a, f_{n+1}(m_2 a, b)) \quad \text{by hypothesis} \\ &\le f_{n+1}(m_1 a + m_2 a + 1, b) \quad \text{using definition of } f_{n+1}(a, b) \\ &\le f_{n+1}(4a + k + 3, b) \quad \text{by (2)}. \end{aligned}$$

Case 5 is immediate.

LEMMA 10. If $n \geq 2$ then $v_n(a, b)$ is an $\mathscr{E}^{n+1}$ function.

Using lemmas 7 and 9 this is established in an exactly similar manner to theorem 8.

(*Note* 1. This is an improvement on the result in [1], but our method will not yield anything when $n=0$ or 1 as $f_2^m(a, b)$ is not an $\mathscr{E}^2$ function. 2. It follows from lemma 10 that for every ϕ in $\mathscr{E}^n$, $n \geq 2$, if for all $m \vdash_n \phi(0^{(m)})$ then $\vdash_{n+1} \phi(x)$.

We have shown now that all the conditions of [3] are satisfied with R_a as $\mathscr{E}^n$-arithmetic and R_b as $\mathscr{E}^{n+1}$-arithmetic, provided $n \geq 2$, and so

THEOREM 11. $\vdash_{n+1}$ Consistency of $\mathscr{E}^n$-arithmetic, where the symbol $\vdash_{n+1}$ refers to derivability in $\mathscr{E}^{n+1}$-arithmetic.

3. Undecidability and categoricity with respect to recursive models

It will be shown in this section that for $n \geq 2$, $\mathscr{E}^n$-arithmetic is undecidable (in fact, creative) and categorical with respect to recursive models, that is, has no recursive non-standard models. Both these results derive from the fact that for $n \geq 2$ certain recursively inseparable sets can be represented in $\mathscr{E}^n$-arithmetic. In preparation for this we examine first certain syntactical properties of $\mathscr{E}^n$-arithmetic.

For any n, let $P(y)$ and $Q(y)$ be formulae (i.e. equations) of $\mathscr{E}^n$-arithmetic each with one free variable y. Let $W_1(y)$ denote $P(y) \& A_z^y[\neg Q(z)]$, $W_2(y)$ denote $Q(y) \& A_z^y[\neg P(z)]$, $X_1(x)$ denote $E_y^x[W_1(y)]$ and $X_2(x)$ denote $E_y^x[W_2(y)]$; these are $\mathscr{E}^n$-formulae. (*Note* $E_n^x[f(n) = g(n)] \equiv \prod_{n=0}^{x}(1 \dot{-} (1 \dot{-} |f(n), g(n)|)) = 0$, so the bounded quantifiers belong to $\mathscr{E}^0$ as $1 \dot{-} |x, y| = (1 \dot{-} (x \dot{-} y)) \dot{-} (y \dot{-} x)$.)

LEMMA 11. $\vdash_n \neg(X_1(z) \& X_2(t))$.

We have

$$\neg(W_1(x) \& W_2(y)) \equiv \neg P(x) \vee E_b^x[Q(b)] \vee \neg Q(y) \vee E_a^y[P(a)]$$

and this formulae holds always because in the disjunction either $P(x)$ or $Q(y)$ occurs with its negation and the result follows.

Now let

$$\phi_1(x, y) \equiv T_1(m_1 x, x, y)$$
$$\phi_2(x, y) \equiv T_1(m_2 x, x, y)$$

where $T_1(e, x, y)$ is the usual Kleene T_1 predicate defined in [10]. Kleene remarks, in chapter XI of [10], that T_1 is a predicate of $\mathscr{E}^3$-arithmetic; in fact it is an $\mathscr{E}^2$ predicate (to show this we have to replace the pairing function using prime numbers by our w function (an $\mathscr{E}^2$ function) and note that, although the iteration of w is not an $\mathscr{E}^2$ function, this does not affect the result as we do not require a Gödel number to be attached to a unbounded number of formulae). It follows that ϕ_1 and ϕ_2 are also $\mathscr{E}^2$-functions. Hence there are formulae $R(x, y)$, $S(x, y)$ in $\mathscr{E}^n$-arithmetic for $n \geq 2$ each with only two free variables such that for all j, k

$$\begin{aligned} &\phi_1(j,k) \leftrightarrow \vdash_n R(0^{(j)}, 0^{(k)}) \\ &\phi_2(j,k) \leftrightarrow \vdash_n S(0^{(j)}, 0^{(k)}). \end{aligned} \tag{3}$$

Now let $R(0^{(j)}, y)$ be the $P(y)$ and $S(0^{(j)}, y)$ be the $Q(y)$ for lemma 11 and let $W_1(0^{(j)}, y)$, $W_2(0^{(j)}, y)$, $X_1(0^{(j)}, y)$ and $X_2(0^{(j)}, y)$ be defined as in that lemma. Then for $n \geq 2$

$$\vdash_n \neg (X_1(0^{(j)}, z) \,\&\, X_2(0^{(j)}, t)). \tag{4}$$

We shall also require

$$\begin{aligned} &\vdash_n X_1(0^{(j)}, t) \,\&\, t < z \rightarrow X_1(0^{(j)}, z) \\ &\vdash_n X_2(0^{(j)}, t) \,\&\, t < z \rightarrow X_2(0^{(j)}, z) \end{aligned} \tag{5}$$

which can easily be shown to hold.

Next let H_1 and H_2 denote the informal counterparts of W_1 and W_2, that is

$$\begin{aligned} &H_1(j,y) \equiv \phi_1(j,y) \,\&\, A_z^y[\neg \phi_2(j,z)] \\ &H_2(j,y) \equiv \phi_2(j,y) \,\&\, A_z^y[\neg \phi_1(j,z)]. \end{aligned}$$

So we have for $n \geq 2$ by (3) and as $X_1(0^{(j)}, 0^{(k)})$ and $X_2(0^{(j)}, 0^{(k)})$ contain no free variables

$$\begin{aligned} &E_x^k[H_1(j,x)] \leftrightarrow \vdash_n X_1(0^{(j)}, 0^{(k)}) \\ &E_x^k[H_2(j,x)] \leftrightarrow \vdash_n X_2(0^{(j)}, 0^{(k)}). \end{aligned} \tag{6}$$

Now it can easily be shown that

LEMMA 12. The sets Π_1 and Π_2, where

$$\Pi_1 = \hat{x}[(Ey)H_1(x,y)] \quad \text{and} \quad \Pi_2 = \hat{x}[(Ey)H_2(x,y)]$$

are effectively inseparable.

We come now to the main results of this section; the properties of $\mathscr{E}^n$-arithmetics we require are (4), (5) and lemma 12. Let $\mathscr{T}_n$ denote the set of (Gödel numbers of) $\mathscr{E}^n$-formulae with at most one free variable which are derivable in $\mathscr{E}^n$-arithmetic. We shall call an $\mathscr{E}^n$-formula $F(x)$ *refutable* if there exsists a provable counterexample, that is, if there exists a number j such that $\vdash_n \neg F(0^{(j)})$. Let $\mathscr{R}_n$ denote the set of Gödel numbers of refutable one variable formulae in $\mathscr{E}^n$-arithmetic.

THEOREM 13. If $n \geq 2$, $\mathscr{T}_n$ and $\mathscr{R}_n$ are effectively inseparable *).

PROOF. Let

$$\Sigma_1 = \hat{\jmath}\left[(Ek)(\vdash_n X_1(0^{(j)}, 0^{(k)}))\right]$$
$$\Sigma_2 = \hat{\jmath}\left[\vdash_n \neg X_1(0^{(j)}, x)\right].$$

We shall show first, in four steps, that Σ_1 and Σ_2 are effectively inseparable.

(a) $\Sigma_1 \cap \Sigma_2 = \emptyset$ (the empty set).

For if $m \in \Sigma_1 \cap \Sigma_2$ then $\vdash_n X_1(0^{(j)}, 0^{(k)})$ for some k since $m \in \Sigma_1$. Further $\vdash_n \neg X_1(0^{(m)}, x)$ since $m \in \Sigma_2$. Hence $\vdash_n \neg X_1(0^{(m)}, 0^{(k)})$ but now, by (6), we have a contradiction and so (a) follows.

(b) $\Sigma_1 \supset \Pi_1$.

Let $m \in \Pi_1$. Then $(Ey)H_1(m, y)$ and so $H_1(m, k)$ for some k, hence $E_x^k[H_1(m, x)]$. So by (6), $\vdash_n X_1(0^{(m)}, 0^{(k)})$ and thus $m \in \Sigma_1$.

(c) $\Sigma_2 \supset \Pi_2$.

Let $m \in \Pi_2$. Then $H_2(m, k)$ for some k and so $E_x^k[H_2(m, x)]$ and (6) gives $\vdash_n X_2(0^{(m)}, 0^{(k)})$. But from (4) we have $\vdash_n X_2(0^{(m)}, 0^{(k)}) \rightarrow \neg X_1(0^{(m)}, x)$, so $\vdash_n \neg X_1(0^{(m)}, x)$ and hence $m \in \Sigma_2$.

(d) It is well known that any two disjoint recursively enumerable supersets of two effectively inseparable sets are themselves effectively inseparable (chapter V of [11]).

From (a)–(d) and lemma 12 we conclude that Σ_1 and Σ_2 are effectively inseparable.

* This result, for full primitive recursive arithmetic, was proved by G. Kreisel in his review of [3] (see Math. Rev. **25**, p. 746).

Now it is clear that there exists a (primitive) recursive function g such that $g(m)$ is the Gödel number of $\neg X_1(0^{(m)}, x)$. So

$$m \in \Sigma_1 \leftrightarrow (Ej)(\vdash_n \neg\neg X_1(0^{(m)}, 0^{(j)}))$$
$$\leftrightarrow g(m) \in \mathscr{R}_n$$

and

$$m \in \Sigma_2 \leftrightarrow \vdash_n \neg X_1(0^{(m)}, x) \leftrightarrow g(m) \in \mathscr{T}_n.$$

Hence (Σ_1, Σ_2) is many-one reducible to $(\mathscr{R}_n, \mathscr{T}_n)$, so again using chapter V of [11], $\mathscr{R}_n$ and $\mathscr{T}_n$ are effectively inseparable as Σ_1 and Σ_2 are.

COROLLARY 14. For $n \geq 2$, $\mathscr{T}_n$ and $\mathscr{R}_n$ are creative.

This follows from theorem 13 using [11] again.

In [4] Kreisel proved that a free variable primitive recursive arithmetic satisfying certain conditions is categorical with respect to recursive models (pp. 173–4); a similar method is given in [12]. We shall not reproduce the proof here but using (4), (5) and lemma 12 it can easily be checked that, for $n \geq 2$, $\mathscr{E}^n$-arithmetic satisfies Kreisel's conditions, hence

THEOREM 15. For $n \geq 2$, $\mathscr{E}^n$-arithmetic is categorical with respect to recursive models.

References

[1] A. Grzegorczyk, Some classes of recursive functions, Rozprawy Matemat. **4** (1953).

[2] R. L. Goodstein, Logic-free formalisations of recursive arithmetic, Math. Scand. **2** (1954).

[3] H. E. Rose, On the consistency and undecidability of recursive arithmetic, Zeitschr. f. Math. Logik **7** (1961).

[4] G. Kreisel, Mathematical significance of consistency proofs, J. Symbolic Logic **23** (1958).

[5] H. Wang, A survey of mathematical logic (North-Holland Publ. Co., Amsterdam, 1962).

[6] J. P. Cleave, A hierarchy of primitive recursive functions, Zeitschr. f. Math. Logik **9** (1963).

[7] A. Lachlan, Multiple recursion, Zeitschr. f. Math. Logik **8** (1962).

[8] P. Axt, Enumeration and the Grzegorczyk hierarchy, Zeitschr. f. Math. Logik **9** (1963).

[9] H. E. Rose, Ternary recursive arithmetic, Math. Scand. **10** (1962).

[10] S. C. Kleene, Introduction to metamathematics (North-Holland Publ. Co., Amsterdam, 1952).

[11] R. Smullyan, Theory of formal systems, Ann. Math. Studies **47** (1961).

[12] A. Mostowski, On recursive models of formalised arithmetic, Bull. Acad. Pol. Sc. **5** (1957).

DISJUNCTION AND EXISTENCE IN FORMALIZED INTUITIONISTIC ANALYSIS[1])

J. R. MOSCHOVAKIS
Occidental College, Los Angeles, Calif., USA

From results of Gödel, Gentzen and Kleene, one would expect any intuitionistic formal system which is an extension of intuitionistic number theory to satisfy the following:

THEOREM. For closed formulas A, B, $\exists x A(x)$:

(i) $\vdash A \vee B$ only if $\vdash A$ or $\vdash B$.

(ii) $\vdash \exists x A(x)$ only if $\vdash A(\boldsymbol{x})$ for some numeral $\boldsymbol{x}$.

In the present paper, we shall establish this theorem for the common portion of intuitionistic and classical analysis, as formalized by Kleene, and for various weaker systems. The method of proof is outlined in §5 and developed in §§6–10; the earlier sections discuss specific axioms for intuitionistic analysis.

1. Introduction

Let **I** be Kleene's intuitionistic formal system of analysis, described in Chapter I of Kleene and Vesley's [2]. We shall assume familiarity with [2] and with Kleene's [3], hereafter referred to as "FIM" and "IM" respectively.

Let **L** (our "least" system) be obtained from **I** by omitting the axiom of choice $^{x}2.1$, the bar theorem $^{x}26.3$, and Brouwer's principle $^{x}27.1$. The systems we consider will be intermediate in strength between **L** and **I**. We shall denote them compactly by ordered triples (α, β, γ), where $\alpha =$

[1]) This paper is a somewhat condensed version of Part I of the author's Ph. D. thesis [1], written under the direction of Professor Stephen C. Kleene, whose encouragement and criticism were alike invaluable. To Professor Richard E. Vesley of Case Institute of Technology, and to Professor Yiannis N. Moschovakis of U.C.L.A., the author is indebted for many helpful conversations.

0, 1, 2, 3 and $\beta = 0, 1, 2$ and $\gamma = 0, 1, 2, 3$ according as $^{\times}2.1$, $^{\times}26.3$, $^{\times}27.1$ are omitted, modified in specified ways or kept intact. For example, (3, 2, 0) is Kleene's basic system **B**, (0, 0, 0) is **L** and (3, 2, 3) is **I**. (In §§ 5–10, we shall also write $(\alpha, \beta, 0)$ for (α, β).)

Occasionally we shall consider classical systems arising from the intuitionistic systems by adding as postulate the classical law of double negation

$$8^{\circ}. \qquad \neg\neg A \supset A \qquad \text{(FIM p. 13, IM p. 82).}$$

These we denote by suffixing°. Thus (3,2,0)° is Kleene's classical system **C**.

2. The axiom of choice $^{\times}2.1$.

2.1. First we consider the axiom of choice $^{\times}2.1$, and two modifications of it, as follows. Here, and in the sequel, the letters are subject to the obvious stipulations (cf. in particular the cited pages of FIM, and in general FIM middle p. 9).

$$^{\times}2.1. \qquad \forall x \exists \alpha A(x, \alpha) \supset \exists \alpha \forall x A(x, \lambda y \alpha(\langle x, y \rangle)) \qquad \text{(FIM p. 14; cf. p. 40).}$$

$$^{\times}2.2. \qquad \forall x \exists y A(x, y) \supset \exists \alpha \forall x A(x, \alpha(x)) \qquad \text{(FIM p. 17).}$$

$$^{\times}2.2!. \qquad \forall x \exists ! y A(x, y) \supset \exists \alpha \forall x A(x, \alpha(x)).$$

By $(\alpha, 0, 0)$ for $\alpha = 1, 2, 3$ we mean the system obtained from **L** by adding the axiom schema $^{\times}2.2!$, $^{\times}2.2$, $^{\times}2.1$ respectively. More generally, (α, β, γ) for $\alpha = 1, 2, 3$ comes from $(0, \beta, \gamma)$ by the addition of $^{\times}2.2!$, $^{\times}2.2$, $^{\times}2.1$ respectively.

By FIM p. 17, each instance of the "axiom of choice for numbers" $^{\times}2.2$ is deducible in **L** from an instance of $^{\times}2.1$; or briefly $^{\times}2.2$ is "derivable" in **L** from $^{\times}2.1$.

Furthermore, the "comprehension axiom" $^{\times}2.2!$ is derivable in **L** from $^{\times}2.2$, since $\exists ! y A(x, y) \vdash \exists y A(x, y)$ whence by $\supset$-introduction $\vdash \exists ! y A(x, y) \supset \exists y A(x, y)$; now use IM *69 and *2 with $^{\times}2.2$.

(In the classical least system $\mathbf{L}^{\circ}$, conversely $^{\times}2.2$ is derivable from $^{\times}2.2!$: use successively $^{\times}149$, $^{\times}174b$, $^{\times}2.2!$, and $\exists \alpha \forall x [A(x, \alpha(x)) \& \forall z (z < \alpha(x) \supset \neg A(x, z))] \supset \exists \alpha \forall x A(x, \alpha(x))$, with *17a, *2, *69. Using *149a instead of *149, this derivation works in **L** when $\forall x \forall y (A(x, y) \vee \neg A(x, y))$

is provable or is taken as an additional assumption formula.)

Thus

$$(0,0,0) \subseteq (1,0,0) \subseteq (2,0,0) \subseteq (3,0,0),$$

or more generally

$$(0,\beta,\gamma) \subseteq (1,\beta,\gamma) \subseteq (2,\beta,\gamma) \subseteq (3,\beta,\gamma),$$

where "$\subseteq$" expresses "is a (proper or improper) subsystem of" or "is not stronger than".

(For the classical systems:

$$(0,\beta,\gamma)^\circ \subseteq (1,\beta,\gamma)^\circ = (2,\beta,\gamma)^\circ \subseteq (3,\beta,\gamma)^\circ.)$$

2.2. Define $\exists!\alpha A(\alpha)$ like $\exists!xA(x)$ (IM p. 199), except using equality for functors (FIM 4.5), then another natural modification of ^{x}2.1 is the following, which however is interderivable in **L** with ^{x}2.2! ([1] pp. 4–6).

^{x}2.1!. $\qquad \forall x \exists! \alpha A(x,\alpha) \supset \exists \alpha \forall x A(x, \lambda y \alpha(\langle x, y \rangle)).$

2.3. We now ask whether the inclusions $\subseteq$ in 2.1 can be strengthened to proper inclusions $\subset$.

A simple classical interpretation (below) shows that $(0,0,0) \subset (1,0,0)$ (and $(0,0,0)^\circ \subset (1,0,0)^\circ$), i.e. that ^{x}2.2!, and hence ^{x}2.2 and ^{x}2.1, are not derivable in **L** (or $\mathbf{L}^\circ$). The stronger result that $(0,\beta,0) \subset (1,\beta,0)$ for arbitrary β, i.e. that ^{x}2.2! is not even derivable in **L** from ^{x}26.3, will be established in 7.4.

To see that ^{x}2.2! is not derivable in $\mathbf{L}^\circ$, we interpret $\mathbf{L}^\circ$ classically as follows. Let N be the class of all natural numbers, let P be the class of all primitive recursive functions (whose arguments are numbers and one-place number-theoretic functions and whose values are numbers), let the formal number variables be interpreted as ranging over N, and let the formal function variables range over the subclass of P consisting of the one-place number-theoretic primitive recursive functions. Let the formal symbols $\supset$, &, $\vee$, $\neg$, $\forall$, $\exists$, $=$, λ have their usual classical interpretations, and let the function symbols $f_0,\ldots,f_p$ have their intended interpretations (FIM p. 9) as specified members of P. Then every closed theorem of $\mathbf{L}^\circ$ is true under this interpretation. By IM Theorem 32, the Ackermann function $\xi(x)$ (which is general, but not primitive, recursive; cf. [4] and IM p. 271) is numeralwise representable (IM p. 200, FIM p. 21) in formal intuitionistic number theory **N** and hence in $\mathbf{L}^\circ$. Say A(x, y) is a formula, containing free only the distinct number variables x and y, which numeralwise represents $\xi(x)$ in $\mathbf{L}^\circ$. Then $\forall x \exists ! y A(x, y)$ is true (since in $\mathbf{L}^\circ \vdash \exists ! y A(\boldsymbol{x}, y)$ for each numeral $\boldsymbol{x}$) but $\exists \alpha \forall x A(x, \alpha(x))$ is false under the interpretation. So $\forall x \exists ! y A(x, y) \supset \exists \alpha \forall x A(x, \alpha(x))$ is a closed instance of $^{\times}2.2!$ which is false under the interpretation, and hence unprovable in $\mathbf{L}^\circ$ (a fortiori in **L**).

2.4. The questions whether $(1, \beta, \gamma) \subset (2, \beta, \gamma)$ and whether $(2, \beta, \gamma) \subset (3, \beta, \gamma)$, i.e. whether $^{\times}2.2!$ is weaker than $^{\times}2.2$ and whether $^{\times}2.2$ is weaker than $^{\times}2.1$, are mostly unsolved [1]).

For $\gamma = 0$ or 1 (cf. 4.1) and β arbitrary, we do not know the answer to either question. Nor do we know whether $(2, \beta, 2) \subset (3, \beta, 2)$, where $\gamma = 2$ indicates that $^{\times}27.1$ has been replaced by $^{\times}27.2$ (FIM p. 73); however, $(1, \beta, 2) = (2, \beta, 2)$ ([1] p. 13). Vesley has shown, moreover, that $(2, \beta, 3) = (3, \beta, 3)$ (see FIM p. 88); by a trivial modification, his proof actually gives $(1, \beta, 3) = (3, \beta, 3)$. So for $\gamma = 3$ both questions are answered in the negative.

---

[1]) However, Kleene observed in FIM (Remark 5.4 and p. 88) that replacing $^{\times}2.1$ by $^{\times}2.2$ would sacrifice (in subsystems without $^{\times}27.1$) at most $^{\times}2.1$ itself and its immediate corollaries *2.1a and *25.8. (Other direct uses of $^{\times}2.1$ in the semi-final draft of FIM were eliminated in 1963 by the present writer and Kleene, cf. FIM p. 88.)

Now we further remark that in FIM Chapter I the replacement of $^{\times}2.2$ by $^{\times}2.2!$ will cause at most the sacrifice (in addition to $^{\times}2.1$, *2.1a, *25.8) of $^{\times}2.2$ itself and its immediate corollaries *2.2a and *25.7 (see [1] p. 15). However, there have been two setbacks to the program of formally bypassing $^{\times}2.1$ and $^{\times}2.2$. In [10], Kleene has an application of $^{\times}2.1$ which we do not know how to bypass ([10] Remark 3). And we see no way to avoid Vesley's double use of $^{\times}2.2$ in the proof of *R1.10 in FIM Chapter III (cf. [1] p. 16).

Our attempts to show that $^{\times}2.2!$, as an axiom replacing $^{\times}2.2$ or $^{\times}2.1$, is intuitionistically adequate are motivated by philosophical considerations (cf. IM top p. 510 and FIM p. 72). By a statement of the form $(a)(Eb)A(a,b)$, an intuitionist presumably means that he has an algorithm $\mathfrak{a}$ which, from any a, will at some point in its operation first produce a b for which $A(a,b)$. Thus he could equally well assert $(a)(E!b)\{(b$ is the first output of the algorithm $\mathfrak{a}$ for the input $b) \& A(a,b)\}$. So the adequacy of a formal system for intuitionistic analysis should not depend significantly on which of $^{\times}2.2!$, $^{\times}2.2$ is postulated; and similarly with $^{\times}2.1!$ (which is interderivable in **L** with $^{\times}2.2!$, by 2.2 above), $^{\times}2.1$.

3. The bar theorem ^{x}26.3

3.1. Now we consider the bar theorem ^{x}26.3 and the fan theorem ^{x}26.6, as follows.

$$^{x}26.3c. \quad \forall\alpha\exists!xR(\bar{\alpha}(x))\,\&\,\forall a[\mathrm{Seq}(a)\,\&\,R(a)\supset A(a)]\,\& \\ \forall a[\mathrm{Seq}(a)\,\&\,\forall sA(a*2^{s+1})\supset A(a)]\supset A(1) \qquad \text{(FIM p. 55).}$$

$$^{x}26.6c. \quad \forall\alpha_{B(\alpha)}\exists!xR(\bar{\alpha}(x))\supset\exists z\forall\alpha_{B(\alpha)}\exists x_{x\leq z}R(\bar{\alpha}(x)) \qquad \text{(FIM p. 61),}$$

where $B(\alpha)$ is $\forall t\alpha(t)\leq\beta(\bar{\alpha}(t))$. The system (α, β, γ) for $\beta=1, 2$ is obtained from $(\alpha, 0, \gamma)$ by adding as a postulate ^{x}26.6c or ^{x}26.3c respectively.

For systems with $\alpha=0$, it may not be immaterial which of the four forms ^{x}26.3a–^{x}26.3d of ^{x}26.3 is used, since the derivation in FIM (p.55) of ^{x}26.3a from ^{x}26.3b uses ^{x}2.2! via Lemma 5.5 (a). For definiteness, we specify ^{x}26.3c, from which the other three forms are derivable in **L** (FIM p. 55). Similarly with ^{x}26.6 (cf. FIM p. 61).

By FIM pp. 61–62 with [1] pp. 14–15, ^{x}26.6c is derivable from ^{x}26.3c in (1, 0, 0). Using a realizability interpretation, Kleene has shown (FIM Corollary 9.9 p. 113) that ^{x}26.6c is not provable in (3, 0, 3). Thus $(0, 0, \gamma)\subset(0, 2, \gamma)$,

$$(\alpha, 0, \gamma)\subset(\alpha, 1, \gamma),$$

and for $\alpha>0$ also

$$(\alpha, 1, \gamma)\subseteq(\alpha, 2, \gamma).$$

(As mentioned in 2.3, we shall show in § 7 that ^{x}2.2! is not provable in any of the systems $(0, \beta, 0)$.)

3.2. In contrast to the intuitionistic relationships just detailed, ^{x}2.2 (or ^{x}2.2! or ^{x}2.1!) is interderivable with *26.1° (or ^{x}26.3) in the classical system **L**°. The derivation of *26.1 from ^{x}2.2 is in FIM (p. 53). Howard, in Section II of Kreisel and Howard's [5], gives a classical derivation of the axiom of choice (for numbers) from the bar theorem; in [1] (p. 19), his proof is adapted to the present formalism.

4. Brouwer's principle ^{x}27.1

4.1. Here we consider Brouwer's principle for a function (^{x}27.1) and for a number (^{x}27.2), with a modification (^{x}27.2!) of the latter.

$^{\times}$27.1. $\forall\alpha\exists\beta A(\alpha,\beta)\supset\exists\tau\forall\alpha\{\forall t\exists!y\tau(2^{t+1}*\bar{\alpha}(y))>0\ \&$
$\forall\beta[\forall t\exists y\tau(2^{t+1}*\bar{\alpha}(y))=\beta(t)+1\supset A(\alpha,\beta)]\}$ (FIM p. 73).

$^{\times}$27.2. $\forall\alpha\exists bA(\alpha,b)\supset\exists\tau\forall\alpha\exists y\{\tau(\bar{\alpha}(y))>0\ \&$
$\forall x[\tau(\bar{\alpha}(x))>0\supset y=x]\ \&\ A(\alpha,\tau(\bar{\alpha}(y))\dot{-}1)\}$ (FIM p. 73).

$^{\times}$27.2!. $\forall\alpha\exists!bA(\alpha,b)\supset\exists\tau\forall\alpha\exists y\{\tau(\bar{\alpha}(y))>0\ \&$
$\forall x[\tau(\bar{\alpha}(x))>0\supset y=x]\ \&\ A(\alpha,\tau(\bar{\alpha}(y))\dot{-}1)\}$.

The system (α, β, γ) for $\gamma=1, 2, 3$ is obtained from (α, β, 0) by adding as a postulate $^{\times}$27.2!, $^{\times}$27.2, $^{\times}$27.1 respectively.

By the classical falsity of $^{\times}$27.2! (cf. FIM p. 70), the obvious $\exists!bA(\alpha, b) \vdash \exists bA(\alpha, b)$, and the proof (using $^{\times}$2.2!) of *27.2 in FIM (p. 73):

$$(\alpha,\beta,0)\subset(\alpha,\beta,1)\subseteq(\alpha,\beta,2),$$

and for $\alpha>0$ also

$$(\alpha,\beta,2)\subseteq(\alpha,\beta,3).$$

We do not know whether $(0, \beta, 2)\subseteq(0, \beta, 3)$, or whether any of the above inclusions $\subseteq$ can be strengthened to proper inclusions.

4.2. Another modification of $^{\times}$27.1 which comes to mind is the following.

$^{\times}$27.1!. $\forall\alpha\exists!\beta A(\alpha,\beta)\supset$
$\exists\tau\forall\alpha\{\forall t\exists!y\tau(2^{t+1}*\bar{\alpha}(y))>0\ \&$
$\forall\beta[\forall t\exists y\tau(2^{t+1}*\bar{\alpha}(y))=\beta(t)+1\supset A(\alpha,\beta)]\}$
(*27.1′ of FIM p. 89).

Only for $\alpha=0$ could this give rise to other systems, since $^{\times}$27.1! is interderivable in (1, 0, 0) with $^{\times}$27.2!. The derivation of $^{\times}$27.2! from $^{\times}$27.1! in (1, 0, 0) is like the proof of *27.2 in FIM (p. 73). Kleene in FIM (p. 89) announced that $^{\times}$27.1! is derivable from $^{\times}$27.2; his derivation, rewritten by him to proceed in **L** from $^{\times}$27.2!, appears on pp. 22–24 of [1].

5. The notion Γ|E

5.1. We now extend part of the theory of Kleene's [6] to twelve systems intermediate in strength between our least system **L** (i.e. **B** minus $^{\times}$2.1 and $^{\times}$26.3) and Kleene's basic system **B** (FIM p. 8). These are the systems

(α, β, 0) of §§ 1–4. Here we denote them simply as (α, β), where $\alpha=0, 1, 2, 3$ and $\beta=0, 1, 2$ depending upon which of the following are added as postulates to **L** (cf. 2.1, 3.1).

α		β	
0	–	0	–
1	$^{\times}$2.2!	1	$^{\times}$26.6c
2	$^{\times}$2.2	2	$^{\times}$26.3c
3	$^{\times}$2.1		

5.2. As aids in this investigation we shall employ some semi-formal systems (which have $2^{\aleph_0}$ symbols), as well as formal systems of the usual sort (with only $\aleph_0$ symbols).

We now adapt the notion $\Gamma|\mathrm{E}$ of [6] 2.2 to any formal or semi-formal system **S** which has the symbolism and formation rules of FIM § 3 with the possible addition of some new one-place number-theoretic function symbols (even $2^{\aleph_0}$ of them) and which has as postulates at least those of **L**. For all our present applications of the notion $\Gamma|\mathrm{E}$, we shall take Γ to be empty; however, we lose nothing by giving the definitions and preliminary results for the general case. We accordingly define $\Gamma|\mathrm{E}$, for Γ,E closed formulas of **S**, by induction on the number of logical symbols in E, as follows. Here "$\Gamma|\vdash \mathrm{E}$" abbreviates "$\Gamma|\mathrm{E}$ and $\Gamma\vdash \mathrm{E}$," where "$\Gamma\vdash \mathrm{E}$" means that E is deducible from Γ in **S**.

1. If P is a prime formula, $\Gamma|\mathrm{P}$ if $\Gamma\vdash \mathrm{P}$.
2. $\Gamma|\mathrm{A}\&\mathrm{B}$, if $\Gamma|\mathrm{A}$ and $\Gamma|\mathrm{B}$.
3. $\Gamma|\mathrm{A}\vee\mathrm{B}$, if $\Gamma|\vdash \mathrm{A}$ or $\Gamma|\vdash \mathrm{B}$.
4. $\Gamma|\mathrm{A}\supset\mathrm{B}$, if, if $\Gamma|\vdash\mathrm{A}$, then $\Gamma|\mathrm{B}$.
5. $\Gamma|\neg\mathrm{A}$, if, if $\Gamma|\vdash\mathrm{A}$, then $\Gamma\vdash 1=0$.
6. $\Gamma|\forall\mathrm{x}\mathrm{A}(\mathrm{x})$, if, for each numeral $\boldsymbol{x}$, $\Gamma|\mathrm{A}(\boldsymbol{x})$.
7. $\Gamma|\exists\mathrm{x}\mathrm{A}(\mathrm{x})$, if, for some numeral $\boldsymbol{x}$, $\Gamma|\vdash\mathrm{A}(\boldsymbol{x})$.
8. $\Gamma|\forall\alpha\mathrm{A}(\alpha)$, if, for each closed functor u, $\Gamma|\mathrm{A}(\mathrm{u})$.
9. $\Gamma|\exists\alpha\mathrm{A}(\alpha)$, if, for some closed functor u, $\Gamma|\vdash\mathrm{A}(\mathrm{u})$.

5.3. Exactly as before ([6] 2.3): *If* $\Gamma\vdash 1=0$, *then, for each closed formula* E, $\Gamma|\mathrm{E}$.

5.4. For each system **S** we consider, we shall establish the following properties (A) and (B).

(A) *For each new function symbol* τ *of* **S**, $\vdash \mathrm{a}=\mathrm{b}\supset\tau(\mathrm{a})=\tau(\mathrm{b})$.

From (A), it will follow that *the replacement theorem* FIM *Lemma* 4.2 *extends from* **L** (for which the proof in FIM p. 16 establishes it) *to* **S**.

(B) *For each new function symbol* τ *of* **S**, *to each x there is exactly one y such that* $\vdash \tau(\boldsymbol{x})=\boldsymbol{y}$.

Putting $\tau(x)=y$ for each of the pairs x, y in (B), we thence obtain a function τ which we interpret $\boldsymbol{\tau}$ as expressing.

Supplementing FIM Lemma 3.3 (p. 12) by these meanings of the new function symbols, FIM *Lemma* 5.2 *on numeralwise representation extends from* **L** *to* **S** (using (B) to treat the new case, at the end of II on p. 22, that s is $\boldsymbol{\tau}(\mathrm{t})$).

Thence also FIM 5.4, on numeralwise expressing, extends from **L** to **S**.

5.5. Having (A) and (B) (with their consequences just noted), we can get as before [6] 2.4: *Let* x *be a number variable,* E(x) *be a formula containing only* x *free,* t *be a closed term, and* ***t*** *be the numeral expressed by* t *under the intended interpretation. Then* (a) $\Gamma \vdash \mathrm{E}(\mathrm{t})$ *if and only if* $\Gamma \vdash \mathrm{E}(\boldsymbol{t})$, *and* (b)$\Gamma \,|\, \mathrm{E}(\mathrm{t})$ *if and only if* $\Gamma \,|\, \mathrm{E}(\boldsymbol{t})$.

Similarly (but not involving (B)): *Let* α *be a function variable,* E(α) *a formula containing only* α *free and* u *and* v *closed functors, and suppose that* $\Gamma \vdash \mathrm{u}=\mathrm{v}$. *Then* (a) $\Gamma \vdash \mathrm{E}(\mathrm{u})$ if and only if $\Gamma \vdash \mathrm{E}(\mathrm{v})$, *and* (b) $\Gamma \,|\, \mathrm{E}(\mathrm{u})$ *if and only if* $\Gamma \,|\, \mathrm{E}(\mathrm{v})$.

5.6. Adapting [6] 2.5: When $\mathrm{E}(\mathrm{y}_1, \ldots, \mathrm{y}_m, \alpha_1, \ldots, \alpha_n)$ is a formula containing free only the distinct variables shown, we say $\Gamma \,||\, \mathrm{E}(\mathrm{y}_1, \ldots, \mathrm{y}_m, \alpha_1, \ldots, \alpha_n)$ if, for each m-tuple of numerals $\boldsymbol{y}_1, \ldots, \boldsymbol{y}_m$ and each n-tuple of closed functors $\mathrm{u}_1, \ldots, \mathrm{u}_n$, $\Gamma \,|\, \mathrm{E}(\boldsymbol{y}_1, \ldots, \boldsymbol{y}_m, \mathrm{u}_1, \ldots, \mathrm{u}_n)$.

5.7. We shall now establish, for certain systems **S**, the version of [6] Theorem 1 for Γ empty:

(*) $\qquad$ *If* $\vdash \mathrm{E}$, *then* $\| \mathrm{E}$.

To prove (*) (when we can), we follow the general plan used in [6] 2.6.

Since now Γ is empty, and since for each system **S** to be considered it will follow from FIM Corollary 9.5 that **S** *is consistent* (i.e., not $\vdash 1=0$), we can dispense with the argument by cases ($\Gamma \vdash 1=0$ or not $\Gamma \vdash 1=0$). The proof then proceeds by induction on the length of a given deduction of E, with cases corresponding to the postulates of **S**.

In writing out each of the cases for an axiom or axiom schema, to simplify the notation we suppose (as in [6] 2.6) that an arbitrary substitution of numerals for the free number variables and (now) of closed functors for the free function variables has already been made.

All the twenty-four postulates of number theory are handled essentially as before. The four postulates 9F–12F (FIM p. 13) of the predicate calculus for function variables are treated essentially as 9N–12N (called 9–12 in [6]) for number variables; but for 10F, 11F the argument is simpler than for 10N, 11N, e.g.:

AXIOM SCHEMA 11F: $A(u) \supset \exists\alpha A(\alpha)$ where (by the substitution already performed) u is a closed functor. Suppose $|\vdash A(u)$. Then immediately by Clause 9, $|\exists\alpha A(\alpha)$.

The remaining postulates of **L** are $^{x}0.1$ and the recursion equations in Group D, which give rise only to prime axioms, and $^{x}1.1$. By Clause 1 in 5.2, $|P$ for each provable closed prime formula; this takes care of $^{x}0.1$ and Group D. We could treat $^{x}1.1$ like Axiom 14, but the following method (also applicable to 8^{I}, 14–17) is more direct.

$^{x}1.1$: $\boldsymbol{a}=\boldsymbol{b} \supset u(\boldsymbol{a})=u(\boldsymbol{b})$. By substitution in the axiom $^{x}1.1$: (a)$\vdash \boldsymbol{a}=\boldsymbol{b} \supset u(\boldsymbol{a})=u(\boldsymbol{b})$. Assume (b)$|\vdash \boldsymbol{a}=\boldsymbol{b}$; we must infer $|u(\boldsymbol{a})=u(\boldsymbol{b})$. By (b), $\vdash \boldsymbol{a}=\boldsymbol{b}$, which with (a) gives $\vdash u(\boldsymbol{a})=u(\boldsymbol{b})$, and hence (by Clause 1, since $u(\boldsymbol{a})=u(\boldsymbol{b})$ is prime) $|u(\boldsymbol{a})=u(\boldsymbol{b})$.

We have now established that (*) *holds for the system* **L** $(=(0,0))$, for which (A) and (B) are vacuously true, as the **S** of the definitions and theorem.

In 6.2 we shall show that (*) holds also for the system (0, 1). We do not know whether (*) holds for the system (0, 2) (cf. however end 7.3). In 5.9 we shall show that (*) does not hold for the systems (α, β) with $\alpha \neq 0$.

5.8. Adapting [6] pp. 11, 14, (*) has the following consequences (for any **S** for which it holds), where the formulas $A \vee B$, $\exists x A(x)$, and $\exists\alpha A(\alpha)$ are assumed closed:

(i) $\vdash A \vee B$ only if $\vdash A$ or $\vdash B$.

(ii) $\vdash \exists x A(x)$ only if $\vdash A(\boldsymbol{x})$ for some numeral $\boldsymbol{x}$.

(iii) $\vdash \exists\alpha A(\alpha)$ only if $\vdash A(u)$ for some closed functor u.

For intuitionistic propositional calculus, (i) was first obtained by Gödel [7]. For intuitionistic predicate calculus, (i) is due to Gentzen [8]. For intuitionistic number theory, (i) and (ii) were first established by Kleene ([9], or IM Theorem 62 (b) p. 504).

5.9. Now we show: (iii) *(and therefore (*) itself) does not hold for any of the nine systems* (α, β) *with* $\alpha \neq 0$.

It is straightforward to show that the Ackermann function $\xi(x)$ is provably recursive in intuitionistic number theory and hence in **L**; thus we may choose the formula $A(x, y)$ of 2.3 so that in **L**, *a fortiori* in $\mathbf{S}=(\alpha, \beta)$: **(a)** $A(x, y)$ numeralwise represents Ackermann's function $\xi(x)$, and **(b)** $\vdash \forall x \exists ! y A(x, y)$.

Furthermore, for $\alpha \neq 0$, in (α, β) we have $^{x}2.2!$ (as an axiom for $\alpha=1$, by 2.1 for $\alpha=2$, and thence by FIM p. 17 for $\alpha=3$). So **(c)** $\vdash \forall x \exists ! y A(x, y) \supset \exists \alpha \forall x A(x, \alpha(x))$. By (b) and (c): **(d)** $\vdash \exists \alpha \forall x A(x, \alpha(x))$. This formula is closed. So if (*) held in (α, β), we would have **(e)** $| \exists \alpha \forall x A(x, \alpha(x))$, so there would be a closed functor u such that **(f)** $\vdash \forall x A(x, u(x))$. By FIM Lemmas 3.3 and 5.2: **(g)** $u(x)=y$ numeralwise represents a primitive recursive function $\varphi(x)$. Since $\xi(x)$ is not primitive recursive, there is a number q such that **(h)** $y_1=\xi(q) \neq \varphi(q)=y_2$. By (g): **(i)** $\vdash u(\boldsymbol{q})=\boldsymbol{y}_2$. By (a): **(j)** $\vdash A(\boldsymbol{q}, \boldsymbol{y}_1)$. By $\forall$-eliminations from (f) and (b): **(k)** $\vdash A(\boldsymbol{q}, u(\boldsymbol{q}))$, **(ɫ)** $\vdash \exists ! y A(\boldsymbol{q}, y)$. From (j), (k), (ɫ) by *172, $\vdash \boldsymbol{y}_1=u(\boldsymbol{q})$, whence with (i): **(m)** $\vdash \boldsymbol{y}_1=\boldsymbol{y}_2$, which with (h) contradicts the consistency of (α, β) as a subsystem of **B** and thence of **I** (FIM Corollary 9.5).

5.10. We now describe a device which will enable us (in §§ 7–10) to get the consequences (i) and (ii) of (*) for each of the systems (α, β) with $\alpha \neq 0$. Let $\mathbf{S}_0$ be such a system (α, β). By adding new function symbols and axioms to $\mathbf{S}_0$, we shall obtain a system **S** which satisfies not only (A) and (B) of 5.4, but also:

(C) **S** *is an inessential extension of* $\mathbf{S}_0$; i.e. if Γ, E are formulas of $\mathbf{S}_0$ such that $\Gamma \vdash E$ in **S**, then $\Gamma \vdash E$ in $\mathbf{S}_0$.

We shall then establish (*) (and thence (i), (ii) and (iii)) for **S**.

Now suppose $A \vee B$ is a closed formula (of $\mathbf{S}_0$) such that $\vdash A \vee B$ in $\mathbf{S}_0$. Then (a fortiori) $\vdash A \vee B$ in **S**, so by (i) for **S**: $\vdash A$ in **S** (so, by (C) with Γ empty, $\vdash A$ in $\mathbf{S}_0$) or $\vdash B$ in **S** (so, by (C), $\vdash B$ in $\mathbf{S}_0$). So (i) holds for $\mathbf{S}_0$.

Similarly, suppose $\exists x A(x)$ is a closed formula (of $\mathbf{S}_0$) such that $\vdash \exists x A(x)$ in $\mathbf{S}_0$, whence $\vdash \exists x A(x)$ in **S**. Then by (ii) for **S**: for some numeral $\boldsymbol{x}$, $\vdash A(\boldsymbol{x})$ in **S** (so, by (C), $\vdash A(\boldsymbol{x})$ in $\mathbf{S}_0$). So (ii) also holds for $\mathbf{S}_0$.

Fortunately, the reasoning for (i) and (ii) fails for (iii). For, if $\exists \alpha A(\alpha)$ is a closed formula (of $\mathbf{S}_0$) such that $\vdash \exists \alpha A(\alpha)$ in $\mathbf{S}_0$, so $\vdash \exists \alpha A(\alpha)$ in **S**, we can conclude (by (iii) for **S**) only that there is a closed functor u of **S** (but not, in general of $\mathbf{S}_0$) such that $\vdash A(u)$ in **S**.

When $\mathbf{S}_0=(0, 2)$, however, we shall be able to establish for our extension **S** the further property:

(D) *If* Γ, $\mathrm{A}(\alpha)$ *are formulas of* $\mathbf{S}_0$ *and* u *is a functor of* $\mathbf{S}$ *such that* $\Gamma \vdash \mathrm{A}(\mathrm{u})$ *in* $\mathbf{S}$, *there is a functor* v *of* $\mathbf{S}_0$, *containing free only those variables which occur free in* u, *such that* $\Gamma \vdash \mathrm{A}(\mathrm{v})$ *in* $\mathbf{S}_0$.

For Γ empty and u closed, this, together with (iii) for $\mathbf{S}$, will imply that (iii) holds for $\mathbf{S}_0$. We remark that, in general, (D) implies (C).

Summarizing: *If* (*) *holds for an extension* $\mathbf{S}$ *of a system* $\mathbf{S}_0$, *where* (A), (B) *and* (C) *are satisfied by* $\mathbf{S}$, *then* (i) *and* (ii) *hold for* $\mathbf{S}_0$. *If also* (D) *is satisfied by* $\mathbf{S}$, *then* (iii) *holds for* $\mathbf{S}_0$.

6. The systems $(\alpha,1)$ (complete treatment for $\alpha=0$, partial treatment for $\alpha=1, 2, 3$).

6.1. We now remark that for each of the (formal and semi-formal) systems $\mathbf{S}$ to be considered: $\mathbf{S}$ is a subsystem of a classical system, and hence *the intended interpretation E of each closed theorem* E *of* $\mathbf{S}$ *is classically true.*

6.2. Using 6.1, we can give a direct treatment of the case (in the proof of (*), begun in 5.7) that E is an instance of the fan theorem ^{x}26.6c. It will follow immediately, using 5.7, that (*) *holds for the system* (0, 1) as the $\mathbf{S}$ of the definitions and theorem. Furthermore, for the case $\mathbf{S}_0$ is $(\alpha, 1)$ with $\alpha \neq 0$, this treatment will apply to any extension $\mathbf{S}$ of $\mathbf{S}_0$ satisfying (A) and (B) in 5.4, under the proviso in 6.1.

AXIOM SCHEMA ^{x}26.6c: $\forall \alpha_{\mathrm{B}(\alpha)} \exists ! \mathrm{x} \mathrm{R}(\bar{\alpha}(\mathrm{x})) \supset \exists \mathrm{z} \forall \alpha_{\mathrm{B}(\alpha)} \exists \mathrm{x}_{\mathrm{x} \leq \mathrm{z}} \mathrm{R}(\bar{\alpha}(\mathrm{x}))$, where $\mathrm{B}(\alpha)$ is $\forall \mathrm{t}(\alpha(\mathrm{t}) \leq \mathrm{v}(\bar{\alpha}(\mathrm{t})))$. Assume **(a)** $| \vdash \forall \alpha_{\mathrm{B}(\alpha)} \exists ! \mathrm{x} \mathrm{R}(\bar{\alpha}(\mathrm{x}))$; we must infer $| \exists \mathrm{z} \forall \alpha_{\mathrm{B}(\alpha)} \exists \mathrm{x}_{\mathrm{x} \leq \mathrm{z}} \mathrm{R}(\bar{\alpha}(\mathrm{x}))$, that is, we must find a numeral $\boldsymbol{z}$ such that $| \vdash \forall \alpha_{\mathrm{B}(\alpha)} \exists \mathrm{x}_{\mathrm{x} \leq \boldsymbol{z}} \mathrm{R}(\bar{\alpha}(\mathrm{x}))$.

I. We first establish the hypothesis $(\alpha)_{B(\alpha)}(E!x)\ \{| \vdash \mathrm{R}(\boldsymbol{a})$ for $a=\bar{\alpha}(x)\}$ for an application of the informal analogue of ^{x}26.6c, where $B(\alpha)$ is $(t)(\alpha(t) \leq \beta(\bar{\alpha}(t)))$, where $\beta(y)$ is the informal function expressed by $\mathrm{v}(\mathrm{y})$ under the intended interpretation (5.4). Thus let α be any one-place number-theoretic function such that **(b)** $B(\alpha)$. Toward (h), assume **(c)** $a=\bar{\alpha}(x)$, and let u abbreviate $\lambda \mathrm{t}((\boldsymbol{a})_{\mathrm{t}} \dot{-} 1)$. Then **(d)** $\vdash \boldsymbol{a}=\bar{\mathrm{u}}(\boldsymbol{x})$. By cases from $\mathrm{t}<\boldsymbol{x} \vee \mathrm{t} \geq \boldsymbol{x}$, using (b), (c), (d) with *166 for the case $\mathrm{t}<\boldsymbol{x}$: **(e)** $\vdash \mathrm{B}(\mathrm{u})$, whence also **(f)** $| \mathrm{B}(\mathrm{u})$ (by 5.2 with $\forall$-elimination from (e)). From (a), $| \mathrm{B}(\mathrm{u}) \supset \exists ! \mathrm{x} \mathrm{R}(\bar{\mathrm{u}}(\mathrm{x}))$, whence using (e) and (f), $| \exists ! \mathrm{x} \mathrm{R}(\bar{\mathrm{u}}(\mathrm{x}))$. So there is a numeral $\boldsymbol{y}$ such that **(g)** $| \vdash \mathrm{R}(\bar{\mathrm{u}}(\boldsymbol{y})) \& \forall \mathrm{x}[\mathrm{R}(\bar{\mathrm{u}}(\mathrm{x})) \supset \boldsymbol{y}=\mathrm{x}]$. Thence by cases ($y=x$ or $y \neq x$) using (c), (d) with 5.5, 6.1: $\{[| \vdash \mathrm{R}(\boldsymbol{a})$ and $R(\bar{\alpha}(x))]$

or $[|\vdash\neg \mathrm{R}(\boldsymbol{a})$ and not $R(\bar{\alpha}(x))]\}$, where $R(a)$ is the classical interpretation of R(a). Thence (discharging (c)): **(h)** $(x)\{[|\vdash \mathrm{R}(\boldsymbol{a})$ for $a=\bar{\alpha}(x)]$ if and only if $R(\bar{\alpha}(x))\}$. Further, from (a) with 6.1, $(\alpha)_{B(\alpha)}(E!x)R(\bar{\alpha}(x))$, whence with (b): **(i)** $(E!x)R(\bar{\alpha}(x))$. By (h) and (i) (discharging (b)): **(j)** $(\alpha)_{B(\alpha)}(E!x)\{|\vdash \mathrm{R}(\boldsymbol{a})$ for $a=\bar{\alpha}(x)\}$.

II. From (j), by the informal analogue of $^{\times}$26.6c, there is a z such that: **(k)** $(\alpha)_{B(\alpha)}(Ex)_{x\leq z}\{|\vdash \mathrm{R}(\boldsymbol{a})$ for $a=\bar{\alpha}(x)\}$. We shall show $|\vdash\forall\alpha_{\mathrm{B}(\alpha)}\exists \mathrm{x}_{\mathrm{x}\leq \boldsymbol{z}}\mathrm{R}(\bar{\alpha}(\mathrm{x}))$. Toward (l), assume u is a closed functor such that $|\vdash \mathrm{B}(\mathrm{u})$, and let $\alpha(x)$ be the function expressed by u(x). Then $B(\alpha)$, so by (k) there is an $x\leq z$ (so $\Vdash \boldsymbol{x}\leq \boldsymbol{z}$) such that $\Vdash \mathrm{R}(\boldsymbol{a})$ where $a=\bar{\alpha}(x)$ (so $\vdash \boldsymbol{a}=\bar{\mathrm{u}}(\boldsymbol{x})$). Using 5.5, $|\vdash \boldsymbol{x}\leq \boldsymbol{z}\,\&\,\mathrm{R}(\bar{\mathrm{u}}(\boldsymbol{x}))$. We have established:
(l) $|\forall\alpha_{\mathrm{B}(\alpha)}\exists \mathrm{x}_{\mathrm{x}\leq \boldsymbol{z}}\mathrm{R}(\bar{\alpha}(\mathrm{x}))$. Now, toward (s), assume: **(m)** B(α), i.e. $\forall \mathrm{t}(\alpha(\mathrm{t})\leq \mathrm{v}(\bar{\alpha}(\mathrm{t})))$. Evidently, there is a k (depending on β and z) such that $\vdash\forall\alpha_{\mathrm{B}(\alpha)}\bar{\alpha}(\boldsymbol{z})\leq \boldsymbol{k}$, whence (by $\forall$-elimination with (m)): **(n)** $\bar{\alpha}(\boldsymbol{z})\leq \boldsymbol{k}$. Now let C(y) abbreviate the numeralwise decidable formula Seq(y) & lh(y) $=\boldsymbol{z}$ & $\forall \mathrm{t}_{\mathrm{t}<\boldsymbol{z}}(\mathrm{y})_{\mathrm{t}}\dot{-}1\leq \mathrm{v}(\prod_{\mathrm{i}<\mathrm{t}}\mathrm{p}_{\mathrm{i}}^{(\mathrm{y})_{\mathrm{i}}})$. Let $\boldsymbol{y}$ be an arbitrary numeral such that $y\leq k$, and toward (p) assume: **(o)** $\bar{\alpha}(\boldsymbol{z})=\boldsymbol{y}$.

CASE 1: $\vdash \mathrm{C}(\boldsymbol{y})$. Then $B(\lambda t(y)_t\dot{-}1)$, so by (k) there is an $x\leq z$ such that $\Vdash \mathrm{R}(\boldsymbol{a})$ where $a=\overline{(\lambda t(y)_t\dot{-}1)}(x)$. Thus $\vdash \boldsymbol{x}\leq \boldsymbol{z}\,\&\,\mathrm{R}(\overline{(\lambda \mathrm{t}(\boldsymbol{y})_{\mathrm{t}}\dot{-}1)}(\boldsymbol{x}))$, whence using (o): $\boldsymbol{x}\leq \boldsymbol{z}\,\&\,\mathrm{R}(\bar{\alpha}(\boldsymbol{x}))$. By $\exists$-introd., $\exists \mathrm{x}_{\mathrm{x}\leq \boldsymbol{z}}\mathrm{R}(\bar{\alpha}(\mathrm{x}))$.

CASE 2: $\vdash\neg \mathrm{C}(\boldsymbol{y})$. Then since $\mathrm{C}(\boldsymbol{y})$ by (o) with (m), trivially $\exists \mathrm{x}_{\mathrm{x}\leq \boldsymbol{z}}\mathrm{R}(\bar{\alpha}(\mathrm{x}))$. Discharging (o), for arbitrary $y\leq k$: **(p)** $\bar{\alpha}(\boldsymbol{z})=\boldsymbol{y}\supset\exists \mathrm{x}_{\mathrm{x}\leq \boldsymbol{z}}\mathrm{R}(\bar{\alpha}(\mathrm{x}))$. Thence by *166a, **(q)** $\forall \mathrm{y}_{\mathrm{y}\leq \boldsymbol{k}}(\bar{\alpha}(\boldsymbol{z})=\mathrm{y}\supset\exists \mathrm{x}_{\mathrm{x}\leq \boldsymbol{z}}\mathrm{R}(\bar{\alpha}(\mathrm{x})))$. By (q) and (n) (with $\bar{\alpha}(\boldsymbol{z})=\bar{\alpha}(\boldsymbol{z})$): **(r)** $\exists \mathrm{x}_{\mathrm{x}\leq \boldsymbol{z}}\mathrm{R}(\bar{\alpha}(\mathrm{x}))$. By $\supset$-introd. (discharging (m)) and $\forall$-introd.: **(s)** $\vdash\forall\alpha_{\mathrm{B}(\alpha)}\exists \mathrm{x}_{\mathrm{x}\leq \boldsymbol{z}}\mathrm{R}(\bar{\alpha}(\mathrm{x}))$. This, with (l), completes the proof.

7. The systems (α,2) (complete treatment for $\alpha=0$, partial treatment for $\alpha=1, 2, 3$)

7.1. Now we turn to the problem of constructing suitable supersystems to carry out the program outlined in 5.10, beginning with the systems (α, β) for $\beta=2$.

We adopt the convention (here and for §§8–10) that, when we are considering simultaneously two or more systems, named by **S** with or without subscripts or superscripts, "$\vdash$", "$|$", "$\|$" with or without the same sub- or superscripts will refer to the corresponding systems (unless otherwise stated). For example here, where we will have $\mathbf{S}_0$ and **S**,

"$\vdash_0$ E" means "$\vdash$E in $\mathbf{S}_0$"; and "$\vdash$E" means "$\vdash$E in $\mathbf{S}$" (unless "in $\mathbf{S}_0$" is indicated).

When $\mathbf{S}_0$ is $(\alpha, 2)$, to form the (semi-formal) system $\mathbf{S}$ we first adjoin to the symbolism of $\mathbf{S}_0$ (FIM 3.3) new function symbols in one-to-one correspondence with the one-place (classical) number-theoretic functions; call the set of these function symbols J^0 ($\bar{\bar{\mathrm{J}}}^0 = 2^{\aleph_0}$). Each one $\boldsymbol{\tau}^0$ of these new function symbols is interpreted as expressing the corresponding function τ^0. To the postulates of $\mathbf{S}_0$ we adjoin the following sets of axioms:
G^0: $\boldsymbol{\tau}^0(\boldsymbol{x}) = \boldsymbol{y}$ for each $\boldsymbol{\tau}^0 \in \mathrm{J}^0$, whenever $y = \tau^0(x)$;
K^0: $\mathrm{a} = \mathrm{b} \supset \boldsymbol{\tau}^0(\mathrm{a}) = \boldsymbol{\tau}^0(\mathrm{b})$ for each $\boldsymbol{\tau}^0 \in \mathrm{J}^0$.
($\bar{\bar{\mathrm{G}}}^0 = 2^{\aleph_0} \cdot \aleph_0 \cdot \aleph_0 = 2^{\aleph_0}$; $\bar{\bar{\mathrm{K}}}^0 = 2^{\aleph_0}$. In the notation of IM p. 266, G^0 is the $2^{\aleph_0}$-union of the sets of equations $\mathrm{E}_{\tau 0}^{\boldsymbol{\tau}^0}$ for $\boldsymbol{\tau}^0 \in \mathrm{J}^0$.)

We call the result of this adjunction to $\mathbf{S}_0$ of symbols and axioms $\mathbf{S}^0$. When $\alpha = 0$, $\mathbf{S}$ is simply $\mathbf{S}^0$. When $\alpha \neq 0$, there will be further adjunctions, which will be described in the succeeding sections.

7.2. Next we verify that, so far as the adjunctions to form $\mathbf{S}^0$ are concerned, (A)–(C) and (with $\mathbf{S}^0$ as the $\mathbf{S}$) (D) are satisfied.

For (A) and (B) this is immediate. (Here we picked the interpretation of the symbol $\boldsymbol{\tau}^0$ first, and then put in the formulas $\boldsymbol{\tau}^0(\boldsymbol{x}) = \boldsymbol{y}$ to satisfy (B) and its sequel in 5.4.)

We now establish (D) (for $\mathbf{S}^0$ as the $\mathbf{S}$), and thence (C). Let Γ, $\mathrm{A}(\alpha)$ be formulas of $\mathbf{S}_0$, let u be a functor of $\mathbf{S}^0$, and suppose we are given a deduction of $\mathrm{A}(\mathrm{u})$ from Γ in $\mathbf{S}^0$. Let $\boldsymbol{\tau}_0^0, \ldots, \boldsymbol{\tau}_q^0$ be the distinct elements of J^0 which occur in the deduction, and suppose $\boldsymbol{\tau}_0^0(\boldsymbol{x}_{00}) = \boldsymbol{y}_{00}, \ldots, \boldsymbol{\tau}_0^0(\boldsymbol{x}_{0k_0}) = \boldsymbol{y}_{0k_0}, \ldots, \boldsymbol{\tau}_r^0(\boldsymbol{x}_{r0}) = \boldsymbol{y}_{r0}, \ldots, \boldsymbol{\tau}_r^0(\boldsymbol{x}_{rk_r}) = \boldsymbol{y}_{rk_r}$ are the distinct axioms from G^0 used in the deduction. For each $i = 0, \ldots, r$, let $x_i = \max(x_{i0}, \ldots, x_{ik_i}) + 1$ and let $a_i = \bar{\tau}_i^0(x_i)$. Now, in the given deduction, for $i = 0, \ldots, r$ substitute $\lambda\mathrm{t}(\boldsymbol{a}_i)_{\mathrm{t}} \dot{-} 1$ for $\boldsymbol{\tau}_i^0$, and for $i = r+1, \ldots, q$ substitute $\lambda\mathrm{t}0$ for $\boldsymbol{\tau}_i^0$. Thereby each axiom from G^0 or K^0 used in the given deduction is transformed into a theorem of $\mathbf{S}_0$. (For $\boldsymbol{\tau}_i^0(\boldsymbol{x}_{ij}) = \boldsymbol{y}_{ij}$: $x_{ij} < x_i$ so $(a_i)_{x_{ij}} \dot{-} 1 = \tau_i^0(x_{ij}) = y_{ij}$, so by FIM Lemma 5.2 and $^{\times}0.1$, $\vdash(\lambda\mathrm{t}(\boldsymbol{a}_i)_{\mathrm{t}} \dot{-} 1)(\boldsymbol{x}_{ij}) = \boldsymbol{y}_{ij}$ in $\mathbf{S}_0$. Each axiom from K^0 is changed into an equality axiom for a functor of $\mathbf{S}_0$, which is provable using $^{\times}1.1$.) Each axiom of $\mathbf{S}^0$ not from G^0 or K^0 becomes an axiom of $\mathbf{S}_0$ by the same schema, and each application of a rule of inference for $\mathbf{S}^0$ becomes an instance of the same rule for $\mathbf{S}_0$. Thus $\Gamma \vdash_0 \mathrm{A}(\mathrm{v})$, where v is the functor of $\mathbf{S}_0$ resulting from u by the prescribed substitutions (which evidently introduce no new free variables).

Thus $\mathbf{S}^0$ satisfies (A)–(C), so (when $\beta=2$) $\mathbf{S}$ does in the case $\alpha=0$; and it will in the cases $\alpha\neq 0$, provided we can similarly deal with the further adjunctions. Under this proviso, the treatment in 5.7 of all the postulates of $\mathbf{L}$ toward the proof of (*) holds good, since that treatment depended only on $\mathbf{S}$ being a supersystem of $\mathbf{S}_0$ satisfying (A) and (B).

7.3. Toward the proof of (*), we now have additional cases for the adjoined particular axioms G^0 and K^0 and for the bar theorem ^{x}26.3c.

The axioms G^0 are closed prime formulas; apply 5.2 Clause 1. The axioms K^0 are treated just as ^{x}1.1 was treated in 5.7.

AXIOM SCHEMA ^{x}26.3c: $\forall\alpha\exists!\mathrm{x}\mathrm{R}(\bar{\alpha}(\mathrm{x}))\,\&\,\forall\mathrm{a}[\mathrm{Seq}(\mathrm{a})\,\&\,\mathrm{R}(\mathrm{a})\supset\mathrm{A}(\mathrm{a})]\,\&\,\forall\mathrm{a}[\mathrm{Seq}(\mathrm{a})\,\&\,\forall\mathrm{s}\mathrm{A}(\mathrm{a}*2^{\mathrm{s}+1})\supset\mathrm{A}(\mathrm{a})]\supset\mathrm{A}(1)$. (This is the closed result of a substitution into any axiom by ^{x}26.3c; cf. 5.7.) Assume (**a**) $|\vdash\forall\alpha\exists!\mathrm{x}\mathrm{R}(\bar{\alpha}(\mathrm{x}))\,\&\,\forall\mathrm{a}[\mathrm{Seq}(\mathrm{a})\,\&\,\mathrm{R}(\mathrm{a})\supset\mathrm{A}(\mathrm{a})]\,\&\,\forall\mathrm{a}[\mathrm{Seq}(\mathrm{a})\,\&\,\forall\mathrm{s}\mathrm{A}(\mathrm{a}*2^{\mathrm{s}+1})\supset\mathrm{A}(\mathrm{a})]$, whence: ($\mathbf{a}_1$) $|\vdash\forall\alpha\exists!\mathrm{x}\mathrm{R}(\bar{\alpha}(\mathrm{x}))$, ($\mathbf{a}_2$) $|\vdash\forall\mathrm{a}[\mathrm{Seq}(\mathrm{a})\,\&\,\mathrm{R}(\mathrm{a})\supset\mathrm{A}(\mathrm{a})]$, ($\mathbf{a}_3$) $|\vdash\forall\mathrm{a}[\mathrm{Seq}(\mathrm{a})\,\&\,\forall\mathrm{s}\mathrm{A}(\mathrm{a}*2^{\mathrm{s}+1})\supset\mathrm{A}(\mathrm{a})]$. We must infer that $|\mathrm{A}(1)$.

I. From (a_1) as in FIM p. 55 "^{x}26.3c from ^{x}26.3a" (which is good in $\mathbf{L}$), $\vdash\forall\mathrm{a}[\mathrm{Seq}(\mathrm{a})\supset\mathrm{R}(\mathrm{a})\vee\neg\mathrm{R}(\mathrm{a})]$. Using also ($\mathrm{a}_2$), ($\mathrm{a}_3$) and ^{x}26.8a (available in $\mathbf{S}$, since ^{x}26.8a is derivable from ^{x}26.3a, and thus from ^{x}26.3c, in $\mathbf{L}$; cf. 3.1 and FIM p. 64): (**b**) $\vdash\mathrm{Seq}(\mathrm{w})\,\&\,\forall\alpha\exists\mathrm{x}\mathrm{R}(\mathrm{w}*\bar{\alpha}(\mathrm{x}))\supset\mathrm{A}(\mathrm{w})$.

II. We now set the stage for an informal bar induction, i.e. an application of the informal analogue of ^{x}26.3c, with $|\vdash\mathrm{R}(\boldsymbol{a})$ as the $R(a)$, and with $\{\vdash\forall\alpha\exists\mathrm{x}\mathrm{R}(\boldsymbol{a}*\bar{\alpha}(\mathrm{x}))$ and $|\vdash\mathrm{A}(\boldsymbol{a})\}$ as the $A(a)$. Toward (e), consider any one-place number-theoretic function τ^0, which is expressed by $\boldsymbol{\tau}^0\in\mathrm{J}^0$. By ($\mathrm{a}_1$), $|\exists!\mathrm{x}\mathrm{R}(\bar{\boldsymbol{\tau}}^0(\mathrm{x}))$, whence for some natural number x, $|\vdash\mathrm{R}(\bar{\boldsymbol{\tau}}^0(\boldsymbol{x}))\,\&\,\forall\mathrm{y}(\mathrm{R}(\bar{\boldsymbol{\tau}}^0(\mathrm{y}))\supset\boldsymbol{x}=\mathrm{y})$, whence (**c**) $|\vdash\mathrm{R}(\bar{\boldsymbol{\tau}}^0(\boldsymbol{x}))$ and (**d**) $|\vdash\forall\mathrm{y}(\mathrm{R}(\bar{\boldsymbol{\tau}}^0(\mathrm{y}))\supset\boldsymbol{x}=\mathrm{y})$. Let $w=\bar{\tau}^0(x)$. From (c) using 5.4 and 5.5, $|\vdash\mathrm{R}(\boldsymbol{w})$. Further, if for any y we had $|\vdash\mathrm{R}(\boldsymbol{u})$ where $u=\bar{\tau}^0(y)$, then (using 5.4, 5.5) $\Vdash\mathrm{R}(\bar{\boldsymbol{\tau}}^0(\boldsymbol{y}))$, whence by (d), $\vdash\boldsymbol{x}=\boldsymbol{y}$, whence by the consistency (cf. 5.7) $x=y$. So (**e**) $(\tau^0)(E!x)\{|\vdash\mathrm{R}(\boldsymbol{a})$ for $a=\bar{\tau}^0(x)\}$.

III (BASIS). Suppose $\mathrm{Seq}(a)$ and $|\vdash\mathrm{R}(\boldsymbol{a})$; we must infer $\vdash\forall\alpha\exists\mathrm{x}\mathrm{R}(\boldsymbol{a}*\bar{\alpha}(\mathrm{x}))$ and $|\vdash\mathrm{A}(\boldsymbol{a})$. IIIa. By *22.6 and $\bar{\alpha}(0)=1$, with $\exists$-and $\forall$-introd., $\vdash\forall\alpha\exists\mathrm{x}\mathrm{R}(\boldsymbol{a}*\bar{\alpha}(\mathrm{x}))$. IIIb. By 5.4, $\vdash\mathrm{Seq}(\boldsymbol{a})$, so (since $\mathrm{Seq}(\boldsymbol{a})$ is prime) $|\vdash\mathrm{Seq}(\boldsymbol{a})$. Also $|\vdash\mathrm{R}(\boldsymbol{a})$ by hypothesis, so $|\vdash\mathrm{Seq}(\boldsymbol{a})\,\&\,\mathrm{R}(\boldsymbol{a})$. By ($\mathrm{a}_2$), $|\vdash\mathrm{Seq}(\boldsymbol{a})\,\&\,\mathrm{R}(\boldsymbol{a})\supset\mathrm{A}(\boldsymbol{a})$. Hence $|\vdash\mathrm{A}(\boldsymbol{a})$.

IV (INDUCTION STEP). Assume (**f**) $\mathrm{Seq}(a)$, and for each s: (**g**) $\vdash\forall\alpha\exists\mathrm{x}\mathrm{R}(\boldsymbol{b}_s*\bar{\alpha}(\mathrm{x}))$ and (**h**) $|\vdash\mathrm{A}(\boldsymbol{b}_s)$, where $b_s=a*2^{s+1}$. We must infer $\vdash\forall\alpha\exists\mathrm{x}\mathrm{R}(\boldsymbol{a}*\bar{\alpha}(\mathrm{x}))$ and $|\vdash\mathrm{A}(\boldsymbol{a})$. IVa. Using (f), 5.4 and *23.6, assume for $\exists$ β- and

$\exists$z-elim.: **(i)** $\boldsymbol{a}=\bar{\beta}(z)$. Using FIM Lemma 5.5(a) (the special case p. 42, which is good in **L**) put (for $\exists\gamma$- and $\exists\delta$-elimination):

(j) $$\forall t\gamma(t)=\begin{cases}\beta(t) & \text{if } t<z,\\ \alpha(t\dot{-}z) & \text{if } t\geqslant z,\end{cases}$$

(k) $$\forall t\delta(t)=\begin{cases}\beta(t) & \text{if } t<z,\\ 0 & \text{if } t\geqslant z.\end{cases}$$

Then using *23.7, $^{\times}$23.1, *B19, *6.3, etc.:
(l) $\forall w\bar{\gamma}(z+w)=\boldsymbol{a}*\bar{\alpha}(w)$, **(m)**$\forall u\,\bar{\delta}(z'+u)=\boldsymbol{b}_0*\overline{(\lambda t0)}(u)$, **(n)** $\forall x_{x\leq z}\,\bar{\gamma}(x)=\bar{\delta}(x)$. After $\forall$-elim. from (a_1), assume for $\exists$x-elim.: **(o)** $R(\bar{\gamma}(x))\&\forall y(R(\bar{\gamma}(y))\supset x=y)$. After $\forall$-elim. from the case of (g) for $s=0$, assume for $\exists$u-elim.: **(p)** $R(\boldsymbol{b}_0*\overline{(\lambda t0)}(u))$. By (m): **(q)** $R(\bar{\delta}(z'+u))$. Assume for $\neg$-introd.: **(r)** $x\leq z$. Then by (n) and (o): **(s)** $R(\bar{\delta}(x))$. By (a_1) with $\forall$-elim., (q), (s), and *172: $z'+u=x$, contradicting (r). So $x>z$. Put (for $\exists$v-elim.) **(t)** $x=z'+v$, so $x=z+v'$. By (o), $R(\bar{\gamma}(z+v'))$, so by (l): **(u)** $R(\boldsymbol{a}*\bar{\alpha}(v'))$. Using $\exists$x-introds., completing the $\exists$v-, $\exists$u-, $\exists$x-, $\exists\delta$-, $\exists\gamma$-, $\exists\beta$- and $\exists$z-elim., and using $\forall$-introd.: $(\mathbf{v}_1)$ $\vdash\forall\alpha\exists xR(\boldsymbol{a}*\bar{\alpha}(x))$, $(\mathbf{v}_2)$ $\vdash\forall\alpha\exists xR(\boldsymbol{a}*\bar{\alpha}(x'))$. IVb. For $\exists\sigma$-elim., put

(w) $$\forall t\sigma(t)=\begin{cases}s & \text{if } t=0,\\ \alpha(t\dot{-}1) & \text{if } t>0.\end{cases}$$

Then (like (l), using also *B3, *B4) **(x)** $\forall x\bar{\sigma}(x')=2^{s+1}*\bar{\alpha}(x)$. By (v_2) (with $\forall$-elim.) and **(x)** (with (f), 5.4, *22.5, *23.5, *22.9), $\exists xR((\boldsymbol{a}*2^{s+1})*\bar{\alpha}(x))$. Completing the $\exists\sigma$-elim., and using $\forall$-introd., $\vdash\forall\alpha\exists xR((\boldsymbol{a}*2^{s+1})*\bar{\alpha}(x))$. Thence using (f), 5.4, *22.5, *22.8 and (b): $\vdash A(\boldsymbol{a}*2^{s+1})$, whence by $\forall$-introd.: **(y)** $\vdash\forall sA(\boldsymbol{a}*2^{s+1})$. Using (h) and 5.4, 5.5: $|\forall sA(\boldsymbol{a}*2^{s+1})$, whence with (y), $|\vdash\forall sA(\boldsymbol{a}*2^{s+1})$. By (f) with 5.4, 5.5: $|\vdash \mathrm{Seq}(\boldsymbol{a})$; so $|\vdash \mathrm{Seq}(\boldsymbol{a})\&\forall sA(\boldsymbol{a}*2^{s+1})$. By (a_3), $|\vdash \mathrm{Seq}(\boldsymbol{a})\&\forall sA(\boldsymbol{a}*2^{s+1})\supset A(\boldsymbol{a})$. So: **(z)** $|\vdash A(\boldsymbol{a})$, completing the proof.

Thus far, we have established (A)–(D) and (*) for the case $\mathbf{S}_0$ is (0,2) (and **S** is $\mathbf{S}^0$). Thence (using 5.10): (i), (ii) *and* (iii) *hold for the system* (0, 2).

For the case $\mathbf{S}_0$ is $(\alpha, 2)$ with $\alpha\neq 0$, we have done all the work toward establishing (A)–(C) and (*) which is attributable to the adjunctions which gave $\mathbf{S}^0$ and to the presence of $^{\times}$26.3c. So, to conclude (using 5.10) that (i) and (ii) hold for $(\alpha, 2)$ when $\alpha=1, 2, 3$, we shall need to handle only the further adjunctions and $^{\times}2.2!$, $^{\times}2.2$, or $^{\times}2.1$ respectively.

7.4. We digress here to show that $^{\times}2.2!$ is not derivable in (0, 2) (a fortiori, $^{\times}2.2!$, $^{\times}2.2$ and $^{\times}2.1$ are not derivable in any of our systems $(0, \beta)$).

Suppose to the contrary $^{\times}2.2!$ were derivable in $\mathbf{S}_0=(0, 2)$. We take over the lettered results in 5.9, where now a sub- or superscript indicates the system $\mathbf{S}_0$ or $\mathbf{S}^0$: $(\mathbf{a})_0$, $(\mathbf{b})_0$ (as before), $(\mathbf{c})_0$ (by hypothesis), $(\mathbf{d})_0$ (as before), $(\mathbf{d})^0$ (a fortiori), $(\mathbf{e})^0$ (using $(*)$ as proved for $\mathbf{S}^0$), $(\mathbf{f})^0$ (as before), $(\mathbf{f})_0$ with a different u (using (D) as proved for $\mathbf{S}^0$), $(\mathbf{g})_0$, $(\mathbf{h})$, $(\mathbf{i})_0$–$(\mathbf{m})_0$ (as before).

It follows that $^{\times}2.2!$ is not derivable in any of the systems obtained from our (0, 2) by replacing $^{\times}26.3c$ by one of the other forms $^{\times}26.3a$, $^{\times}26.3b$, $^{\times}26.3d$ of the bar theorem, since all three of these forms are derivable in **L** from $^{\times}26.3c$ (FIM p. 55).

8. The systems $(1, \beta)$

8.1. For $\beta=0,1$, $\mathbf{S}^0$ shall be $\mathbf{S}_0=(1, \beta)$ itself; for $\beta=2$, $\mathbf{S}^0$ shall be the system so named in 7.1.

Starting with $\mathbf{S}^0$ as basis, we define by recursion an increasing sequence

$$\mathbf{S}^0 \subset \mathbf{S}^1 \subset \mathbf{S}^2 \subset \ldots$$

of (semi-formal) systems, of which $\mathbf{S}$ is to be the union. Thus $\mathbf{S}=\mathbf{S}^{\omega}=$ $=\bigcup_{n<\omega}\mathbf{S}^n$ and $\{\vdash \mathrm{E}\}\equiv\{\vdash^{\omega}\mathrm{E}\}\equiv(En)_{n<\omega}\{\vdash^n \mathrm{E}\}\equiv(En)\{\vdash^n\mathrm{E}\}$.

$\mathbf{S}^{n+1}$ is defined from $\mathbf{S}^n$ thus. Consider the set of all formulas of $\mathbf{S}^n$ of the form $\forall x\exists! y A(x, y)$ where $A(x, y)$ contains free at most the distinct number variables x and y, where x is free for y in $A(x, y)$, and where

(1) $\vdash^n \forall x\exists! y A(x, y)$,

(2) for each x there is a y such that $\vdash^n A(\boldsymbol{x}, \boldsymbol{y})$.

To these formulas $\forall x\exists! y A(x, y)$ we correlate one-to-one new function symbols τ^{n+1} (i.e. distinct function symbols not used in $\mathbf{S}^n$, and therefore not in $\mathbf{S}_0, \mathbf{S}^0, \ldots, \mathbf{S}^{n \dot{-} 1}$), which we adjoin to the symbolism of $\mathbf{S}^n$; call the set of these function symbols J^{n+1}. To the postulates of $\mathbf{S}^n$ we adjoin the following set of axioms:

$$\mathrm{H}^{n+1}: \quad \forall x A(x, \tau^{n+1}(x)) \quad \text{for each} \quad \tau^{n+1} \in \mathrm{J}^{n+1} \text{ where}$$

$\forall x \exists ! y A(x, y)$ is the formula of $\mathbf{S}^n$ to which τ^{n+1} is correlated. The system thus obtained is $\mathbf{S}^{n+1}$.

8.2. To extend (A)–(C) to $\mathbf{S}^n$ for any finite n, we use induction on n. Instead of (C), we shall establish for each n the following property (C′), of which (C) (with $\mathbf{S}^n$ as the $\mathbf{S}$) is an immediate corollary.

(C′) $\mathbf{S}^n$ *is an inessential extension of each of* $\mathbf{S}_0, \mathbf{S}^0, \dots, \mathbf{S}^{n \dot{-} 1}$.

Basis. Using §§ 5, 7: (A)–(C) hold (vacuously for $\beta=0,1$; by 7.2 for $\beta=2$) for $\mathbf{S}^0$ as the $\mathbf{S}$. Thus also (C′) holds for $n=0$.

Induction step for (A). Assume (A) holds for $\mathbf{S}^n$. Toward (A) for $\mathbf{S}^{n+1}$ assume $\tau^{n+1} \in \mathrm{J}^{n+1}$, and assume (for $\supset$-introduction in $\mathbf{S}^{n+1}$) **(a)** $a=b$. Thence by the replacement theorem in $\mathbf{S}^n$, a fortiori in $\mathbf{S}^{n+1}$: **(b)** $A(a, z) \supset A(b, z)$, where $\forall x \exists ! y A(x, y)$ is the formula of $\mathbf{S}^n$ to which τ^{n+1} is correlated. From (b) by substitution IM p. 101 (in $\mathbf{S}^{n+1}$): **(c)** $A(a, \tau^{n+1}(a)) \supset A(b, \tau^{n+1}(a))$. By $\forall$-eliminations from the axiom $\forall x A(x, \tau^{n+1}(x))$ of $\mathbf{S}^{n+1}$: **(d)** $A(a, \tau^{n+1}(a))$, **(e)** $A(b, \tau^{n+1}(b))$. By (d) and (c): **(f)** $A(b, \tau^{n+1}(a))$. By $\forall$-elimination from the provable formula $\forall x \exists ! y A(x, y)$ of $\mathbf{S}^n$: **(g)** $\exists ! y A(b, y)$. From (f), (e) and (g) by *172, $\tau^{n+1}(a) = \tau^{n+1}(b)$. By $\supset$-introduction (discharging (a)), $a=b \supset \tau^{n+1}(a) = \tau^{n+1}(b)$.

Induction step for (C′). Assume (C′) holds for $\mathbf{S}^n$. Then to establish (C′) for $\mathbf{S}^{n+1}$ we need only prove that $\mathbf{S}^{n+1}$ is an inessential extension of $\mathbf{S}^n$, since the property of being an inessential extension is obviously transitive. Thus let Γ, E be formulas of $\mathbf{S}^n$ such that $\Gamma \vdash^{n+1} \mathrm{E}$. Let $\tau_0^{n+1}, \dots, \tau_q^{n+1}$ be the distinct elements of J^{n+1} which occur in a given deduction (in $\mathbf{S}^{n+1}$) of E from Γ. Let $\mathbf{S}_0^n$ be $\mathbf{S}^n$, and for each $i=0, \dots, q$ let $\mathbf{S}_{i+1}^n$ be the system obtained from $\mathbf{S}_i^n$ by adjoining the symbol τ_i^{n+1} and the axiom $\forall x A_i(x, \tau_i^{n+1}(x))$ where $\forall x \exists ! y A_i(x, y)$ is the formula of $\mathbf{S}^n$ to which τ_i^{n+1} is correlated. Then $\Gamma \vdash_{q+1}^n \mathrm{E}$. Furthermore, by an unpublished theorem of Kleene (extending IM Theorem 42 p. 408), τ_i^{n+1} with its axiom $\forall x A_i(x, \tau_i^{n+1}(x))$ is eliminable from $\mathbf{S}_{i+1}^n$ in $\mathbf{S}_i^n$, for each $i=0, \dots, q$. It follows immediately that S_{i+1}^n is an inessential extension of $\mathbf{S}_i^n$ for $i=0, \dots, q$, and thence by transitivity that $\mathbf{S}_{q+1}^n$ is an inessential extension of $\mathbf{S}^n (= \mathbf{S}_0^n)$. Thus $\Gamma \vdash^n \mathrm{E}$.

Induction step for (B). Assume $\tau^{n+1} \in \mathrm{J}^{n+1}$, and let $\forall x \exists ! y A(x, y)$ be the formula of $\mathbf{S}^n$ to which it is correlated. Then by (2), for each x there is a y such that **(a)** $\vdash^n A(\boldsymbol{x}, \boldsymbol{y})$. By $\forall$-eliminations from (1) and the corresponding axiom in H^{n+1}; **(b)** $\vdash^n \exists ! y A(\boldsymbol{x}, y)$, **(c)** $\vdash^{n+1} A(\boldsymbol{x}, \tau^{n+1}(\boldsymbol{x}))$. From

(a) and (b), a fortiori: **(d)**$\vdash^{n+1} A(\boldsymbol{x}, \boldsymbol{y})$, **(e)**$\vdash^{n+1} \exists! y A(\boldsymbol{x}, y)$. By *172 from (c), (d), (e), **(f)**$\vdash^{n+1} \tau^{n+1}(\boldsymbol{x})=\boldsymbol{y}$. Now assume **(g)**$\vdash^{n+1} \tau^{n+1}(\boldsymbol{x})=\boldsymbol{z}$. By replacement in (c): **(h)**$\vdash^{n+1} A(\boldsymbol{x}, \boldsymbol{z})$. By *172 from (d), (h), (e): **(i)**$\vdash^{n+1} \boldsymbol{y}=\boldsymbol{z}$, whence by (C′) as just established for all finite n, **(j)**$\vdash_0 \boldsymbol{y}=\boldsymbol{z}$, so the consistency of $\mathbf{S}_0$ (included in FIM Corollary 9.5) demands $y=z$.

Now (A) and (B) for $\mathbf{S}(=\mathbf{S}^{\omega})$ follow immediately, as does (C) in the form: (C″) $\mathbf{S}\ (=\mathbf{S}^{\omega})$ *is an inessential extension of each of* $\mathbf{S}_0$, $\mathbf{S}^0$, $\mathbf{S}^1$, $\mathbf{S}^2$, ...

8.3. To establish (∗) in **S**, we show by course-of-values induction on m that, if $\vdash^m$ E, then $\|$ E.

Since (A) and (B) hold in **S**, the treatment in 5.7 applies to all postulates of **L**, and for $\beta=1$ or 2 the argument in 6.2 or 7.3 applies to ${}^{\times}$26.6c or ${}^{\times}$26.3c respectively.

AXIOMS H^{n+1}: $\forall x A(x, \tau^{n+1}(x))$, where $m=n+1$. We must show that $|\forall x A(x, \tau^{n+1}(x))$, i.e., that, for each x, $|A(\boldsymbol{x}, \tau^{n+1}(\boldsymbol{x}))$. By (2), for each x there is a y such that $\vdash^n A(\boldsymbol{x}, \boldsymbol{y})$, so by the induction hypothesis $|A(\boldsymbol{x}, \boldsymbol{y})$; moreover, by the reasoning used (for (f) in the induction step for (B)) in 8.2, $\vdash^{n+1} \tau^{n+1}(\boldsymbol{x})=\boldsymbol{y}$, whence $\vdash \tau^{n+1}(\boldsymbol{x})=\boldsymbol{y}$. Using 5.5 (which depended only on (A) and (B), which we have) for **S**, $|A(\boldsymbol{x}, \tau^{n+1}(\boldsymbol{x}))$.

AXIOM SCHEMA ${}^{\times}$2.2!: $\forall x \exists! y A(x, y) \supset \exists \alpha \forall x A(x, \alpha(x))$. This (under the convention in 5.7) is the closed result of a substitution (which may introduce symbols of higher systems) into an axiom of $\mathbf{S}^m$ by ${}^{\times}$2.2!; say it is a formula of $\mathbf{S}^p$. We must show $|\forall x \exists! y A(x, y) \supset \exists \alpha \forall x A(x, \alpha(x))$. Suppose **(a)**$|\vdash \forall x \exists! y A(x, y)$. Thence (using (C″)), **(b)**$\vdash^p \forall x \exists! y A(x, y)$. Also by (a), **(c)** $(x)(Ey)\{|\vdash A(\boldsymbol{x}, \boldsymbol{y}) \,\&\, \forall z[A(\boldsymbol{x}, z) \supset \boldsymbol{y}=z]\}$, whence (using (C″)): **(d)** $(x)(Ey)\{\vdash^p A(\boldsymbol{x}, \boldsymbol{y})\}$. From (b) and (d) by H^{p+1}, for some $\tau^{p+1} \in J^{p+1}$: $\vdash^{p+1} \forall x A(x, \tau^{p+1}(x))$, a fortiori **(e)** $\vdash \forall x A(x, \tau^{p+1}(x))$. Now consider an arbitrary numeral $\boldsymbol{x}$. From (c), there is a y such that **(f)** $|\vdash A(\boldsymbol{x}, \boldsymbol{y}) \,\&\, \forall z[A(\boldsymbol{x}, z) \supset \boldsymbol{y}=z]$, whence **(g)** $|A(\boldsymbol{x}, \boldsymbol{y})$ and **(h)** $\vdash \forall z[A(\boldsymbol{x}, z) \supset \boldsymbol{y}=z]$. By $\forall$-elim. from (e): **(i)** $\vdash A(\boldsymbol{x}, \tau^{p+1}(\boldsymbol{x}))$. Thence with (h) (after $\forall$-elim.): **(j)** $\vdash \boldsymbol{y}=\tau^{p+1}(\boldsymbol{x})$. By (g) and (j), using 5.5 for **S**: $|A(\boldsymbol{x}, \tau^{p+1}(\boldsymbol{x}))$. We have established: **(k)** $|\forall x A(x, \tau^{p+1}(x))$, whence with (e), $|\vdash \forall x A(x, \tau^{p+1}(x))$. So $|\exists \alpha \forall x A(x, \alpha(x))$. Thus (∗), as well as (A)–(C), holds for $\mathbf{S}(=\mathbf{S}^{\omega})$, so (by 5.10): (i) *and* (ii) *hold in each of the systems* $(1, \beta)$.

9. The systems $(2, \beta)$

9.1. Modifying 8.1, we now define $\mathbf{S}^{n+1}$ from $\mathbf{S}^n$, thus. Consider the family of all denumerable classes $\mathscr{L}$ of theorems (i.e. provable formulas) of $\mathbf{S}^n$ such that, for some formula A(x, y) containing free at most the distinct number variables x and y, where x is free for y in A(x, y):

(1′) $\forall x \exists y A(x, y) \in \mathscr{L}$,

(2′) for each x there is exactly one y such that $A(\boldsymbol{x}, \boldsymbol{y}) \in \mathscr{L}$, and no other formulas $\in \mathscr{L}$. We call $\forall x \exists y A(x, y)$ the *pilot formula* of $\mathscr{L}$. To these classes $\mathscr{L}$ we correlate one-to-one new function symbols τ^{n+1} (call the set of them J^{n+1}), and adjoin these to $\mathbf{S}^n$. As postulates we adjoin the following sets of axioms:

H^{n+1}: $\forall x A(x, \tau^{n+1}(x))$ for each $\tau^{n+1} \in J^{n+1}$ where $\forall x \exists y A(x, y)$ is the pilot formula of the class $\mathscr{L}$ to which τ^{n+1} is correlated,

G^{n+1}: $\tau^{n+1}(\boldsymbol{x}) = \boldsymbol{y}$ for each $\tau^{n+1} \in J^{n+1}$, each x, and the image y of (2′) for the class $\mathscr{L}$ to which τ^{n+1} is correlated,

K^{n+1}: $a = b \supset \tau^{n+1}(a) = \tau^{n+1}(b)$ for each $\tau^{n+1} \in J^{n+1}$.

9.2. For these systems $\mathbf{S}^n$, we establish (A)–(C′) as in 8.2 by induction on n.

Basis. As before: (A)–(C), and thus (C′), hold for $\mathbf{S}^0$.

Induction step for (A). This is immediate, using K^{n+1}.

Induction step for (C′). Again it will suffice to show $\mathbf{S}^{n+1}$ is an inessential extension of $\mathbf{S}^n$. Thus let Γ, E, $\tau_0^{n+1}, \ldots, \tau_q^{n+1}$ be as before. For each $i = 0, \ldots, q$, let $\forall x_i \exists y_i A_i(x_i, y_i)$ be the pilot formula of the class $\mathscr{L}_i$ to which τ_i^{n+1} is correlated, and suppose $\forall x_i A_i(x_i, \tau_i^{n+1}(x_i))$, $\tau_i^{n+1}(\boldsymbol{x}_{i0}) = \boldsymbol{y}_{i0}, \ldots, \tau_i^{n+1}(\boldsymbol{x}_{ik_i}) = \boldsymbol{y}_{ik_i}$ include all the axioms from H^{n+1} and G^{n+1} involving τ_i^{n+1} which are used in the given deduction. Let $\beta_0, \ldots, \beta_q$ be distinct function variables, none of which appears in Γ, in the given deduction, nor in any of the formulas $\forall x_i A_i(x_i, \tau_i^{n+1}(x_i))$. For each $i = 0, \ldots, q$, let $C_i(\beta_i)$ be the following formula of $\mathbf{S}^n$: $\forall x_i A_i(x_i, \beta_i(x_i)) \,\&\, \beta_i(\boldsymbol{x}_{i0}) = \boldsymbol{y}_{i0} \,\&\ldots\&\, \beta_i(\boldsymbol{x}_{ik_i}) = \boldsymbol{y}_{ik_i}$. Then $\vdash^n \exists \beta_i C_i(\beta_i)$. For, using &-introd. on the appropriate elements of $\mathscr{L}_i$, $\vdash^n \forall x_i \exists y_i A_i(x_i, y_i) \,\&\, A_i(\boldsymbol{x}_{i0}, \boldsymbol{y}_{i0}) \,\&\ldots\&\, A_i(\boldsymbol{x}_{ik_i}, \boldsymbol{y}_{ik_i})$, whence (by cases from $x_i = \boldsymbol{x}_{i0} \vee \ldots \vee x_i = \boldsymbol{x}_{ik_i} \vee (x_i \neq \boldsymbol{x}_{i0} \,\&\ldots\&\, x_i \neq \boldsymbol{x}_{ik_i})$) $\vdash^n \forall x_i \exists y_i [A_i(x_i, y_i) \,\&\, (x_i = \boldsymbol{x}_{i0} \supset y_i = \boldsymbol{y}_{i0}) \,\&\ldots\&\, (x_i = \boldsymbol{x}_{ik_i} \supset y_i = \boldsymbol{y}_{ik_i})]$, whence by $^{\times}$2.2 (for $\mathbf{S}^n$): $\vdash^n \exists \beta_i \forall x_i [A_i(x_i, \beta_i(x_i)) \,\&\, (x_i = \boldsymbol{x}_{i0} \supset \beta_i(x_i) = \boldsymbol{y}_{i0}) \,\&\ldots\&\, (x_i = \boldsymbol{x}_{ik_i} \supset \beta_i(x_i) = \boldsymbol{y}_{ik_i})]$, whence (using first *87) $\vdash^n \exists \beta_i C_i(\beta_i)$. Now for $\exists$-eliminations assume successively $C_0(\beta_0), \ldots, C_q(\beta_q)$. In the given deduction of E from Γ in $\mathbf{S}^{n+1}$, for each $i = 0, \ldots, q$ substitute β_i for τ_i^{n+1}. By this procedure, each axiom from H^{n+1} or G^{n+1}

used in the deduction is transformed into a consequence (by &-elimination) of $C_i(\beta_i)$ for some i, each axiom from K^{n+1} into a theorem of **L** (by substituting into $^{x}1.1$), each other axiom of $\mathbf{S}^{n+1}$ into an axiom of $\mathbf{S}^n$ by the same schema, and each application of a rule of inference of $\mathbf{S}^{n+1}$ into an instance of the same rule for $\mathbf{S}^n$; the formulas Γ and the end-formula E of the original deduction remain unchanged. Thus, after $(q+1)$ $\exists$-eliminations (since Γ, E contain none of $\beta_0, \ldots, \beta_q$), $\Gamma \vdash^n \mathrm{E}$.

INDUCTION STEP FOR (B). This is immediate. For given $\tau^{n+1} \in J^{n+1}$ and arbitrary x, from G^{n+1} we have $\vdash^{n+1} \tau^{n+1}(\boldsymbol{x}) = \boldsymbol{y}$ for one y. If also $\vdash^{n+1} \tau^{n+1}(\boldsymbol{x}) = \boldsymbol{z}$, then by replacement (which we have by (A)) $\vdash^{n+1} \boldsymbol{y} = \boldsymbol{z}$, whence (by (C′)) $\vdash_0 \boldsymbol{y} = \boldsymbol{z}$, so (by the consistency of $\mathbf{S}_0$) $y = z$.

As before: (A), (B) and (C″) hold for $\mathbf{S} = \mathbf{S}^\omega = \bigcup_{n<\omega} \mathbf{S}^n$.

9.3. To establish (*) in $\mathbf{S}(=\mathbf{S}^\omega)$, we show (as in 8.3) by course-of-values induction on m that, if $\vdash^m \mathrm{E}$, then $\Vert \mathrm{E}$.

The cases for the postulates of **L**, and for $^{x}26.6c$ (if $\beta = 1$) or $^{x}26.3c$ (if $\beta = 2$), are treated as in 8.3. The cases for G^{n+1} and K^{n+1} (where $m = n+1$) are like those for G^0 and K^0 in 7.3. The case for H^{n+1} is handled as in 8.3, except that now (2′) is cited instead of (2), and then $\vdash^{n+1} \tau^{n+1}(\boldsymbol{x}) = \boldsymbol{y}$ directly from G^{n+1}. (For $j+1 < m$, the cases for G^{j+1}, K^{j+1} and H^{j+1} are taken care of by the induction hypothesis.)

AXIOM SCHEMA $^{x}2.2$: $\forall x \exists y A(x, y) \supset \exists \alpha \forall x A(x, \alpha(x))$. As before (for $^{x}2.2!$ in 8.3), this is a closed theorem of $\mathbf{S}^p$ for some $p \geq m$. Suppose **(a)** $| \vdash \forall x \exists y A(x, y)$. Thence (using (C″)), **(b)** $\vdash^p \forall x \exists y A(x, y)$. Also by (a), **(c)** $(x)(Ey)\{| \vdash A(\boldsymbol{x}, \boldsymbol{y})\}$, whence (using (C″)): **(d)** $(x)(Ey)\{\vdash^p A(\boldsymbol{x}, \boldsymbol{y})$ and $| A(\boldsymbol{x}, \boldsymbol{y})\}$. Then $\forall x \exists y A(x, y)$ is the pilot formula of the class $\mathscr{L}$ of theorems of $\mathbf{S}^p$, satisfying (1′) and (2′), given by (b) and (d). For the τ^{p+1} correlated to this $\mathscr{L}$, from H^{p+1}: $\vdash^{p+1} \forall x A(x, \tau^{p+1}(x))$, a fortiori **(e)** $\vdash \forall x A(x, \tau^{p+1}(x))$. Now consider an arbitrary numeral $\boldsymbol{x}$. From (d), there is a y such that **(f)** $| A(\boldsymbol{x}, \boldsymbol{y})$, where (by G^{p+1}): $\vdash^{p+1} \tau^{p+1}(\boldsymbol{x}) = \boldsymbol{y}$, a fortiori **(g)** $\vdash \tau^{p+1}(\boldsymbol{x}) = \boldsymbol{y}$. From (f) and (g) using 5.5 for **S**: $| A(\boldsymbol{x}, \tau^{p+1}(\boldsymbol{x}))$. So $| \forall x A(x, \tau^{p+1}(x))$, whence with (e): $| \exists \alpha \forall x A(x, \alpha(x))$.

Thus, as before: (i) *and* (ii) *hold in each of the systems* $(2, \beta)$.

10. The systems $(3, \beta)$

10.1. As before (8.1, 9.1) we take $\mathbf{S}^0$ to be $\mathbf{S}^0 = (3, \beta)$ for $\beta = 0, 1$; for $\beta = 2$, $\mathbf{S}^0$ shall be as in 7.1.

Now we define an increasing sequence of semi-formal systems $\mathbf{S}^\zeta$ indexed by the ordinals of Cantor's first and second number classes; i.e. $\mathbf{S}^\zeta$ is to be defined for each ordinal $\zeta<\Omega$ (= the first uncountable ordinal), and $\mathrm{S}^\xi \subset \mathrm{S}^\zeta$ whenever $\xi<\zeta<\Omega$. Then $\mathbf{S}$ shall be $\mathbf{S}^\Omega=\bigcup_{\zeta<\Omega}\mathbf{S}^\zeta$.

$\mathbf{S}^0$ has already been defined. At limit ordinals $\zeta(<\Omega)$, we let $\mathbf{S}^\zeta$ be $\bigcup_{\xi<\zeta}\mathbf{S}^\xi$.

If ζ is a successor ordinal $(<\Omega)$, say $\zeta=\xi+1$, we define $\mathbf{S}^\zeta$ from $\mathbf{S}^\xi$ as follows. Consider the family of all denumerable classes $\mathscr{L}$ of theorems of $\mathbf{S}^\xi$ such that, for some formula $\mathrm{A}(\mathrm{x}, \alpha)$ which contains free at most the number variable x and the function variable α and in which x is free for α:

(1″) $\forall \mathrm{x} \exists \alpha \mathrm{A}(\mathrm{x}, \alpha) \in \mathscr{L}$,

(2″) for each x there is exactly one closed functor u such that $\mathrm{A}(\boldsymbol{x}, \mathrm{u}) \in \mathscr{L}$, and no other formulas $\in \mathscr{L}$. We call $\forall \mathrm{x} \exists \alpha \mathrm{A}(\mathrm{x}, \alpha)$ the *pilot formula* of $\mathscr{L}$. To these classes we correlate one-to-one new function symbols $\boldsymbol{\tau}^{\xi+1}$ (call the set of them $\mathrm{J}^{\xi+1}$) and adjoin them to $\mathbf{S}^\xi$. As postulates we adjoin the following sets of axioms:

$\mathrm{D}^{\xi+1}$: $\forall \mathrm{x} \mathrm{A}(\mathrm{x}, \lambda \mathrm{y}\, \boldsymbol{\tau}^{\xi+1}(\langle \mathrm{x}, \mathrm{y}\rangle))$ for each $\boldsymbol{\tau}^{\xi+1} \in \mathrm{J}^{\xi+1}$ where $\forall \mathrm{x} \exists \alpha \mathrm{A}(\mathrm{x}, \alpha)$ is the pilot formula of the class $\mathscr{L}$ to which $\boldsymbol{\tau}^{\xi+1}$ is correlated,

$\mathrm{E}^{\xi+1}$: $\lambda \mathrm{y}\, \boldsymbol{\tau}^{\xi+1}(\langle \boldsymbol{x}, \mathrm{y}\rangle)=\mathrm{u}$ for each $\boldsymbol{\tau}^{\xi+1} \in \mathrm{J}^{\xi+1}$ and each x and closed functor u such that $\mathrm{A}(\boldsymbol{x}, \mathrm{u})$ is in the class $\mathscr{L}$ to which $\boldsymbol{\tau}^{\xi+1}$ is correlated,

$\mathrm{F}^{\xi+1}$: $\boldsymbol{\tau}^{\xi+1}(z)=0$ for each $\boldsymbol{\tau}^{\xi+1} \in \mathrm{J}^{\xi+1}$ and each z such that $z \neq \langle (z)_0, (z)_1\rangle$,

$\mathrm{K}^{\xi+1}$: $\mathrm{a}=\mathrm{b} \supset \boldsymbol{\tau}^{\xi+1}(\mathrm{a})=\boldsymbol{\tau}^{\xi+1}(\mathrm{b})$ for each $\boldsymbol{\tau}^{\xi+1} \in \mathrm{J}^{\xi+1}$.

10.2. By transfinite induction on ζ, we now show that for each $\zeta \leq \Omega$: $\mathbf{S}^\zeta$ satisfies (A), (B), and the following condition (C′) (which includes (C)).

(C′) $\mathbf{S}^\zeta$ *is an inessential extension of* $\mathbf{S}^\xi$ *for each* $\xi<\zeta$, *and of* $\mathbf{S}_0$.

The cases for $\zeta=0$ (using 7.2 for $\beta=2$), and for ζ a limit ordinal $(\leq \Omega)$, are immediate. Only the cases for $\zeta=\xi+1$ $(<\Omega)$ require comment.

Successor case for (A). This also is immediate, using $\mathrm{K}^{\xi+1}$.

Successor case for (C′). It will suffice to show that $\mathbf{S}^{\xi+1}$ is an inessential extension of $\mathbf{S}^\xi$. Thus let Γ, E be formulas of $\mathbf{S}^\xi$ such that $\Gamma \vdash^{\xi+1} \mathrm{E}$. Let $\boldsymbol{\tau}_0^{\xi+1}, \ldots, \boldsymbol{\tau}_q^{\xi+1}$ be the distinct elements of $\mathrm{J}^{\xi+1}$ which occur in a given deduction (in $\mathbf{S}^{\xi+1}$) of E from Γ. For each $i=0, \ldots, q$, let $\forall \mathrm{x}_i \exists \alpha_i \mathrm{A}_i(\mathrm{x}_i, \alpha_i)$ be the pilot formula of the class $\mathscr{L}_i$ to which $\boldsymbol{\tau}_i^{\xi+1}$ is correlated, and suppose $\forall \mathrm{x}_i \mathrm{A}_i(\mathrm{x}_i, \lambda \mathrm{y}_i\, \boldsymbol{\tau}_i^{\xi+1}(\langle \mathrm{x}_i, \mathrm{y}_i\rangle))$, $\lambda \mathrm{y}_i\, \boldsymbol{\tau}_i^{\xi+1}(\langle \boldsymbol{x}_{i0}, \mathrm{y}_i\rangle)=\mathrm{u}_{i0}, \ldots, \lambda \mathrm{y}_i\, \boldsymbol{\tau}_i^{\xi+1}(\langle \boldsymbol{x}_{ik_i}, \mathrm{y}_i\rangle)=\mathrm{u}_{ik_i}$, $\boldsymbol{\tau}_i^{\xi+1}(z_{i0})=0, \ldots, \boldsymbol{\tau}_i^{\xi+1}(z_{ih_i})=0$ include

all the axioms from $D^{\xi+1}$, $E^{\xi+1}$ and $F^{\xi+1}$ involving $\tau_i^{\xi+1}$ which are used in the given deduction. Let $\beta_0, \dots, \beta_q$ be distinct function variables, none of which appears in Γ, in the given deduction, nor in any of the $\forall x_i A_i (x_i, \lambda y_i \tau_i^{\xi+1}(\langle x_i, y_i \rangle))$. For each $i=0, \dots, q$, let $C_i(\beta_i)$ be the following formula of $\mathbf{S}^{\xi}$:
$\forall x_i A_i (x_i, \lambda y_i \beta_i(\langle x_i, y_i \rangle))$ & $\lambda y_i \beta_i (\langle \boldsymbol{x}_{i0}, y_i \rangle) = u_{i0}$ & ... & $\lambda y_i \beta_i(\langle \boldsymbol{x}_{ik_i}, y_i \rangle) = u_{ik_i}$ & $\beta_i(\boldsymbol{z}_{i0})=0$ & ... & $\beta_i(\boldsymbol{z}_{ih_i})=0$. Then $\vdash^{\xi} \exists \beta_i C_i(\beta_i)$ essentially as before (9.2), but using $^{x}2.1$ instead of $^{x}2.2$. For $\exists$-elims. assume successively $C_0(\beta_0), \dots, C_q(\beta_q)$. In the given deduction of E from Γ in $\mathbf{S}^{\xi+1}$, for each $i=0, \dots, q$ substitute β_i for $\tau_i^{\xi+1}$. Thus each axiom from $D^{\xi+1}$, $E^{\xi+1}$, or $F^{\xi+1}$ used in the deduction is transformed into a consequence (by &-elimination) of some $C_i(\beta_i)$, each axiom from $K^{\xi+1}$ into a theorem of **L**, and each other axiom or use of a rule of inference of $\mathbf{S}^{\xi+1}$ into an instance of the same schema or rule for $\mathbf{S}^{\xi}$, while Γ and E remain unchanged. After $\exists\, \beta_i$-eliminations, $\Gamma \vdash^{\xi}$ E.

SUCCESSOR CASE FOR (B). For $\tau^{\xi+1} \in J^{\xi+1}$ and arbitrary z, we have two cases, as follows:

SUBCASE 1: $z = \langle (z)_0, (z)_1 \rangle$. Then (using 5.4) $\vdash_0 \boldsymbol{z} = \langle \boldsymbol{x}, \boldsymbol{y} \rangle$ where $x=(z)_0$, $y=(z)_1$, whence (**a**) $\vdash^{\xi+1} \boldsymbol{z} = \langle \boldsymbol{x}, \boldsymbol{y} \rangle$. From $E^{\xi+1}$, (**b**) $\vdash^{\xi+1} \lambda y\, \tau^{\xi+1}(\langle \boldsymbol{x}, y \rangle) = u$ for some closed functor u of $\mathbf{S}^{\xi}$, whence by $\forall$-elimination with $^{x}0.1$: (**c**) $\vdash^{\xi+1} \tau^{\xi+1}(\langle \boldsymbol{x}, \boldsymbol{y} \rangle) = u(\boldsymbol{y})$. By 5.4 for $\mathbf{S}^{\xi}$ (using the induction hypothesis) there is a w such that $\vdash^{\xi} u(\boldsymbol{y}) = \boldsymbol{w}$, so (**d**) $\vdash^{\xi+1} u(\boldsymbol{y}) = \boldsymbol{w}$. From (a), (c), (d), using replacement (which we have by (A)) for $\mathbf{S}^{\xi+1}$: (**e**) $\vdash^{\xi+1} \tau^{\xi+1}(\boldsymbol{z}) = \boldsymbol{w}$. If also $\vdash^{\xi+1} \tau^{\xi+1}(\boldsymbol{z}) = \boldsymbol{t}$ then (using (e)) $\vdash^{\xi+1} \boldsymbol{w} = \boldsymbol{t}$, whence (by (C′)) $\vdash_0 \boldsymbol{w} = \boldsymbol{t}$, so (by the consistency of S_0) $w=t$. SUBCASE 2: $z \neq \langle (z)_0, (z)_1 \rangle$. From $F^{\xi+1}$: $\vdash^{\xi+1} \tau^{\xi+1}(\boldsymbol{z}) = 0$. If also $\vdash^{\xi+1} \tau^{\xi+1}(\boldsymbol{z}) = \boldsymbol{t}$, then (as in Subcase 1) $0=t$.

10.3. To establish (*) in **S** $(=\mathbf{S}^{\Omega})$, we show by transfinite induction on $\zeta \leq \Omega$ that, if $\vdash^{\zeta}$ E, then $\Vert$ E.

The cases for the postulates of **L**, and for $^{x}26.6c$ or $^{x}26.3c$ if present, are treated as before (8.3, 9.3). The cases for $F^{\xi+1}$ and $K^{\xi+1}$ (for $\zeta = \xi+1$) are like those for G^0 and K^0 respectively in 7.3. The case for $D^{\xi+1}$ is essentially like that for H^{n+1} in 9.3, with a closed functor u (of $\mathbf{S}^{\xi}$) in place of the numeral $\boldsymbol{y}$, except citing (2″), $E^{\xi+1}$ instead of (2′), G^{n+1} respectively. For $E^{\xi+1}$, use $\forall$-elimination from the axiom and apply 5.2 Clauses 1 and 6.

AXIOM SCHEMA $^{x}2.1$: $\forall x \exists \alpha A(x, \alpha) \supset \exists \alpha \forall x A(x, \lambda y \alpha(\langle x, y \rangle))$. This is a closed theorem of some $\mathbf{S}^{\xi}$ where $\zeta \leq \xi < \Omega$ (cf. $^{x}2.2!$ in 8.3, $^{x}2.2$ in 9.3). Assume (**a**) $| \vdash \forall x \exists \alpha A(x, \alpha)$. We must infer $| \exists \alpha \forall x A(x, \lambda y \alpha(\langle x, y \rangle))$. By (a), to each x there is a closed functor u_x (say of $\mathbf{S}^{\eta_x}$, where $\eta_x < \Omega$) such that (**b**) (x) $\{\Vdash \mathrm{A}(\boldsymbol{x}, u_x)\}$, whence (**c**) (x) $\{| \mathrm{A}(\boldsymbol{x}, u_x)\}$. The sequence $\xi, \eta_0, \eta_1, \eta_2, \ldots$ has an upper bound $\eta < \Omega$, so $\forall x \exists \alpha \mathrm{A}(x, \alpha)$ and (for each x) $\mathrm{A}(\boldsymbol{x}, u_x)$ are formulas of $\mathbf{S}^\eta$, whence (using (C′) for $\mathbf{S}$ with (a), (b)): (**d**) $\vdash^\eta \forall x \exists \alpha \mathrm{A}(x, \alpha)$, (**e**) (x) $\{\vdash^\eta \mathrm{A}(\boldsymbol{x}, u_x)\}$. Then $\forall x \exists \alpha \mathrm{A}(x, \alpha)$ is the pilot formula of the class $\mathscr{L}$, satisfying (1″) and (2″), given by (d) and (e). For the $\boldsymbol{\tau}^{\eta+1}$ correlated to this $\mathscr{L}$, by $\mathrm{D}^{\eta+1}$: $\vdash^{\eta+1} \forall x \mathrm{A}(x, \lambda y\, \boldsymbol{\tau}^{\eta+1}(\langle x, y \rangle))$, a fortiori (**f**) $\vdash \forall x \mathrm{A}(x, \lambda y\, \boldsymbol{\tau}^{\eta+1}(\langle x, y \rangle))$. Moreover, by $\mathrm{E}^{\eta+1}$: (x) $\{\vdash^{\eta+1} \lambda y\, \boldsymbol{\tau}^{\eta+1}(\langle \boldsymbol{x}, y \rangle) = u_x\}$, so (**g**) (x) $\{\vdash \lambda y\, \boldsymbol{\tau}^{\eta+1}(\langle \boldsymbol{x}, y \rangle) = u_x\}$. By (g) and (c), using 5.5 for $\mathbf{S}$: (**h**) (x) $\{| \mathrm{A}(\boldsymbol{x}, \lambda y\, \boldsymbol{\tau}^{\eta+1}(\langle \boldsymbol{x}, y \rangle))\}$. By (h) and (f), $| \vdash \forall x \mathrm{A}(x, \lambda y\, \boldsymbol{\tau}^{\eta+1}(\langle x, y \rangle))$, whence $| \exists \alpha \forall x \mathrm{A}(x, \lambda y \alpha(\langle x, y \rangle))$.

Thus, as before: (i) *and* (ii) *hold in each of the systems* $(3, \beta)$. In particular (when $\beta = 2$), they hold for the basic system **B**.

References

[1] J. R. Moschovakis, Disjunction, existence, and λ-eliminability in formalized intuitionistic analysis, Thesis, University of Wisconsin, 1965.

[2] S. C. Kleene and R. E. Vesley, The foundations of intuitionistic mathematics (North-Holland Publ. Co., Amsterdam, 1964).

[3] S. C. Kleene, Introduction to metamathematics (North-Holland Publ. Co., Amsterdam; P. Noordhoff N.V., Groningen, 1952).

[4] W. Ackermann, Zum Hilbertschen Aufbau der reelen Zahlen, Mathematische Annalen **99** (1928) 118–133.

[5] G. Kreisel and W. A. Howard, Reports of the seminar on foundations of analysis, Stanford University, Summer 1963.

[6] S. C. Kleene, Disjunction and existence under implication in elementary intuitionistic formalisms, J. Symbolic Logic **27** (for 1962, pub. 1963) 11–18. Errata: p. 16 lines 11 and 16, for "⊢" read "|". An addendum, Ibid. **28** (for 1963, pub. 1964) 154–156.

[7] K. Gödel, Zum intuitionistischen Aussagenkalkül, Akademie der Wissenschaften in Wien, Mathematischnaturwissenschaftliche Klasse, Anzeiger **69** (1932) 65–66, reprinted in: Ergebnisse eines mathematischen Kolloquiums, Heft 4 (for 1931-2, pub. 1933) 40.

[8] G. Gentzen, Untersuchungen über das logische Schliessen, Mathematische Zeitschrift **39** (1934-5) 176–210, 405–431.

[9] S. C. Kleene, On the interpretation of intuitionistic number theory, J. Symbolic Logic **10** (1945) 109–124.

[10] S. C. Kleene, Classical extensions of intuitionistic mathematics, Proc. 1964 Intern. Congress of Logic, Methodology, and Philosophy of Science (North-Holland Publ. Co., Amsterdam, 1965) 31–44.